Trading Up

Nancy Goldstone was [...]
graduate of Cornell Un[...]
from the Columbia Gra[...]
in New York.

She was a loan officer at [...] before joining
the commodity lending department of a major US bank
where she was promoted to assistant vice president. Soon
after transferring to its capital markets division, she became
vice president and manager of the Options Trading Unit.

She resigned in 1986 to write *Trading Up*. She is married and
lives in New York.

Nancy Goldstone
Trading Up

Pan Books London
Sydney and Auckland

First published in Great Britain in 1988 by
Sidgwick & Jackson Limited
This edition published 1989 by Pan Books Ltd,
Cavaye Place, London SW10 9PG
9 8 7 6 5 4 3 2 1
© Nancy Bazelon Goldstone, 1988
ISBN 0 330 30312 0
Printed and bound in Great Britain by
Richard Clay Ltd, Bungay, Suffolk

Author's note

The events in this book really happened, although a
series of events in some instances has been telescoped
to a single scene. The characters in this book are based
on real people; although again some individuals
appearing in the book are composite characters,
and I have disguised the identity of the people
upon which the characters are based.

to Larry, who gave me back my dreams

CONTENTS

PROLOGUE   1

1 ▲ THE BEGINNING   5

2 ▲ TRADING   23

3 ▲ THE LEARNING PROCESS   52

4 ▲ THE TIDE TURNS   73

5 ▲ THE COMPANY SHE KEEPS   81

6 ▲ WOMAN'S WORK   96

7 ▲ G-5   110

8 ▲ LIFE AT THE TOP   120

9 ▲ THE HEIGHT OF POWER   145

10 ▲ GROWING PAINS   164

11 ▲ WE WISH YOU A MERRY CHRISTMAS . . .   175

12 ▲ . . . AND A HAPPY NEW YEAR   194

13 ▲ TAKING STOCK   205

14 ▲ OUT OF THE FRYING PAN . . .   216

15 ▲ . . . AND INTO THE FIRE   228

16 ▲ OPTIONS   238

17 ▲ CUTTING TIES   251

18 ▲ TRADING UP   259

Trading Up

Prologue

8:29 A.M.: The trading room of a large commercial bank on Wall Street. The room is filled with people. The United States government is about to release key information on the state of the economy. It is deadly quiet.

The head foreign-exchange trader stands nervously behind his desk. He knows this information will move the dollar. If the data are good, the dollar will go up. The head trader will order his traders to telephone their counterparts at other banks and buy. If the numbers are very good, he will buy at least $100 million. If the numbers are bad the dollar will fall; the head trader will sell. The decision to buy or sell must be made immediately because the price will begin to change the instant the information is released. The head trader alone will make this critical decision. There is no time for consultation. If he is correct, he may earn a million dollars for his bank in minutes. If he is wrong, he could lose a million just as quickly.

8:30 A.M.: A junior trader stands at the Telerate machine. A bell rings. The news is moving across the wire.

"Up 3.4 percent!" the junior trader shouts. He runs back to his desk and grabs his telephone.

Great news!

"Buy!" the head trader orders.

Six traders scream into six telephones.

"Mine! Mine!" they shout, buying the dollar.

8:31 A.M.: Countless traders at other institutions across the globe are also trying to buy. The value of the dollar jumps. The head trader takes a quick look at the scrawl on his trading blotter. His traders have bought $150 million in the first minute. The head trader grins. The dollars he bought have risen in value. A profit of $1.25 million.

8:32 A.M.: The bell at the Telerate machine rings again. The junior trader drops his phone and races to read the new information on the wire.

"Revision!" he shouts. "Last month's numbers revised down by 4.5 percent!"

The head trader freezes. The economy is weaker than expected because it grew less in the previous month than the first flash indicated. The dollar will crash.

"Sell it!" he hollers.

Six heads bend once again to their task.

"Yours! Yours!"

But other traders at other institutions have also seen the revision. No one is willing to buy the dollar. The traders have no one to sell to. The dollar begins to

2

plummet. The head trader looks on helplessly. Finally, after what seems like an eternity, the price falls so low that traders at some of the other banks are ready to buy the dollar again. The head trader sells his dollars.

8:40 A.M.: From plus $1.25 million to a loss of two million dollars. Lunch is still three hours away.

On Wall Street, decision making is power. A head trader can make or lose millions in seconds. That's power.

This is the story of how I, Nancy Bazelon Goldstone, at age twenty-seven, with no previous experience in currency trading, became the head trader for currency options at one of the largest financial institutions in the country. I did it in three months. Was it talent? No. Was it experience? No. I didn't know a deutsche mark from a benchmark. Suddenly I was making decisions on millions of dollars of the bank's capital every day. My friends were impressed. My peers were envious. My family was horrified.

1 The Beginning

I grew up in Highland Park, Illinois, an upper-middle-class suburb of Chicago. Highland Park is one of those places untouched by the current of human drama. Be there war, famine, pestilence, economic, political, or social upheaval in other cities or nations, Highland Park will remain aloof. Through the filter of a television set, sitting in a living room surrounded by prints of Expressionist art, with a scotch in one hand and a handful of Planters dry-roasted peanuts in the other, the residents of Highland Park monitor, judge, and finally dismiss the passion and turmoil of the outside world. These things happen, of course, they murmur. But not in Highland Park.

Upon reaching adolescence, I experienced an acute

sense of guilt over having to grow up in such a privileged environment. I considered it quite unfair. It was the early 1970s and we were at the tail end of the Vietnam War. Many people had suffered. The country was divided. New issues were coming to the fore.

At my house, the principal topic of conversation was whether to have lamb chops or broiled chicken for dinner.

Applying a fairly standard technique for relieving my conscience, I took everything out on my parents.

Striking out blindly against them, I rarely missed an opportunity to do the opposite of what they said. Their reasoning was dismissed out of hand. They were my parents, and, by definition, always wrong.

I saw my struggle as a noble act of rebellion and an assertion of independence. As it turned out, my parents made very convenient foils. After all, there's no safer way of asserting independence than when you know full well you aren't going to get it.

So how did I rebel? Did I drop out of society and go to work on a commune? Did I run away and join the French Foreign Legion? Did I start a home for unwed mothers in my bedroom?

Don't be ridiculous. I told you, this was Highland Park.

My rebellion took the tangible form of: (1) heroically resisting all of my mother's entreaties to straighten up my room; (2) boycotting the country club during the summer; (3) wearing torn Levi's instead of stonewashed Calvin Kleins; (4) turning down an invitation to the prom; (5) refusing to learn to play either golf or tennis; and (6) applying to colleges outside of the Chicago area.

Tough measures, but necessary.

But, like all teenagers, while fighting them, I desperately sought my parents' approval. One way to win their respect and affection was through education. They thought grades were important. As schoolwork always came easily to me, this seemed at first a painless way of earning their praise. But, after a while, it seemed they expected good grades. I brought home As, and, although they still praised me, they no longer went to the trouble of hiring a marching band or writing their congressman.

Interpreting this slight falloff in enthusiasm as disapproval, I raised my already high standards. You could say I was something of an overachiever.

To escape the pressure, I sought a refuge. Some kids do drugs. Some kids do sports.

I did books.

Long books. Short books. I read all the time— everything I could get my hands on, never bothering to discriminate. Thus I would finish Hemingway and begin on Irving Wallace.

(My mother, noting my attachment to the written word, suggested that perhaps I might wish to try my hand at writing. I immediately registered for an advanced mathematics course.)

I remember stumbling onto *War and Peace* during my senior year in high school. I loved *War and Peace*. I read it day and night to the exclusion of all other activities, intensely displeasing my high school sweetheart. Why would I want to stay home all night with a book, he asked plaintively, when I could spend the evening with him watching the Celtics play the Lakers on television?

Whenever I read, I give myself up to the world I'm reading about, unconscious of events happening right under my nose. In the case of *War and Peace*, this state of affairs lasted for over a month.

Consequently, I missed the announcement of an impending examination in European history.

I found out about the test thirty seconds before class,

7

in the hallway outside the room. All the other kids were standing around comparing notes. I froze. I'd read not one word of the assigned text and had not listened in class for nearly a month. What time period were we covering? What countries? I had no idea. Mechanically, I followed the rest of my classmates into the room and sat down at my desk. Everyone was quiet with the usual hush that precedes an examination.

The teacher handed out the test. It consisted of a single question: "Do great men make their circumstances, or do circumstances make great men?"

I stared down at the question. What luck! For over an hour, taking everything directly from *War and Peace,* I wrote happily about Napoleon invading Russia. Tolstoy and I received one of the highest grades in the class.

Though I didn't know it at the time, it was a sign of things to come. All I thought was, Thank God it wasn't math.

I went on to an Ivy League university, my first time away from home. Independent at last! Time to show my parents that I could manage perfectly well on my own, thank you very much.

My major changed three times in the first year and a half, running the gamut from playwriting to nuclear physics. (I had an idea that I would look terrific in a white coat— a notion I got from an old episode of "I Spy.") Finally, I came under the influence of a professor who taught power politics under the guise of American history. It was rumored that he'd be up for secretary of state if so-and-so were elected. So-and-so never made it, and neither did my professor. However, he did manage to pass on his ambition to most of his students.

Determined to follow in my professor's visionary though frustrated footsteps, I enrolled in graduate school at Columbia University in New York City to prepare for an entry-level position in the State Department. There I met Tom Smith, a graduate student in the School of Business. Tom was brilliant and determined. He knew exactly what he wanted. He had his whole life mapped out. He was going to enter an investment bank and become rich and powerful.

I was attracted to his intelligence and self-confidence. We started to date. I confided in him my scheme to enter the State Department, do great works, become famous, etc., etc.

He shuddered.

"What do you want to go there for?" he demanded. "That's just a bunch of bureaucrats."

He said it as though they were a new species of vermin.

"Well, where should I go?" I asked.

He never hesitated.

"Wall Street."

At first I thought he was crazy. Wall Street? I didn't know very much about Wall Street, but it seemed incompatible with my ideals. I was interested in doing good works. I wasn't particularly interested in making money.

But Tom was very determined. Unsure myself of what I wanted out of life, I began to listen to him. Suddenly, I noticed that most of the intelligent people I knew at school were following his example. Surely they knew what they were doing. Besides, power and money were attractive lures. I didn't want to spend my life as an ineffective naïf. It became something of a competition for me, trying to prove that I was every bit as determined and ambitious as my peers.

I didn't know it at the time, of course, but I was falling prey to one of the most insidious influences of my generation.

I was becoming a Yuppie.

Switching out of my World Hunger class, I enrolled in Basic Accounting and Finance. For the first time in my life, I read the business section of the newspaper and saw reports of billion-dollar deals and million-dollar salaries. Approaching graduation, I dreamed of power, money, action.

What I got was a job as a loan officer.

And a loan officer I remained for three years, achieving the position of assistant vice president at $40,000 a year.

It was my job to lend money to companies who traded in gold and silver. From my customers I was able to pick up a rudimentary knowledge of the precious-metals market and the basics of gold trading. Unfortunately, my term as a loan officer coincided with a slump in the demand for precious metals. The companies I was supposed to lend to didn't really need the bank's money. Faced with this reality, my days flew by at the breakneck speed of an English cricket match.

I came to dread my morning strategy sessions with my manager, Charles. Charles had dark hair and eyes, and a moustache of which he was very proud. He went out almost every night with customers of the bank so that he could eat at the most expensive restaurants and carouse at the liveliest nightclubs. In this way he affected a jet-set life-style without the necessity of a jet-set income.

Our conversations were nearly always the same.

"Good morning, Nancy," Charles said, examining his fingernails. Charles was always a bit superior, an attitude due, no doubt, to his keen regard for the high position he held within the bank. Charles was a "global manager." This meant he managed me and three others. I never did figure out why we were global.

"Good morning, Charles," I replied. "What can I do for you?"

"Nancy, how many customers do you have?"

"I have five customers, Charles."

"In that case, I expect you to lend out $10 million today to each customer. That's $50 million altogether."

"Wait. I called them all yesterday and they told me they don't need money this week."

"Call them back. Make them take the money." Charles glared at me.

"What do you mean, 'Make them take the money'? I can't force people to borrow, can I?"

"Call them."

With that Charles stalked off to his desk in a corner and stared at me until I picked up the phone. Then he folded his arms across his chest, put his feet up on the desk, and fell asleep.

I was driven to despair by Charles's rigidity and my customers' lack of enthusiasm for more money, despite my offer of a free toaster for every $10 million borrowed. So I approached Charles one day at 3:00 P.M. Months of experience had taught me that Charles was at his best immediately following his afternoon nap but previous to his cocktail hour. I caught him just as he was finishing up a telephone conversation. He had been trying to scrounge up a date for the evening's entertainment. This activity generally took up several hours of his day.

"Charles, may I speak with you for a moment?"

"Of course, Nancy." Charles was genial. He had apparently scored.

"I've been thinking, " I said. "Since I'm having so much trouble lending to our usual customers, why don't you let me go out and try to drum up some new business?"

Charles frowned slightly and lit a cigarette.

"Are you sure you have the time for it?" he asked suspiciously.

I assured him I had.

11

"Whom do you intend to visit?"

I told him about a relatively new product I'd heard of called *options*. I understood that there were companies that were devoting themselves entirely to trading options. I thought these companies might need to borrow to finance their purchases and sales.

"I don't think so," said Charles. "Sounds too risky for us."

But I knew how to get to Charles.

"Just think, Charles!" I exclaimed. "This is a new product. We could be the first people on Wall Street to finance options. People get their names in the newspaper for being the first to try something new."

"I suppose," said Charles, straightening up a bit, "there's no real harm in letting you investigate. Just make sure that I'm informed every step of the way. With something innovative like this, you'll need my signature on every memorandum."

"Of course, Charles."

Cheered by the thought of having something to do, I made an appointment with the treasurer of an options trading company. The treasurer told me that the company traded options on foreign currencies, U.S. government bonds, stocks, metals, and other commodities. He threw out technical terms, like *delta*, *gamma*, *theta*, and *volatility*. He was eager to borrow money and offered to post options as collateral.

I was quiet during this first interview. The terms the treasurer used were unfamiliar to me. However, I would have died rather than let him detect my ignorance. Smiling sweetly, I promised to get back to him.

I went to a bookstore and bought every book on options I could find. I spent the next two weeks studying. I learned that an option was like an insurance policy against an adverse price movement in the value of

12

a commodity. The purchaser of an option pays a premium up front for the right to buy or sell a commodity at a specific price for a finite period of time. This premium fluctuates with the price of the underlying commodity and the time left on the option. I became reasonably familiar with the term *delta*, which was a measure of how much the option's premium would increase or decrease in value given a change in the price of the underlying commodity. I never did figure out what *gamma*, *theta*, or *volatility* meant.

Charles was suspicious, but impressed by the flood of memorandums I produced for his signature. As copies of all memos were reviewed by the bank's senior management, it got around that Charles was becoming something of an options expert.

The more I learned, the more interested I became in trading. Although I couldn't pretend to understand everything I'd read, that didn't stop me from daydreaming about becoming an options trader. It seemed glamorous, fast-paced, and exciting. After three years of lending, I was in the mood for a little excitement.

This daydream haunted me so, that I actually did something about it. I went to apply for a job with the bank's trading department.

Most people don't know that banks speculate with their own capital. In fact, when I told my father, a respected lawyer in Chicago, that I intended to get a job trading options at the bank, he told me that I was crazy to think that a bank gambled with its depositors' money.

Of all the false images ever perpetrated on an unsuspecting public by advertising, surely the myth of the commercial bank as a financially conservative institution is the most blatant. Commercial banks are among the largest, and are certainly the most uncontrolled, gambling institutions in the world. This is a simple fact.

13

The trading departments of every major commercial bank in this country (and abroad, for that matter) are responsible for openly speculating with the bank's capital on the value of the dollar or the direction interest rates will take. More often than not, a bank trader will be allowed to bet a significant portion of the bank's actual capital base at any one time. The only difference between the trading room of a major commercial bank and a Las Vegas gambling casino is that in Las Vegas you can't lose more than you bet.

Therefore, I ignored the parental comment and approached the man in charge of the bank's Options Trading Unit, Paul Pepper.

He was large and genial, in his mid-thirties, possessed of masses of curly brown hair and an engaging grin. Though still young, he gave the impression of being middle-aged, which I attributed to the pressures of his job.

Paul had begun his career as an administrative assistant to a government bond trader. Later he became interested in options and succeeded in convincing senior management that the bank was falling behind the competition by not making this product available to its customers. He offered to study the situation and set up a currency options desk for the bank. His study took a year and a half, and at the end of that time he was appointed to head the bank's newly organized Options Trading Unit.

Trying to change jobs within a large organization such as a commercial bank is very tricky business. The whole matter has to be handled with delicacy, or you're liable to lose your old position without gaining the new one. The object is to get your prospective boss to think that hiring you was his own idea.

"Can I have a job trading options with you?" I asked Paul.

He looked at me, surprised.

"Do you know anything about options?" he asked me.

I handed him the pile of memorandums I'd written for Charles's signature. He looked them over.

"I wrote these," I said.

"Okay, leave them with me and give me a call tomorrow around four o'clock."

I walked away, holding my breath, dizzy with excitement. I'd done it! I'd made the first move! I rushed home to tell my fiancé, Larry, who gave me a thorough dose of reality.

I had known Larry for about a year. He had worked for a client of the bank, and one day he'd walked into my lending department. We gazed mutely at each other across the word processors.

Larry was unlike anyone I'd ever met before. Until now, all of my boyfriends had been a lot like Tom Smith: upright, industrious, boring.

Larry was anything but boring.

During his professional career, Larry had been (among other things) a political consultant, a banker, a gold trader, a model, an actor, and a member of a think tank. He'd helped organize a major gold-trading operation on Wall Street. He'd devised sophisticated risk-management programs as an outside consultant.

He was charming and extremely good-looking. He was also brilliant: it took him all of two years to get his Ph.D. in political science. His varied experiences had given him the kind of real-life outlook that is significantly underrepresented on Wall Street.

Larry had one motto in life: Go for it.

He was ten years older than I. I had a great deal of respect for his opinion.

"Do you have any idea," asked my fiancé, "how difficult it is to secure a junior trading position?"

I admitted I had no idea.

"Very difficult. Do you have any idea how many people want to get into trading who are far more qualified than you, and how few positions they compete for?"

I allowed ignorance as to the exact number of applicants in the field, or the size of the field, for that matter.

"Let me enlighten you, then," said my beloved. "The competition for a position in trading is fierce, because the potential rewards are enormous. It is the most sought-after career on Wall Street."

I pointed out, a bit defensively, that I wasn't without some skills. I had read books on the subject.

"I just don't want you to get your hopes up," said Larry, more gently. "The odds are a hundred to one against you. Go in there and give it your best shot. But know that it's an outside chance at best."

I didn't sleep all night.

I spent the next day at my lending desk, frantically poring over my books. The more I read, the more confused I became. By early afternoon I was absolutely convinced that I knew nothing whatsoever about options and could never learn. I would never get the job.

At 3:00 P.M., the phone rang.

"Nancy? This is Paul Pepper. Can you come up and see me in about half an hour?"

"Uh . . . well . . . sure," I stammered.

"Good," said Paul. "I'm going to have you sit down with Bob Green and myself. Bob is the other member of the team. Just come by the desk when you're ready." He hung up.

My hand trembled as I hung up the phone. I wanted the job so bad. But how to get through the interview? I prayed for divine intervention.

I made an excuse to Charles and escaped to the

16

trading room at the appointed time. Paul and Bob were there waiting for me. We shook hands, and they led me into an empty office away from the noisy, crowded room. We sat down facing one another. The moment of truth had arrived.

"Nancy," Paul began pleasantly, "you have excellent timing. As it turns out, Bob and I were looking for a third member of the options trading team."

So there was a job available! I prayed harder. I offered God my firstborn male child.

"There are a few questions we'd like to ask you first," the interview began.

Here it comes! I threw in the rest of my family.

"Could you start within two weeks?" Paul asked.

I said I thought it could be arranged.

"As a junior trader, you would have to come into work earlier than you do now, say seven-thirty instead of nine. Do you have a problem with that?"

I assured him that I was an early riser anyway. I am proud to say that this was the only real lie I told to get the job.

"Well," said Paul, settling back into his chair, "those are my questions. Bob, do you have any questions?"

"I don't think so," said Bob, looking bored.

"All right, then," said Paul, standing up, "I'll talk to John."

I looked from one to the other, bewildered.

"Did I get the job?" I asked Paul.

"Well," said Paul. "I've got no problem with you. Bob has no problem with you, right, Bob?"

"Right," said Bob, who was already on his way out of the office.

"Then it's only a matter of having you meet John."

"Who is John?"

"John Anderson," Paul explained, "is the head of the bank's trading operation. Our unit falls within his jurisdiction. If he agrees, the job is yours. Provided," he added quickly, "that you are willing to start within two weeks."

"Oh, absolutely," I said, just as quickly.

"Good," said Paul, shaking my hand. "I'll set you up with an appointment with John. Will you be available sometime tomorrow during the day? Okay. I'll call you tomorrow and let you know."

Larry made me repeat the conversation word for word that evening when I got home from work. He shook his head.

"There's something wrong here," he said when I had finished recounting the interview for the third time. "Are you sure that's all they asked you?"

I replied with dignity that I thought I could remember a five-minute conversation as well as the next person.

"Well," he said, "it must be that John Anderson makes all the decisions. That will be the tough interview. The one today must just have been part of the screening process. Still, it's odd that the two people that you will be working most closely with didn't bother to find out more about you."

Even I had to admit that the initial interview had been less than rigorous.

"Perhaps my memos were so good that they spoke for themselves," I suggested.

"Perhaps."

I kept the part about sacrificing the family to myself. But how else was I to explain the ease with which I had sailed through that first interview?

The next day I received a call from Mr. Anderson's secretary, Linda, who arranged for me to come and see him at 2:00 P.M. I spent the morning trying to find out everything I could about John Anderson.

It turned out that John was a rising star at the bank. He had come up through the ranks to achieve, at the age of forty-two, the coveted position of executive in charge of the Trading Sector. This meant that he was responsible for managing all of the bank's trading in its most sophisticated and complex financial instruments—everything from foreign-exchange options to interest-rate swaps.

The more I found out, the more impressed I became. I was to be interviewed by a man who was only two positions removed from the chairman of the board. No wonder the first interview had been so simple. A man of John's caliber would certainly detect my rudimentary knowledge of foreign-exchange and options trading immediately. I was keenly aware of my shortcomings.

Nonetheless I arrived at his office at the appointed time for the interview. I was ushered into the neat, uncluttered room and found myself face-to-face with one of the bank's most senior managers.

My first impression was of a well-groomed executive. Everything about him proclaimed his professionalism. He was perfectly dressed, from his immaculately clean white shirt to the gleam of the polish on his wing-tip shoes. He even had a freshly laundered handkerchief peeking out of the breast pocket of his conservative dark suit. Gold cuff links, a Rolex watch, and a wedding band were his only accessories. He was slim, energetic, and youthful in appearance, with an almost boyish charm. His posture was excellent. Although it was the dead of winter, he sported a beautiful suntan. He looked as if he hadn't a care in the world. He shook my hand briskly and asked me to sit down.

19

"Let's see," he began in a no-nonsense way. "Nancy. Yes. You're interviewing for a spot on the options team, is that it? You'll have to excuse me for not being entirely focused at the moment. You see, I've just come from a major meeting on asset-liability management."

I assured him that I understood.

"And in twenty minutes I must attend a senior-level risk-management meeting."

I thanked him for taking time out of so obviously busy a schedule to talk to me. He seemed to like that.

"Fascinating subject, risk management. Do you know much about risk management, Nancy?" He looked at me searchingly.

So Larry was right. This was going to be a difficult interview. I opened my lips to answer, but, to my surprise, he cut me off.

"I think that risk management is one of the most important issues facing those of us responsible for overseeing trading operations today. How, for example, do you manage the risk of an option position—?"

Worse and worse! Once again I started to answer, but he continued.

"—or of a forward rate agreement, or of a swap? What about forward foreign-exchange positions, Treasury positions?"

Damn! How was I to answer so many difficult questions during the course of a single twenty-minute interview? At least I did have some opinions on foreign-exchange options positions. I opened my mouth to speak but he interrupted again.

"These are the questions someone in my position has to deal with. Do you know my background, Nancy? No? Well, let me begin by telling you that I was an officer in the Marines during the Vietnam War. I joined the bank in 1973. . . ."

He spent the next eighteen minutes reviewing his

career. From combat he moved to junior bank clerk. From junior bank clerk to senior bank clerk. Then came a promotion to managing bank clerk. Then junior operations assistant, senior operations assistant—on and on, up and up, until his present position. Although I tried to listen attentively, I barely heard him. I thought he was just filling the time until the interview was over. I had obviously failed somewhere.

He had just finished speaking when there came a knock on the door. Linda poked her head into the office and reminded John that it was time to attend the next meeting.

He thanked her and rose to his feet. I stood up as well, not knowing what else to do, quite sure that I hadn't gotten the job. Now I was going to be dismissed.

He held out his hand to me. I took it limply.

He shook hands energetically, grinned, and exclaimed:

"Glad to have you on board!"

Larry didn't believe me when I told him I had gotten the job.

"Just like that?" he asked.

"Just like that," I replied.

"I don't understand it," he said. "All you know about trading is from what you've read in books." Suddenly he jerked his head up. "Unless . . . "

"Unless what?"

"You're certainly as smart and as capable as the next person. But you're also a lot better-looking than the next person, who would most assuredly be male. I'm sure that didn't hurt."

"That's not true!" I said, stung.

"Well, how many women did you see when you visited the trading room?"

"There were a few."

"Mostly secretaries or salespeople, I bet. How many of them were in their twenties? How many were pretty? How many had great legs?"

"I don't have great legs."

"You do have great legs. That's why I'm marrying you."

"I didn't get this job because of my legs."

"Are you sure?"

"I'm positive. It wasn't like that. There were no sexual vibes. I'm not sure they even noticed that I was a woman."

"Nancy," said Larry, "they always notice."

"I don't care. I've got the job now, and I'm going to keep it."

It was arranged that I would begin working on the options desk as soon as possible. I had to give Charles two weeks' notice, of course, and he would probably put up a bit of a fight about it, but since I had a firm offer from the trading side of the bank, there wasn't much he could do.

I spent those last two weeks as a loan officer in a happy daze. My associates were choked with envy. The trading side of the bank paid much better than the lending side. Although I wasn't getting a raise to begin with, my potential earning power was far greater as a trader. And I was going off to do something new and exciting. Already I could taste the fruits of success.

2 Trading

Reality smacked me full in the face that first morning when the alarm went off at 5:30 A.M.

It was a bitterly cold day in early February 1985. The sun wouldn't be up for another hour and a half. Larry rolled over as I struggled out of bed.

"Good luck, babe," he murmured sleepily.

I was only half awake myself when I pushed open the swinging glass doors that marked the entrance to the trading room. I woke up with a start.

There were desks and computer screens every-where. Wires hung down from the ceiling or lay piled in ropes on the floor. The fluorescent lighting intensi-fied the glare from the machinery. The room was puls-ing with heat and energy. It was only 7:15 A.M., but already the trading room was full of people sipping coffee and smoking their first cigarettes of the day. I made my way over to the options desk. Paul Pepper was already there, turning on computer screens and talking into the phone.

The trading room is the symbol of the life-force of Wall Street. It is the source of energy. Its fuel powers the impressive boardrooms where negotiations are conducted by quiet men in dark suits—negotiations that allocate and then reallocate the world's resources. Its influence pervades the deepest recesses of the financial community here and abroad. Traders sit in judgment on every action taken, every policy determined. The trading room is the arena in which modern-day gladiators meet to do battle for their institutions and for themselves. Telephones and computer screens may have replaced the swords and shields of days of yore, but the principle remains the same.

The telephones and computer screens relay information. Traders suck in information the way other people breathe. Trading rooms virtually hum with an incessant undertone of news. Improvements in communications systems over the last decade have made it possible for news reports to be almost instantaneous. Many traders keep Reuters screens at home so they can check on the overseas markets long after their office has shut down for the day. The whole world is on real time. What this means for the trader is that, from the moment of awakening in the morning until bedding down for a few hours of much-needed sleep at night, he or she is constantly bombarded with information.

All different kinds of news affect the market; it's not limited to "business" data per se. Factors such as political news: What candidate is running for which office and in which country? What bill is being passed in Congress and what effect will that have on other nations as well as our own? Then there is international news: riots have broken out here; terrorist activities are taking place there. And economic information: At what rate did the economy grow last month? What's predicted for next month? Who says so? Then there's general gossip: The Arabs are buying! No, they're selling! No, it's the Japanese!

Every new detail, fact or rumor, must be absorbed. To be unaware of even the most innocuous news item can mean the difference between winning and losing millions of dollars in a single day, even in a single hour, in what many consider to be the only game in town: the market.

The market is the sum total of all the traders in the world. It has a dynamic all its own, the result of a continual assessment of the value of a given commodity. For every buyer there is a seller. Price is determined literally by the total, on a macroeconomic scale, of what one trader is willing to pay versus what another will take to sell. As new information becomes available, opinions change, and so do the prices.

Successful traders are among the most respected individuals in the financial community. To do the job properly, a good trader must have, in addition to intellect, of course: stamina, to withstand the constant pressure and round-the-clock hours; boldness, to hold a position or risk large sums in the face of uncertain information; discipline, to acknowledge an error and take a loss today to save a larger loss tomorrow; speed, to grasp all of the implications of a piece of information instantaneously as one hears it; and creativity, to stay ahead of a community that places a high premium upon innovation. No other position demands all of these particular qualities to the extreme that trading does, and well the trader knows it. This usually adds arrogance to the list.

Trading rooms are large, open areas, filled with many people, mostly men. (Trading is one of the most purely male-dominated fields. It is almost taken for granted that one's masculinity, as much as one's capital, is on the line when one trades.) Some are standing, others sitting, but all are peering intently into tiny computer screens that transmit even tinier fluorescent numbers, while speaking into telephones—sometimes two at once. A trader is very conscious of time and never wastes words. The price could change during the exchange of even the most limited pleasantries and an opportunity to buy or sell would be gone. The atmosphere crackles. The air is hot and dry, fired by the heat given off by both the computer equipment and the sheer number of people crammed in per square foot.

Traders buy and sell and hope to make a profit by the effort. Gold traders buy and sell gold. Stock traders buy and sell stock. Currency option traders buy and sell currency options.

A gold trader's responsibility is to make money by betting that the price of gold will rise or fall. If, for example, the gold trader thinks that the price of gold will rise in the future, he will go into the marketplace and buy gold. He will buy the gold from traders at other banks (who are betting the price of gold will fall) or from one of the public exchanges that were established for this purpose. (Just as there is a stock exchange where it is possible for an individual to buy and sell stock, so there is a commodities exchange where it is possible to buy and sell gold.)

Currency options, of course, are harder to visualize than gold. Unlike gold, a tangible asset (something we can see and touch), a currency option is an intangible asset, a right. A currency option is the right to buy or sell foreign currency at a specific price for a specific period of time. Although not something you can touch or see, rights are real nonetheless. Since it is difficult to imagine a "right," think of a currency option as a piece of paper on which is written "The Right to Buy" or "The Right to Sell."

Like the gold trader, the currency option trader's responsibility is to make money by betting that the price of currency options will rise or fall. Currency options can be bought from traders at other banks, or from a public exchange, just like gold. Currency option prices rise or fall in correlation with the rise or fall of the dollar.

Traders are hired by banks for one reason and one reason alone: to make money.

Paul and Bob traded currency options from a desk in the center of a large room. To their right were the spot foreign-currency traders; to their left the interest-rate desk. The spot currency traders were responsible for speculating on whether the dollar would increase or decrease in value. The interest-rate traders were supposed to do the same thing for long-term and short-term interest rates. Both of these desks were run by men with ten or more years of experience in the marketplace.

But this was not the case at the options desk. Paul had only been trading options for a little over a year, and Bob for eight months. The options market was not so developed as the interest-rate or spot foreign-currency markets. Options were a new and complex financial instrument that not that many people understood, certainly not senior management at the bank. Paul and Bob could trade pretty much as they pleased.

By the time I arrived on the scene, Paul and Bob had managed to amass quite a sizable options portfolio—close to $1 billion in face value. Every option has a *face value*. For example, Paul and Bob could buy an option to purchase $5 million at a specific price for a specific date. The face value of that option would be $5 million. The aggregate of all the options they had purchased and sold was the face value of the portfolio. They were very proud of the size of the portfolio and of their reputation as being "aggressive" traders. They were willing to buy or sell at prices under the market in order to increase their volume of business. They said this was the best way to promote the bank's name throughout the industry.

The first few days at any new job are difficult. The first few days on a trading desk were bewildering.

Paul and Bob sat at a small table on which were stacked six computer screens, four push-button phones, and a telephone console. The phones rang constantly so it was often necessary to speak into two receivers at once. The computer screens blinked little green numbers that changed from second to second. Occasionally a bell would ring and one of the screens would flash an important news item.

Paul went out of his way to be helpful. In between phone calls and trading he would explain how one screen was linked to an exchange in Chicago, and another to Philadelphia; a third reported spot currency prices in New York; a fourth, options prices out of Switzerland. Whenever he bought or sold an option he would stop to show me exactly what he'd done and how he had priced the trade.

Nothing I had done as a loan officer prepared me for the grueling work and absolute concentration of those first few days in the trading room. There is no aspect of lending that can be remotely characterized as fast-paced, unless you count the speed at which everyone runs for the elevators at lunchtime.

But by 11:00 A.M. of that first day I was exhausted. I wanted to go home. The level of attention demanded was staggering.

And nothing I had read in any of the books I'd

studied so religiously prepared me for the reality of trading. Forget learning about the options market. I had to learn about the spot foreign-exchange market before I could attempt to understand the options market.

Paul called my attention to a screen that listed the current prices of each of the major currencies: deutsche marks, Swiss francs, Japanese yen, British pounds, Canadian dollars. I stared at that screen. Concentrate. Concentrate. Every time one of the numbers on that screen changed I would ask myself a series of questions. The deutsche mark number changed. Was the dollar going up or down against the deutsche mark? Up—no, down. No—up. Okay. If the dollar was going up, did that mean other traders were buying it or selling it? Selling it—no, buying it. Wait! The British pound number just changed. Did that mean the dollar was going up or down against the British pound . . . ?

I could hear the spot foreign-exchange traders, at their desks across the room, trading. Mine! They shouted. Did *mine* mean they were buying or selling the dollar? I asked Paul. Buying. Okay, if they were buying did that mean the dollar was going up or down? And against which currencies?

Wait! A bell is ringing! That means there's news. Oh my God! *All* the numbers are changing! The mark, the pound, the franc, the yen! Are they going up or down? What does that mean . . . ?

All day long. Constant. Unremitting.

"How'd it go?" asked Larry when I got home that first evening.

I collapsed on the sofa.

"That bad, huh?" he murmured sympathetically, sitting down beside me and putting his arm around me.

"Oh, Larry," I sighed, stifling a sob, "I can't do it. It's too hard."

"Don't you think you should give yourself more than one day at it before you chuck it?"

"I guess so," I sighed again. I was very depressed.

"Why don't you let me help you a little?" Larry asked.

"Oh!" I said, eagerly. "Do you think you can?"

"Sure. I know how the market works. C'mon, keep your chin up." He winked at me.

I'd written down every one of the trades that Paul had done that day. He'd tried to explain them to me at the time, but I hadn't understood. I figured if I wrote them all down, there was a chance of making some sense of them later. I showed the sheets to Larry.

"Terrific!" he said. "Now we've got something to work with. Let's look at this very first trade. What does it say?"

I looked at the trade steadily for about five minutes.

"Beats me," I said.

"Well, let's go through it slowly," said Larry, laughing. "It looks to me like you bought $5 million worth of a put on the deutsche mark expiring in June."

I looked at the trade again. Now that he mentioned it, it did look like Paul had bought $5 million of a put on the deutsche mark expiring in June.

"Now, what does that mean?" Larry encouraged.

I closed my eyes and tried to concentrate. I remembered something I'd read in one of my books.

"Well," I said slowly, "when you buy a put on the deutsche mark, you are buying the right to sell deutsche marks at a specific price for a specific period of time."

"That's right," said Larry, nodding. "Who says you don't know your stuff? Now what does that mean, the 'right to sell deutsche marks'?"

I closed my eyes to concentrate again. Then I opened them.

"Beats me," I said.

"Well," said Larry, "when you sell deutsche marks, doesn't that mean you are going short the deutsche mark? And when you go short the deutsche mark, doesn't that mean that you are actually going long the dollar? Isn't that the same thing as buying dollars?"

"You really think so?" I asked.

"Think about it," he said.

I hadn't thought about it that way before. It seemed right. At least, I could see nothing wrong with the reasoning.

"Did the dollar go up or down against the deutsche mark today?" Larry asked.

I'd remembered to write down the price of all the currencies when I came in in the morning and just before I left. I dived for the paper. After some intense calculating (I had to start over once from the beginning when I lost track in the middle), I was able to answer the question.

"The dollar went up against the deutsche mark today," I said finally.

"There you go!" said Larry. "So if you bought a put—buying a put is the same thing as buying dollars—and the dollar went up, did you make or lose money on this put?"

"I guess if we bought dollars and the dollar went up we made money on the put," I said.

"Exactly."

"Gee! We made money on that put?" I asked, looking at the sheets with renewed interest.

"Looks like," said Larry, dryly.

"Think of that," I said, just as pleased as if I'd thought to buy the put myself.

"Don't get cocky," said Larry. "Let's look at the

next one. It looks to me like you bought a put on the Japanese yen. . . "

Larry never lost patience. I don't know what I would have done without him. Day after day of those first two weeks I would struggle out of bed in the morning and steel myself for another day of frustration and concentration. Night after night I would bring home handwritten notes of the trades that Paul and Bob had executed that day, and Larry and I would go over them, painstakingly, one at a time. It took hours.

But bit by bit I started to learn. I didn't learn enough to trade. But I learned enough to start asking questions.

There is no one standard method for trading options. In many ways, it's like going to the racetrack. A bettor can make educated guesses by studying the racing form and knowing something about the horses, but it's best to have luck on your side. The most successful options traders try to structure trades that make money in three out of four scenarios—and then hope that the fourth doesn't happen.

Paul tried to explain the rationale behind some of his trades.

"Now this trade," he said, pointing an ink-stained finger to one of many numbers scrawled on a handwritten sheet, "this trade makes money if the dollar increases in value anytime during the next two months. It has a maximum profit potential of $100,000."

I looked at the trade.

"What if the dollar doesn't increase in value?" I asked.

"Well," Paul answered, "if the dollar stays pretty much where it is today for the next two months, this trade will make about $20,000."

"And if the dollar declines in value?"

"If the dollar declines slightly in value, the trade will lose about $30,000. You always have to take some risk," he added.

"What if the dollar declines significantly in value?"

"If the dollar declines significantly in value?" Paul repeated. "Nancy, I've been trading options for over a year and a half now. In all that time I have never seen the dollar decrease significantly in value. In fact, the dollar has been steadily increasing in value during the entire time I've been trading. It is extremely unlikely that the dollar will decrease significantly in value during the next two months, which is the time period of this particular trade."

"But what if it does?" I persisted.

"Well, if the dollar started to fall dramatically, the loss on this particular trade would be unlimited. But I tell you, it's not going to happen."

"I see," I said.

Almost all of my instruction came from Paul. Bob just ignored me.

Bob came from Connecticut. His father was a corporate lawyer, his mother a psychiatrist. Bob's scholastic credits read like a sample from a how-to book on résumé writing: prep school, Ivy League university, Harvard Business School. (Hobbies: golf and tennis.) He had wavy blond hair and blue eyes. The freckles on his nose belied his real age, which was close to thirty.

The first thing that struck me about Bob were his clothes. His expensive suits were cut in the European style and were tailored to perfection. Cary Grant would have envied the crease in his trousers. He scorned the traditional red or yellow neckties popular on Wall Street in favor of muted colors and patterns. A pink silk handkerchief adorned his breast pocket. When I was intro-

33

duced to him, we shook hands, and I noticed to my chagrin that his fingernails were better manicured than mine.

Bob had begun his career marketing foreign exchange to the bank's customers. His sense of self-assurance combined with an understated humor held a universal appeal. He charmed both men and women (particularly the latter) and was considered to be one of the bank's most successful young salesmen. Bob could, and often did, convince people who had no need whatsoever for foreign currency to buy large quantities of it, and at overstated prices.

Bob loved to trade. Here was an opportunity to sell anything to anybody. He was particularly interested in selling options that no other trader was willing to sell.

"Why did you sell that option?" I would ask Bob of a particularly complex trade. Bob never volunteered information; he would only respond to a direct question. Whenever I spoke to him, he would look at me so blankly that I was never sure he remembered who I was.

"Because it puts customer business on the books."

"Isn't it risky, though?" I would ask.

"What do you mean, risky?"

"Can't you lose a lot of money on it?"

"Nancy," Bob would say, with a finality that signaled his patience was at an end, "these are options. You can't lose a lot of money trading options."

I believed everything they told me. It seemed that they traded with ease and confidence. I wanted to know how much money they made for the bank, but something in their attitude suggested that it was inappropriate to ask.

It turned out I didn't have to.

Once a month, the options position was assessed for profit and loss. One day, soon after I'd started, Paul,

Bob, and I sat down to value all the options in the portfolio. That is, we had to decide what every option was
worth on that day. This is called *finding the market value
of an option*. The difference between that market value
and the amount of money that had been paid for the
option if the option had been purchased, or the amount
of money received for that option if it had been sold,
was then tallied by hand by the accounting represen-
tative, Kashir Rameshwar. Whatever the resulting
number came out to be was assumed to be the profit
or loss for the month.

Paul handed me a sheet of paper on which were
listed the options that I was supposed to value. There
were over one hundred options on my list.

Some of the options had been purchased from or
sold to one of the public exchanges that offer currency
options. The exchanges list the market value of all their
options on a daily basis, so for exchange-traded options
I just put down whatever the exchange said was the
market value of that particular option.

But exchange-traded options were only a very small
percentage of the options in our portfolio. For over 80
percent of the portfolio there were no listed market
values.

"How should I calculate the market price for the
options that are not listed on the exchange?" I asked
Paul.

"Eyeball it," he advised me.

Eyeball it?

Paul's method for determining the price of an option that was not listed on the exchange was to pretend
it was listed on the exchange, and extrapolate a price.
He showed me how to do that, and I copied his method
and went to work. It took about three hours for all of
us, working steadily, to value the portfolio this way.

I was aware almost immediately that there were
two dangers with this system. The first was that be-

cause Paul and Bob and I were assigning the market values (using the rigorous "eyeball" method), we could more or less assign any value we wished. There didn't appear to be any second checks. Almost no one at the bank knew what an option was, so there was no one to monitor our work. This meant that, if we'd wanted to, we could have shown whatever profit we wished.

The second danger was that Kashir seemed to have absolutely no idea of what he was doing. Not only could he not provide the necessary second check on our calculations, he didn't seem to know what to do with the data we provided.

However, as no one but I seemed to have any problem with this arrangement, we handed in our market values to Kashir and awaited the result.

A week after we assigned the month-end market values, Kashir, whose office was located just off the main trading room, came by holding a slip of paper behind his back. Kashir was of medium build. He wore his jet-black hair slicked back off his face, and had a fondness for bow ties. He spoke with a heavy accent.

Kashir had been with the bank seemingly since its inception, and over time had performed a wide variety of tasks all having to do with the operations side of the bank. That's where the bank performs its internal accounting, makes and receives payments, and monitors the traders' positions. The operations department of any commercial bank or trading house is absolutely crucial to the financial health of the institution. Operations are ultimately responsible for guarding the bank against fraud and theft. Unfortunately, operations work is also boring, which results in a high turnover rate for personnel. Kashir had achieved his position principally by outlasting the competition. As the most senior person in his department, he was responsible for verifying the profit and loss of the entire trading floor. When Paul and Bob started up the options desk, senior management deemed it unnecessary to go to all the trouble and expense of hiring an individual experienced in accounting for currency options, and assigned the additional task to Kashir.

Kashir made his way over to the desk and addressed himself to Paul.

"Ahem!" he began, clearing his throat and rolling his eyes nervously. "I haf here de profit-and-loss numbers," he announced, sneaking a glance at Paul to determine his reaction to this piece of information.

"Yes?" Paul replied pleasantly.

"I haf here de profit-and-loss numbers," Kashir repeated for emphasis.

"Yes?" Paul replied again, a shade less pleasantly. "What is the number?"

Here Kashir lost his nerve. "Ahh . . . " he drew in his breath, held it, and then finally let it out. "Ahh . . . " Suddenly, his face brightened with a new thought. "What number do you think eet should be?"

"It doesn't matter what number I think it is," Paul replied. "You're the accounting person. It's your responsibility to determine the profit or loss on the position for the month. It's you who are representing to senior management how well or how poorly this area is performing on a monthly basis." Here Paul paused for effect. "If you misrepresent the number, it's your head, not mine."

"Yes, I know." Kashir cleared his throat again. "But what number do you think eet should be?" he persisted, finally raising his eyes to meet Paul's pleadingly.

"I told you, it doesn't matter what I think!" Paul was exasperated now. "What is the number?"

Kashir couldn't bring himself to say the number, so instead he handed Paul the slip of paper he had been twisting around and around in his hands. "Here eet is," he said glumly.

"A loss? A $250,000 loss?" Paul's voice reflected astonishment and anger. "It's wrong."

"Eet's wrong?" Kashir repeated hopefully, his eyes still on the ground. After all, he had finally ascertained one figure the profit and loss was not. "You think maybe dees loss is too beeg? You think maybe de loss should be smaller?"

"I think it should not be a loss," Paul said emphatically.

Kashir lifted his head, his eyes searching Paul's face as if to find the answer there. "You think eet should not be a loss," he repeated thoughtfully.

"Of course," Paul's tone was more casual now, "if you wish to represent this number to senior management . . . " He left the sentence unfinished.

"No, no," Kashir interrupted hurriedly. "Dees ees only an interim number," he explained. "I haf to go back and recheck eet."

"Okay," Paul said, turning his back to end the conversation.

Two days later Kashir reappeared and sidled up to the desk, clutching a new piece of paper. He stood behind Paul's chair, a little off to the side, waiting to get his attention. Paul made him wait about five minutes before turning toward him.

"Yes, Kashir," he said. "What can I do for you?"

"I haf now de profit-and-loss number," Kashir announced, head slightly bent, staring at Paul's kneecaps. "You were right. Eet ees not a loss." He paused.

"Oh?" Paul queried. "What is it?"

"Eet ees a gain."

"Yes?" Paul stared directly into Kashir's bowed head, where a heavy film of hair tonic combined with the overhead lighting to produce a rainbow effect. "How much of a gain?"

Pause.

"Eet ees a gain of $5,000," Kashir whispered, staring at the paper in his hand.

Now Paul paused.

"Five thousand dollars?" he said incredulously. "Five thousand dollars? Do you think I worked that hard last month for a lousy $5,000? Five thousand dollars is not a gain! You can make more than $5,000 a month if you invested the money in a Treasury bill!" Paul sputtered. "Jesus! You could make at least $250,000 a month just investing the money in a crummy Treasury bill!"

Kashir caught the magic number. Raising his eyes to Paul's belt buckle, he repeated, "Two hundred and fifty thousand dollars a month?"

"Of course!" Paul was contemptuous. "Over $250,000 a month," he added.

"I see," Kashir nodded slowly.

"Of course, if you want to represent this figure to senior management—"

"No, no!" Kashir cut in. "Dees ees only an interim number."

About a week later Kashir returned, beaming. We were by this time two weeks into the next month, not yet having a profit-and-loss number to show management for the preceding month. Kashir walked proudly up to Paul's desk and waved a piece of paper under his nose.

"I haf here de profit-and-loss number for last month," he announced.

"What is it?"

"Eet ees a gain of $300,000!"

"Really?" Paul broke into a smile. "Hey, that's terrific! Hey, John!" Paul called over to the boss. "Come over here! Kashir has the profit-and-loss number for last month!"

"Finally!" John came racing over to the desk. "What is it?"

Before Kashir could say anything, Paul cut in.

"It's a gain of $300,000! Isn't that so, Kashir?" Paul turned and stared at Kashir.

"Ahh . . . well . . . ahh . . . "

"Wonderful!" John bellowed. "Let me congratulate you!" he shook Paul's hand. Then he turned back to Kashir. "Now, are you sure that number is correct?" he asked.

Both pairs of eyes bored into Kashir's bowed head. "Ahh . . . yes, eet's right," he mumbled.

"Wonderful!" John took the paper to his office.

Kashir slunk back to his desk.

The first time I saw this happen, I approached Paul, puzzled.

"If you knew the profit for the last month was $300,000, why didn't you just tell Kashir what you thought in the first place? Couldn't you have gone over his numbers with him to find the error, so it wouldn't happen again next time?"

Paul looked at me. "I didn't know that the profit for last month was $300,000," he said.

"You didn't?" I asked, surprised. "What should it have been then?"

"How should I know?" Paul shrugged. "It might have been a loss for all I know."

"But . . . ," it was my turn to stammer. "Kashir . . . "

"Hey." Paul was stern. "It's Kashir's job to figure out the profit-and-loss number, not mine. It's not my fault if he misrepresents the situation to senior management."

Thus were the profit-and-loss numbers determined monthly for the options section of a large commercial bank.

I was coming home from work one night. It was about six-thirty on a Thursday evening. I had been working at my new trading job for almost two weeks.

I got off the subway and climbed the steps to the open air, bracing myself for the chill of the February night. I moved slowly. I was still unaccustomed to my new hours. Having to wake up every morning at five-thirty was throwing off my internal clock. It was like having perpetual jet lag.

I fought the wind, clutching my copy of the day's work to me. After two weeks, I had a grasp of the absolute basics. In order to avoid confusion, I turned over my newfound knowledge constantly in my mind, memorizing it until it took on the unreal singsong quality of a nursery rhyme.

> If I buy a call, I'm long the currency, short the dollar.
> If I sell a call, I'm short the currency, long the dollar.
> If I buy a put, I'm short the currency, long the dollar.
> If I sell a put, I'm long the currency, short the dollar.

A vast improvement in understanding from a mere two weeks ago. Still, something less than what was needed actually to trade.

But tonight I did not repeat my lessons under my breath. Tonight I had other things on my mind.

For the first time I had discovered that the dollar was actively traded abroad while I was at home asleep. According to Paul, the Far Eastern market, which included Singapore and Tokyo, began trading at around eight o'clock in the evening New York time, and stayed open until the traders in Europe and London came in. Although I knew that the dollar traded while I was sleeping (the morning price was almost always different from that of the previous afternoon), I had not understood that the foreign markets were every bit as active as the one I traded in. In fact, the London market was actually larger than the New York market.

I had been surprised to learn that Paul regularly monitored the market in the Far East from his home at night. I myself was exhausted when I got home from work. It was all I could do just to force myself to work through the day's trades. How did Paul manage? My respect for him increased.

Then the blow fell.

Paul was bemoaning his inability to trade the London and European markets when they first opened in the morning, sometime around 3:30 A.M. New York time. He couldn't very well trade Singapore until 11:30 P.M., get up again at 3:00 A.M., and expect to put in a full day's work at the office.

Suddenly he looked at me.

"Hey! I've got a great idea," he said. "Why don't you come in every morning at three-thirty and trade London for us?"

I looked around to see whom he was talking to. There was nobody else in the immediate vicinity.

"Me?" I choked.

"Sure. Why not? It's not like you'd have to stay all day. I wouldn't be so unreasonable as to expect you to work until six every night. You'd be the early morning shift. You come in at three-thirty and stay until, say two-thirty in the afternoon. Bob and I would come in at our regular time." He thought about it. "We could even come in a little later. I mean, you'd be here to cover."

I started to laugh.

"It's a joke, right?" I giggled. "You're putting me on?"

"What's wrong with it?" Paul demanded.

I stopped laughing.

"Why . . . uh . . . ." I searched frantically for an irrefutable objection. "Why, I can't even trade yet! I

42

haven't put on a single trade by myself. I just sit here and watch you. I don't even know what to do yet when somebody calls and wants to trade. I can't be here all by myself!"

"Well, I'm not saying we have to start tomorrow," said Paul. "Maybe in a couple of months. You can always call me at home if there's a problem."

"But, Paul!" I was desperate. "I can't. I mean, I wouldn't feel comfortable alone here . . . at that hour . . . "

"Nancy," said Paul. "Sit down."

I sat.

"Nancy," said Paul. "I look at you, and Bob, and myself, as a professional team playing an intensively competitive sport, like football. We have to give up everything to win. It's a question of giving it our all. Of self-sacrifice and determination." He saw the blank expression on my face. "Maybe you don't watch football," he continued. "But do you know what I'm talking about? It's like a team sport. Everybody plays team sports in school. Nancy, what sport did you play in high school?"

"Water ballet."

Now, walking home from the subway, I reviewed this conversation. This is going to be some short career, I thought. If I say no, I will not come into the office at 3:30 A.M., Paul will probably fire me. If I say yes, I will come into the office at 3:30 A.M., I'll be killed taking the subway alone at that hour. That's not quite correct. I'll be killed walking out of my apartment building at that hour of the morning. I'll never make it to the subway.

On this cheerful note, I put my key in the lock and opened the door of my apartment.

For a second I thought I was in the wrong place.

The apartment had been cleaned, and there were

three big bunches of roses in vases around the room. The table had been laid for a candlelight dinner for two. There was a bottle of champagne cooling in an ice bucket. From the kitchen came the pleasant aroma of food cooking. The room was warm and cozy, and shadows flickered on the wall from all the candles. The scene was romantic and inviting.

Larry, dressed in black tie, was standing at the table lighting candles.

"What's all this?" I asked.

"Happy Valentine's Day," said Larry, putting his arms around me.

Valentine's Day! I'd forgotten all about it.

"Dinner for two coming up," he said. "May I pour you a glass of champagne?"

I just stood there.

"You can put your papers down now," said Larry. "We're not doing any options tonight." He went to open the champagne.

"It's beautiful," I said finally. "It's wonderful."

We ate the dinner and drank the champagne. All thoughts of the bank, the market, and Paul's latest suggestion were forgotten.

Later that evening, lying in bed, I told Larry of Paul's suggestion.

"That's absurd," he laughed. "You can't ask a young, attractive woman to be traipsing around Manhattan in the dead of night. Besides, you don't have a clue to what you're doing. If they really want to trade London, they should hire an experienced trader to work out of the bank's London office."

"You mean you think I can tell him that I won't do it?" I asked.

"Absolutely. Stick up for yourself."

By the end of February I had advanced to the point that I could handle several tasks: confirming the daily

44

trades with the proper counterpart, writing out instructions for wire transfers, computing premiums. However, I was no closer to knowing what Paul and Bob's trading strategies were than I was when I was a loan officer. I told Paul that I really couldn't see myself coming in alone for the opening of London every day. At first he protested, but then he dropped the subject altogether. I could tell that he didn't like my refusing him like that.

To make matters worse, I became aware that Paul and Bob were paying more and more attention to each other and less attention to me. They were always whispering together, or speaking in half-sentences that I knew they didn't mean for me to understand. This made me feel left out, and I wondered if they were disappointed with my progress. When I first took over the administrative duties, I had made some mechanical errors, like sending a payment to the wrong bank. But these mistakes were corrected quickly, and I never made the same mistake twice. Still, I couldn't shake the suspicion that something was very wrong.

I was ready for the worst when Paul approached me on the last day of the month.

"I'm calling a staff meeting this evening at five. Just you and me and Bob. We'll meet in my office."

We had never had a staff meeting before. What was on Paul's mind? He'd said it pleasantly enough, but by now I knew that Paul was always pleasant.

Paul and Bob were already in the office when I arrived. They clearly had been discussing something, but stopped when I entered. I pulled a chair over to where they were sitting.

"So what's up?" I asked, to break the silence.

Paul and Bob exchanged glances. In their look I read my doom.

"Bob and I have some news for you," Paul began

cheerfully. "There's good news and there's bad news. Which do you prefer to hear first?"

I'm of the school of thought that believes in getting the worst over quickly.

"The bad news," I said.

"The bad news is that Bob and I are both resigning from the bank. I am going to run the options desk at another bank. Bob is going to work for a brokerage operation."

"How soon?"

"By Friday."

Three days!

"Does John know yet?"

"He'll know tomorrow."

I was speechless. No one at the bank except Paul and Bob knew anything whatsoever about options.

"Don't you want to hear the good news?" Paul asked.

"Of course."

"I'm recommending that you take over the desk."

"Well!" said Larry that evening after I had relayed these latest developments to him. "That explains a great many things."

"What do you mean?" I asked. I was still grappling with the enormity of the situation.

"Well, the kind of deals that Paul and Bob made take months to come to fruition."

"So?"

"So they knew they were going to leave when they hired you."

"What exactly are you saying?"

"I'm saying that they needed to hire someone so that they could both leave the bank at the same time without appearing overly irresponsible. They probably

46

would have hired a chimpanzee if they thought they could get away with it."

Early the next morning, I saw Paul disappear into John's office. Bob flashed me a conspiratorial smile.

Already I had noticed a change in Bob's manner. Normally he would have been too absorbed in his own affairs to take much notice of me. This morning, however, he made an effort to be friendly.

"When this is all over," he whispered, "you and I will go out for a drink and we'll have a nice talk."

I said I thought that would be fine.

"And before I go," Bob continued, "I want to give you my new phone number. You know, I'm going to be brokering currency options. I don't see any reason why you and I shouldn't do some profitable business together. After all, I feel kind of responsible toward you. You know I've always tried to help you whenever I could."

Paul came out of John's office and wandered over to where Bob and I were standing.

"Your turn," he said to Bob.

"Right!" said Bob. "This is going to be fun!"

I asked Paul how John had taken the news.

"Not badly," he said. "But then again, he doesn't know about Bob yet."

"I see."

John came tearing out of his office.

"Both of you?" he asked Paul.

Paul nodded.

"Back into my office!" John ordered.

Paul, Bob, and John were closeted for the whole day. I waited to see if John intended to talk to me, but they were still at it at six-thirty in the evening. I decided to give up and go home. I was relieved. I needed time to appraise the situation.

"What do you think I should do?" I asked Larry.

"Well, that depends," he replied. "Do you want to run the desk?"

I weighed the advantages and disadvantages of the situation. On the negative side I listed the following: I didn't know how to trade; I didn't understand Paul's and Bob's trades that were already on the books; the bank had no accounting system to help me keep track of the position or the profit and loss; there was no one at the bank who could help me to learn the business; and Paul and Bob were leaving approximately $1 billion worth of trades to manage, too much for one person to handle alone. The amount of work involved would be staggering, as I would have to watch the New York, London, and Singapore markets by myself. That alone was a twenty-four-hour job.

On the positive side there was only one factor: I would never have this chance again.

"I want to do it," I said.

Paul had been induced to stay on an extra week. I spent as much time with him as I could, working frantically to understand the trades that would be left to my management.

John asked to see me.

"We have to talk," he said.

"Certainly," I replied.

"Why don't you come into my office right now so we can chat for a minute?"

I decided to set the rules immediately.

"I think that what we have to say to each other will take longer than a few minutes. Besides, I have to trade now."

He was taken aback.

"Oh! Of course." He thought for a moment. "Well, how about dinner tonight after work? That should give us enough time."

"That will be fine."

That evening, John relaxed comfortably against the soft leather of the booth.

"I hope you like steak," he said. "This place has the best T-bones in town."

We ordered drinks. John raised his glass.

"Cheers," he said, taking a long pull of scotch and soda.

"Cheers," I seconded, sipping my wine.

Silence. I waited for him to begin.

"Nancy," John said, breaking the silence, "have I ever outlined for you my global plan for the trading sector of the bank?"

I said I didn't think so. I didn't bother to mention that, as this was only the second time we'd ever spoken, it seemed unlikely that I'd know of his global scheme.

"Well then!" He sat up a little straighter. "Let me give you some background. I was an officer in the Marine Corps during the Vietnam War. When I joined the bank back in 1973 . . ."

Drinks came and went. Appetizers were served.

"After I was promoted to vice president I was assigned to London . . ."

The steaks came. Mine was quite good.

"I told the chairman of the board that I wanted to run a global operation . . ."

The waiter cleared the plates and brushed the tablecloth for crumbs. Dessert menus were passed around. I ordered chocolate cake.

"I'm planning on expanding into Hong Kong . . ."

Finally, coffee was served.

"Well, that's about all I have to say." John paused to take a sip of coffee. "By the way, do you have any questions?"

"Just one," I replied.

"What is it?"

"Have you considered that I am the only person at the bank with any experience whatsoever in trading options, the only person who has any idea of the extent of the bank's exposure in currency options? That if I walk out of this restaurant and get hit by a truck the bank is at risk for millions and millions of dollars?"

He choked on his coffee.

"Something wrong, sir?" the waiter asked.

"Huh?" John asked, and then recovered. "No, everything's fine here, thank you."

Silence.

"So what do you want?" John asked, finally.

"I only want what's fair," I replied. "If I'm to take on all of this work and all of this responsibility, I deserve the benefits of the position as well."

"What do you intend to ask for?"

I took the plunge.

"I want an immediate 100 percent raise in salary. I want a bonus plan at the end of the year tied to my performance. And I want an immediate promotion to vice president and manager of the Options Trading Unit."

"That's rather a tall order," John replied uneasily.

"Look, John," I said. "We both know it will cost you twice as much to go out and hire an experienced trader and you still take the risk that whoever you get won't be able to handle the trades the bank has been left with. I at least have some familiarity with Paul's and Bob's trading styles and with our current exposure."

Silence.

"This is what I can do for you," John sighed. "A 50 percent increase in salary immediately. The other 50 percent increase in three months."

"What about the promotion and the bonus?"

"Promotions are harder to come by than raises. However, I believe that I can swing a promotion to vice president at the end of the three months."

"Vice president and manager," I corrected.

"Of course, vice president and manager," he echoed.

"And the bonus?"

"The bonus plan has to be approved by the board of directors," he said.

I waited.

"I'll do my best," he said.

I waited.

"All right," he said. "I'll recommend a bonus plan that is tied to performance. That's all I can do," he added quickly.

I thought about it.

"Okay," I said. "I'll do it. But there's something else."

"What is it?" John asked anxiously.

"I want all of this in writing."

"What's the matter?" John asked. "Don't you trust me?"

The next morning I walked into the trading room and over to the options desk. Both Paul's and Bob's chairs sat empty. Everyone in the room knew that I was going to try and fill the position of two seasoned options traders with only a little over a month's experience behind me. I could feel myself being sized up by both the spot foreign-exchange traders on my right and the interest-rate traders on my left.

I turned on all the computer screens as I had been taught to do. I took out the handwritten sheets that comprised the options position. I sipped black coffee as I examined the papers.

I was now the head currency options trader at the bank with a $1 billion options portfolio to manage.

What to do now?

3 The Learning Process

What I didn't know, couldn't have known, was that my solitary apprenticeship would mark by coincidence the advent of one of the most violent periods in the history of the currency markets: the beginning of the decline in the value of the dollar. In March 1985, when I assumed my new duties, the dollar was so high that it was difficult for producers of U.S. goods to sell their products abroad. American manufacturers were having trouble selling their products at home as well. Foreign goods were so much cheaper. The U.S. automobile industry, for example, was extremely threatened by a strong dollar. It seemed as if everybody was buying a Japanese car. The seriousness of the problem was reflected in the magnitude of the U.S. trade deficit.

The leaders of the industrialized world, led (some say coerced) by those in the United States, embraced the downward trend in the dollar as a panacea for the worsening economic climate. Not two weeks after the departure of Paul and Bob from my bank, the market began what was to become a two-year, all-out, free-for-all, come-and-get-'em, going-out-of-business, children-eat-free, fire sale on the dollar. This fire sale was punctuated every few weeks by panicked buying on the part of incredulous traders who, after watching the dollar appreciate for months and months, couldn't rid themselves of a strong-dollar bias and continued to buy the dollar periodically, almost from force of habit, as if against their wills. On the other hand, more astute traders profited by understanding that a major shift in opinion was taking place, and only waited for the chance to sell more. These competing impulses—the overwhelming rush to sell followed by short bursts of intense buying—resulted in wild swings in the value of the dollar, swings of such speed and violence that many veteran traders who understood the magnitude of the risks involved became frightened by the upheaval and chose to abstain from trading for short periods of time. I was not one of them.

I entered the world of trading with two advantages. As I had spent the last year and a half as a lending officer, I was oblivious to the dollar's recent appreciation in value and so had no bias in favor of a strong dollar. Furthermore, I was so inexperienced that I didn't know enough to be frightened. This resulted in my being able to take risks that would have made a seasoned trader shudder. Not that I knew I was taking risks. I thought I was just trading.

During those first three months of trading, through one of the most traumatic periods in market history, John left me completely alone. I was never asked to report on my position. I was never given any guidelines by which to trade. I was never told to limit the size of my positions. I'm not sure he knew that I was taking positions. (I'm not sure *I* knew that I was taking positions.) We communicated on the average of once a month, at which time Kashir would present the profit-and-loss numbers.

I found out later—much later—that the bank's board of directors approved limits under which each of its traders was to operate. But as nobody ever bothered to tell me what my limits were in the beginning, and as the bank had no system in place that enabled management to monitor my positions, I confess I don't see what purpose the limits served. In retrospect I realize that I must have been substantially over my limits often in those first few months. But who could tell?

To give an idea of the complete power that I was exercising, let me explain that if an officer of the bank wanted to commit $1 million of the bank's resources in the form of a loan to a customer, that officer would have had to have the decision approved by a bank credit committee. The decision to lend $1 million would have taken weeks, perhaps months. But for me to commit $20 million, $50 million, $100 million of the bank's resources to the purchase or sale of foreign-currency options, I had only to pick up the phone and make the trade. No one asked me what I was doing. No one seemed to care.

In the absence of any semblance of control or direction, I simply assumed that I had an unlimited source of funds behind me and operated accordingly.

The trading world reacted to the news of my taking over after Paul's and Bob's departures in the same way sharks react to the sight of a wounded man set adrift at sea.

My telephone console was blinking furiously with

unanswered calls by the time I got into the office at 7:20 A.M. The conversations were short and to the point.

"Options desk," I said, answering a call at random.

"Halloo?" said the voice on the other end of the phone through the static that indicated an international call. "This is Franz calling from Geneva, Switzerland. May I please speak with someone on the options desk?"

"Hello, Franz. This is Nancy on the options desk. How may I help you?"

"Can you make me a price?" Franz asked.

Making a price is trader jargon. It means: I-wish-to- trade- an- option- but- I- don't- want- you- to- know-whether- I'm- a- buyer- or- a- seller- so- that- I- can- take-advantage-of-you-if-possible. It is far easier to react to someone else's price than it is to have to make one up yourself. But that was a lesson that I learned later on.

"Certainly," I replied.

Franz wanted a price on a call option. The price of an option is determined by a number of factors: the current spot price of the dollar relative to the foreign currency in question; the date the option is to expire; the forward price of the dollar against the currency; the current U.S. interest rate; the interest rate in the country of the foreign currency; and the volatility of the currency in the market. I fed my computer this information as Paul had taught me to do. The computer responded with the price I should be willing to pay if I were buying, and the price I should be willing to take if I were selling. I quoted these two prices to Franz.

"Okay," said Franz immediately. "I sell $10 million to you."

I knew by the quickness of his response that I had made a mistake and that my price was too high. I'd seen Paul trade and knew that when there was no hesitation in the other trader's voice, there was something wrong. However, in trading your word is your handshake. I had just bought $10 million worth of an option from Franz.

"Done," I said, writing down the trade on a sheet of paper.

"Have you more to do there?" Franz asked casually.

Damn! The price must have really been high. Franz wanted to sell me more than $10 million.

"Not at that level," I hedged.

"Can you make me another price then?" Franz asked.

The man had no shame.

What could I do? I made him a new price but this time I lowered my bid substantially.

"Okay," said Franz. "I sell another $10 million to you."

Would this never end? What was I going to do with $20 million worth of a call option that gave me the right to sell the dollar at a much lower price than it was currently trading at, anyway? Buy a call, long the currency, short the dollar. That meant that the dollar would have to fall for me to make any money. Everybody knew that the dollar was going to rise in value, not fall. Here I was paying Franz all this money for an option that would most likely end up being worthless. Franz's gain; my loss.

"Done," I said again.

At this point I was thoroughly sick of talking to Franz. Before he had a chance to breathe, let alone ask me for another price, I cut in.

"I'm so sorry Franz, but the other phones are all ringing. I have to go now."

I hung up quickly without saying good-bye. I considered myself lucky to have escaped without having bought $50 million. The nerve of some people! Taking advantage of me like that!

Still, I took it in stride. After all, I consoled myself, they couldn't all be like Franz.

With renewed spirit I answered the next phone call. The voice on the other end of the phone was English this time.

"Can you make me a price?" it asked.

On the other hand, maybe they could.

Despite the merciless attack by colleagues here and abroad, I was able to turn my first few weeks of trading to good advantage. This didn't exactly happen by design. It was just that when the dollar started to fall, I panicked. I knew that I had inherited a large number of trades from Paul and Bob that were predicated on a strong dollar. If the dollar went down, these trades would lose money. So I sold a whole lot of dollars on the theory that if the dollar continued to fall I would make more on the dollars I'd sold than I would lose on the inherited trades. If the trend toward a lower dollar had reversed itself, I would have lost far more on the dollars I'd sold than I would have made on the inherited trades. It was a risky thing to do.

As it turned out, selling dollars was exactly the right thing to do.

In addition to that, the call options I had purchased as a result of my overly high price making turned out to be quite valuable once the dollar started to fall.

Looking back over the situation I see now that I was the beneficiary of a phenomenon not unknown to the trading community: beginner's luck.

I was just starting to breathe a little easier when events took a turn for the worse.

I was hard at work at my desk one afternoon when I heard a sound behind me. I turned around to find Kashir standing there holding a slip of paper in his hand.

I realized that the March profit-and-loss numbers were due.

This first profit-and-loss number was very important to me. I regarded it as justification for the long hours I had spent struggling through an extremely difficult period.

Although a lack of detailed information on the positions that I had inherited from Paul and Bob made it impossible for me to calculate the exact profit-and-loss number, I knew that I had been trading profitably. My most conservative estimate for the month's profit and loss was a gain of $250,000. I felt that I was actually doing better than this, but I didn't know how much would be recognized immediately, and how much would be deferred until the next month. In any event, I looked forward to hearing Kashir's report.

"Ahem!" Kashir cleared his throat.

"Yes?"

"I haf here de profit-and-loss number," he began.

There was something very different about Kashir today. He seemed to have had a change in attitude. He wasn't staring at the floor or twisting the paper nervously in his hands. His posture was erect; his manner threatening, even defiant.

"Yes?" I repeated.

"Eet ees a loss!" he announced, staring directly into my eyes.

A loss! "How much?" I asked.

"Eet ees a loss of $300,000!" he trumpeted.

A $300,000 loss! It wasn't possible! "Are you quite sure?" I asked, shocked.

"Absolutely!" He was actually grinning.

"Show me the numbers," I ordered.

Kashir handed me a disorganized pile of papers that represented his work sheets. On the sheets were scrawled figures in varying degrees of legibility.

"Leave these with me," I said. "I don't have the time to look at them right now."

"You don't haf to look at them," said Kashir. "I tell you de number ees correct."

It was my turn to stare Kashir in the eye.

"We'll see," I said.

He turned and walked away.

I studied the work sheets after Kashir had left. They were indecipherable. I called Kashir on the telephone, asking for explanations on some of his calculations. His answers were confused. The profit-and-loss numbers were produced by comparing this month's market values to last month's market values, so all of Kashir's calculations were based in part on numbers generated while Paul managed the desk. Last month's numbers had already been accepted by senior management and could not be changed. Nor, I realized helplessly, could they be disproved.

I knew that I had traded profitably in March. The only possible explanation for the loss Kashir was showing was that the profits that had been reported in prior months had been overstated. The overstatement (now reflected as a loss) was being reported in this, my first month of trading. And there was nothing I could do to prevent it. I was too inexperienced, too new at my job, for my version of events to carry any weight. Kashir had been with the bank forever. I had been there for fewer than four years. Kashir was a man in his late forties. I was a woman in my mid-twenties. I knew that if I attempted to argue with Kashir's results I would be branded as a troublemaker and, worse, as a woman who tried to blame her own mistakes on others. This, I knew, was an unacceptable sin in the eyes of the trading community. There was nothing to be done at the moment. I conceded the first round to Kashir.

But that didn't mean I wasn't going to get even.

▲ ▲ ▲

I was understaffed and needed some help. I pressed John, and in April I was assigned the services of an administrative assistant by the name of Phillip Lee. Phillip had been with the bank for over a year. He had spent most of this time on the spot foreign-exchange desk, where his most demanding duty was fetching the senior traders their coffee and doughnuts. Even after he was officially assigned to me, the spot desk refused to part with him for an additional two weeks. After that, they were forced to get their own coffee.

Of Asian descent, Phillip had come to New York to pursue a career in banking. He had received his graduate degree from Stanford, where he had graduated near the top of his class. His passion was computers.

In January, Paul and Bob had persuaded John to buy an options software package designed for personal computers. This software had arrived just before they left. The problem was that nobody (including me) knew how to use it. I asked Phillip if he thought he could adapt the software to accommodate our needs. We needed reports that were organized along the lines of our general trading style, rather than simply listing a long series of trades in no particular order. It was done within the week. I asked Phillip to generate a series of reports that would measure our overall exposure in the event of large currency moves. If the dollar rose or fell substantially overnight, what would be the effect on our portfolio? Should we be buying or selling the dollar? The reports were on my desk the next morning. I asked Phillip if it would be possible to produce daily profit-and-loss statements, rather than monthly. The reports were produced every afternoon and were on my desk by the time I went home in the evening.

I kept the existence of the profit-and-loss statements to myself for a while. As no one ever bothered to ask me how I was doing or what positions I was taking, this was not hard to do.

I continued to trade, and tried to keep my risk to a minimum by buying as many options as I sold. However, the daily P and L reported that while this conservative trading strategy made money consistently, the profits accrued slowly. I wanted a strategy that would make a whole lot of money quickly. After all, I had a $300,000 loss to make up, didn't I?

I decided to take a large position by either buying or selling dollars. It was, I knew, the only way for me to make back all of March's loss in April.

I analyzed the situation carefully. I was beginning to discuss the market on a much more detailed and informed basis with some of my colleagues on the spot foreign-exchange desk, and with traders at other institutions. I reviewed past data on the U.S. economy, and investigated what experts were predicting for the future. I analyzed technical data and surveyed charts. By degrees I arrived at a well-informed conclusion. I decided to buy the dollar.

Wrong.

I can still close my eyes and remember the horror of that first loss. The dollar started to fall precipitously in value almost from the moment I put on my position.

Not having yet learned the importance of exercising discipline in such cases, I stubbornly refused to cut my losses. It seemed impossible to me that the market wouldn't come back at least to where I'd bought in the first place. I held on to that thought and the dollars for three days, at the end of which time I had lost $500,000. That was in addition to the $300,000 loss that Kashir had already reported for March.

At this point I felt it was in my best interest to inform John of the situation.

I approached John's secretary first thing in the morning.

"I'd like to see John today," I said.

She looked over her glasses at me.

"Is it important?" she asked.

Was a half-million-dollar loss in three days important?

"Reasonably," I said.

She glanced down at her calendar.

"He's busy all day," she said. "But I think he can spare fifteen minutes between lunch and the weekly senior management meeting."

"I'll take it," I said.

I spent the next couple of hours contemplating my future. I felt terrible about losing the money. I understood now that I'd taken a risk with the bank's capital. I was playing with other people's savings deposits. Even though I had made the decision to buy dollars after an intelligent appraisal of the situation, I understood that it was the urge to make a quick and easy profit that had undermined me. I had become greedy, and the bank had paid. I had been rash, and the bank had paid. Although I recognized that everything I'd done had been motivated by the best of intentions, I was apprehensive about telling John. I wasn't sure but that I could be fired for making a mistake of this kind.

I was at John's office at the appointed time, but his luncheon ran late, and five minutes of my precious fifteen were wasted waiting for him to show up. Not that I minded the wait. It wasn't as if I were looking forward to this conversation.

"Have a seat," John said, breezing in. He flung himself into the chair behind his desk. "Sorry I'm late. I just couldn't get away."

"I understand," I said.

"So what's this all about?" John asked.

I took a deep breath.

"I've lost some money," I said. "Quite a lot of money, actually."

"I know," John said cheerily. "I saw Kashir's March figures."

"No," I said. "This is in addition to the March loss. This is the April loss." Before he could speak I rushed on. "I took a position. It was the wrong position to take. I lost $500,000. I'm sorry. It won't happen again."

"So you are now down almost $1 million, is that what you are saying?"

I nodded my head in misery. I couldn't even look him in the eye.

"Well, I suppose it can't be helped," said John. "Happens to everyone."

This was unexpected. He was taking it so well.

"You think you can make it back quickly?" John asked.

"Oh, absolutely," I lied.

"Well, then," said John smiling at me. "That's fine. I have to go to the senior management meeting now. But, hey! Thanks for letting me know."

"Don't mention it," I said.

I walked out of that meeting confused, but relieved. John must know, I reasoned, that the only way for me to "make it all back quickly" was to take yet another, larger position. In fact, I got the definite impression that it was my job to do so.

This time, though, I vowed to learn from my mistakes. If the position began to be a losing one, I would take an immediate loss rather than wait and thereby risk substantially more. If I was right, I would take some of my profit immediately, or hedge my exposure by using some of my profit to purchase options, which would increase in value if the market turned around and went against me. And, most important, I would take a large position only when I was thoroughly convinced that the market would go my way—not just because I had taken a loss the week before. I would take a large position

63

only when I felt that technical and economic factors were signaling a move, and then only after I'd discussed the market with some of my colleagues at other institutions. These rules, in combination with a whole lot of luck, just might see me through this difficult period.

I continued to transact the conservative day-to-day trading that accumulated slow but steady profits, while waiting for the chance to take a large position. I did not contest Kashir's April figures, even though he reported a larger loss than was indicated by my own daily P and L.

Throughout this entire period, Phillip stood by me and became my friend and compatriot. I was lucky to have him.

Phillip is without doubt the most compassionate individual I have ever met. He always considers the other person's feelings and goes out of his way to be helpful or simply a good friend. I have never heard him say anything negative about another person. He is quiet and never volunteers advice. If you ask him for his opinion, he will choose his words carefully and they are always worth listening to.

Phillip is very intelligent. English is not his native language, so his speech is textbook-perfect. His manners are unparalleled; he could have taught Emily Post a thing or two.

Phillip's strengths complemented my own. I relied on him for computer prowess and technical analysis, two areas in which I was dangerously deficient.

On the whole I adored Phillip. There was only one small problem. Hardly worth mentioning.

He lived in another world.

▲ ▲ ▲

While Phillip was excellent at the large, terribly important computer-related aspects of the job, small human details utterly defeated him. My first tip-off of his problem came at lunchtime. The bank let us order free lunches from the cafeteria every day and had them delivered at noon in boxes so we could eat at our desks. That way we wouldn't miss a single second of trading. I ordered one of these free lunches once and decided not to repeat the experience.

Phillip, however, did not seem to mind the food, and took advantage of the bank's largess. He ordered the same thing every day: overcooked roast beef on Wonder Bread with raw onions, mashed potatoes accompanied by an unidentified green and brown gravy, and watered-down orange juice.

Unlike the other traders in the room, Phillip didn't wolf down his food as though it were his last meal. On the contrary, he would carefully unpack his lunch and then forget all about it.

The first time I saw this happen, I tried to be helpful.

"Phillip," I said, pointing to the sandwich, "why don't you eat your food now? It's one o'clock already. Aren't you hungry?"

"Huh?" he said, startled.

"Your lunch," I reminded him. "Eat your lunch."

"Oh!" He picked up the sandwich and opened his mouth to take a bite. Then he remembered his manners.

"May I offer you some?" he asked, extending the sandwich toward me.

"No, thank you anyway," I said, recoiling from the smell of raw onion.

"Oh! Okay!" he said, putting the sandwich down.

Another hour passed.

"Phillip, you still haven't eaten."

"Huh?"

"Your food. Eat your food."

He reached for the mashed potatoes. The gravy had hardened, coating the surface with a shiny cover of congealed fat.

"May I offer you some?"

"No, really, I'm not hungry."

Another hour passed.

"Phillip."

"Huh?"

"Please eat your food."

He ate.

"Oh! It's cold!" he said, surprised.

Lunch was only the beginning. This dreamlike state extended into other, more pressing areas.

"Phillip?"

"Huh?"

"Did you write the tickets yet so that the operations department can enter today's trades into the computer?"

"Oh! No! So sorry."

"It's one o'clock already. Let's try and get them done early today, okay? Otherwise the operations people have to stay late."

"Oh! Okay."

"Phillip?" I said later.

"Huh?"

"I don't see those tickets."

"Oh! So sorry! I forgot."

"Phillip, it's three o'clock," I reminded him after a while.

"Okay. I'll do them right now."

"Phillip?"

"Huh . . . ?"

This happened every day.

The simpler the task, the more difficult it was for Phillip to perform it. If it didn't relate to what he was plugging into a terminal, for Phillip it simply didn't exist.

"Phillip?"

"Huh?"

"The phone is ringing. Could you please answer it? I'm already on the other line."

"Oh! Sure! So sorry." He reached for the phone. "Good day? Good day?"

"No, I'm on that line," I said patiently. "Get the other line, please."

"Oh! Sure! So sorry," he said, starting to hang up.

"No! Wait!" I said. "You're about to—"

He hung up.

"—disconnect me."

"Oh! So sorry!"

"That's all right. Just get the other phone, okay?"

"Huh?"

I think I could have lived with all of this, except for one last thing. Phillip didn't like to trade options. It's not that he couldn't, it's just that he didn't want to. This can be a significant handicap for an options trader.

"Phillip?"

"Huh?"

"Could you please price this option for me?"

"Oh! Sure!"

"Phillip?"

"Huh?"

"Did you make that price I asked you for earlier?"

"Oh! So sorry!"

"Phillip, you can't leave people waiting like that. It's unprofessional."

"Yes, of course. So sorry!"

"Phillip?"

"Huh?"

"Did you make that price yet?"

He started to open his mouth.

"Never mind. I'll do it."

I decided I needed a third member of the team.

I gave the subject some thought and decided on an associate of mine from the lending side of the bank, Peter Poska. Peter was my friend.

He was two years younger than I, with a broad, open face that always had a well-scrubbed look to it. He kept his brown hair short and neatly parted on the side.

I had known Peter for two years. He'd been assigned to my unit while I was still in the lending department. He was just out of the bank's training program then and had graduated at the top of his class.

Peter's background was unusual. He came from a tiny town in the Midwest where his father raised cattle. It was an atmosphere as far removed from that of the city as it is possible to get without venturing into outer space, and even then I'm not sure that a small town set in the deep cold of the farm belt isn't one of the ends of the universe. There were no theaters, no restaurants, no social life for a teenager. The nearest farm was a half hour's drive, and the nearest movie (there was only one, of course) was even farther away.

In Highland Park, I spent my time going out with my friends or scooping ice cream at the local Baskin Robbins (a terrific after-school job; not only did I get to eat all the free ice cream I wanted, but as I regularly gave it away to members of the football and basketball teams I was enormously popular whenever one of them was hungry). By contrast, Peter was getting up at four o'clock in the morning to milk the cows or bale the hay or do whatever it is that is done on a cattle farm at four in the morning.

Peter is a quiet man. I put this down to his having spent most of his waking hours in the company of cows. Until you get to know him (and even then) it is difficult to get more than a "Yes" or "No" out of him, and then only in response to a direct question. Yet he had a dry wit and a commonsense way of looking at things that I found particularly refreshing.

What made Peter decide on commercial banking as a career is a mystery. No farmer has much respect for bankers, probably because farmers are actually forced to work with the financial community on a more or less regular basis.

Peter helped to handle his family's financial affairs at an early age.

"What was it like?" I asked.

Peter shrugged.

"Every couple of years or so the bank would give us a new loan officer," he said. "The new guy would drive out to the farm, and Dad would have to spend hours with him explaining the business." Peter shook his head. "Always the same questions. Always the same answers."

"What kind of questions did they ask?"

" 'Just how many head of cattle do you have, Mr. Poska?' " Peter imitated the fictitious banker in a high, squeaky voice. " 'We have ten thousand head of cattle, Mr. Banker,' " reverting to his usual delivery. " 'My! That seems like quite a lot, Mr. Poska.' " " 'Yes, sir, especially around milking time.' "

"I take it the cattle were put up as collateral," I said.

"Yup. They were always wanting to check out the collateral." Peter switched back to his banker voice. " 'Mr. Poska, I'm afraid that it's part of my job to count

69

the cattle.' 'Count the cattle, Mr. Banker?' 'Yes, please, Mr. Poska.' 'All of 'em, Mr. Banker?' 'All of them, Mr. Poska.' "

"Well," Peter continued, "it was my job to drive those bankers around so they could count the cattle. I thought I'd make my job a little easier. First I'd drive around in circles to get them good and confused."

"Yes?" I prompted.

"And then I'd drive to the closest pasture and show them the one thousand head of cattle there. Then I'd drive around a little more and go back to the same pasture and show them the same one thousand head. I'd do it over and over until they'd counted their ten thousand head, and then they'd go home until the next time."

Peter went through a period of culture shock when he first moved to the big city. He had made a conscious decision to leave his past behind him and to mold himself in a new direction. But because he was trying so desperately to fit into an environment so different from that of his early years, he was unsure of himself. He hid his roots, but he was never quite satisfied that he wasn't giving himself away unconsciously.

Peter's lack of self-assurance touched me. I have a younger brother just Peter's age, living in Chicago. How would I feel if my brother moved to a strange city to begin a new career? Wouldn't I want someone to look after him, to protect him in his new endeavor?

Accordingly, I adopted Peter.

While we were still in the lending area, I encouraged him in every way possible. I gave him the benefit of my experience. I tried to protect him from superiors. If we stayed late at the office, I always made sure that he had enough money to get home and told him to call me when he got in so I would know he was all right.

"Don't worry, Mom," he would say.

I guess I overdid it a little, but my heart was in the right place.

When I got to be a trader, it was natural for me to want Peter on the desk. It was clearly better for his career. There was more money in it. It was more stimulating intellectually. I could continue to watch over him.

I secretly discussed the matter with Peter and found him enthusiastic. The next step was to take it up with his boss, Ralph Johnston.

Ralph had been with the bank for over ten years and was technically my senior. He was jealous of my advancement and would certainly object to my hiring Peter.

I put a phone call through to Ralph. "Hello, Ralph," I said when he answered. "This is Nancy on the options desk. How are you today?"

"What do you want?" he asked.

"Well, actually, Ralph," I said, "I'm calling about Peter."

"What about Peter?"

"I think you know, Ralph, that the options desk is somewhat understaffed due to the recent loss of some of our more senior people."

"So?"

"The fact is, the need for extra personnel is becoming increasingly urgent. Peter is the only person in the bank with any real knowledge of options—"

"Not a chance," Ralph cut me off. "No way."

"Just let me explain a little . . ."

"There's nothing to explain. Peter is to remain here. You are not to mention this to him, do you hear?" He hung up.

Six weeks, even a month, earlier, Ralph's attitude would have intimidated me. By nature a shy and reserved person, I would have abandoned any idea that led me into direct conflict with a superior. But regularly trading and managing large sums of money was beginning to have its effect. It was time to flex my muscles.

It was possible to advertise job openings throughout the bank by circulating a memorandum outlining the responsibilities associated with the work and listing the minimum qualifications. No one could be forbidden to apply.

I had such a memorandum circulated. I made the qualifications specific. So specific, in fact, that as far as I knew they fit only Peter.

I told Peter about the memo, and he was the first person to apply. In all, I had seven applicants. Three were grossly unqualified for the position. Two were discouraged by the amount of work involved. Peter had only one serious rival, and that person's knowledge of options was cursory.

"Phillip?"

"Huh?"

"Who do you think we should hire, Peter or the other applicant?"

Silence while Phillip considered the question. "Let me see," he said finally. "They are both very good."

"But Phillip, we can't hire both. Who would you prefer working with?"

"It's very hard to make a choice."

"I know. But I would really appreciate your opinion."

Silence while Phillip struggled to avoid saying anything negative, even by implication. "I think Peter is a little bit better."

Peter it was.

I had won my first round.

4 The Tide Turns

Peter caught on to trading quickly and was soon able to take over some of the day-to-day responsibilities. This left me free to concentrate on the market.

By May I was convinced that the turmoil of March and April was coming to a close. One look at the spot foreign-exchange desk told me that the traders there could not keep up their frenzied pace for much longer. I concluded that the market would cool down during the summer and the dollar would once again begin a slow, measured descent. My conviction was so strong that I took by far the largest position that I had yet dared to take. If I were right, I knew that I would make back all of the losses in one fell swoop. If I were wrong . . .

It was the first week of July. I was once again hard at work at my desk when I heard a noise.

I recognized the sound immediately and turned to find Kashir standing upright behind me.

"Yes?" I encouraged him.

"I haf here de profit-and-loss number for June," said Kashir.

"Yes?"

Apparently my manner was not properly submissive because he repeated himself with more authority.

"I haf here de profit-and-loss number for June!"

"I heard you the first time," I answered. "What is the number?"

"Eet ees a loss!" Kashir had by this time developed a real flair for the dramatic.

"Really?" I asked. "How much of a loss?"

"Eet ees a loss of $300,000!"

I decided to give Kashir his one and only chance.

"Are you quite sure, Kashir?" I asked.

"Absolutely!" he insisted, throwing the papers on my desk and turning to go. "They will be distributed to senior management this afternoon."

"I wouldn't do that if I were you," I said.

Something in my tone made him turn around in midstride.

"Huh?" said Kashir.

"I wouldn't do that if I were you," I repeated.

"Why not?"

"Because it's not correct."

"How do you know?" he challenged.

I opened my desk drawer and took out a stack of my daily computerized profit-and-loss statements.

There is nothing so impressive as the sight of a stack of computerized reports. They are especially useful against the weak-minded.

Kashir took one look at the reports and turned pale.

"What are those?" he whispered.

"These," I said, patting the papers lovingly, "are a set of daily profit-and-loss statements recording our progress over the last two months. Phillip and I have checked them over to ensure that there are no errors. The entire position has been input into the computer as a matter of record, and the computer automatically values the position. I can assure you that all of these figures are correct and can be accounted for."

I waited a moment to let the full impact sink in.

"I can also assure you that the computer reports are not showing a $300,000 loss for June."

Kashir was beginning to hunch over.

"What . . . what number are you showing?" he asked.

"Why do you care?" I countered. "You told me that you were absolutely sure that your number was correct."

"I . . . I never said that," he mumbled.

"Oh? I must have misunderstood you then. What was it that you said?"

"I said . . . I said . . . eet ees only an interim number."

"Oh?" I said. "You mean that you want to go back upstairs to recheck your work?"

"Yes."

"All right," I said.

Kashir didn't move.

"Yes?" I said.

"Perhaps I should take a copy of one of those reports with me," pleaded Kashir.

"Kashir," I said, "I will give you the reports so that you can check your work." He made a movement toward the papers. I held up my hand to stop him. "Please

75

be advised that this information has been saved in the computer's memory, so that if any report is stolen or damaged I can always print a new one. If you have any questions, you can talk to Phillip about it. But I want you to work quickly. I intend to distribute my reports tomorrow afternoon to senior management whether or not you agree with them."

Not surprisingly, Kashir found that he had made a number of errors in his original calculation of the June profit-and-loss. After correcting these mistakes, he found that he agreed with the profit-and-loss figure demonstrated by the computer reports.

Senior management was pleasantly surprised to find that the options desk was recognizing a gain of $500,000 in June.

I was on my way.

My first three months as head trader were up.

In retrospect I understood that I had undertaken a task of almost Herculean proportions. I thought I'd done pretty well for the bank. Instead of a one-woman fiasco they had a three-person, fully functioning trading unit that was well on its way to profitability. Instead of a manual, error-filled accounting system they had a computerized program that monitored profit and loss and risk management on a daily basis. Instead of anonymity, they had a name that was recognized in the marketplace as a growing force.

Even though my three months had been up and I was owed a promotion and raise, I had not pressed the issue. I hadn't had the courage. Now that the desk was becoming profitable, my nerve returned. It was time for John to come through with his side of the bargain.

I went up to Linda's desk.

"I want to see John," I said. "Today."

Linda opened her appointment book.

"He hasn't got a second all day," she said. "He's booked all the way up until 6:30 P.M.."

"Fine," I said. "Tell him I'll see him at 6:30."

John was already in his office when I arrived promptly at 6:30. I walked in and shut the door behind me.

"Hello, Nancy," said John. "Have a seat."

I sat down in the chair across from his desk.

"Everything all right in the trading room?" he asked.

I assured him that everything was fine.

"That's good," he said.

Silence.

"So what can I do for you?" he asked finally.

"It's been three months," I said. "We had a deal."

"Is it three months already?" John asked vaguely.

"It's actually more than three months," I said.

"Oh," he said. "You know I've been so busy . . ."

I indicated that I appreciated the demands on his time.

"Well," said John. "I'm glad you reminded me. Let me get out your file and we'll discuss it."

Discuss it?

John called Linda into his office.

"Will you find Nancy's personnel file for me, please?" he asked her.

Linda went over to a file cabinet, picked out the appropriate folder, handed it to John, and left, closing the door behind her.

"She's just a wonder," said John. "Don't know what I'd do without her."

Silence.

John opened the file and flipped through a few pages.

"Let's see," he said. "What was it we had talked about?"

"We didn't just talk about it, we had an agreement," I reminded him. "After three months I was to be raised by another 50 percent, and promoted to vice president and manager. There was also to be a recommendation to the board of directors concerning my bonus."

"Nancy," said John, "let's examine each of these issues one at a time."

"Yes?"

"Let's begin with the additional 50 percent raise in salary," he said.

"Yes?"

"Although your performance has been adequate to date . . ."

Adequate?

"I don't see where you've earned an additional raise in salary," he said.

Silence.

"After all, you are still operating at a loss for the first three months, aren't you?" he asked.

More silence.

"I understand your difficulties and appreciate your efforts," said John. "I think you've made a fine start. Perhaps in another three months . . ."

Another three months? We'll see about that.

"I inherited those losses. I put in all new systems. We get daily profit-and-loss statements. Accurate profit-and-loss statements. By the end of this month the unit will be operating at a profit for the year. I've two people working for me that I've spent a significant amount of time training, and who show enormous potential. The bank's name is known in the market. The Options Unit is stronger today than it was the day that Paul and Bob resigned."

"I repeat that I commend your efforts," said John, "but I just don't see that an additional raise is justified."

Silence.

"I'm afraid I'm firm on this," he added.

"I'm sorry you feel that way," I said. "I'm afraid I don't agree with you." I stood up and started to leave the room.

"Where are you going?"

"Well," I said, "clearly there's nothing more to talk about. I'll have to reexamine the situation now. Perhaps I'll take a few days off to think about it. Of course, the market's pretty active now and someone else will have to try to run my position—"

Even John knew that there was no one else to run the position.

"Just a second," John cut in. "Let's not be too hasty."

I sat down again.

"Perhaps I was wrong after all," said John. "You have been working pretty hard and have had a number of obstacles to overcome."

I waited.

"All right," said John. "You'll get your raise."

"Thank you," I said.

"But about the promotion," he continued. "You know, Nancy, I feel very strongly about the title, vice president and manager. It's not a title one gives away lightly."

I waited.

"It usually takes at least seven years to receive such a title. As I understand it, this is only your third year with the bank; is that correct?"

I nodded.

"Don't you see that if I promote you you will be the youngest vice president and manager at the bank?"

Silence.

"I don't think you are ready to be a vice president and manager just yet," said John. "In another three months, perhaps . . ."

I stood up again.

"All right, all right," he sighed. "Vice president and manager it is."

I sat down.

"Thank you," I said.

"I don't suppose that you'd be willing to discuss the bonus recommendation . . . no, of course not. . . . I'll submit the recommendation to the board of directors at the end of this month."

"Thank you."

This time we both rose to our feet and shook hands. John smiled at me.

"Keep up the good work!" he said.

John kept his promise and I received both my raise and my promotion immediately. He was also successful in persuading the board of directors to approve a bonus arrangement that linked compensation directly to the earnings contributed by each trading unit. This made me one of the highest-paid individuals in the entire bank.

As it turned out, John didn't do too badly either. For the next six months I made one successful trading decision after another. He was more than justified in his decision to raise and promote me.

My power grew daily. I was alternately respected, feared, and hated throughout the bank. In three short months I had gone from a lowly loan officer to a position of recognized authority in a highly visible area of the bank.

My star was on the ascendancy.

It seemed that nothing could go wrong.

5 The Company She Keeps

I fingered the cream-colored engraved invitation that had just arrived in the mail. A cocktail party was being given at the Waldorf-Astoria Hotel by one of the principal exchanges dealing in currency options. My presence at this function was requested.

I sighed as I turned the card over in my hand. Until now I had pretty much ignored the outside world, preferring to concentrate on matters closer to home. I had a hundred excellent excuses for putting off meeting my counterparts at other banks and financial institutions face-to-face. I told myself that I had my hands full at the bank; I had to organize my department, install computer systems, master my trade. Valid reasons, one and all.

But the truth was, I was scared. I wasn't sure I'd measure up to industry standards. It was safer and easier to hang back.

On the other hand, meeting the rest of the trading industry was something of a challenge. I couldn't get it out of my mind. Suddenly, it wasn't enough to have succeeded at the bank. I wouldn't be satisfied until I was respected as a professional by a jury of my peers.

Under the circumstances, there didn't seem to be much point in putting it off any longer. I was going to make my debut into trading society.

I took several deep breaths in front of the mirror in the ladies' room of the Waldorf-Astoria. The ladies' room at the Waldorf is a very nice place. There are dressing tables and complimentary cosmetics and a flowered sofa. At that moment I felt as if I could easily spend the night there.

This is it, I thought. I'm about to meet the most powerful and experienced traders in the options market. The crème de la crème. The elite. The chosen.

They know what they're doing. I don't. They're tough. I'm not. They'll be out there looking for weakness. My inexperience alone makes me an easy mark.

I'm in big trouble.

How can I even the odds? How earn the respect of people whose only definition of success is a personal net worth in excess of $20 million? These guys are killers! Sharks!

Sharks. That's it. That's the key.

I'm walking into a high-stakes poker game, aren't I? I thought suddenly. That's exactly what trading is all about. It's poker.

What wins in poker? Well, the cards, of course. But that's not enough. Good cards don't make a good poker player. Experience helps, too. I mean, you have to know the rules to win. But experience alone won't do it.

What really wins in poker is attitude. Attitude is the one quality that is absolutely necessary to win the game. There's only one thing to do, I decided.

Bluff 'em.

I walked into the crowded room.

The party was already in full swing. A rose-colored banquet room had been reserved for the occasion. The pinkish glow of the walls was set off nicely by the steel-gray cloud of cigarette smoke that forever shadows the trading industry.

I had been in New York for six years. This was the first time that I'd seen this many men all in the same place at the same time. There were men huddled in small groups. There were men clustered around the bar. There were men sitting and men standing up. There were men everywhere.

I had often heard my unmarried girlfriends wonder aloud at where all the men were in New York. Now I knew.

I'd never had any problem dealing with men in the past. It's just that I wasn't used to being in one room with quite so many all at once.

Oh, God, I thought. What'll I do if nobody talks to me?

At that moment a man stepped up to me.

Oh, God, I thought. Somebody's about to talk to me. What am I going to say?

The man in question was of less-than-average height with a mop of unruly dark hair that he made even messier by running his fingers through it every few minutes. He wore smudged horn-rimmed glasses and his shirt was wrinkled under his unbuttoned double-breasted blue pin-striped jacket. I judged him to be in his mid-twenties, perhaps a year or two younger than I. He was wearing a ridiculous bright orange name tag that read: "Hi! My Name Is Brian Henry!"

I recognized the name as belonging to a junior trader who worked at a competing bank.

He held out his hand to me. I took it.

"I'm Brian," he said.

"I'm Nancy," I said.

So far, so good.

"Pretty good turnout tonight," he commented, surveying the room.

"Oh, yes," I agreed, cautiously.

With this he fell silent, apparently having used up his entire store of snappy cocktail-party patter. Accordingly, I struggled to come up with something to talk about.

"How was your day today?" I asked.

Brian brightened immediately.

"Exhausting but profitable," he confided, grinning. "I captured 35 percent volatility in my Swiss book today and 28 percent in my yen book. And our theta curve is averaging $150,000 a day."

I stared at him. Was he speaking English? Perhaps this was some kind of a joke. I smiled uncertainly.

"Ah!" he said, puffing out his chest, which served to emphasize the food stains on his tie, "I see that you don't believe me. I don't blame you. Those are pretty impressive numbers."

What was the correct response? I searched frantically for some kind of answer.

"I believe you," I said.

"Listen," he said. "I can tell there's something else going on here. Maybe you think those numbers aren't so hot."

"I didn't say that—" I began.

"So what's the story?" he interrupted me. "You trying to tell me you're doing better than that? What's your time-decay number?"

I suppose if he could have told me what *time decay*

84

was, I might have been able to give him a number. As things stood, however, I could think of nothing better than to smile again.

"Not going to tell me, huh? What's the big secret? I told you mine."

I judged it best just to keep smiling.

"Two hundred thousand dollars a day?" he asked. "More? Two hundred fifty thousand dollars a day? Jesus! You telling me you're doing those kind of numbers?"

"I didn't say that," I objected again.

"You don't have to. I can see it on your face. I'm a pretty good judge of character, you know," he continued modestly.

"I think I need a drink," I said, edging away from him.

"Oh! Sure. But listen, let's sit down sometime and discuss the market, just you and me, okay? I have a feeling I could learn something from you."

"Uh . . . sure . . . sometime . . ." I said, backing off.

I went back into the ladies' room and wrote down every word he'd said. Perhaps there was a book somewhere that would explain it.

I returned to the party and moved in the direction of the bar, keeping as far away from Brian as possible. It was very crowded, and thus difficult to navigate.

I was stopped by a large group of traders who were arguing heatedly with one another. I was trying to find the best way of getting around them without simply pushing through. One of them noticed my efforts and pointed out my dilemma to the person next to him. They moved over to include me.

"Having trouble?" The trader laughed. He was about my age, but he had already lost a lot of his light brown hair and so looked older. His distinguishing characteristic was his height: he stood barely five feet four inches. As I stand five feet eight inches in my stocking feet and was at the time wearing three-inch heels, I'm sure we made an interesting couple.

"I'm afraid I am," I said, smiling down at him. I was trying to read his orange name tag to find out who he was, but I don't see long distances very well without my glasses.

"I'm John Wilson. You're Nancy, aren't you?" he said, taking me off the hook.

" Yes. Hi, John. I thought I recognized your voice." John worked for another major commercial bank and I spoke with him often.

"Nancy, this is Chuck Brown. Chuck, this is Nancy," he said, introducing the man next to him.

Another bank trader whose name sounded vaguely familiar.

"Pleased to meet you, Nancy," said Chuck. "I think we might have done some business last month."

"That's right," I said. "I remember."

"How's the market treating you?" John asked.

"Pretty well, I guess," I said cautiously. I certainly did not want a repetition of the last conversation. To throw him off, I changed the subject. "John, didn't I hear somewhere that you accepted a job at another bank?"

"That's right," he said. "This is my last week."

"What happened?" I asked. "Were you unhappy?"

"Not particularly," he said.

"Were you being held back?"

"On the contrary, I was given a free hand."

"What was it, then?"

Before John could answer, Chuck stepped in.

"It was the three months' supply-and-demand cycle," he said.

"The what?"

"The three months' cycle," Chuck repeated. "You know, every three months or so a new bank decides to get into the options business. So they steal an options trader from another bank. There is only a limited supply of us, so every time it happens the value of options traders in general rises."

"Then, of course," John continued for Chuck, "three months later another bank gets into the picture and steals the options trader from the first bank for a premium."

"You're kidding," I said. "I mean, I knew there was a high turnover rate . . ."

"I'm not kidding at all," said John seriously. "There's a good living in trading your salary. For instance, in the past two years I've worked for three different banks. I started out making $60,000 a year with a $10,000 bonus. Now I make $150,000 a year, and have an opportunity to make another $150,000 in bonus. Of course," he added quickly, "to make that kind of money I'd have to stay with the same bank for a whole year. I'm not sure I'd want to do that. It might be more profitable simply to move again, especially if prices keep moving up the way they've been."

"And if you keep trading the way you've been," Chuck cut in. "You don't earn much of a bonus for showing a loss at the end of the year."

"Who said I left a loss?" countered John.

"Oh, come on," said Chuck. "It's all over the Street."

"Who said I left a loss? I never left a loss! Who said I left a loss?"

"I must have been mistaken," snickered Chuck.

"You mean a new bank will hire you even if you've lost money at the old one?" I asked.

"Of course," said Chuck. "They don't care about

performance. They just want someone with experience."

"I see," I said, even though I didn't.

"Who said I left a loss?" John repeated hotly. "I never left a loss!"

"Oh, calm down, John," said Chuck. "How's the new house?"

"Great," said John sullenly.

"And the new car? What'd you get this time, a Porsche?"

"No," said John warming up slightly. "A Maserati."

"What color?"

"Fire-engine red."

I couldn't help smiling at the picture of this little balding guy zooming around in a red Maserati. How did he see over the dashboard?

"Well, I guess it's about time I went and got my drink," I said. "It was a pleasure meeting you both in person, finally. Be sure and call me if you want to do business."

As I walked away I heard John repeating:

"Who said I left a loss? I never left a loss!"

I got close enough to the bar this time to stand in line for a drink. The man in front of me smiled and held out his hand.

"Hi, I'm Sam."

"I'm Nancy."

"Nice to meet you. What can I get you?"

"Oh, just a glass of white wine, thanks."

He got the drinks and we moved out of the way of the bar.

"Cheers," he said, raising his glass.

"Cheers," I echoed, sipping my wine.

"The dollar's going down, you know," he said.

"What?"

"The dollar's going down."

"Is it?"

"Sure," he said. "Have a look."

He took a small metal object out of his pocket that looked rather like a hand-held calculator.

"What's that?" I asked.

"Why, it's my portable Reuters screen," he said, surprised. "Don't you have one?"

"Not only don't I have one, I've never seen one," I said. "What does it do?"

"It tells me the current prices for everything on a twenty-four-hour basis. See? I've got the Australian market right now. Pretty soon the Tokyo market will start trading. This way I always know exactly where everything is."

As I was staring at the tiny screen, I noticed that his hand was shaking. He quickly put the machine away and lit a cigarette.

"You must work awfully hard," I said.

"Twenty-four hours," he said proudly.

"Aren't you tired?" I asked with real curiosity.

"Sure I get tired. But I trade better when I'm tired."

"You do?"

"I love pressure. It sharpens my concentration."

"Don't you ever take any time off?"

"Not really."

"What does your wife think about that?"

"My wife?"

"I couldn't help noticing that you were married," I said, nodding toward his wedding ring.

"I haven't seen my wife in four days," he said.

"You haven't?"

"Nope. Either I'm working late or she is. She's a lawyer. She's asleep when I get up. She can't stand my trading at night. Says the phone calls wake her up."

"I can't understand why," I said under my breath.
"What?"

"I said, she doesn't seem to be very understand-ing," I recovered.

"Those are the breaks," he said. "It's the business. You've got to be tough to take it. Especially if you want what I want."

"What do you want?" I asked.

"I want to be the best. I've got it all planned out."

"You have?"

"Uh-huh. First I have to move to an investment bank."

"Where are you working now?"

"A commercial bank."

"What's so special about an investment bank?"

"The money."

"Is it really that much better?" I asked doubtfully. It seemed to me the pay was pretty good at commer-cial banks.

"See that guy over there?" asked Sam. "The one with the light-blue tie?"

I looked and saw an attractive man in his early thirties with blond hair cut very short. He was stand-ing with an air of self-assurance, talking quietly to an-other man.

"Yes," I said. "I see him. What about him?"

"I hear he takes home almost $1 million a year."

I took a closer look. Damn! I wished I had my glasses.

"And there are others who make even more," said Sam.

"I see."

"It's not just the pay. It's the connections. The perks. The power."

"Are you close to making a deal?" I asked.

"Soon," he said. "But it's a secret. Don't tell any-one."

"I won't," I promised.

"I mean, I'm only telling my closest friends."

I made my way back to the bar and got myself another glass of wine. I stood back for a moment and surveyed the room.

"Allow me to introduce myself," said a voice be-hind me.

I turned around quickly, narrowly missing spilling my wine down the front of my blouse. It was the trader in the light-blue tie.

"Whoa!" said my new acquaintance. "Be careful. I don't usually have this strong an effect on women until the second or third date."

"Very funny."

"No, really." He stuck out his hand. "I'm Adam Tyler."

"Where's your orange name tag, Adam?"

"It doesn't go with my eyes."

"Well, it's nice to meet you, Adam. I'm Nancy."

"The pleasure is all mine, believe me."

I ignored his tone. He stared at me critically.

"I was wondering what you looked like," he said.

"I hope I haven't disappointed you."

"Not at all." He winked at me.

I laughed. He was so direct it was almost refresh-ing. I began to loosen up a little. Of course, the wine wasn't hurting any.

"That's better," he said, leaning over confiden-tially. "Listen. There's nobody here worth meeting other than me. Honest. Cross my heart. Why don't you and I blow off this group and go for a nice, quiet, intimate dinner somewhere? I know a lovely place not too far from here . . ."

"That sounds terrific, Adam," said another male voice at my elbow. "May I come along, too?"

A man of average height, also in his early thirties, had come up unobserved while we were talking. His dark hair curled over his collar, and his eyes seemed to take in the whole room at a glance. He was very intense. He exuded such a strong sense of confidence that he somehow diminished Adam's assurance.

"Thomas!" said Adam. "How wonderful to see you again. Why don't you get lost now?"

"Just when the conversation was getting so interesting? Not a chance," said Thomas, laughing. "I'm Thomas Richards," he said, shaking my hand.

I recognized Thomas as being an options dealer at another investment bank, one of Adam's principal competitors.

"Tell me," he said, nodding toward Adam, "has this man been bothering you?"

"Thomas," said Adam, "don't you have to go check the market in Australia or something?"

"That's funny coming from you. You're the one with the risky position."

"That's because you don't have the balls to go long the dollar."

"No, it's because I'm not stupid enough to go long the dollar."

They seemed to have forgotten about me completely.

"By the way," said Adam. "I haven't seen your name in the market for a while. Have you decided to take the summer off?"

"I was just about to ask you the same question," Thomas replied coolly. "We've been handling some pretty large deals. Too bad you couldn't get a piece of the action. I just figured you weren't up to it."

"You know I'm always ready to do size," Adam retorted. "Just name it."

"Fine. Make me a price."

"Here?"

"Sure. What's the matter?"

"This is a party, for God's sake."

"So? You have a problem with that? Are you telling me you don't know where the market is? Come now, Adam, I know you better than that." Thomas winked at me. "Unless, of course, you've started to slip in your old age . . ."

"Not at all. My market's 10 bid at 30." This meant that Adam was willing to buy at 10 or sell at 30.

"I don't call that being very aggressive," said Thomas. "I have to say that I'm disappointed in you, Adam. I thought you could do better than that. My market's 15 bid at 25."

"For how much?"

"Your size."

"Fine. Twenty dollars sold at 15." Adam had just sold Thomas $20 million worth of an option.

"Done," said Thomas. "Twenty bid for another 100."

Thomas was ready to buy another $100 million worth of options from Adam for five points higher than he had just paid.

I held my breath. I'd never seen anyone raise his own bid. It was a sign of real confidence. And for such a large sum, too! And not even being in the office!

Adam hesitated. In this business, he who hesitates is lost.

"I'll pass," he said, finally.

"Fine," said Thomas. "Well, it's been fun, but I've got to go make a phone call now. It's always a pleasure doing business with you, Adam." He turned to go.

"Oh, by the way, Adam," said Thomas, turning back for just a second. "You should have hit me. The real market's 10 bid at 15. Nancy, it was a pleasure meeting you. Do yourself a favor and don't listen to anything this guy says while I'm gone." He walked away laughing.

"Son of a bitch," said Adam to Thomas's back.

The cocktail party continued on for several hours. I had a wonderful time. Everybody wanted to talk to me. I learned more about the market in one evening than I had in four months on the trading desk.

I had walked in hoping that no one would notice that I was a woman, that I would be treated like one of the guys. What a mistake! Being a woman in this environment was a powerful advantage.

Sure, there were a few other women in the room. One or two of them were even traders. But I'd gotten most of the attention. Men who earned fabulous salaries, and who threw around hundreds of millions of dollars in the market as if it were so much chicken feed, had fallen over themselves competing for my attention. Nobody had tested my knowledge or experience. If anything, they'd gone out of their way to prove to me how intelligent, tough, and powerful they were.

Suddenly, I realized that it was very late. Larry had been expecting me at home hours ago. I'd been reveling in all the attention so much that I'd lost all track of time.

I started rummaging in my purse for cabfare home. In the process of the struggle I came across my notes. My elation was marred only slightly by the reminder.

What the hell was a theta curve?

I ran out into the warm summer night to hail a cab.

Larry was waiting up for me when I got home.

"Do you have any idea what time it is?" he asked.

"I'm sorry," I began. "I didn't realize—"

"Didn't realize that it was nearly one o'clock? That

you'd gone to a cocktail party that was supposed to be over by nine? Did it occur to you that I might be worried about you? That I had visions of you lying in the street somewhere alone and hurt?"

"Why would you be worried about me?"

"Why? You're four hours late without even bothering to call me, and you ask me why? Are you telling me you didn't once notice the time?"

"I'm sorry. The time just got away from me."

Boy. This was the last thing I needed.

I told myself that it was my success that was causing the argument. That he didn't like the fact that it was I who was holding her own among the big boys. Well, I wasn't going to split the credit with anybody, not even Larry, who'd helped me get started in the first place. I turned and went into the bedroom.

About half an hour later Larry followed me in and went to sleep.

I tried to sleep as well. But when I closed my eyes all I could see was Thomas's face offering to buy another $100 million at 20.

6 Woman's Work

There's one little piece of information I've neglected to mention. Larry and I were newlyweds. We'd been married one month after I got the trading job.

We didn't plan it that way; it just happened. We were engaged in September after having known each other for nine months. My mother had been firm in her insistence that it takes at least six months to organize a proper wedding (please note that this is approximately twice the time it takes to become a head options trader at a major commercial bank), so we'd set the date for April, never dreaming I'd have any trouble getting away. After all, who cares when a loan officer takes her vacation?

Much to John Anderson's displeasure, when the time

came, I actually insisted on attending my own wedding and—inexcusable irresponsibility—my own honeymoon. I must confess that I was surprised by his reaction. He showed so little interest in what I was doing that I naturally assumed his indifference would extend to my vacation plans. In this I was wrong; while he didn't particularly seem to care what I did on the desk, he did seem to care that I be there to oversee personally whatever it was that I did that he didn't care about. I think he believed he could talk me out of leaving right up until the time I got on the plane.

Mom did a great job, the wedding was beautiful, the honeymoon was even lovelier, and the whole event was marred only slightly by the fact that Phillip lost an additional $250,000 in my absence. Oh, well, you can't have everything.

I completely adore Larry. His good looks and intelligence are a hard combination to beat, and there's an energy about him that I find very attractive. You can't meet Larry, even briefly, without his leaving a definite impression on you, good or bad. How did I wind up with this spectacular guy? Timing. He's divorced. Twice.

Until this point, Larry and I had been living a fairytale existence. We had a terrific apartment, for one thing. Now, I know that in most cities, procuring an adequate living space is not a cause for wild rejoicings, but this is Manhattan. I, for example, had lived the first four years in New York without benefit of direct sunlight, unless you count the fact that if I stuck my head out of the window at exactly 5:33 P.M. between October 13 and December 10 I could see the reflection of the sun as it struck the windows of the thirty-fifth floor of the building directly opposite mine.

By contrast, Larry had an apartment on the fifteenth floor of a building on Central Park West. Not only was his spacious one-bedroom apartment flooded with direct sunlight whenever there was direct sunlight to be had, but to the apartment was attached a terrace, and to the terrace was attached—Oh, wonder! Oh, marvel! Oh, joy!—an unimpaired view of Central Park and the city surrounding it. On cold winter nights you could see all the way down to the Empire State Building. All this, and the man himself, for the unbelievably low price of $400 a month ($440 if you wanted to rent a parking space as well).

Naturally, I took the deal.

"How in the world did you ever get this wonderful apartment so cheap?" I asked Larry when he told me what he paid in rent.

"I've been here for ten years," Larry replied. "It was only $250 when I first moved in, but the neighborhood's changed a lot in ten years. It wasn't quite this nice when I first got here."

"How bad could it have been?" I asked.

"Let me put it this way," said Larry. "When I first moved in, on Sunday nights I would hear the sound of drums beating and weird chanting coming from the park. It was scary, let me tell you. Then, on Monday mornings, the park would be littered with dead chickens. I mean it, chickens with their heads cut off."

"Ugh!" I said.

"Yep," he said, nodding his head. "Dead chickens. The occasional dead goat. But mostly chickens."

"Why didn't you go to the police?" I asked. The Twenty-fourth Precinct was right down the block.

"I did," said Larry. "Talked to a sergeant. He told me he knew all about it. Told me it was the Haitians practicing their voodoo and such."

"Well, why didn't they go in there and break it up?"

"I asked the cop that very same question."

"What did he say?"

"He said: 'Didn't you hear what I said, man? It's the Haitians! That's voodoo going on in there!'"

"I see his point," I said.

Anyway, what the NYPD was unable to do, the Yuppies did. By the time I arrived on the scene the war had already been fought, and all that was left was to iron out a few of the finer terms of surrender: exactly which corner would be left available for drug distribution and during what hours; the exact period of time before the Army-Navy store would be converted into a Tex-Mex charcuterie; just the usual last-minute details. All I had to do was to relax and enjoy it.

When I first met Larry, he had chucked his business career in favor of the theater. It had always been his dream to be an actor, and he felt that this was his only chance to give it a try. We'd agreed that he'd give himself a full year to get a start in the theater. If he hadn't made it by that time, we would reevaluate.

Greater naïveté, I am convinced, does not exist on this planet. It would be easier to break into Fort Knox in a year's time than into the New York theater community.

We were therefore in the process of reevaluating. When I got the trading job, and Larry and I spent so much time going over the basics of options, he'd gotten the idea of trading himself from home. He was just getting started that summer.

But in the meantime, because it cost us so little to live, there was always enough money around for a good time, even before I got the trading job. Larry and I would get all dressed up and go dancing late at night during the week (while I was still a loan officer and it wasn't necessary to be awake to do the job). We went to the movies. We went to the theater. We went to the ballet. I love the ballet. We went to the Mets games. Larry loves the Mets.

We made love all the time. I couldn't have been happier.

Then I got the trading job.

The morning after the cocktail party, the sound of the alarm wrenched me from a deep sleep at 5:30. I longed to throw the clock across the room, turn over, and fall immediately back into a deep, satisfying sleep lasting a mere twelve hours or so. Then I remembered the fight.

We'd had fights before, of course, but this was our first major argument since we'd been married. In the quiet of the dark bedroom I suddenly felt terribly lonely.

I looked over at Larry, lying peacefully on his stomach, still fast asleep. His dark hair was curling around his face and his long lashes rested against cheeks flushed with the warmth of sleep. I felt a great rush of love for him.

He'd been right. It had been thoughtless of me not to call. He'd had every right to be upset. And why had I stayed at the party so long anyway? All the attention had gone to my head.

I nestled up closer to him and put my arms around him.

"Ummm," he mumbled sleepily.

"Honey, I'm sorry," I whispered tenderly, kissing his ear. "You were right. It was horrible of me not to call. I love you. I don't know what came over me. I acted like a big jerk last night."

He turned his head toward me and cocked open one eye.

"I know," he said.

The result of the cocktail party was that I found myself at the center of a network of information and shifting alliances.

Traders are the biggest gossips in the world. Bigger than professional gossip columnists like Rona Barrett. Bigger than male sports commentators. Bigger even than my aunt Agnes.

Until I'd had the chance to meet my fellow traders, I never realized the extent of this underground advisory service. Now I picked up bits and pieces of information almost daily. Suddenly, a large portion of the industry was calling just to talk.

What was the cause of my sudden popularity?

They liked talking to a woman.

A woman who knows how to trade is a great anomaly. Male traders feel more comfortable with a woman trader than they do with their wives or girlfriends. They can talk about the market with a woman who really understands what they are saying. A spouse who has never traded may appreciate the amount of time and effort her husband puts into his career and certainly respects the money he brings in as a result, but she could not identify with the feeling of doubling up on a losing position, nor could she properly admire the brilliance of a decision to buy when prevailing thought says sell.

But I could.

"Options desk."

"Hi, Nancy. This is Chuck."

"Hi, Chuck. How are you?"

"I'm hanging in there. What about yourself?"

"I'm just fine. What can I do for you? Do you want me to make you a price?"

"No, I shut down for the day. I was up late last night."

"Really?" I asked. "What happened?"

"Oh, I was the wrong way when the Japanese prime minister decided to open his big mouth."

Translation: Chuck had bought yen, expecting the yen to strengthen overnight. The Japanese prime minister had unexpectedly issued a statement that the market had interpreted in favor of a weaker yen. The yen had fallen. Chuck had lost money.

"Oh, I'm sorry," I said, sympathetically. "Don't worry. I know you'll do better next time."

I was getting used to my role as surrogate girlfriend, cheerleader, and den mother.

"I know it, too," he said. "I'm not worried. I just found out that a very large player in Switzerland will be in there buying Swiss francs at ———." He named a price.

"They will?" I asked. "How do you know?"

"I have a very good contact in Europe. Trust me."

If that was true, the Swiss franc could be expected to appreciate in value as soon as it reached that price.

"Oh!" I said. "Thanks for the information."

"Anytime," he said, ringing off.

I watched and waited until the price of Swiss francs got to the level that Chuck had indicated, and then I bought a very small amount just to see. Sure enough, someone came into the market and started buying large amounts of Swiss just as Chuck had predicted. The price of Swiss started to rise. Although I hadn't taken very much of a position, I still made some money.

Well! I thought. This is turning out better than I'd expected.

"Options desk."

"Nancy," said a deep male voice, "how nice to hear from you again."

"But, Adam," I replied, recognizing the voice instantly, "you called me."

"Did I? In that case, why haven't you called me?"

"I didn't have anything to say."

"That makes no difference," said Adam. "You'd be surprised the number of people who call me with nothing to say."

"I'll keep it in mind," I promised. "Now, what can I do for you?"

"I was hoping you'd ask that. Let's start with drinks and then dinner and then—"

"Let me rephrase the question," I said, cutting him off. "Do you want me to make you a price?"

"You cut me to the quick. Of course I don't want you to make me a price. I can get a price from anybody. But I can't go for a walk with just anybody. And it's a beautiful day for a walk. Don't you want to go with me?"

"I'd love to but I have to work."

"Work! That's a lame excuse."

"Lame but true," I said.

"What do you have to do?"

I sighed.

"For one thing, I have to figure out which way the dollar is going," I said. "I don't suppose you know the answer to that question?"

"Nobody knows the answer to that question, my sweet," said Adam. "But if it will allow you to unchain yourself from the desk for an hour or so and accept my gallant invitation to stroll along the streets of downtown New York, I can tell you that all the signs indicate that a rebound is in the works."

"You think the dollar's going up, then?" I asked, zeroing in.

"Well," said Adam. "From a completely technical point of view, a correction in the downward trend is long overdue. Just take a look at your charts."

The *charts* Adam referred to are graphs that record the price of the dollar over the recent past. Some charts are extremely sophisticated, utilizing all kinds of market information in addition to price histories. However, anyone can draw a simple chart by taking the price of the dollar relative to another currency (say, deutsche marks) and plotting it over time on a piece of ordinary graph paper.

People who follow these charts are, appropriately enough, called *chartists*. Chartists believe that there are patterns to market behavior. Properly interpreted, the charts reveal these patterns and help predict future prices.

Chartists, like the charts they employ, come in a variety of types. The most effective spend a great deal of time at their craft and have elevated charting to a science.

Unfortunately, because anyone can pick up a pencil and draw a crude graph without much effort, the vast majority of those who call themselves chartists are individuals who believe that any chart (particularly theirs) can predict the future. In their unrelenting search for quick and easy profit, these chartists have reduced the science to art.

This is how it works. The standard method for drawing charts is based somewhat loosely on the children's game Connect-the-Dots. You remember Connect-the-Dots. Children play it in school, behind the teacher's back. The essence of chart interpretation, then, is to draw lines through the dots on the graphs and to hunt for pictures resulting from this effort.

For example, a chartist will suddenly lift his head from his work to chortle: "Aha! A perfect head-and-shoulders formation!" He will offer to show you his work. You look, and, sure enough (after he has lovingly traced the outline for you with his finger) you will see a clumsy picture of what could be interpreted as a person's head and shoulders, particularly if that person were a hunchback. "What does it mean?" you ask the chartist. "It means the dollar is going down!" he shouts happily. "Sell the dollar!"

The first time I was introduced to a chartist's methods I made the mistake of wondering aloud whether he wasn't working too hard, and didn't perhaps need a vacation. But then I noticed something important. When all the chartists in the world (and their number is growing every day) decide to sell the dollar, there are so many of them selling that the dollar, by virtue of being sold so much, actually does go down. Chartists make fortunes during these periods.

Accordingly, I have learned to pay attention to the charts.

"In addition to that," Adam continued, "most of the economists on the Street are predicting a slight improvement in economic growth over the near term. Not very much, but enough. But none of that is really important. The really important thing is . . ."

"Yes?" I asked, all attention.

". . . I feel like the dollar is going up," he finished.

"You feel like it," I repeated.

"Yep," he said.

Well, there's no arguing with research. "Thanks for the insight," I said.

"Now, what about that walk?"

"Some other time," I said. "I promise." I hung up the phone.

"Phillip?" I said.

"Huh?"

"What do the charts say?"

"Huh?"

"The charts. Your charts," I repeated patiently. "Do they seem to indicate a rebound in the dollar?"

"Ah! My charts! Let's look at my charts!" Phillip loved his charts. He spent hours on them, keeping them up to date, drawing lines through points, erasing these lines and then redrawing them. Now he tenderly unfolded a large chart depicting the value of the dollar relative to the deutsche mark over the past three years.

"Let's see," he said, scrutinizing his own work. "Why, yes! I don't know why I didn't see it before! Look here. It's oversold. The dollar should be going up! Let's buy some!"

"Not so fast," I said. I wanted to make sure that Adam's information was real. "Do we have any numbers coming out this week?"

"Yes. Housing starts and the consumer price index," said Phillip, referring to a calendar that indicated the dates on which economic data were released monthly by the Commerce Department.

"What's expected?" I asked. "A slight improvement?"

"Yes," said Phillip. "A slight improvement is expected."

"Okay," I said. "Let's buy some."

We bought some.

Adam was right. The dollar was oversold. The correction began in Tokyo that very night and continued for a few days. The dollars that Phillip and I bought increased in value. We sold them for a nice profit.

And this industry has a reputation for being cut-throat! I thought. Why, everyone is being just as helpful as they can be!

"Options desk."

"Hello, Nancy. This is Roger calling from London."

"Hello, Roger. What can I do for you?"

"Nothing much. Just calling up to chat."

I was surprised and pleased. I hadn't met Roger face-to-face yet. I guessed that my name was getting around the market as a good person to talk to.

"How's it going for you, anyway?" Roger asked. "You getting along okay?"

"Pretty well," I said. "How about yourself?"

"Great month. Couldn't be better. What do you think of the dollar?"

I was thrilled. Imagine Roger asking me for my opinion! I had finally arrived.

"I think the dollar's going down," I said firmly.

"Really?" Did I imagine it or was there a hint of disapproval in his voice?

"I mean . . ." I faltered, "all the signs are there for a weaker dollar. . ."

"You think so?" This time there was no mistaking his tone.

"Of course, I could be wrong," I admitted, suddenly very unsure of my position.

"Did you hear about the retail sales number?" Roger asked.

Retail sales is a statistic released every month by the U.S. government. It's an indication of how well the retailing sector of the economy did in the previous month.

"What about the retail sales number?"

"Rumor says it's going to be up 6.5 percent."

Up 6.5 percent! For the past few months, retail sales had been averaging under 3 percent.

"But . . . the dollar will fly," I said, aghast. I was at the moment running a short dollar position. That meant that I had sold dollars I didn't own, intending to buy them back when the dollar was cheaper. A 6.5 percent retail sales number could kill me.

"Exactly."

I made some quick calculations. Today was Thursday. Retail sales didn't come out until tomorrow. I still had time to turn my position around and go long dollars.

As if he could read my thoughts, Roger continued: "Just look at the bonds."

I looked at the bonds. Bond prices were falling. This could be interpreted in favor of higher interest rates.

Such an interpretation was in line with a stronger dollar.

"Gee," I said. "Thanks for the information."

"Don't mention it," said Roger, hanging up.

I bought back all the dollars I had sold, and more. I also bought some very expensive options that would increase in value when the dollar went up.

I wasn't the only one buying. By the time I went home Thursday night the dollar was stronger. It was even higher in Tokyo when I checked the market at eleven-thirty before going to sleep.

Another example of male chivalry. I hardly knew Roger and I felt rather guilty for not having been friendlier toward him in the past. I wished I had had some information to pass along back to him. Maybe I could send him some flowers or something instead.

Friday morning at eight o'clock found me pacing back and forth behind my chair. The dollar had started to fall in London at three o'clock in the morning my time. It was already lower than where I'd bought it yesterday, so I was running a small loss at the moment.

I wasn't really worried, though. I knew how far up a 6.5 percent retail sales number would push the dollar. My only question was whether to buy more dollars at the cheaper price before the number came out at 8:30, or stay with the position I had. I decided to stay put.

8:30: One of the junior spot traders was at the Telerate machine. The bell went off. Silence. Then: "Up 1.5 percent!" shouted the junior trader.

Phillip and Peter and I exchanged looks of horror. It was a terrible number. Much weaker than expected. The dollar started to fall.

"Wait for the revision," I ordered.

Sometimes the government revises the previous month's retail sales number on the basis of more accurate information. I could only assume that Roger's information referred to last month's number.

We waited breathlessly to see if there would be a revision. The dollar continued to fall.

Suddenly the bell went off again. Ding ding ding ding ding!

"Revision!" shouted the junior trader.

Thank God, I mouthed silently.

"Last month's number revised down by 1.2 percent!"

I didn't even have to say anything.

"Yours!" shouted Phillip.

"Yours!" shouted Peter.

"Yours! Yours! Yours!" I shouted, selling dollars at a loss.

"London speaking."

"May I please speak to Roger?"

"Roger speaking."

"Hello, Roger. This is Nancy."

"Nancy, old girl! How are you?"

"I've been better."

"Really? Sorry to hear that. What's the matter?"

"Your information wasn't exactly accurate."

"What information?"

"The retail sales number," I said coldly. "Remember? Up 6.5 percent?"

"But—you don't mean—didn't you hear the later rumor?"

"What later rumor?"

"The rumor that said it was going to be up only 1.5 percent."

"I must have missed that one."

"What a pity. I hope you didn't get burned too badly?"

So much for male chivalry.

7 G-5

Something was happening to me. It crept up on me so slowly that I didn't even notice it. But it was there nonetheless. And it was growing stronger every day.

I was developing trader head.

Trader head is a syndrome in which one's ego grows at an accelerated rate at the expense of all other personality traits. Manifestations of the disease include a tendency on the part of the victim to look down his or her nose at other human beings, particularly those people who don't trade large sums of money for a living.

My exposure to other traders aggravated the pace of the illness. As I spent more and more time socializing with colleagues, I picked up not only their mania for all things market-related, but their arrogance as well.

I came home later and later in the evening and my talk was increasingly about who had sold what and to whom. I felt very important, being accepted as part of such an elite group. Home and husband lost by comparison.

My working environment contributed to the condition. On the trading desk, my word was law. No one questioned my decisions, or my right to throw ever-increasing sums of money at the market. If I told Peter or Phillip to do something, they did it. Fast.

This approach, however, did not seem to work as well at home.

It was the third Sunday in September. Larry and I were having a fight.

"What's your problem?" I asked coldly.

"You're my problem," he responded.

"That's not very helpful. Perhaps you could elaborate."

"Let me make myself clear."

"Please do."

"We don't spend any time together anymore."

"I have to work."

"Not all the time. Trading has become your whole life. When was the last time you took the initiative in this relationship? You're too tired to go dancing. You're too tired to see a film. You're too tired to go out with friends. The only thing you're not too tired to do is trade. That's a big drag."

"Anything else?"

"You are completely self-absorbed. The only thing that's growing in this relationship is your ego."

"It's my business," I retorted.

"It's not your business to turn into a walking, talking Reuters screen."

"You're just jealous. You're jealous of my success."

"That's untrue and unfair and you know it. I've helped and encouraged you from the beginning. That's

111

why I'm disappointed to see you turning out this way."

"Just leave me alone."

"Have it your way."

Larry went to read the Sunday paper outside on the terrace. I stayed in the apartment, fuming. What right had he to criticize me that way? Nobody else would dare do such a thing. Why was it that everyone else could see how important I had become but my own husband still treated me as though I were a mere mortal?

A half hour later Larry came back inside.

"Much as I hate to encourage you at this point in your chosen profession, I feel obliged to inform you that there's an article in the paper today which it behooves you to read."

I ignored him. Nothing he could say would interest me.

"Front page," he said, reading over my pointed silence. " 'Members of the five industrialized nations met today and decided to work together toward weakening the overvalued U.S. dollar. This initiative on the part of the Group of Five, or G-5 as it's now being called, represents an entirely new policy for the industrialized nations.' "

I continued to ignore him. I was so angry that if he'd told me the Russians had invaded I wouldn't have listened.

"This is really big news. It says here they've agreed to intervene to devalue the dollar."

"So what?" I said irritably.

"Honey, the dollar's going to react to this news. There's going to be a big move tonight in the Far East."

My wounded ego flared up again in anger. How dare he presume to tell me my own business! I was the head trader, not he!

"Don't be ridiculous," I said haughtily. "You don't know what you are talking about. Nothing's going to happen tonight."

"You'd better check it out," he warned.

"Forget it," I said, dismissing him. "Not only am I not going to read the article, I'm not even going to call the market tonight. I'm going to bed, and I'm going to turn off all the phones."

Larry doesn't argue with me when I'm in this mood.

"Fine," he said, shrugging.

I turned on my heel and went into the bedroom, closing the door behind me. What did he know about anything? I'd show him a thing or two.

I sure did.

I rode up in the elevator to the trading room on Monday morning, well rested for once. I nodded good morning to one of the spot foreign-exchange traders. He returned the greeting.

"Some move, huh?" he said, shaking his head in wonder. "I've been in the business for fifteen years and I've never seen anything like it."

I started to get a queasy feeling.

I hurried into the trading room. A crowd had gathered at the spot foreign-exchange desk. I recognized the president of the bank among them.

Now, the president of the bank does not make regular visits to the trading room. Correction: he never visits the trading room. In fact, I'd never even seen him in person before. Yet there he was, clapping the spot trader on the back, and smiling at the rest of the desk.

The queasy feeling in my stomach increased.

I walked over to my own desk and looked at the glum expressions on Peter's and Phillip's faces. Then I looked at the Reuters screen.

It was the single largest overnight move in the history of the currency markets. As a result of the G-5 initiative, the dollar had lost almost 10 percent of its value in fewer than five hours. And I'd missed it.

I sank into my chair. Peter saw the expression on my face.

"You didn't hedge anything last night?" he asked, horrified.

I shook my head in misery. I'd never seen a move of such magnitude. I hadn't thought such a move was possible. I didn't have any idea of how much we'd lost.

John chose this moment to stop by the desk.

"Isn't it terrific!" he gloated. "The spot desk was short dollars and they made a fortune overnight!"

"Wonderful," I smiled wanly.

It was difficult to hide the tremor in my voice. Even John picked it up.

"Everything's okay over here, isn't it?" he asked.

"Just fine. I mean, wonderful." I corrected myself.

"Good!" he said, relieved. "How much did you make?"

"How much did I make?" I repeated stupidly. "How much—uh—it's hard to tell exactly. You know how complicated options are."

"Are you sure you're all right?" he peered at me.

"Perfectly," I was recovering now. "You know, it was just an exciting night for me."

"Oh! Of course," he said. His attention was drifting back to the spot desk. The president of the bank was making movements as if to leave. "Well, let me know your P and L when you're sure," he shouted over his shoulder as he ran back to hold the door for the president.

As soon as he was out of earshot, I turned to Phillip and Peter.

"Input the new information into the computer and get me some updated reports right now!"

Our computer system was so slow that it took almost two hours to print out new reports. Two hours later I knew where I stood.

We'd lost the half million dollars in profit we'd been accruing for the month of September, and were now showing an additional loss of $250,000.

I decided that John did not need to know the specifics of the situation right away. If I avoided him, perhaps I could even make some of it back before he found out. As it turned out there was no need for covert maneuverings: in his joy over the spot desk's performance, John forgot all about me.

I had ten days to act before my month-end results would be available to senior management.

The first thing I noticed about the G-5 initiative was that it turned much of the trading community from snarling wolves into bleating sheep.

Options provide protection in the event of large currency moves. The more likely people consider the prospect of a significant currency move, the more expensive options become. Potential buyers compete with each other for the privilege of paying, and potential sellers, sensing danger, back away from their offers. The risk to the buyer is that he or she will end up purchasing a very expensive option only to see the market quiet down and the option expire worthless, resulting in the loss of the entire premium. The risk to the seller is that, after the option has been sold, the market will fluctuate even more wildly than before the sale, and the money earned through the sale of the premium will not make up the loss incurred trying to hedge the damn thing. The buyer acts conservatively, the seller acts aggressively, and both risk loss. The mediating factor is the price of the option. At some point the option becomes so expensive that the risk of loss flip-flops away from the seller and over to the buyer. It's like buying a house at the height of a real estate boom: you find to your chagrin that the house was not worth the money you paid for it.

All my rough-and-tumble-big-brave counterparts at the other banks saw the big overnight move and behaved precisely the way you would expect them to. They panicked.

Traders who had sold options before G-5 were desperate in their attempts to buy them all back as quickly as possible. "Mine! Mine!" they shouted into their phones, bidding up the price. Tension heightened as other members of the community took their lead. Soon everybody was buying. The price of options soared. Potential sellers became confused. If everybody was buying, what were they doing selling? Offers of "Yours! Yours!" dwindled, and were replaced by the now-frantic screams of "Mine! Mine!" as the sellers, too, rushed to turn their positions around from short to long.

I watched this process, bemused. Had everyone gone completely crazy? We'd just had the largest overnight move in recent memory, a direct result of a specific action taken on the part of the industrialized nations. The damage was done, in my opinion. Did people really expect the dollar to move like that every night? I mean, when were we all going to sleep?

In addition, every newspaper report I'd read about G-5 had emphasized that one of the key objectives of the initiative was a slow, nondisruptive but steady decline in the value of the dollar. No shocks. No roller-coaster rides. Just the gentle, wafting motion of a feather, as it drops ever so slowly to the floor.

Does that sound to you like a cause for panic?

Maybe, I thought, there's a way out of this mess after all.

▲ ▲ ▲

The very first thing I did was to sell dollars. It's not often that a trader gets the kind of broad hint on currency direction that the G-5 nations dropped that weekend. If the leaders of the industrialized world wanted to devalue the dollar, I certainly wasn't going to argue with them. As the dollar trended down, I knew this position would become profitable. The only thing I had to worry about was where we'd eventually hit bottom, but I figured that we still had a ways to go before that became an emergency.

I then turned my attention to the options market. The prices were unbelievably high! If I acted quickly, I could make back everything I'd lost and more.

I got Bob on the phone.

Bob was now working for a successful brokerage operation. We were on much better terms now that I was a customer. He even remembered my name. It didn't hurt that when he was first getting started I had helped him by giving him all of my business. At the time I had wanted a friend in the industry, and I sensed great potential in Bob. He was so clearly superior in terms of charm and intelligence that I knew he would make enormous inroads into the other brokers' territories. That meant he would get the best and most competitive prices, and I would be one of the first to see them. At least, I hoped I would be one of the first. You could never tell with Bob.

"Nancy, my dear," said Bob as soon as I got him on the phone, "how nice to hear from you. What can I do for you, my love?"

"You can get me a bid, my love," I said.

"Right!" he responded. "Be back in a jiffy."

I waited impatiently.

"The bid is 150," he came back.

Too good to be true.

"For how much?" I asked.

"Five dollars."

That's broker jargon. He meant $5 million.

"Yours for $5!" I said.

"Done."

"Who is it?" I asked.

He named a large commercial bank, a competitor of mine in the market.

"Ask them if they've more to do."

Silence while Bob consulted the other bank.

"They say nothing more at that price," he came back.

"Where's their new bid?" I asked.

"They say they can only bid 145 now," Bob replied after another brief silence.

"For how much?"

"Another $5."

"Yours again!"

"Done."

"More to do?"

"No. They hung up."

"Get me somebody else."

"The next bid is 142."

"Yours! Any more there?"

Pause.

"They say no," said Bob.

"Fine. Get someone else."

"The bid's only 140 now."

"For how much?"

"Ten dollars."

"Yours. Ten dollars done. More?"

I did this every day for a week.

The price dropped steadily. Soon the people who were holding options started to worry. Their options were losing value daily. The market was quieting down, as I had predicted. Other traders started to sell. Suddenly everybody was selling.

118

I decided to hold the position and milk it for everything it was worth.

"Well!" said John when he saw my September results. "I see that everything is going well for the options desk. How do things look for October?"

"October will be even better," I assured him.

"Great! Keep up the good work!"

G-5 was a turning point for the currency markets, and a turning point my career. No one at the bank (except for Phillip and Peter, of course) ever knew what had actually happened. I got off scot-free.

In retrospect it would have been better for me if things hadn't gone so well. My impulsive reaction to the fight with Larry should have highlighted some of the more serious problems that were beginning to evolve.

The ease with which I glided through the G-5 fiasco exacerbated my worsening condition for the next few months. The only lesson that I drew from the entire experience was that I was one terrific trader.

8 Life at the Top

I was not alone in that opinion.

The money I had earned in the aftermath of G-5 was enough to cement my already strong position within the bank. Pleased with the undeniable success of my operation, John Anderson began to take more notice of me. Not more notice of what I was doing or how I was doing it; more notice of me, personally.

In recognition of my efforts, he showed his appreciation in the only way he knew. He rewarded me with those tributes that lay closest to his own heart.

He signed me up for meetings.

There is a very simple way to tell when you get to be a somebody at a bank. It's not by title, because titles are often misleading. In fact, most titles were invented to mislead people into believing that what they were getting was more power, more authority, more money (oh, yes, people can even be fooled into believing they are getting more money when they're not), when actually all they were getting was more title. I know of one man who was demoted three times in one year and never knew it. But I knew it because at the end of that year he had the longest and most impressive title at the bank.

You're not a somebody only if you have a great income, either. You can earn a healthy income at a bank simply by standing around doing nothing for years and years and years. In fact, this is the position that most people in banks aspire to with the greatest energy.

Importance at a bank isn't determined by seniority. Seniority works pretty much the way income does.

The way to tell if you're a somebody is not by any of these things. It's by the meetings you are invited to attend.

And so, in reward for a job well done, John began to invite me to a variety of meetings. These meetings fell into two basic categories: private meetings between John and myself, and group meetings.

On the private side were our lunch meetings. These were arranged so that John could "bring me up to date" on all of the various and sundry projects associated with his global strategy, and the management of the trading floor in general. ("Now that you are one of my managers," he told me, "I feel that we should see each other on a more regular basis.") These lunches were held upstairs in the bank's executive dining room. The bank had two dining rooms, and management was none too subtle in its distinctions.

Downstairs in the basement was the employee cafeteria, which was available to all employees of the bank but used primarily by those persons who had not yet achieved the rank of vice president. Upstairs on the fifty-first floor was the executive dining room, which was available only to people holding at least a vice presidential title. Downstairs it was dark and rather unpleasant smelling, with plastic tables and chairs crammed together for the staff. Upstairs was light and airy, with a panoramic view of lower Manhattan and carefully arranged tables draped in long white tablecloths. Downstairs you stood in line with a plastic tray, and your food was dished out by a surly individual dressed in a soiled gray uniform; upstairs you were seated by an appropriately obsequious maître d' in black tie, and served by a battery of waiters dressed in clean white uniforms.

Accordingly, one of the principal benefits associated with becoming a vice president was the ability to dine upstairs, away from the common hordes. Remember that it often took as long as ten years to achieve this title. Most people looked forward with great eagerness to the exercise of this particular privilege, having spent many years imagining the culinary delights of those who dined above. It therefore came as a disappointment to the newly promoted to discover that the two cafeterias, so different in appearance, were bound together by a common thread. The same food was served at both. Thus it was possible for a piece of meat labeled "chopped meat with gravy" downstairs to masquerade as "Salisbury Steak Supreme" on the printed menus distributed upstairs.

No one ever let on, however.

My lunches with John were conducted in the following manner. I would meet John at his office at 1:00 P.M. sharp, and we would ride the elevator together to the fifty-first floor. We would make polite conversation during these rides, being careful to discuss nothing of a sensitive nature in front of the other passengers, who might or might not be employees of the bank. This served a dual purpose: to protect the integrity of the trading floor, at the same time increasing our importance in the eyes of the other passengers, who couldn't help but notice from John's conspiratorial manner that our meaningless chatter was merely a smoke screen for more weighty topics.

After being escorted to our regular table by the maître d' ("Oh, yes, Mr. Anderson! Of course your table by the window is ready!"), we would order our lunch and get down to business.

After the obligatory discussion of the "global plan," John would turn to more pressing management issues. Today's subject was the high turnover rate that was currently decimating the trading floor. Many people were leaving the bank to go to work for the competition. The most recent blow was also the most crushing: the man in charge of the interest-rate desk, a ten-year veteran of the bank, had announced his intention to accept a similar position elsewhere.

"Why do you think everyone is leaving?" John asked, as the Consommé Brunoise was served (Vegetable Soup downstairs).

"The bank isn't paying them at a competitive rate," I replied, eyeing my bowl uneasily. You never knew what was floating around in the vegetable soup.

"But we're implementing a new bonus system," John protested.

"But no one's exactly sure how it's going to work," I observed. "You haven't named any figures yet."

"It's still with the board of directors," said John. "It's out of my hands at the moment. I've done what I could. I honestly want to keep good people working here."

"I understand your problem," I said, "but you must

understand mine as well. Options traders, for example, are greatly in demand at the moment. I must pay Peter and Phillip competitively at the end of the year or I'll lose them."

I didn't say anything about myself, but the implication was clear.

"Have they been approached by anyone?" John asked quickly.

I shrugged.

"I don't think so," I replied. "But there are lots of banks looking. Most of them are looking for head traders, but it's only a matter of time before they begin on more junior people."

"I see," he said.

The soup was removed. Golden Glow Aspic (Jell-O with Mixed Fruit) was served.

"Nancy," said John. "I've been meaning to congratulate you. Your unit is doing very well."

"Thank you," I said.

"And it appears not to be a one-shot deal," John continued. "I mean, the income flow is pretty consistent month to month."

"That's true," I said.

"How is it done?" John asked.

"Excuse me?"

"How is it that you produce a fairly constant flow of income on a monthly basis?"

Well! I thought. This is encouraging! John wants to know something about what I do.

I started to give a very simple explanation outlining the nature of options trading in a general way. Knowing that the subject was complicated, I tried only to explain the basics. John listened attentively, occasionally nodding his head. My commentary continued through the arrival of the main course, Glacé Boeuf à la Mode (Pot Roast).

"And that," I said in conclusion, "is pretty much how we do it."

John nodded again and finished swallowing a potato. He wiped his mouth with his napkin.

"That's very interesting," he said. "But I have a slightly different concept of the way it's done."

"You do?" I asked.

"Uh-huh," he said. "I figured it out for myself. Every option has a premium associated with it, correct?"

"That's correct," I said.

"So the way you make money is simply by selling all of these options and pocketing the premium. Isn't that really it?"

"No, not really . . ." I started over. I explained that sometimes we bought more options than we sold, because we expected the price of options to increase. And that even when we sold more options than we bought, we didn't just pocket the premium because we had to manage the risk of the options we'd sold and that cost money.

When I finished speaking he looked at me.

"I still say it's the premium income," he insisted.

I gave up. After all, he was the boss.

"If you say so," I said.

We decided against dessert, which was Blanc-mange (Tapioca Pudding), and returned to our respective posts: I to the options desk, he to his next meeting.

Then there were the group meetings. Group meetings were regularly scheduled affairs with specific names, like Strategic Planning or Policy Analysis. These meetings were generally attended by the same people and were usually chaired by John.

One of the first meetings that I was invited to was the Risk-Management meeting.

There is nothing more important to a financial institution than the management of risk. On a trading floor, where enormous sums are involved, the stakes are that much higher. In a sophisticated trading environment, the Risk-Management meeting is the place where senior management sets the parameters within which its traders must operate.

Before G-5 I had been left out of this meeting. It was a testament to my new success that I was asked, and I was aware of the honor of being admitted into its select confines.

There was one little problem. Risk-Management meetings were held every Thursday at 10:00 A.M.

In most areas of business, 10:00 A.M. is the ideal time to hold a meeting. It's early enough in the morning for everyone to still be fresh, but not so early that everyone is still asleep.

But on a trading floor, it's different. By 10:00 A.M. you are in the heat of battle. Trading is extremely active. The London, European, and New York markets are all open at that hour.

Important economic information is sometimes released at 10:00 A.M. Senior officials like the chairman of the Federal Reserve Board give speeches to members of Congress at that hour, and their remarks (accompanied by an appropriate storm of bells and whistles) are broadcast over the Reuters and Telerate machines. These remarks are dissected with surgical accuracy, then digested at light-speed by members of the trade, causing the markets to roll and pitch with each successive inference.

Corporate treasurers like to get their funding and foreign-exchange requirements accomplished at 10:00 A.M. because they know the market is liquid at that hour and they are able to get the best prices from their banks. Traders are in the act of establishing large positions at

10:00 A.M.. Literally billions of dollars trade at 10:00 A.M.

Not the best time for a meeting.

Having only just earned the right of attendance, however, I judged it best not to begin by questioning the scheduling. When the time came, I simply left the desk to Peter and Phillip and proceeded down the hall to the conference room.

Risk-Management meetings were held in a small conference room close by John's office but away from the noise and energy of the trading floor.

The conference room was a long, thin, airless room, fitted with a long, thin table, a blackboard, and a grim portrait of the chairman of the board. I was there promptly at 10:00 A.M. A handful of people were there, lounging around in their chairs or staring vacantly out of the only window. I recognized a bank economist and the credit manager responsible for the trading floor. I nodded hello and took a seat in the corner at the foot of the table.

A few more people drifted in slowly. I glanced at my watch. The meeting was already ten minutes late in starting. I couldn't resist the urge to tap my foot with impatience. I wasn't used to being away from the desk during the most active period of the morning. I didn't like leaving the desk in the hands of junior traders.

Finally John arrived, having only just come from an earlier meeting that had run over into this one.

"Everybody here?" John asked. "Good. Let's get started then."

Conspicuous by his absence was the head spot foreign-exchange trader. A fifteen-year veteran of the markets, he handled all of the bank's positions in foreign exchange (except for those I took in options). But whereas I would often try to hedge my positions, the nature of his business was to take large, outright positions. He traded successfully with hundreds of millions of dollars. His knowledge of the markets was unparalleled at the bank. His gains and losses made everyone else look as if they were playing pinochle instead of trading. How any risk-management meeting could be held without him was beyond my comprehension.

Yet clearly he had no intention of showing up. A slight feeling of uneasiness crept over me but I ignored it.

"Today's discussion focuses on the probable direction of the dollar and interest rates in the near term," said John, referring to some handwritten notes for a moment.

He began to speak on the current climate affecting the foreign-exchange market, referring often to his notes. I was impressed to see how well prepared he was. His appraisal was concise and to the point. I relaxed a little. I didn't mind being away from the market if my time was spent usefully.

I listened carefully. After all, this was my field.

He was in the middle of a careful analysis of the significance of some recent actions taken by the Federal Reserve Bank when I realized that I knew what he was going to say before he said it. His comments were based upon a column that had appeared in the previous week's *Wall Street Journal*. In fact, he seemed to have lifted whole paragraphs from the article.

I glanced furtively around the room to see if anyone else recognized the analysis. If others did, they gave no sign.

I settled back into my chair, wondering once again what was happening in the market in my absence.

"Well," said John, finishing up his remarks, "I think

I've set a context for the rest of the discussion. Does anyone else have something to add?"

"I do." It was Hal White, the economist.

John indicated that he had the floor.

"Well," said Hal importantly. "As you know, I've just returned from a high-level policy meeting in Washington. There is a great deal of sympathy for the concept of fixed exchange rates. In my opinion, exchange rates will be fixed by year end."

I sat bolt upright in my chair.

Fixed or stabilized exchange rates would radically affect the price that people would be willing to pay for foreign currency options. In fact, it could wipe out my market altogether. If what he was saying was true, and he seemed quite confident that this was indeed the case, it meant at the very least that I would have to change my current trading strategy radically, and possibly close down the currency options book altogether.

Hal was elaborating on the subject.

"It's almost a fait accompli. . . ," he was saying.

"Excuse me," I interrupted.

Everyone looked at me.

"Yes?"

"Fixing exchange rates is a pretty drastic step," I pointed out. "People have been talking about returning to a fixed exchange rate system for years, but the suggestion has not, to my knowledge, been seriously considered before this. Are you quite sure that the government has definitely decided in favor of this proposal?"

"Jack Kemp has been talking about it for some time," Hal responded.

"That's true," I agreed, "but Jack Kemp is only a congressman, and doesn't have responsibility for the decision. Was the chairman of the Federal Reserve Board at this meeting?"

"No."

"The secretary of the treasury?"

"No."

"How about the German, Japanese, or British finance ministers? Were any of them there?"

"No."

"Well," I said, "who was there?"

"Well, let me see now," said Hal. "There were several economists from the banking community, along with a smattering of academicians from some of the better schools. There were also some congressmen present. And the assistant to the under secretary of commerce dropped by."

I decided not to change my trading strategy on the basis of the assistant to the under secretary of commerce's word, and relapsed into silence.

The meeting continued.

John called on one of the traders responsible for the bank's interest-rate position.

"What is your opinion of the direction that interest rates will take?" he asked.

The interest-rate trader reported that while it was anyone's guess which way interest rates were going, he, the interest-rate trader, assumed that they would stay put if they didn't go up or down.

John then called on the gold trader to discuss possible outlooks for gold in the near term.

Although he had no firm opinion on the direction that gold would take, the gold trader was willing to venture an opinion on interest rates.

"Interest rates are going up," he said.

Here the interest-rate trader felt called upon to speak out—on the subject of gold.

"Gold is going down," he said.

The gold trader acknowledged this bit of advice by pointing out that, with all due respect, the interest-rate trader didn't know the gold market and that gold was a much more difficult instrument to predict than interest rates.

The interest-rate trader responded that, on the contrary, interest rates were much more difficult to call than gold.

The meeting continued on in this vein for the better part of an hour. It was finally ended by the necessity of John's having to attend another meeting.

It was almost noon by the time I got back to my desk. I'd missed the most active part of the day.

At about four o'clock, when trading slowed down and everyone was sitting around waiting for reports of the day's activities to be printed by the operations department, the head spot foreign-exchange trader approached me.

"Did you attend the Risk-Management meeting today?" he asked.

"Yes," I replied.

"What did they have to say?" he wanted to know.

"Not much," I answered.

"Yeah," he sighed. "That's what they always have to say. That's why I never go."

It was the end of October. I'd just had one of my best months ever.

It was late in the day. All of us were engaged in our normal postmarket activity. The gold trader was playing Yahtzee with the Canadian dollar dealer. The Bankers Acceptance dealer was in the middle of a fierce paper-airplane duel with the Fed Funds trader. And my intrepid crew, Peter and Phillip, were testing their athletic mettle at Computer Olympics. This is a computer game in which each player uses the keyboard to participate in a variety of Olympic events. For example, if Peter and Phillip were competing in the 100-yard dash, each would be assigned two keys on the keyboard and they would have to press these keys as fast as they could in order to make each of their little men on the screen (actually, it was more like each of their little dots) run. When the winning man (dot) crossed the finish line, the computer launched into a stirring rendition of the Olympic theme. Peter and Phillip took these contests very seriously.

Consequently, when the phone rang they took no notice.

"Options desk," I answered.

"May I please speak with Nancy?" asked an unfamiliar voice.

"This is she."

"Hello, Nancy. You don't know me but my name is Fred Berkstein and I work for C.W. Associates."

"C.W. Associates?" The name sounded vaguely familiar.

"We are an executive-recruitment firm."

Translation: headhunters.

"What can I do for you, Fred?" I asked.

"Nancy, believe me, it's not what you can do for me. It's what I can do for you," said Fred. "We're not just any executive-recruitment firm. We're the best in our business. And our business is you."

"Right."

"People are our business. We're not in this for ourselves. We're in this for people."

"Right."

"You, Nancy," said Fred, "are our kind of person."

This guy's in the wrong business, I thought. He should be selling used cars.

"Yes?" I prompted.

"Nancy, have I got a job for you!"

"You have?"

"Yes, I have. Do you want me to tell you all about it?"

132

"No."

"It's a great . . ." Fred continued, then stopped. "No?" he asked incredulously.

"That's right. No."

"But why not?"

"Because I'm quite happy where I am, thank you."

"But this is a wonderful opportunity. . . . Just let me tell you about it. . . . It's at another major commercial bank . . . you'd be running the whole show. . . ."

"I run the show here," I pointed out.

"I know you do, but this is even more visibility, more challenge . . . this bank has had a high turnover in options traders and this time they are really committed to doing the job right . . . ," Fred hurried on.

Of course I knew which bank it was. Everybody in the industry knew which banks were looking for options traders.

"The base salary's going to be $100,000 . . . ," Fred continued.

"That's not enough," I said. "I make that now." (Small lie.)

"It's negotiable, everything's negotiable. The bonus will be up to 100 percent of your salary . . ."

"That's not enough," I said. "I make that now. More than that." (Another small lie.)

"Like I said, everything's negotiable. They may be willing to pay anything you want. Why don't you just let me make you an appointment? . . ."

"I'll tell you what," I said, to get him off the phone, "I'll consider it and let you know."

"All right," said Fred, accepting the compromise, "I'll call you again tomorrow."

"You needn't bother—" I began, but he was already gone.

I hung up to the rousing strains of the Olympic March.

C.W. Associates, I mused. Now where have I heard that name before?

Then I remembered.

While I was still a loan officer, but wanted to move into trading, I'd thought to approach a headhunter to see if there were any jobs available in the field. Larry had done business with a number of these firms and suggested I talk to David Silverman at C.W.

I'd called up and spoken to David. I gave him my credentials, and told him a little bit about what I wanted to do. He suggested that I come in and see him at his office.

I went to C.W. Associates' offices, bringing along a copy of my résumé. David looked it over as I sat beside him in his office.

"Let's see," he said, reading aloud. "Bachelor's and master's degrees from two excellent Ivy League schools. That's good."

He sounded encouraging. I relaxed a little.

"Went into commercial banking immediately upon graduation. Passed the bank's MBA training program. That's good."

I relaxed a little more.

"Assigned to the commodity lending department. That's good!" He looked up and smiled at me.

I smiled back.

"Nancy," said David. "I think we're in business."

"That's great!" I said. "Do you have any positions available right now?"

"I sure do. With your experience, I have some terrific positions available in the lending areas of a number of commercial banks."

"But, David," I said. "You don't understand. I told you on the phone that I don't want to go to the lending area of another commercial bank. Of course I've got experience! I've been in lending for three years! That's why I want to get out!"

134

"You want to get out of the lending business?" David asked. "But everything on your résumé points to commercial banking."

"Of course it does!" I said. "I've only been working for three years. Commercial banking was just the first thing I did, before I knew better. Now I want to get into something else."

"Like what?" David asked.

"Like trading," I said.

David laughed.

"You must be dreaming," he said.

I looked at him.

"Nancy," said David. "Let me explain the facts to you. You've been in commercial banking for three years now, right?"

"Right," I said, glad to see we'd made headway on that point.

"By staying in commercial banking for three years you have labeled yourself a commercial banker for life. No trading department is going to pick you up."

"Really?" I asked.

"Really. I'll tell you something else. I've been in this business a long time."

By which I assumed he meant three years.

"I know people," David continued. "I can look at you and see that you couldn't do the work of a trader. I wouldn't even send you up for the interview, you understand? Stick with what you got, kid. Why don't you let me place you at another bank for, say, a 15 percent increase? If you don't like it I can place you again in another six months."

"No, thank you," I said. "I don't need you to place me at another job just like the one I have already. I guess I'll just look around on my own."

"Suit yourself," said David, shrugging. "But you can take my advice and save your energy. You'll never be a trader."

▲ ▲ ▲

Fred called me every day for a week.

"Come on," he urged. "I hear you are one of the best traders on the Street. What harm can there be in just going and checking it out?"

I went home and asked Larry what harm there could be in just going and checking it out.

"None that I can see," said Larry.

"But what if someone at the bank finds out?" I asked.

"So much the better, really. The bank is more likely to place a higher value on you if they think you're wanted elsewhere. It might even help you with your upcoming bonus negotiations if they think you've received a competing offer. Also, it never hurts to see what you are worth in the open market."

I arranged for an appointment with the other bank.

The day of the interview arrived.

I was in a very good mood. Everything seemed to be going so well that I went into the cosmetics store across the street from the bank and bought myself $100 worth of the best makeup as a treat for myself. (One hundred dollars' worth of the best makeup buys you one mascara, one lipstick, some face powder and a little eyeshadow. A very little eyeshadow.)

Slightly startled by the meager purchasing power of $100 in what most people would classify as a drugstore, I struck off for the interview, carrying my very expensive cosmetics in a very inexpensive brown paper bag.

Fred had told me to report to the ninth floor. I'd made only one request when we made the arrangements.

"Listen, Fred," I'd said, "since I'm only going to the bank to listen and am not really interested in the position, I don't think it's necessary that I go through the personnel office. Just have me speak with whoever is in charge. There's no need to get Personnel involved until we are close to a deal, and we are certainly not close to a deal at the moment."

I lived in dread of personnel offices. They perform no real function and are notorious for all kinds of bureaucratic nonsense. I wanted to get the interview over quickly and not waste anyone's time (particularly mine) in the process.

"Fine. No problem," said Fred.

I got off the elevator at the ninth floor.

It was the personnel office.

I tried to make the best of the situation. I went up to the receptionist and gave her my name.

"Yes, you are expected," said the receptionist. "Please fill out this form."

I looked at the form. It filled two sides, single-spaced, of a sheet of legal-size paper. It asked for all kinds of interesting information, including the color of my eyes, which I was not aware was a component of the job description. It also asked for my last five places of employment, including summer jobs held during high school, and for the names, addresses, and telephone numbers of my immediate superiors at each of those positions.

Aside from the fact that it was not common practice for me to carry around the addresses and telephone numbers of my previous employers, I objected to filling out the form. As I didn't really want the job, and didn't expect to take the job, and was only there to discuss the position because I'd been talked into it by a headhunter, I didn't expect that the bank would ever need a record of the color of my eyes.

Accordingly, I handed the form back to the receptionist, politely responding that I had no intention whatsoever of filling out the form.

Apparently, no one had ever refused to fill out the

form before. I could see that I was shaking the receptionist's belief in the system as a whole.

"But you must fill out the form," she said. "It's procedure!"

"I don't care what it is," I responded. "I'm not filling out the form."

The receptionist decided that it was time to call in the big guns, in the form of her boss, an overweight man in his mid-thirties.

"What's the problem?" he asked abruptly.

The receptionist explained that I had refused to fill out the form.

"Oh!" said her boss. Evidently deciding that the misunderstanding must be due to physical infirmity on my part, he turned to me and spoke very slowly, enunciating clearly.

"You-have-to-fill-out-this-form," he said.

I looked at him.

"I'm-not-going-to-fill-out-that-form," I said.

"You- have- to- fill- out- the- form- to- get- the- job," he said.

"If-I-take-the-job-then-I'll-fill-out-the-form," I said.

This threw him so much that he forgot to enunciate.

"But that's not standard procedure!" he said.

"I don't care," I said.

He glowered at me.

"I have to check it out with the person in charge," he said.

"Do so," I said.

He got on the telephone. When he got off, he turned to me.

"Okay, you can go to the interview without filling out the form first," he said. "The interview is upstairs on the thirtieth floor."

"Thank you," I said.

I turned toward the elevators.

"Don't forget!" he cried as I stepped into the elevator. "If-you-get-the-job-you-have-to-fill-out-the—"

The elevator closed on his last words.

I got off the elevator on the thirtieth floor. A woman in a dark suit and bow tie was waiting for me.

"Nancy?" she asked.

"Yes?"

"My name is Jane. Please follow me."

I followed her. Along the way I stopped her to ask a question.

"Jane?"

"Yes?"

"The headhunter . . . er . . . executive recruiter neglected to mention the name of the person I'm to be meeting. What is his name, please?"

"Her name is Kathy Arnold."

This took me aback.

"And what is Kathy Arnold's position?" I asked.

"She is administrative head of the trading department," Jane replied.

John Anderson's position!

Just as there are very few women who run their own trading desks, so are there equally few women administrators in the field. In fact, Kathy was the first one I'd ever heard of.

I began to look forward to the meeting.

Jane ushered me into a small office at the far end of the bank's trading floor. A brunette woman wearing a dark suit and white shirt (but no bow tie) held out her hand to me.

"Nancy? I'm pleased to meet you. I'm Kathy Arnold."

Her grip was as strong as any man's.

I took a quick glance at Kathy. She was a woman

of medium weight, which is to say that although she didn't strike me as heavy, she didn't strike me as thin either. What she did strike me as was the kind of girl who played field hockey in school. She was reasonably attractive, with regular features.

"I'm very glad to meet you," I said.

"Sit down," said Kathy, "and we'll begin."

I took a seat across from her. Jane sat down in a chair by the door, pen and notebook in hand.

"Tell me about yourself, Nancy," said Kathy.

"What do you want to know?"

"Why don't you begin with how long you've been trading and what made you go into trading in the first place?" she suggested.

I gave her the short version of my rags-to-riches tale. Periodically she would nod in Jane's direction and Jane would take notes of whatever it was I was saying.

"Very interesting," she said when I'd finished. "And how do you trade now?"

I explained a little about the way I traded.

"*Volatility* trading, is it?" she said, picking up on one of the words I'd used. "Yes, all you volatility traders are in vogue right now." She said it as though I were the result of someone's fashion sense.

"Now for the important questions," she said, leaning forward in her chair.

"Yes?" I replied, leaning forward in mine.

"Do you have any brothers or sisters?" she asked.

I was unprepared for the question. It took me a moment to remember that I did, in fact, have a brother, and I said so.

"Aha!" she said. "An older brother or a younger brother?"

"A younger brother," I said, slightly puzzled.

"No sisters?"

"No sisters."

140

"That makes you the oldest child," she said.

Upon reflection I agreed that that did seem to sum up the case pretty well.

Kathy nodded approvingly. Jane wrote.

"Very good!" said Kathy. "And where are your parents?"

"In Chicago," I said.

"Are they both alive?"

"They are," I said.

"And you left them in Chicago?" asked Kathy.

"Uh, yes," I replied, slightly confused by this line of questioning.

"Very good again!" said Kathy, smiling at me. "Eldest child, a woman, leaves home, strikes out independently! Exactly the pattern I was looking for!"

I took this to mean that she was satisfied with my credentials.

"Now," said Kathy. "Before we go any further, do you have any questions?"

Well, yes, I had a few. Could she describe the job?

"Oh, yes," said Kathy. "Well, as you probably know, we've had a number of options traders here in the past, and they've all left for one reason or another. We want our bank to become a force in the options market and we're willing to devote the resources necessary to do the job."

Really? Such as?

"Well, we were thinking of hiring someone like you, and a junior trader of your choice."

What about the back office?

"Well," said Kathy, hesitating for the first time, "the back office does need a little work. We'd expect you to take care of that."

How is your back office currently accounting for the bank's options portfolio?

141

"Well," said Kathy, looking more and more uncomfortable, "they're . . . not."

Should I take that to mean that I would have to install a fully functioning accounting system?

"Well," said Kathy slowly. "You don't have to, but I'd imagine it would be difficult to work without one."

Translation: Yes.

What about credit lines? Would I be able to trade size with all the other banks if I wanted to?

"Well," said Kathy, "credit lines have always been a problem at this bank. If you wanted to trade options with another bank, you would have to get approval from the credit department."

And how long does that take?

"Approximately six months," said Kathy. "Per bank."

Since the bank is committed to becoming a force in the market, couldn't the process be speeded up a little?

"Unfortunately not," said Kathy. "It's against bank procedure."

So I would be walking into a position where there is no back office and no credit lines available to trade under.

"That's right," said Kathy, nodding.

Jane wrote.

"But do let me point out the advantages of the position," said Kathy.

Please do.

"It's a position of high visibility within the bank," said Kathy. "Very prestigious. You'll get to go to all sorts of high-level meetings!

"Nancy," said Kathy, "I'm going to be honest with you. I like you. I like your background. I think you're perfect for the job."

"Thank you," I said.

"Let's talk about salary and bonus," said Kathy.

I knew I was in trouble.

To walk into another bank with no back office and no credit lines meant that I would have to spend a minimum of six months working just to establish the unit, with no real trading income to speak of. As bonus is usually related to trading income, that meant I would have only six months of trading income to show for my first year at the job. To say nothing of the fact that I would be leaving a fully functioning options unit in order to work under conditions that were at least as bad as (if not worse than) those I had started out with originally.

In other words, I didn't want the job. I prayed she wouldn't offer me so much money that I would be tempted to take it.

"What are you offering?" I asked.

"We are offering $120,000 plus bonus," said Kathy. "Bonus would be up to 100 percent of your salary, depending on performance."

I breathed a sigh of relief.

"That's not enough," I said, gathering up my makeup and my coat.

Kathy stopped me.

"What would be enough?" she asked.

"What?" I asked.

"I said, what would be enough?" she repeated. "I'd really like to have you. What kind of money were you looking for?"

"What I want doesn't matter," I said, "It's what you are offering that counts. Are you improving your offer?"

"Just tell me what you want," she pressed.

I made some rapid calculations. I really didn't want the job. Also, I'm a trader. I wanted to make sure I wasn't going to ask for anything less than what she was willing to pay. I came to a figure. But what if I named an amount and she agreed? What was I going to do then?

I made my decision.

"I wouldn't do it for less than a quarter of a million dollars," I said. Then, seeing her face, I added "plus bonus," just for safety's sake.

"I see," said Kathy, nodding her head.

Jane wrote.

"Well, Nancy—" said Kathy, standing up and holding out her hand.

I held my breath.

"—while the bank is committed to becoming a force in the options market, it is not committed to that extent. It was nice to meet you."

"My pleasure," I said, shaking her hand and escaping out the door.

Who would ever have imagined that I'd be so relieved at not being offered a job that paid somewhere between $120,000 plus bonus and $250,000 plus bonus? I thought. Oh, well, that's life at the top, I guess.

How would I ever explain this to my father?

9 The Height of Power

John Anderson stopped by the desk.

"I have something important to discuss with you," he said. "Can you come by my office around four o'clock today?"

"Certainly," I replied.

"Good. See you then," he said, abruptly turning his back and walking away.

I stared after him. He was visibly upset. This was highly unusual. He rarely lost his equilibrium. What could it be?

Had he heard about my interview at the other bank? Impossible. Besides, I'd turned that job down. Was somebody else leaving the trading floor? The only person left of any importance was Andy, the head spot trader. I looked over at Andy. He was standing at his desk, screaming into two telephones at once, happy as a clam.

No, that wasn't it.

Perhaps the board of directors had turned down the bonus requests? This was likely, but it wasn't the kind of thing that would upset John in this way. After all, it wasn't John's compensation that was affected by the bonus negotiations; it was just his staff's.

No, I decided, no way to guess. Have to wait for four o'clock to find out.

John's office door was closed when I arrived promptly at four. I knocked.

"Come in," came John's voice from inside.

I opened the door and went in. My eyes widened with surprise.

John was sitting at his desk, waist-deep in papers. The normally neat and uncluttered office was littered with documents and files.

"Have a seat," said John, flinging an arm in the direction where the table and chairs had once been.

I followed his signal to an unusually high stack of papers and notebooks and started digging. Sure enough, the initial search revealed the presence of a chair somewhere beneath the piles. I redoubled my efforts and eventually cleared off enough space to be able to sit precariously on the end of the seat.

"Sorry about that," John said glumly.

I looked over at John. There was clearly something wrong. For one thing, his hair was slightly disheveled. Not the "casually tousled" style he usually sported. No, this was definite muss, as though he'd actually run his fingers through it before he'd remembered not to. Another surprise: he wasn't wearing his jacket. In fact, I couldn't even find his jacket. Also, he had actually loosened his tie. He was the very picture of the careworn executive.

Totally out of character. Something was terribly amiss. I almost felt sorry for him.

"What is it you wanted to see me about?" I asked.

He turned to me.

"It's London," he said, his voice trembling with rage.

"London?"

"London," he confirmed. He could barely speak.

I was having trouble understanding him. Surely he wasn't upset with the city as a whole.

"Can you be more specific?" I asked.

John started to explain.

Our bank was owned by a large foreign bank that had offices all over the world. It was so large it actually had three offices of its own in London. As our bank also had an office in London, that meant that there were four representatives of the same organization in that city.

This would have been all right if each of those offices had had its own specialized function. For example, one office could have lent funds for the development of real estate, another could have financed the import-export business, a third could have handled trading, and so on. In this way, each branch would have its particular expertise and all the offices would have flourished.

But our parent bank, it appeared, believed in a decentralized environment. So each of the offices operated as a separate little bank, trying to handle every type of banking function. The result was that no office was able to establish an expertise in any one area. They were much too busy competing with each other for the same business.

Our parent bank had no real expertise anywhere in trading. Up until now, our bank had been the recognized source of all market knowledge and initiatives. It was very much a feather in John's cap, for instance, that I ran the only options unit in the whole organization.

But now it appeared that one of our parent bank's London offices wanted to compete with us by trading options.

"They want to trade options?" I asked, surprised. Options are very complicated financial instruments. They aren't usually the first choice for a beginner.

John nodded.

"Well," I said. "Why don't they send somebody over here for six months or so and I'll train them to trade options and then they can handle all the options business for us out of London?"

"They don't want to do that," said John.

"Well," I said, "what do they want to do?"

"They want to give all the business to an outside trading organization."

"Why would they want to do that?" I asked. "They are just giving away income that would go to the organization as a whole."

"They don't want to give us the business," said John. "That would make us more important than them."

"Of all the ridiculous . . ." I didn't know what to say.

"I know," said John, shaking his head in misery. "And the worst part is—do you know what this does to my 'global plan'?"

"You're sure they won't cooperate with us?" I asked.

"I'm positive," said John. "They already paid the outside trading organization something like $250,000 for an options accounting system."

"You're kidding," I said. "But they could have had mine for free! All they had to do was ask me! And mine is just the kind of system they need to start an operation!"

I eyed John with new respect. And I thought senior

management at our bank was bad! The parent bank's management was beginning to make our management look like the three wise men.

"What are we going to do?" John asked.

I was angry, too. I didn't like the London office's approach. Incompetence on that level bothers me. Also, I didn't like having my turf invaded like that.

"When are they scheduled to begin trading?" I asked John.

"Sometime after the first of the year," he replied.

I made my decision.

"If it's competition they want, it's competition they'll get," I said grimly.

"What do you mean?" John asked.

"I mean we're going to open up an options trading desk in London, too."

John perked up.

"Nancy, I like your thinking," he said. "Can it be done?"

Can it be done? Hadn't I learned to manage a billion-dollar options portfolio while on the job? Hadn't I put together a terrific team in New York? Hadn't I traded brilliantly through G-5?

"Of course it can be done," I assured him.

He stood up and shook my hand.

"I'm glad you're on my team," he said.

"Thank you," I said.

I turned to go.

"By the way," he asked. "How quickly can you get it set up?"

"What choice do we have?" I asked. "I'll have it open by the first of the year."

It was November 15.

On the way back to my desk I thought about it. The thing about a London desk was that, clearly, somebody had to go there and run it. Later on, additional traders could be hired, but to begin with someone would have to go.

Who was that someone going to be?

Well, there were only three of us to choose from. It shouldn't be that difficult to decide.

I ruled out Phillip immediately. I wasn't sure Phillip could find London.

That narrowed the choice to Peter or me.

Whoever went might have to go for an indefinite period of time, perhaps as long as six months or a year. I was married, Peter was single. (I could just imagine Larry's reaction to my going abroad for six months without him. I could take him with me, of course, but then there was the problem of finding him something to do. I wasn't up to that kind of challenge.) Besides, as I pictured it, the London office would take most of its instructions from New York. The head trader had to be in New York. That narrowed the choice to just Peter. Peter it was.

Good, I thought. That's decided. Of course, sending Peter might be a little inconvenient. That would leave me alone with Phillip, and Peter alone in London. It's difficult to trade with just two people and impossible to trade alone.

Well, I thought, there's a very simple solution to all of this. I will simply hire a new trader in New York, train him or her before Peter leaves, and instruct Peter to hire someone immediately upon arriving in London.

No problem.

I held a short staff meeting when I got back to the desk. I told Peter and Phillip about the parent bank's London office. They were both indignant. I informed them of my decision to open an options desk in London. They applauded. I asked Peter if he would be willing to go to London for a few months to start up the operation. He was enthusiastic.

(Actually, Peter had an English girlfriend whose visa was up and who was going to have to return to London shortly anyway. So it wasn't an entirely altruistic decision on his part.)

I told them we'd have to have the whole thing up and running by the first of the year in order to beat the competition.

No problem, they said.

I went home that night and told Larry. He listened carefully until I'd finished explaining. Then he spoke.

"Are you crazy?" he asked.

"How difficult can it be? I just scoot Peter over there, get our name established in the London market, hire a few new traders, and presto! a London office."

"Why don't you open up in Timbuktu as long as you're at it?" Larry commented.

"Maybe I will," I returned.

"How do you intend to control your London operation?"

"Control?" I asked.

"Yes. How do you intend to keep from overtrading? How will you manage two positions? How will you get information back and forth between the two offices?"

"The operations department will have to come up with something, I suppose," I answered. "They must have the capability to communicate between the two offices by some sort of on-line computer system."

"I'd check that out if I were you," said Larry.

"Don't worry about it," I said. "That won't be a problem."

"Well, assuming that that is no problem, how do you intend to trade?"

"What do you mean?"

"I mean, how do you intend to staff your unit?"

"I told you," I said. "I'm going to hire someone in New York right away and train him before Peter leaves."

"Someone with experience, I hope," Larry said.

I thought about everyone I knew with experience. Most of them weren't worth hiring. The ones that were made more money than I did.

"No," I decided. "I'm going to hire someone with little or no experience. That's the best way."

"And train him in less than a month?"

"Of course," I said. "Why, anyone can trade options."

"Of course!" said Larry. "I forgot that!"

I ignored the sarcasm.

"I'm not kidding. Nancy! Have you thought about the kind of commitment involved in expanding along these lines? You'll have to trade for two operations; you know you'll be helping Peter trade while London is open. You'll have to train new people. You'll have to supervise the installation of communications equipment."

He paused for breath.

"By my calculations, it will take at least three of you to do the job."

Larry's words notwithstanding, I continued with my plans for expansion. The first thing to do was to hire someone in New York.

This was not as easy to do as I had first imagined.

As soon as word got out that the Options Unit was expanding into London and that there were positions in New York opening up as a result, I suddenly became everybody's best friend.

Thoughtful people from all over the bank took time out of their busy schedules to stop by my desk and congratulate me on how well I was doing and to impart to

me the interesting information that they'd wanted to
be an options trader since the fifth grade. Women would
stop me in front of the mirror in the ladies' room to
compliment me on my choice of lipstick, and before I
knew it these tête-à-têtes would turn into hard-sell job
applications. It got so that I couldn't walk into an elevator without being flattered or fawned over by some
devoted acquaintance, and then pitched to with the
practiced adroitness of a theatrical agent.

Unfortunately, none of my newfound admirers met
any of the qualifications of the job. I was forced to look
outside the bank for a suitable applicant (to the intense
displeasure of all my new friends who promptly re-
verted to their old attitude of haughty disdain).

Two people were immediately recommended.

The head spot trader referred me to an intelligent
young woman who was currently working for a computer company. I interviewed her twice and was sorely
tempted to hire her. She was obviously diligent and
industrious. Unfortunately, she hadn't the vaguest idea
what an option was, or what trading was all about.
There was no telling how quickly she'd catch on, or if
trading was even the right place for her. Although I
was convinced that I could "teach anyone" to trade options, the prospect of training someone who lacked even
a rudimentary knowledge of the marketplace daunted
even me.

I turned down her application.

At John Anderson's insistence I interviewed a man
in his late thirties who held a Ph.D. in something or
other. Market knowledge was not a problem here. This
man had plenty of experience with options, having just
lost a significant sum of money trading them for his
own account. Actually, losing money is not, in itself, a
reason for turning down someone's application. Every
trader loses money at one point or another. But this

man had picked up a lot of bad habits in his trading that would be hard to break him of. He thought he was a great trader and blamed everything on the market. It was easy to see why he'd lost money. I wanted someone with rather more experience than the head spot trader's choice and rather less experience (or at least a better quality of experience) than this man. Besides his questionable attitudes, there would be the additional problem of having the junior trader on the desk (him) being a good ten years older than the senior trader on the desk (me).

I turned down his application.

Having interviewed all of two people, my patience was wearing thin. There was also the pressure of time running out. Thanksgiving was just around the corner. I was ready to hire the next person who walked through the door.

The next person to walk through the door was a handsome blond man in his early twenties who had just graduated from the University of California at Berkeley. His name was Randy Miller.

On the surface Randy's credentials were excellent. He'd graduated the spring before and had gone to work for a small California investment bank for the summer. This meant that he was familiar with the way the markets worked. And, wonder of wonders, he'd written his senior thesis on options! Perfect. Now he was looking for a job in New York. This was where it was at, he drawled.

I arranged for a series of interviews.

Randy arrived at 5:00 P.M., after the market had closed. I sent him off with Peter and Phillip for the next round of interviews. When they had finished, I sat down with him myself.

I asked Randy a number of questions about options. He had all the right answers. Although his

154

knowledge was limited, he appeared to be on the right track. I was encouraged.

He was enthusiastic about the position, yet I felt a certain spark was missing from his manner. Nonsense! I chided myself. That's just the way they talk on the West Coast. You'd better watch yourself. You're turning into an Eastern snob.

I sent Randy on to interview with John Anderson. While he was gone I talked to Peter and Phillip about him.

We all agreed that he seemed like a nice guy, and had a basic knowledge of the business. They, too, found him lacking in energy, but were willing to discount the feeling.

"Well," I said, finally. "What do you think? Should we hire him?"

"He seems all right," said Phillip.

"It's so hard to tell after just one interview," said Peter.

"Look, guys," I said. "I've got to make a decision. Peter's leaving in one month. This guy seems okay. Unless one of you has an objection to him, I think we should take him."

The truth was that I was bored with the whole interview process. Besides, I was sure that I could fix whatever was wrong with him. More evidence of trader head. I was deep in the throes of the disease. Perhaps it was all the attention. Perhaps it was all the meetings.

John came out of his office after Randy had left.

"What did you think of him?" I asked.

"On a scale of one to ten," said John, "I'd say he's about a five. He didn't impress me very much. He actually seemed kind of slow."

I explained about the California mentality.

"I don't know," said John.

What does John know? I thought. He'd sent me a university professor with a midlife crisis.

"Look," I said. "I'm not looking for a rocket scientist. I'm looking for a junior trader. This guy knows enough about the business already that he should be able to pick it up pretty easily. We have to get somebody quickly, you know. The first of the year will be here before you know it."

"Well," said John, "it's your decision."

I hired Randy on the condition that he start work right after Thanksgiving. He accepted.

We were on our way to London.

November turned out to be significantly less profitable than any of the preceding months. We made less than $100,000. I blamed the reduced income on a slow market and on all the time I'd had to spend interviewing people and planning for the London office.

John stopped by the desk a few days after I had hired Randy. He motioned me away from the others.

"Great news," he said. "The board of directors has approved the bonus plan."

"That's terrific!" I said.

"Why don't you stop by my office later this week and we'll discuss some of the specifics," said John.

"Fine," I said, returning to my work.

Larry and I had talked of little else but my bonus for weeks.

"How much do you think you'll get?" Larry asked every other night.

"I don't know," I replied, never tired of discussing the subject.

"You must have some idea," said Larry.

"It's so hard to say," I said. "The bank has never really paid bonuses before."

"That's why they're losing everybody," said Larry. "They have to begin to pay competitively."

"Yes," I said. "I know that, and you know that, but the question is, Do *they* know that?

"I think you should prepare for your bonus negotiations," Larry said.

"Prepare? What do you mean?"

"Well, what are you going to say to John? Suppose they only give you a bonus of $10,000. Will you stay working for the bank for that?"

"They wouldn't!" I said, shocked. "All the work I've put in! All the money I've made for them!"

"I didn't say they were going to. But what if? It is a possibility, you know."

"What would I do?" I said hotly. "I'd quite on the spot, that's what I'd do. Let John or the board of directors run the portfolio if they think it's so easy."

"Calm down," said Larry. "I'm just asking. You see my point? You should go into any negotiation knowing your price in advance. Not only does it save a lot of time, but it will help you to bargain more effectively."

But I was still mumbling to myself.

"Ten thousand dollars, indeed! Let them do it if they think it's so easy!"

"Nancy," Larry said, "Stop dwelling on the $10,000. I just used it as an example. Much more likely would be, say, $30,000. How would you feel about $30,000?"

I thought about it.

Thirty thousand dollars was more money in one lump sum than I'd ever been paid before in my life. Nine months ago, $30,000 would have been a sheer impossibility. I would have laughed if anyone would have suggested it to me.

But I'd just turned down a job at another bank for a salary of $120,000 and a bonus of up to 100 percent of that amount. Thirty thousand dollars didn't seem like such a big deal in the light of that offer. And there were plenty of other banks still looking for head options traders.

157

"For $30,000," I said, "I'd leave. I wouldn't quit on the spot, but I'd leave. I'd start interviewing immediately."

"Okay," said Larry. "You'd quit on the spot if it's $10,000, and you'd leave at your leisure if it's $30,000. What amount would you be satisfied with? What amount would you stay for?"

I thought again.

I didn't really want to go to another bank. I loved working with Peter and Phillip. They were my friends. We had a good time together. If I left, there was no telling who I would have to work with.

"I'd be satisfied with $50,000," I said, finally. "I think I deserve more, but I'd stay for $50,000."

"That's what I was thinking," said my spouse.

"I deserve more," I pointed out. "They should pay me more."

"I agree," said Larry, "but what you deserve has nothing to do with it. This bank has not paid substantial bonuses in the past. This is entirely new for them. If you get $50,000 you'll be fine."

I was forced to agree with him.

"Now," said Larry. "Let's talk about attitude."

"Attitude?"

"Yes," he said firmly. "Before every big game the coach always lectures about attitude."

"Big game?"

"In the first place," said Larry, ignoring my questions, "no matter what number he gives you, you will not quit on the spot."

"But, Larry . . ."

"You will not quit on the spot, do you hear me? It doesn't do you any good. The object is not to ride off into the sunset like Clark Gable."

"Gary Cooper."

"Whoever. The object is to get the money. You have

to set the tone of the negotiations," he continued. "If he gives you an unreasonably small number, you might want to tell him that the number is so much below what you consider to be fair that you are unprepared to discuss it at the present time, and ask to reschedule the meeting."

"Why would I want to reschedule? I'd rather get it over with in one sitting."

"Because the second you leave, he'll assume that you intend to look for another job, and he knows you'll get it."

"So you think he'll increase the offer at the second meeting?"

"If he can, he will."

"Why doesn't he just give me a fair number to start with?"

"Because he has to try to get away with anything he can. He's trying to keep *his* P and L for the bank showing a profit too, you know."

"That's true."

"On the other hand, if he gives you $50,000 to start with, you probably shouldn't act too pleased."

"Why not?"

"Because if he thinks you're unhappy with that number he might make some other concessions. I don't think he'll give you more money, but he might give you some other form of recognition."

"I don't know," I said. "There are only so many meetings one can attend in a day."

"You know what I mean. All I'm trying to say is, play to win. You're in an excellent negotiating position. You've done a fantastic job."

"Yeah!" I said.

"They don't want to lose you. You are more likely to walk away from the table than they are."

"Right!" I said.

"People spend their lives dreaming about holding the kind of cards you're holding."

"Yeah!" I said.

"So go out there and win, win, win!"

I went to John's office to discuss the details of the bonus plan. His door was closed when I got there. I took several deep breaths before knocking. This was it!

"Come in," John said in response to my rap.

I went into the office.

Both John and his office had returned to their normal state. The office was neat and uncluttered. So was John. He seemed perfectly in control.

"Have a seat," he said, gesturing to the now-visible table and chairs.

I sat down. He came and sat next to me. He had a folder in his hands. Inside the folder were some papers with numbers on them.

"Nancy," said John, "I can't tell you how pleased I am that this bonus package went through. I knew we were going to have to start paying people competitively, and I pushed for it."

I thanked him for his efforts.

"Now," said John, opening the folder, "let me explain how the bonus package works."

I drew closer to him.

"It's based on a percentage of what you earn," he said. "Your section gets about 15 percent of your bottom line."

I made a rapid calculation in my head. My section had earned $1.8 million before expenses in the last six months. Of course, this did not include the half-million-dollar loss left by my predecessors. My direct expenses, except for brokerage, were about $150,000. Brokerage was another $250,000. That left me with $1.4 million. Fifteen percent of $1.4 million was $210,000!

I couldn't help smiling.

"Now," John was continuing, "for your section, we have the income you earned for the year. That's $1.3 million less expenses."

So he was going to subtract the initial loss. I did another quick calculation: $1.3 million less about $400,000 in expenses was $900,000; 15 percent of $900,000 was still $135,000.

"Your direct expenses for the year came to about $400,000," said John.

"That's correct," I said.

"Now, your indirect expenses came to—"

"My indirect expenses?" I asked.

"Of course. Your bottom-line percentage comes after indirect expenses. That's what bottom line means."

I still wasn't worried. I mean, how much indirect expense could a three-person section have incurred?

"How do you calculate indirect expense?" I asked.

"It's done as a percentage of the indirect expense allocated to the whole floor."

"And how much is that?" I asked.

"Twelve million dollars," he said.

"Twelve million dollars?" I repeated. "Twelve million dollars? Why, that's absurd! How could the trading floor have spent $12 million in indirect expense?"

"Easy," said John, smiling at my naïveté. "This floor makes a lot of money. We have to help pay for everything at the bank from the library to the president's limousine."

I wasn't sure, but I didn't think it was right that the president's car should get a part of my bonus. I didn't remember the automobile having contributed much to the formation of key trading decisions.

"And how much of the $12 million will be allocated to my section?" I asked.

"About $750,000," he said.

▲ ▲ ▲

"Three quarters of a million dollars in indirect expenses?" exclaimed Larry later that evening when I had finished explaining about the bonus plan. "Three quarters of a million dollars for a three-person unit? What did you guys have for lunch every day? Caviar?"

I explained about the president's limousine.

"Nancy," said Larry, "$900,000 less $750,000 leaves $150,000. Fifteen percent of $150,000 is $22,500. Are you telling me that you are expected to pay your entire unit out of that stock? Why, you have to pay Phillip and Peter at least $10,000 apiece just to keep them."

"More," I said miserably.

"Well, you can't pay them more unless you want to go without entirely. As it is, you'd be paying each of them $10,000 and you'd be left with $2,500."

"I know," I said. "It's even worse than I expected. What should I do?"

"Don't spend it all in one place," Larry suggested.

"How can you joke about it?" I asked.

"Because it's just too ridiculous for words. You have only one choice."

"What's that?"

"Throw away the formula completely and go in there and tell him what you want."

I knocked on John's door again.

"Come in," he said.

"I'd like to discuss the bonus plan again," I said.

"Something wrong?" asked John.

"Nothing's wrong exactly," I said uneasily. I was nervous. "It's just that I'd like to say something."

"Yes?"

"About the indirect expenses . . . they seem rather high . . ."

"Well," said John. "I'll tell you what. Why don't

we sit down and go over your bonus recommendations for your people?"

"That would be fine," I said, relieved.

"What do you suggest we give to Peter and Phillip?" John asked, pencil in hand.

"Well, you know, John," I said, "Peter and Phillip have worked very hard this year."

"I know that."

"And they've done very well. They are intelligent, diligent individuals. They are assets to the organization."

"That's right," said John.

"I really think we should try to keep them. I've told you that options traders are greatly in demand."

"And I've told you that I intend to keep them," said John. "So what is your recommendation?"

I made my recommendation. He wrote down the number. He didn't even blink.

"Do you agree?" I asked, cautiously.

"I expected something like this," he said.

"What about the indirect expenses?" I asked.

"Well, we'll have to be flexible with the indirect expenses," he said, winking. "This has been a good year for all of us. I want next year to be just as good. That means I have to keep people around."

I was completely floored. He was being so reasonable.

"Now, for your bonus," he said. "I've been thinking about it."

"Yes?"

"Would you be satisfied with $80,000?"

"What happened to the indirect expenses?" asked Larry when I told him what happened.

"I guess," I said slowly, "that they were indirectly applied—somewhere else."

10 Growing Pains

Larry and I went out to dinner to celebrate my bonus. Larry selected a beautiful restaurant on the river, and made sure we were given a table by the window. We got all dressed up for the occasion. Heads turned as we made our way to the table. Larry knows how to make an entrance.

We sat down and ordered champagne. It was poured into delicate crystal flutes.

Larry raised his glass.

"To you," he said. "I want you to know how proud I am of you. This is your night."

We touched glasses and drank. The crystal rang pleasantly.

"That's nice," said Larry. "Let's do it again." He

raised his glass. "You're beautiful and I love you. I wouldn't want to be married to anyone else."

"Me either," I said.

This time we kissed.

"Isn't it wonderful!" I said, looking out over the water and toward the lights of the city across the river.

"Yes," Larry agreed, holding my hand.

"No," I said, realizing he thought I meant the view. "I meant about the job and all. How well everything has turned out. And it's certainly nice to have the money."

"Nancy," said Larry, "it's not the money. It's never the money. It's that you tried. That's what you should be proud of."

"Sure, sure," I said, a little impatiently. "And I bet I can make three or four times as much next year. Look at Adam. He makes twice that."

The waiter came to take our order.

"Which way do you think the dollar's going?" I asked, as soon as we were alone again. "There seems to be sentiment on both sides—"

"Nancy." Larry stopped me. "No market talk tonight, okay?"

"Oh, right. I'm sorry. What would you like to talk about?"

"How about your eyes?" Larry suggested. He paused. "Hey, why don't we go away next weekend?"

"Where?" I asked.

"I don't know. Let's go out to Montauk. There's no one there this time of year."

"Sure," I answered without much conviction. "We'll see."

I smiled at him. We drank some more champagne. The first course arrived.

"Randy starts this week," I confided over the lobster salad. "I'll have to whip him into shape quickly."

"Nancy," said Larry. "Go slowly here. You don't realize what you're getting yourself into. It takes a long time to train someone properly. And opening a new office, especially overseas, is more work than you expect. A lot more. You don't have the resources. Frankly, I don't know how you're going to do it."

"What are you talking about?" I asked. "It's not that big a deal."

"We've had this discussion before," said Larry, shaking his head. "Let's just drop it and try to enjoy dinner."

"You just don't think I can do it," I accused. "You think I've just been lucky this whole time."

"I'm not saying *you* can't do it," said Larry. "I'm saying it would be difficult for *anyone* to do it. And you have been lucky. There's a lot of luck involved in trading. You know that as well as I do."

The main course arrived. We ate in silence.

"How did we get off the subject of your eyes?" Larry asked finally.

"You started it."

Like all junior traders, Randy was caught between his position and his ignorance. He knew he had to ask questions in order to learn. I recognized this necessity as well. But that didn't make it easier for either party.

For example, suppose you are the head trader. You have just made a decision to buy the dollar, expecting it to go up. As soon as you buy it, the dollar drops in value. You are losing money.

"Why did you do that?" asks the junior trader.

A perfectly reasonable question. A perfectly innocent question. Not, however, the question that you most feel like answering at that moment.

Possible responses include:

1. "I did that because I'm pretty sure the dollar is

going up, but I could be wrong, so I have to concentrate a little bit on the market right now."

2. "I did that for a very good reason but I don't have the time to discuss it with you right now."

3. "Shut up and watch the screen."

Although I was confident that I could teach Randy to trade in no time flat, I'd never considered how annoying it could be to have someone new on the desk. From the very beginning, Peter and Phillip and I had worked in complete harmony. Trading demands total concentration. We knew when to avoid idle conversation and unnecessary questions. Each of us had different strengths and weaknesses, which we understood and to which we deferred. Each of us did what we had to do. We were comfortable with one another. There were strong, unspoken bonds between us.

Into this environment, I had suddenly thrust a complete stranger. Under the best of circumstances, it was a difficult situation. And Randy did nothing to help. In fact, from the very first day, I could find nothing in his manner reminiscent of the person I'd interviewed. Gone was the quiet, respectful, junior trader, eager to learn. In his place was a chattering, boisterous know-it-all.

Randy's biggest problem was that he was insensitive to his surroundings. I had assumed that, coming from a trading environment, Randy would already understand the cardinal rules of trading etiquette. The most important was, it is all right to ask questions, but it is definitely not all right to say whatever comes into your head no matter what the circumstances.

I watched Randy and Phillip together. As I have already mentioned, Phillip is one of the nicest individuals on the planet, with the patience of a saint.

Phillip bought some dollars.

"Why did you do that?" asked Randy.

Phillip explained that he thought the dollar would be having a correction soon (it had been going in one direction—down—for about nine months). He took out his charts and carefully unfolded them for Randy's benefit. He started to teach him, in a painstakingly thorough way, how to read the charts. While he was explaining, the dollar started to fall again. Phillip began to lose a little money on his position.

Still he ignored the market in an effort to teach Randy about the charts.

"Oh!" said Randy, looking from the charts to the screen. "Well, I wouldn't have bought the dollar where you did. I would have sold the dollar. Maybe I would have bought it back here," he added.

Now, there is nothing so irritating to a trader as a person who announces what he or she would have done after the fact. Hindsight does a lot for someone's trading ability.

Phillip showed considerable restraint and said nothing. But I saw that he set his mouth a little firmer, and he put his charts away.

A little while later, after the dollar had fallen substantially more, and Phillip had been forced to take out his position at a loss, Randy approached him once again.

"I would have bought my dollars back here," he said, continuing with the conversation as if nothing had happened.

"I thought you said you would have bought them back fifty points ago," Phillip reminded him.

"I didn't say I would have, I said maybe I would have," Randy began.

"You have the right to your opinion, of course," said Phillip, cutting him off.

It was the sharpest I'd ever heard him get.

It was also a part of Randy's style to pretend to

know everything—even questions to which it was clear he couldn't possibly know the answers. His was a very chipper ignorance. It never occurred to him that he made a bigger fool of himself by pretending to know the answer to something than by simply admitting he didn't. Thus, no matter how many times he was caught in a blunder, he continued cheerfully to bluff his way through his training. This made it very difficult to isolate what he did know from what he didn't.

"Did you figure out the delta position of that trade?" I asked him.

"I don't have to—I know the delta position," came the response.

"Really? What is it, then?"

"It's—it's—let me see, the delta position would be . . ." Randy would start to mumble and stare at the trade.

"Do you know how to figure out the delta position?" I asked.

"Of course I know how to do it!"

"Well, then, if you know how to do it, tell me what it is."

Of course he didn't know how to do it, and I had to show him.

Randy's omniscience went far beyond simple trading matters. He was, it appeared, an expert on everything. One day Peter and I were having a discussion of the application of one of the rules of the exchange.

"I know that rule," said Randy, butting in to our conversation. "I know how it applies."

Peter and I looked at each other. It was a pretty obscure ruling. We only knew about it because we were having a problem with the exchange. It was odd that Randy would know the rule as well.

"Really?" said Peter. "What is the rule, exactly, Randy?"

"Well, yes, I suppose so. Let's see," he said, "there are two little screens built nicely into the desk."

"What information is transmitted by those screens?" I asked.

"Well," he said, hesitating again, "I don't really know. . . ."

"Try turning them on," I suggested.

"Oh, yes, of course!" he said, vastly relieved. "Yes, I see now that they relay information concerning the spot foreign-exchange market."

So I had two machines that performed the function of a Reuters screen. A good start.

"Thank you," I said. "That's very helpful."

"Don't mention it," he said.

"Now," I said. "Are there any PCs on the desk?"

"PCs?" he asked, puzzled.

"Personal computers. We're going to need two personal computers. IBM personal computers. Do you think that you can get them for us?"

"Oh, certainly," he said. "But I'm afraid I'll have to call you back tomorrow about that."

"All right," I said. "And thank you very much for all of your help."

"Don't mention it," he said.

Three days later he called back.

"I found you some personal computers," he said.

"Wonderful!" I said.

"Yes," he continued. "Just imagine! The bank has twelve computers available that nobody is using."

"Twelve!" I said. "That's terrific, but I only need two. What kind are they, AT or XT?"

"Well, let me see," he said, "I have one right here. It says 'Wang' on it—"

I stopped him. "Wang computers?"

"Yes. The bank discovered that Wang computers

were cheaper than IBM computers so they bought a dozen of them."

"But I can't use Wang computers," I said. "I need IBM."

"We don't have any IBMs," he said. "But you can have all twelve Wangs, if you like."

"But I don't need twelve Wangs," I persisted. "I need two IBMs."

Silence.

"I'll tell you what," I said. "This is much too difficult to organize over the phone. Why don't I just come to London for a few days and handle all of these administrative problems?"

"I'd appreciate that," said the London manager.

"Don't mention it," I sighed.

I decided to go to London the week before Christmas. The market appeared to be quieting down for the holiday season.

Peter was going with me, to find a place to stay and to help sort out some of the organizational problems. He would return to New York for the holidays and then move to London on a more permanent basis.

I tried not to think about what it was going to be like without Peter on the desk. Oh, well, I thought. It's only for about six months.

Concerned about possible operational problems resulting from the expansion, I decided that I needed someone with operations experience along on the London trip. The obvious choice was Sam Antonio from the back office. Sam knew his job cold. So far, in my experience with the operations department, this type of expertise was rare, almost unheard of.

The back office was responsible for the smooth functioning of my department. It was their job to make sure that payments went out to the right place and on

172

time, and that all payments received were properly accounted for. Margin requirements at the exchanges had to be proved and met lest the exchange close out our position for lack of funds. Every day, Sam's department had to enter the day's trades into its computers and print out the reports that were so necessary to the managing of the position.

Operations people at the bank were generally underpaid, and there was always the risk of their being lured away by the competition. Sam had done such a terrific job over the past eight months that I wanted to reward him in some way. The trip to London was the perfect vehicle.

I asked Sam if he would like to go to London for a few days right before Christmas. He was thrilled.

"But I'll have to ask the Field Marshall," he said.

"The Field Marshall?" I asked.

"My boss. William Hambrecht."

"Oh!" I said. "I don't know him."

"I know you don't," said Sam, grinning. "If you knew him you wouldn't have to ask."

Sam's group didn't report to me, even though they provided my section with technical support. The bank kept the supervision of the operations department separate from that of the Trading Sector in order to reduce the risk of theft or fraud.

"Okay," I said, smiling back at Sam. "You ask the Field Marshall for permission."

Two days later, Sam came up to me at the desk. He looked unhappy.

"What's the matter?" I asked.

"The Field Marshall says I can't go to London," he said.

"Why not?"

"He says it's too expensive and, besides, I'm too junior to go."

"Too junior to go?" I repeated. "Why, that's ridiculous! Who would I take besides you? Nobody else knows how everything works."

"I guess," said Sam slowly, "that the Field Marshall thinks that if anyone should go, it should be him."

"But he doesn't know anything about our requirements," I said. "What does he expect to do in London?"

"I don't know," said Sam. "I hear it's a good place for shopping."

"Well," I said, "in that case why don't you just go back to your Field Marshall and tell him that I'll pay for your trip and that you are plenty senior enough for me."

"You mean it?" asked Sam.

"I mean it."

The Field Marshall was hard pressed to find a reason for forbidding Sam to go to London once it became clear that I was willing to absorb the expense. He couldn't very well claim that Sam was needed in New York when I said he was needed in London. Sam was allowed to go.

It was my first encounter with the Field Marshall.

I paid very little attention to the market in December. The dollar started to fall again, but I barely noticed. Between training Randy and organizing the expansion and getting ready to go to London, I was only vaguely aware that the market, contrary to my expectations, hadn't really quieted down at all.

What did I care? My bonus was set. I was one of the highest paid officers of the bank. I'm not sure, but I think I was the highest paid woman.

I gave myself until the first of the year to get the unit organized. I was in too good a humor to bother about the market. I was successful! It was the holidays! And I was going to London for the very first time!

11 We Wish You a Merry Christmas . . .

"I'm going to London on business," I announced to Larry.

"When?" he asked, barely looking up from his newspaper.

"The week before Christmas."

We had just finished dinner, a delicious repast of leftover Chinese take-out.

"How long will you be gone for?"

"Three or four days." I hesitated. "You won't even notice I'm gone."

"I don't notice when you're here."

He rose and started to clean up the empty cardboard chow mein boxes.

"Let me do that," I said, jumping up.

"That's all right, I can do it," he said. "It's not like there are any dirty dishes."

I followed him into the kitchen.

"I'll tell you what," I said. "If I leave on the red-eye I can go right to the office and if I plan things right I can finish everything in two days. How's that?"

"Suit yourself. It doesn't seem to matter to you what I say anyway."

"Of course it matters."

"What do you mean, of course? I've been trying to talk to you for months now—" he stopped himself.

"Larry. It's only a two-day trip."

"Why bother to take a plane at all? Why don't you just slip into your red cape and fly to London yourself?"

"What's the matter with you?"

"I don't know why the hell you got married. It doesn't seem to be what you want. I think you'd be much happier at this stage of your life living alone."

"How can you say that?" I was stunned.

"How can I say that?" Larry shook his head in disbelief. "How can I say that?" He threw up his arms and walked into the bedroom.

I stared after him. Go to hell! I thought. Who needs this?

I stuffed the rest of the garbage into a bag, stalked out to the incinerator, and threw out the remains of the dinner with a vengeance. Who does he think he is, I fumed. I probably would be happier living alone!

No, I wouldn't.

I had a brainstorm. The perfect solution.

I went back into the apartment and stood at the bedroom door. Larry was lying on the bed reading a book.

"Why don't you come to London with me?" I said.

176

He looked up.

"It'll be great." I hurried along. "I'll schedule all my meetings in the morning so we can have the afternoons together. And we can stay for the weekend. It will be romantic."

"It's a nice thought, but I don't see how it's possible to organize a new operation in three mornings. It's far more likely you will not only spend the entire day at the bank, but you'll end up having dinner with them, too."

"No, I won't. I promise."

"Look, Nancy, I've been to London. I don't want to end up spending three days wandering around by myself. If you don't think you can do it, be honest. I'd rather you went alone."

"No, no. I can do it. I want to be with you. I want things to be the way they were." I sat down next to him on the bed.

"In that case, we'll have a great time. I know all kinds of wonderful little places. I'd love to show you around."

I began to get excited.

"We could go to the theater," I said. "And out to lunch."

"Shopping," said Larry. "You'd like that."

"And tea!" I said. "I've always wanted to have a real English tea, with scones and clotted cream and raspberry jam!"

"I know just where to go," said Larry.

We started kissing. The phone rang.

"Don't answer it," he whispered.

Two rings. Three rings.

"You know I have to." I pushed him away.

"Ah, yes. This is Singapore calling," said the voice on the other end of the wire. "Is Nancy there?"

"This is Nancy."

Randy made up a rule on the spot for our benefit. He showed great imagination, but little factual knowledge.

"Right," said Peter, smiling his funny little smile, and turning back to me.

I began to wish that I was going away to London instead of Peter.

In addition to training Randy, I was spending a large part of my day helping Peter set up the London office. This, too, was taking more time than I'd imagined.

We were in daily contact with the man who was the administrative head of the bank's trading room in London, a very pleasant gentleman who had never heard of options. That was all right; we didn't expect him to trade. We simply wanted him to arrange for the delivery of the necessary equipment.

Before we could determine what equipment was needed, however, we had to find out what was already there.

"We've found a lovely spot for you in the corner of the room," said the London manager, when I'd gotten him on the phone. "It's right by the tea table."

"That's terrific," I said. "Thank you very much."

"Don't mention it," he said. He was always very polite.

"Does the space you've so kindly provided for us—" I began.

"Don't mention it," he said.

"—have any equipment associated with it?" I asked.

"Oh, yes!" he said. "There is some equipment here."

"Good," I said. "What kind of equipment is it?"

"Well," he said, doubtfully. "I don't really know the proper names for some of these machines. . . ."

"Can you describe them for me?"

170

"Ah, yes! Good evening, Nancy! The market is remaining relatively calm. . . ."

We landed at Heathrow Airport on a Tuesday evening in December and checked into the hotel. The next morning I left Larry still sleeping soundly in the big double bed and went downstairs to look for Sam and Peter. The desk clerk told me that they'd already left. I hurried off to the London office, located somewhere in the financial section of town, known simply as the City.

I didn't have a map or a guide; I didn't need one. I simply found the subway and followed all of the men wearing bowler hats and Burberry raincoats. They led me directly to the London office.

The London manager was waiting for me when I got to the office that first morning. He was a thoroughly nice man, very reserved, who wanted only to do his job.

And do his job he did. He was as much a fixture of the London office as the electric light bulbs. He'd started with the bank when he was nineteen years old, beginning as a clerk in the back office. He worked hard, going from job to job, promotion to promotion, slowly inching along the path to success.

A full twenty years after walking into the bank as a young man, he finally reached his ultimate destination: manager of the entire office. Since the office of London manager carried with it the title of vice president, he and I were of equal rank.

He hurried up to greet me. He was very tall. Even with my heels on, he towered over me.

"You must be Nancy," he said. "I'm Alec Carter. How do you do?"

"How do you do?" I asked, shaking his hand.

"Won't you come into my office?" he asked, leading the way.

I'd walked into, out of, and through trading rooms
in New York for nearly nine months. I knew what to
expect, and it didn't even bother me anymore. It
shouldn't come as a surprise to anyone that the atmosphere inside most trading rooms is overwhelmingly
male. Walking into a trading room is the closest I'll
ever come to visiting the inside of a men's locker room
immediately following the big game.

I had learned to live with the jokes. Traders love
tasteless, off-color jokes. Thanks to my experience in
trading, I was now the master of an almost unlimited
number of these knee-slappers (an accomplishment that
unfortunately does not carry over well into other areas
of social discourse).

I could stand the jabs. Whenever a piece of equipment broke down on my desk, there was always someone there to ask if I was sure I'd plugged it in. Or, "It
figures a woman wouldn't be able to fix a printer," a
male colleague would announce to the room at large,
neglecting to mention that he couldn't fix it either. I
was used to veiled looks, double entendres, half-con-
cealed smirks. I thought I was ready for anything they
could dish out.

I was not ready for the London office.

For all its talk, the New York trading community
is much more receptive to the concept of women's rights
than it cares to admit. There is an underlying acceptance that times have changed and women have to earn
a living just like everyone else. Remember that the
trading community comprises mostly men under the
age of thirty. These men went to school with women.
They've been beaten, first at spelling, and later at math,
by women. They've had to compete for the same jobs
as women, and they've had to take that competition
seriously. Consequently, they have lost some of that air
of male superiority held by their fathers and grandfa-

thers. It can take some of the wind out of your sails to discover that the woman standing next to you on the subway platform earns four times as much as you do.

But in London it's different. The all-male networks are much stronger there. The core group resists the persuasions of the intruder. When I walked into the London trading room that first morning, I felt the shock ripple through the room.

What's the matter with these guys? I thought. You'd think they'd never seen a woman trader before.

They hadn't.

I followed Alec into an office just off the trading floor. We sat down facing each other. He stared at me.

"How . . . uh . . . how long have you been with the bank?" he asked me, to break the silence.

I explained that I'd been with the bank about three years.

"Three years," he repeated blankly. Then: "And how long have you been trading options?"

I told him I was in my ninth month.

"Had you had much experience in trading before this?"

"None whatsoever," I replied.

He struggled manfully to suppress his horror.

"Well," he said finally. "We're very pleased to see that you are opening shop here. I'll do everything in my power to help you."

"Thank you," I said, touched. He really was a nice man.

"Don't mention it," he said. "Shall we have a look at your space?"

We walked through the room toward the back. On the way I saw something that made me start: *Playboy* centerfolds had been tacked to the wall. Alec walked right by them. He gave no sign of having noticed.

Alec ushered me to a desk in the corner of the room. It was exactly as he had described it.

"What do you think?" Alec asked anxiously. "Will this do?"

"Oh, yes," I hastened to reassure him. "This will do nicely."

"As for the two computers you need, I thought that we might put one right here, and the other one back there," he flung his arm in the direction of the wall, some twelve feet away.

"No, both will have to go right here," I said, slapping the top of the desk with my hand.

"Where?" started the London manager. "Oh no! It can't go on top of the desk!"

"Why not? We need both PCs right on the desk so we can price options while we are on the phone."

"You couldn't run back and forth I suppose?" he asked hopefully.

"I'm afraid not."

"But it can't go on the desk!"

"Why not?"

"It will ruin the decor," he said dramatically.

I looked around. Sure enough, all the other traders' screens were built into their desks.

That stopped me. I have to confess that interior design was an issue I hadn't considered before. (Although now that he mentioned it, I certainly wouldn't want to do anything to ruin the effect of the centerfolds.)

"I'm afraid we have no choice in the matter. One of the PCs must go on the desk."

"Yes . . . well . . ." Alec struggled between his loyalty to aesthetics and his innate politeness. Politeness won. "Yes, of course, whatever you want," he murmured unhappily.

While we were talking one of the junior spot traders approached Alec and whispered something in his ear. Alec turned to me.

"There's a phone call for you," he said. "Why don't you take it in my office?"

On the way back to Alec's office I glanced at one of the spot traders' screens. The market wasn't particularly active. Still, it could only be Phillip calling from New York with some problem. I braced myself for trouble.

"Hello?" I said into the phone.

"Hello, sweetie. How's it going?"

My husband.

"Larry," I said. "Is something wrong?"

"Nope. Just calling to see how you're doing over there."

"I'm just fine, honey," I said. "But I'm busy."

"Well, I won't keep you," he said. "I just called to see where you wanted to meet for lunch."

"Lunch?"

"I thought afterward we could do a little sightseeing. . . ."

"Honey," I said sweetly, praying that no one was listening in (you never can tell on a trading floor; the phone lines are communal and most of them are taped as well). "I'm afraid I'm running a little behind schedule. I can't take the whole afternoon off as we'd planned."

"Well, when can you get off?"

"I think it's safer to skip lunch today. Why don't we meet for tea?"

"Fine. See you then."

I caught Sam as he was coming out of the back office. He was laughing.

"What's so funny?" I wanted to know.

"They can't get our accounting program up. They're using the wrong kind of computer," he said.

I groaned. "Not the Wangs again," I said.

"Yep. They want to use Wangs," he said, shaking his head. "I can't for the life of me figure out why. I told 'em Wangs won't do the job."

"It appears," I said, "that the bank is having a fire sale on Wangs and we are supposed to be the happy recipients."

"Yeah," he said. "That's another thing. They want to give us twelve of the things. What would we possibly do with twelve?"

"Never mind," I said. "What are we going to do about it?"

"Well," said Sam, "just to show me, they've got someone coming over from Wang today to give us a demonstration. He is supposed to know how to get our accounting program up on his computer."

"Any chance of it working?" I asked hopefully.

"None," Sam grinned. "But it ought to be fun watching him try."

I saw Sam again later that afternoon.

"Did it work?" I asked.

"Nope."

"Tell them to order some IBMs," I said.

"I already have," said Sam.

Peter, who had been meeting with some of the other traders, met me in Alec's office to discuss where he'd be living during his stay in London.

"Nothing to worry about," said Alec. "We've arranged a place for you."

Peter and I exchanged looks.

"You have?" I asked.

"Yes. A terrific little efficiency apartment not far from here," he continued.

"Well," I said. "I must say it's very nice of you to have gone out of your way like that to find Peter an apartment."

"I'm afraid I can't take the credit for it," said the London manager. "The bank keeps an apartment all year round for visiting executives. You can have it rent-free."

That stopped me. Having had some experience by this time with the London office's free equipment, I thought it behooved me to find out a little more about the free apartment before accepting it.

"What kind of neighborhood is it in?" I asked.

"One of the best in London," Alec replied.

"What kind of condition is it in?"

"I've had assurances that it is in excellent condition."

"How large is it?"

"There's a bedroom, living room, dining room, and a small kitchen attached," he answered. "I'm sure it's quite suitable for Peter. You know, all the bank's executives, including the president himself, stay there whenever they are in town."

I had to admit it sounded perfect. I threw out one more question, just to make sure.

"How are all of those executives going to feel about having to stay at a hotel whenever they come to London?" I asked.

"Stay at a hotel?" The London manager repeated. "Now, why would they stay at hotels?"

"I mean, because Peter will be staying in the apartment," I explained.

"They won't be staying at hotels," said Alec. "Peter will be."

"You mean Peter's supposed to move out of his apartment every time some official of the bank comes into town?" I asked.

"Why, yes, of course," Alec said.

"And just how often do you anticipate that to be?" I asked.

"Oh, no more than two or three times a month," he replied.

We decided to turn down the free apartment.

A spot trader poked his head in the door.

"Telephone call for Nancy," he said.

Alec and Peter looked at me.

"I'll take it in the other room," I offered. "I won't be but a minute."

"Hi!" said a familiar voice when I answered the phone. "Me again."

"Hello, Larry," I said.

"How's everything going?"

"Just fine. But I can't talk now."

"Just confirming. The Connaught, three o'clock."

"Better make it four."

I returned to Alec's office.

"Everything all right in New York?" Alec asked.

"As far as I know," I answered honestly.

"Now," said Alec, "I understand that you need my help in one last area."

I swallowed nervously. I'd already had just about all of the help I could stand for one visit.

"I have been informed," he continued, "that you intend to hire a trader here in London to supplement your group."

"Actually," I said, "we are looking for two people. A senior trader and a junior trader. Peter's job is to find them, train them, set up the desk, and get back to New York as quickly as possible."

He didn't seem to hear me.

"I have just the person for you," he said. "I'll have him assigned to your group."

Free computers, a free apartment, and now a free person. I was instantly on my guard.

"Do you mind if I ask a few questions?"

"Not at all," he replied.

"Who is he?"

"He's a very nice young chap who is currently working in our back office. His name is Robert Wilkins, but everyone around here calls him Bobby."

"How old is he?"

"Nineteen."

I blanched. It's a young business, but not that young. Even the junior trader would have major responsibilities. I shuddered to think how I would have behaved if someone had hired me to trade options at nineteen. I'm quite sure Wall Street would never have lived through the experience.

"How did you happen to choose him—I mean, Bobby—for this position?" I asked casually. "Does he show a special aptitude for options?"

"Oh, dear, no," Alec laughed. "I daresay he's never heard of options."

"Has he a quantitative background then?" I asked.

"Pardon?"

"Does he know math?"

"Oh, yes. I've never had any trouble with his addition or subtraction. He's splendid in the back office. Rarely an error."

"What about his calculus?" I asked.

"Calculus? Don't tell me you need to understand calculus to trade options?"

"I'm afraid it helps," I said. "You know, options trading is a little bit more complex than straight-out foreign-exchange or eurodollar trading."

"No," said Alec. "I didn't know that."

"Well," I said. "How did you pick him for the job?"

"The same way we always do," he replied. "He's the next in line. I promised him the very next job to open up on the trading floor. That's yours."

"I see," I said.

Having only just hired Randy, and having lived for an entire month with the results of my handiwork, I wasn't quite so cavalier about adding personnel as I'd been in November. I was just beginning to see what the addition of a grating personality could do to the over-

186

all atmosphere of a trading desk. The wrong disposition was as much of a distraction to the orderly functioning of the unit as hiring someone to bang on a drum during working hours. I had no intention of making the same mistake twice.

"Well," I said. "I don't suppose you'd mind if Peter and I talked to Bobby before you assigned him to our group?"

"No," Alec said slowly. "I don't see why that couldn't be arranged. In fact, I know he's looking forward to meeting you."

"He knows we're here, does he?"

"Oh, yes! I've already told him that he'll be working with you."

Peter and I exchanged looks.

Bobby sat nervously on the end of the couch in an office adjacent to Alec's, where Peter and I had arranged for a short interview. He was tall and skinny. His jacket was too small. His pants were too large. His skin showed traces of a liberal application of Clearasil.

"Hello, Bobby," I said. "I'm Nancy, and this is Peter. We're glad to meet you."

"Same here," he murmured.

"Bobby," I said. "I understand that you want to be an options trader. Is that true?"

"Yes."

"Why do you want to be an options trader, Bobby?"

He mumbled something about its being fun to trade.

I felt very bad about all of this. It wasn't his fault that he was so young, and so terribly unsuited to the position. Who knows but that in four or five years he wouldn't be one of the most successful traders in London? It's just that I didn't have four or five years to spare.

"Wouldn't you rather trade foreign exchange or eurodollars?" I suggested hopefully.

The reply was indistinct, but I did catch the words "doesn't make much difference."

"Oh, but there is a difference," I said, seeing a way out of the situation. "Options are very difficult to trade."

"They are?"

Peter caught my meaning instantly.

"You'll have to work very hard," he cautioned. "You'll have to begin right away. You've a lot to learn."

"That's right," I nodded. "Don't worry. I've a number of books I can lend you on the subject. And don't be put off by how long and difficult they are. They're quite useful."

"I'm going on holiday," said Bobby. "It's Christmas."

"So much the better!" I said. "You'll have plenty of time for reading then."

"Now, as to your hours," said Peter.

"I work nine to five," said Bobby. "Sometimes they let me out at half past four, though."

"Well," said Peter. "I'll be getting into the office at seven-thirty sharp every morning, and of course I expect you to do the same. We'll have to stay later than the others because we need our reports from New York and we'll have to discuss the position with Nancy."

"Oh!" said Bobby, not very enthusiastically.

"And then, of course," I said, "because we're new in town, there'll be a great deal of socializing after work."

"At the pub?" Bob perked up.

I realized I'd overdone it. Besides, I had no idea what the legal drinking age was in London.

"We can't drink too much," said Peter, coming to my rescue. "We have to always be on top of our game. We often have to trade in the evenings as well."

"In the evenings?" asked Bobby, amazed. "You mean, after work?"

"We all have to be available on a twenty-four-hour basis," I said. "We might need to consult with you at any time."

"We're not asking you to do anything that we don't do ourselves," Peter reminded him.

"Oh!" said Bobby looking from me to Peter and then back again.

I popped back into Alec's office. "May I speak to you for a moment?" I asked.

"Certainly," he said.

"Peter and I have just had a little chat with Bobby," I said.

"How did you like him?"

"He's lovely," I said honestly. "But I'm afraid he doesn't want to trade options."

"What?" asked Alec, amazed.

"Haven't you a spot for him on your eurodollar desk?" I asked quickly. "That's where he really wants to be."

"Well," said the London manager. "If that's what he wants. . . . You're sure you don't mind?"

"Not at all," I said, graciously.

"Well, thank you, then," said Alec.

"Don't mention it."

The spot trader knocked on the door again. "Pardon me, but there's a phone call. . . ."

"I'll be right there," I sighed.

I never did meet Larry for tea. We had dinner that night with people from the bank. The next two days were more of the same.

I met with Sam and Peter on Friday afternoon.

"Let's sum up the situation," I said. "We'll begin with the equipment. Sam?"

"I've two IBMs on order," said Sam.

"When are they expected?" I asked.

"Not for three weeks," he replied.

"Oh!" I winced. "We can't hurry them at all?"

"No," Sam shook his head. "It's Christmas. Everyone's on vacation. If they'd only been ordered earlier . . ."

"Right," I sighed. "What about the other equipment?"

"Well," said Sam. "It seems the phone company takes awhile around here as well. I've ordered you some additional phone lines. I assume they'll get here about the same time as the computers."

I looked at Peter. "That pushes your starting date back to the third week of January," I said.

"It's just as well," he said. "I'll need some time to round up my things. I can get here a little early and start looking around for people to hire. Start making friends with the rest of the community, that kind of thing."

"Right," I said. "Did you find housing?"

"Yes, I did. It's available immediately."

"So you'll leave on schedule," I said. "Will you be all right on your own for a while?"

"Yes, Mom."

"I'm not being motherly. I'm being professional," I snapped. "Nobody trades well on his own. There are too many mistakes made that way."

"I'll be careful."

"You'll call me if there's anything going on?"

"You'll be the first to know," he assured me.

I went to say good-bye to Alec.

"Thank you for all your help," I said.

"Don't mention it," he returned. "How did you find your first trip to London?"

"Hectic," I said, laughing. "I had no idea it was so much work organizing a desk."

"What do you mean?" he asked.

"You know," I said. "Ordering all the equipment, getting the people, and the space, and the phone lines. I'm glad I don't have to do this again!"

"Why—" Alec stopped. "Don't you know?"

"Know what?" I asked.

"Why, the bank has decided to move the entire London trading floor to a new building in six months. We'll have to rearrange everything at that time. I'm surprised you weren't informed."

I got back to the hotel Friday evening to find Larry waiting for me.

"Get everything done?" he asked coldly.

"Larry, honey, I'm sorry," I said. "I had no idea how much work was involved."

"That's always the problem, isn't it?" he said.

I was silent. We stared at each other.

"We have a choice here," I said finally. "We can spend these last two days fighting, or we can make up and try to enjoy ourselves."

"I would certainly rather we had a good time," said Larry.

"So would I."

And we did. We had breakfast in bed. We took long, hot bubble baths in the room's gigantic tub. We walked all over London and I finally had a chance to see some of the world's most breathtaking architecture. We shopped, we had tea at the Savoy Hotel. We went dancing. We were lovers again.

We were walking down South Moulton Street, one of the most fashionable shopping areas in London. Larry stopped in front of a lingerie shop, which sported a life-size picture of a beautiful woman clad only in a silk chemise and sheer stockings with rhinestones up the back.

"Stop drooling," I said.

"I'm not drooling," he protested, wiping his mouth. He continued to stare.

"You'd look great in those stockings," he said. "I want to buy them for you."

I hugged his arm.

"That's not necessary," I said.

"I know it's not necessary," he said. "I want to. You'd look better in them than she does," indicating the model.

"I don't know," I said, hesitating. "This place looks expensive."

"Who cares? You're worth it."

"I don't know," I said again. I'd had some experience with lingerie shops.

He was in the shop before I could stop him.

"This place is great!" he said when I'd followed him inside. "Just look at all of these terrific stockings!"

The stockings were sensational.

"I like this one and this one and this one," he said. "What do you think?"

"They're great," I said. "But one's enough. They must be expensive."

"How much can panty hose be?" demanded my husband.

Before I could tell him, he walked over to a saleswoman who had been watching the proceedings.

"We'll take these," he said, giving her three pairs.

"Are you sure you want all three?" she asked slowly.

"Of course," said my husband, with a grandiose gesture.

The saleswoman hurried to wrap up the purchase in lilac-colored, perfumed tissue paper.

"What do I owe you?" asked Larry, while she was busy folding.

"Ninety-six pounds," she replied.

There was a moment of silence while Larry tried to compute the exchange rate in his head.

"Ninety-six pounds," Larry repeated. "That's $140."

He seemed to think he had either heard wrong or calculated wrong.

"That's right," the saleswoman nodded to him.

"For three pairs of stockings?" asked Larry, struggling to maintain his composure.

"That's right," the saleswoman repeated.

He turned to me.

"Let me put them back," I said.

Larry recovered gallantly. "Do you like them?" he asked.

"Of course I like them."

Larry turned back to the saleswoman. "We'll take them," he said.

The saleswoman smiled sympathetically and gave him a piece of chocolate at no extra charge.

12 . . . and a Happy New Year

I had a plan.

After the weekend in London, Larry and I spent the holidays with some friends in a big, old house in the Pennsylvania countryside. It snowed Christmas morning, right on command. In this peaceful environment, I realized something important: romance and passion must be worked at in a marriage, just like everything else.

If anyone had asked me what was more important to me, my marriage or the direction of the dollar, I would have instantly answered "my marriage" and would have vehemently denied that my behavior implied otherwise. But, in fact, I had been siphoning all of my energy away from my husband and into the bank.

I decided to put a stop to it. I was determined to make the marriage work.

In this I was being completely selfish. It's no great secret that the most satisfying experiences in life are those you share with someone close to you.

Don't misunderstand me. I had no intention of giving up my job. I recognized that my marriage could be truly successful only if both parties involved led full, satisfying lives outside the bounds of the union. For me, this meant continuing along my chosen career path. But it was necessary to begin to balance the requirements of a very demanding vocation with the responsibilities of being a wife.

Hence my plan.

I needed to spend time with Larry, I needed to spend time at the office, right? The solution seemed to me to be a very simple one. I would trade brilliantly in January, so brilliantly that I would earn the whole year's income for the bank in that one month. Management would be more than satisfied with the results, and I could relax and pay attention to my husband for the other eleven months of the year.

This is not as crazy as it sounds. The nature of the market is such that most traders make the bulk of their profits in two or three months of the year. The difference is, they don't pick the month in advance.

The alarm went off at 5:30 A.M. on January 2, 1986. As usual, I groaned as I came to.

Getting out of bed was the hardest part of the day for me. I love to sleep. Given a choice, I would probably spend ten hours out of every twenty-four unconscious.

I pulled myself together in the morning long enough to get dressed, and lured myself out of the apartment by picturing the freshly baked, piping hot, homemade cherry turnover I'd buy when I got to the croissant shop directly across from my office. At 6:15 A.M. I plunged into the cold darkness of pre–rush-hour Manhattan, and hurried down the block to the bowels of the universe, otherwise known as the New York City subway system. I picked my way carefully down the subway stairs, avoiding the large puddle of evil-smelling liquid on the last step, misting suspiciously, like some terrible lake. I put my token in the slot and hurried to the subway platform.

No train. Silence, relieved only by the steady drip, drip, drip of moisture leaking from a crack in the ceiling and the mumbling of a bag woman stretched out on one of the platform's four benches. It was in this congenial atmosphere that I put the finishing touches on my master plan.

Clearly, I reasoned, the only way to earn an entire year's income in one month was to take an enormous position as soon as possible. But what position to take? That was the question. That was always the question.

I started my analysis with a quick review of the market's past performance. The dollar had been falling pretty steadily since March 1985. There had been a short period in August when the dollar rallied, but the charge was short-lived. Fresh troops, in the form of the industrialized world's finance ministers at G-5 in September had taken deadly aim and killed the dollar for all intents and purposes. What most of us were engaging in at the moment was merely a mopping-up exercise. The dollar had lost a full 15 percent of its value since September, 25 percent if you took March as your starting point, when the dollar was at the height of its power.

That was past history. But what would the future hold?

The arrival of the train (heralded by a shriek that has always conjured up for me the vision of ten thousand souls being whipped simultaneously by ten thousand fiends) interrupted my thought pattern. I followed my fellow travelers into the car and found a seat. One good thing about getting into work so early in the morning is that at least you get a seat on the train. The doors closed. The engines roared. The conductor screamed piercingly but unintelligibly over the microphone. We were off!

I returned to my analysis. Because the dollar had been steadily falling for such a long time already, market perception was that 1986 would be a much quieter year than 1985. Volatility, the market's measure of how rapidly the value of the dollar would fluctuate in the upcoming months, was low. I knew that some people (including the bank's gold trader, who, as usual, had an opinion on everything except gold) were loudly predicting that the dollar wouldn't move very much at all; that all of the major moves had already taken place, and that volatility would collapse even further.

Fifty-ninth Street. Time to change for the express. No express yet. I wait patiently on the platform, surrounded on all sides by the human condition. It's rather early in the morning to appreciate fully the human condition. Consequently, I do my best to ignore it. I escaped back to the market.

I didn't believe what the other traders were saying. I didn't think that the market would stay calm. It's not human nature to stay calm, and the market is, after all, made up of human beings. Everything in life works in cycles, and the dollar is no exception. Besides, nobody makes any money when the market's quiet. How would all the foreign-exchange traders on Wall Street justify their existence (not to mention their salaries and bonuses) if the dollar spent a whole year trading in a narrow range?

The express train arrived. Because all of the trains

were running late, a crowd had formed. I was unable to secure a seat this time. I returned to my analysis.

The problem was, I had no clear feeling which way the dollar was going to go—up or down. It had already fallen so far so fast that I was afraid we were in for a correction. A *correction* is the technical term for everybody's deciding to take their profit all at once. Since the only people with profit were the people who were short the dollar (which was just about everybody in the market by this time), taking that profit meant buying back all those dollars they'd sold. The force of all that buying could propel the dollar up.

But, on the other hand, the Reagan administration did not seem to want the dollar to go back up. They wanted to improve the trade deficit. There are two possible ways to improve the trade deficit. The first is to force American producers of goods and services to make their products more competitive by cutting costs or by producing a better product that everyone (even other Americans) will want to buy. To choose this way is to invite a possible confrontation with American labor. The second way is willy-nilly to make all foreign goods and services more expensive than American goods so that, even if the foreign goods are better, Americans will buy American goods because they are so much cheaper. To choose the second way is to face a possible confrontation with America's trading partners: the Germans, the Japanese, the French, the British.

The choice for American politicians was simple. Foreigners don't vote.

Decisions, decisions. What to do? And then, suddenly, somewhere between Forty-second and Fourteenth streets, it hit me: the perfect position.

Don't bet on direction at all. Bet on volatility. Options were cheap now. Buy every option in sight and then sit back and wait for a breakout in the dollar. Make sure that you have options on both sides. Whichever way the dollar goes, the options on that side will more than pay for the cost of the others.

Well satisfied with my plan (after all, hadn't I devoted nearly an hour to it while trying to get downtown?), I got off at the World Trade Center and made my way to the little croissant shop directly across from my office. I was painfully disappointed to discover that the store had changed management during the Christmas holidays, and that the new proprietor thought it a good idea to substitute the previous day's stale cherry turnovers for freshly baked ones, a ruse that was detected with the first bite.

Could it have been an omen?

I walked into the office and immediately got to work buying options. I bought and bought and bought. I spent three days buying everything I could find. I didn't distinguish between long-term and short-term options. I didn't care about the price. I bet heavily on a big move.

Usually when somebody comes in buying big, the price goes up. But when I bought, the price went down. That meant there were plenty of people in the marketplace who held a view directly opposite to mine, who were more than willing to sell to me. Did that discourage me? Not a bit. I bought more. By the time I was finished buying, I had the largest position I had ever accumulated.

Nobody at the bank noticed. Nobody at the bank asked. Nobody at the bank seemed to care. And the market remained ominously quiet.

Peter was gone. In his place was a squawk box that was supposed to link us to him in London. As the box disconnected on the average of once every twenty minutes, transcontinental communication was spotty. This was actually a lucky break. I found out later how much it costs to leave a telephone line open all day to London.

So, Phillip and I continued to man the desk. Of course, there was also Randy.

Sam came by at the end of the day with our reports.

"I think there's something wrong here," he said.

I looked at the reports. They showed a gain of $9 million in one day. While I am a good trader, I'm not that good.

"There's obviously an error here," I said.

A thorough examination of the reports revealed that one trade had earned us over $9 million.

"Here's the error," I said, pointing out the trade to Sam. "The information on that trade must have been entered incorrectly into the computer."

"Let me get the ticket," suggested Sam.

Everyday we wrote up the tickets detailing the day's trades, which were later used to process the reports vital to understanding and trading the position. Recently I had given this job to Randy.

Sam returned with the ticket.

"Here's the problem," he said. "The handwriting is so sloppy we misread the information and entered the wrong date into the computer."

I turned to Randy. "Please try to be more careful in the future," I said. "Now Sam will have to reprint all of our reports." I turned to Sam. "How long will it take to fix the error and reprint?" I asked.

"About an hour and a half," he replied.

I sighed. It was already 5:30 P.M.

"Do it, please," I said wearily.

The very next day Sam again arrived with the reports.

"You're not going to believe this," he said, handing me the thick sheaf of papers.

I looked. This time, we were down $11 million. Once again, it was easy to find the error. Once again, inspection of the ticket revealed that Randy had been careless. Once again, I had to wait until 7:00 P.M. to get the new reports.

The next day I taught my secretary how to write the tickets. She learned how to do it in fifteen minutes. Careless errors on tickets became a thing of the past.

Randy's carelessness extended beyond routine chores. He tried to do everything so quickly to prove that he was on top of the situation that he made senseless errors. I understood that the mistakes were a result of his nervousness at wanting to do a good job, but good intentions are not enough on a trading desk. He often miscalculated the number of contracts that were necessary to cover a trade, and would end up buying too few or too many. Since I didn't check his multiplication and division every step of the way, I wouldn't find out about the problem until it was too late and we'd already lost money.

But it was his continuing insensitivity to his surroundings that bothered me the most. He chattered constantly. He said anything that popped into his head. Even ordering lunch became a big production.

"I'm hungry," I announced around one o'clock. "I'm going to order in some food. Does anyone want something?"

"No, thank you," Phillip declined politely. "I have some lunch here." He indicated the ever-present cold beef and mashed potatoes. "May I offer you some?"

"No, thanks, Phillip," I smiled at him. "I'll just order my own. What about you, Randy?"

"Sure, I'd like some lunch," Randy replied.

I picked up the phone to dial for a delivery.

"What do you want?"

"Let's see," said Randy. "Do I want a hamburger? No. Do I want ham and cheese? No, I don't really feel

201

like ham and cheese. It's not a ham-and-cheese kind of day. Do I want tuna fish?"

I put down the telephone. Experience had taught that this process could take up to a quarter of an hour.

"Just let me know when you've decided," I sighed.

"Do I want egg salad? Uh-uh. Do I want bologna? I hate bologna. Do I want . . ."

I have to admit that I wasn't in the best spirits to begin with. It had been two weeks already and so far the market had stubbornly refused to live up to my subway revelation. Meanwhile, Peter was in London, attempting to trade without benefit of instruments or reports.

"We have a problem, Sam," I said one afternoon.

"What's the matter?" Sam was instantly on the alert.

"It's the reports. Peter's not getting copies of our reports for the opening of London. He can't trade without those reports. He doesn't know what the position is."

"Well," said Sam. "It's a sticky problem. After the reports are printed out in the evening, I've been having one of my people Rapifax the pages to Peter in London."

"I know," I said. "But the Rapifax doesn't work that well. All the pages come out blurry and Peter can't read them."

"I also send him copies by courier," Sam pointed out.

"I know," I said again. "But the courier doesn't get to London until noon. That means he has to trade for four or five hours without crucial information."

"I don't know what else we can do," said Sam, shaking his head. "Rapifax is the only way to get it there in time. We'll just have to keep trying."

Eventually what happened was that Peter would call me at home when he got into the office at 8:00 A.M. London time (3:00 A.M. my time) and I would read the position to him over the phone. I can't tell you how thrilled Larry was with that arrangement.

It's only temporary, I kept saying to myself. The market will heat up and the position will come in and I'll look back over these last few weeks and laugh.

As I got less and less sleep, Randy's behavior seemed to get worse. The time I spent with him decreased as I tried to focus on the market. Instead of using his spare time to study options or to go over his position, he would play video games on the computer. After a while you couldn't tell the difference between the desk and a penny arcade.

I started to hate him.

Something happened to me in those last three weeks of January. The strain of expansion, with the resulting overflow of operational and management problems, combined with insufficient sleep, were beginning to take their toll. Gone was the confident, optimistic, bright-eyed trader of the previous year. In her place was a frothing maniac: unsure, overworked, exhausted.

I put every ounce of faith that I had in that position. It was, I thought, the one thing that could rescue me from the unhealthy atmosphere that was beginning to surround me at work like some toxic cloud. It was to be my salvation. The deeper I sank into the morass of operational quagmire, the more I clung to that position.

Suddenly, I had completely lost my perspective. And perspective is the one quality a trader needs most.

It was the end of January. Phillip was poring endlessly over his charts. Randy was playing Yahtzee on the computer with the gold trader. Sam delivered the day's reports.

I was exhausted. I had been up in the middle of the night every day for a week giving Peter the position. As it was late Friday afternoon, I picked up the reports without looking at them and decided to go home.

I read the reports on the subway. I walked into the apartment. Larry was out shopping for dinner. I took off my coat and hung it up in the closet. I went into the bedroom. I carefully removed the spread from the bed. I took off my shoes. I took off my earrings. Then I threw myself on the bed and cried.

I cried long and hard. I cried at the top of my lungs. I cried uncontrollably, inconsolably. Instead of going up as I had predicted, volatility had crashed. The market was as quiet as I'd ever seen it. My beautiful position had lost approximately $350,000 in just three weeks.

13 Taking Stock

Wait a minute. Hold everything. A $350,000 loss? Why, that's nothing. That's peanuts. I'd lost more than that in one night during G-5. And made it all back and more. So why the hysteria? The uncontrollable sobbing?

Because during G-5 I was still new. Even by my own inflated standards, success was measured in those first few months by the barest survival. Now, however, I was a seasoned professional. I was paid to be right. Everyone else—Adam, Thomas, Chuck—all of them must know my position. I had bought from all of them. Surely they were all laughing at me now, raking in their profits at my expense. No doubt, I agonized, I had replaced Qaddafi as their favorite source of trading-room humor.

Never mind that it was impossible for my competitors to know my position or my P and L. Never mind that they had their own problems. Some of them were probably losing a good deal more than I, and were sitting up nights worrying that everyone was laughing at them. But I didn't think about any of that.

Over the past months I had enjoyed the spotlight that comes with success. I had just received an enormous bonus. My parents, my friends, my associates—everyone was proud and envious. Now all of that was gone, I thought—lost forever.

I guess you could say I took it personally.

As the situation was clearly hopeless, I just lay there wailing at the top of my lungs.

Larry chose this moment to return from shopping.

I heard him turn the key and open the door. Thank God Larry's home! He'll understand.

Larry came running into the bedroom.

"Nancy!" He was pale. "My God! What is it? Are you hurt? Did something happen to you?"

"No, no," I reassured him, between gulps. "I'm not hurt. I'm perfectly all right. Nothing happened to me. I'm fine."

He sat down on the bed and tried to put his arms around me.

"Nancy, sweetheart," he said tenderly. "I've never heard you cry like this before. What's the matter?"

I cried louder.

"Please, honey, tell me what it is," he said, stroking my hair.

"Oh, Larry," I sobbed. "I . . . I . . ."

"Yes? You what?"

"I . . . I . . . I'm losing money!" I wailed.

There was a moment of silence.

"You're what?" he asked.

"I'm losing money! Oh! I've lost $350,000 in just three weeks!" The statement brought on fresh sobs of self-pity.

Larry stopped hugging me. He stood up.

"Let me get this straight," he said. "You are crying over an options position?"

I cried harder.

"You are crying over a $350,000 loss?"

Heartrending sobs punctuated by hiccups. Another moment of silence. I could feel him glaring at me. Finally, he spoke.

"Are you nuts or something?"

Not the reaction I was expecting.

"Stop it," he said. "That's enough. I mean it."

Surprised, I raised my head from the pillow to look at him.

"You are not going to cry like this over an options position," he said. "That's the stupidest thing I've ever heard of."

"What do you know about it?" I sniffled.

"What do I know about it! Do you think you're the only person who ever lost a little money?"

I stopped crying.

"But don't you see?" I demanded. "Everybody will know I've lost. They'll laugh at me!"

"Who cares if they laugh at you? Who are they? Every trader loses! Did you think you were an exception? Did you think you'd be right every time? You're in the wrong business. You want to be right every time? Sell Hondas.

"This has been coming on for months," Larry continued. "You've been running around like a maniac, begging for disaster."

"What are you talking about? I've never worked this hard in my life!"

"Just working hard isn't enough. You have to work

effectively. You know what it takes to be a good trader? I'll tell you. Discipline, management, and attention to detail. You, my dear, are lacking some of these traits."

"Which ones?" I demanded.

"All of them."

"That's not true," I said.

"Oh, yes, it's true. You've sown your own seeds. Your management style is worse than bad. It's non-existent. Look at how bad Randy has turned out. Let me tell you something. That's your fault. Not his. And why take on the burden of a London office at this time? I told you to make sure you had support systems in place before you went ahead with it."

That I knew was true.

"But what can I do?" I asked.

"The first rule of trading is knowing when to take a loss. If the London office was a mistake, close it. Bring Peter back to New York and wait until the thing can be organized properly."

"No! No way!" I was adamant.

"Why not?"

"Because that would be admitting I was wrong and I'm not going to do that. The whole world knows we opened a London office. We can't back down now. That would mean the whole bank would lose face. I won't do that. I'll work harder, I'll try to rectify my mistakes. But I can't close a desk I just opened."

"All right," said Larry. "Leave it open then. But get your act together or get out."

He went to put the groceries away.

How could I argue with him? He was right. I'd brought all these problems on myself. Well, I thought grimly, if I got myself into this, I can surely get myself out. It's simply a matter of putting my mind to it.

I got up and washed my face. It's hard to take yourself seriously with streaks of mascara running down your cheeks.

I spent the weekend strategizing. Looking at the matter from a cool, dispassionate point of view I came to the conclusion that what was needed in this situation was a three-pronged approach.

Lack of adequate operational support was the most significant obstacle in my path. The absence of a satisfactory communications network between New York and London was causing unnecessary foul-ups. In addition, the sheer volume of my trading had increased to the point where I was having trouble controlling the position. At present, the operations department was incapable of generating the kind of reports that were necessary to the smooth functioning of my unit.

Rather than using a computer system to give me accurate, up-to-the-minute information (as all of my competitors did), I was calculating the position by hand. Calculating the position by hand when you're dealing with millions of dollars and hundreds of trades is ludicrous. Punching the wrong number on your calculator can cause an error. Skipping a trade by accident can cause an error. Adding the thirty-third number wrong out of a string of fifty can cause an error. And, of course, by the time you've finished (it takes about two hours to do the job properly), the market has already changed, so your labored calculations are no longer relevant. But they are the best you have, so you use them anyway. It was like living in the Stone Age.

I'd seen other banks' trading operations so I knew it was easy to purchase or develop a system that was capable of calculating in two seconds what currently took me two hours. Not only that, but an on-line computer system could constantly update as the market changed and could show what would happen to the position for a number of different scenarios. Having a good support system does not guarantee good trading, but it certainly helps.

I'd let my section fall behind in installing the necessary support systems. Luckily, I thought, this was a problem easily rectified.

But operational support wasn't the only problem I had to tackle. There was a management problem as well. Larry was right. I wasn't a manager at all.

Trading is a very straightforward business. A trader deals only with numbers. Managing people is a different business altogether. People tend to complicate otherwise rational issues with irrational tendencies to have hopes, dreams, desires, ambitions, and so forth. A good manager has to take all of this into account for each of her subordinates and plot the one course that will maximize that person's potential—a very difficult task, requiring much hard work and patience. A task significantly more difficult than trading.

My most obvious problem was Randy. Instead of ignoring him, I was going to have to sit down and talk to him and tell him all the things that were bothering me and find out what was bothering him. An uncomfortable interview, but necessary if Randy was ever to become a productive member of the group.

The last area of self-improvement was in my actual trading style. I was simply going to have to be more disciplined. I was going to have to take my loss this time and work harder to make it back. I was going to have to think up new trades and watch the markets more closely.

Here once again I came back to the computer system. I knew that there were ways to trade options more conservatively than I'd done in the past. But to analyze the market and find the appropriate strategy required precise data; hand calculations were out of the question.

For the first time I realized the full importance of upgrading my system.

▲ ▲ ▲

The first thing Monday morning I put my plan into action. I began by speaking to Sam.

"I want to talk to you about our computer system," I told him.

"Yes?" said Sam.

"It's not working out," I said flatly. "We need a better system. We need more sophisticated reports and we need them instantaneously. We can't wait two hours every time we have to update the position. And we desperately need to link London to New York."

Sam broke into a smile.

"What's so funny?" I demanded.

"Nothing," he said. "It's just that I couldn't agree with you more."

"I want you to investigate possible ways to improve the situation," I said.

"I'm way ahead of you," said Sam. "I've already started to look into it."

I was impressed. "Fantastic," I said. "Make it a top priority. I need to know my alternatives as soon as possible."

"Got you," said Sam.

"And I want to know everything," I emphasized. "Cost, time to installation, possible problems. Everything."

"Got you," said Sam.

I went back to my desk and looked at the screen. The currency prices had barely moved. I sighed. Time for part two.

"Randy," I said. "I'd like to talk to you."

"Sure," he replied, surprised.

"Not here," I said. "Let's go find someplace quiet."

Randy and I sat facing each other in an empty office off the trading floor.

"So what's the deal?" Randy asked.

I opened my mouth to speak and then closed it.

Now that the time had come for a heart-to-heart, I didn't know what to do. I've always shied away from unpleasantness.

"Are you happy here?" I said finally.

"Happy?" Randy repeated. "Sure. I mean, yeah, I'm happy here."

"Well," I said, getting up my nerve and plunging in, "I'm not."

"Not happy here?"

"No. Not happy with you."

"Oh."

"I don't know quite what to do about it. I'd like to talk about it."

"Go ahead," Randy said coldly.

"You know," I said slowly, trying to choose my words carefully, "it's very important that the atmosphere on a trading desk be congenial to all the participants."

"So?"

"So, I'm afraid that you are detracting from the overall productivity of the desk," I said, hating myself. "I'm sure you don't mean to do it, and that's why I thought if I pointed it out to you we could rectify the situation."

"What do you mean?"

"I mean that sometimes—often, actually—you show a lack of sensitivity to your surroundings. I'm afraid that you tend to chatter during the course of the day and this disturbs the people working around you."

"What do you mean, chatter?"

"Well, Peter and Phillip and I are all pretty quiet people and we need time to concentrate. I don't think you are paying enough attention to that."

"But—" Randy began.

"Let me finish." As long as I had begun, I figured I might as well get it all out before I lost my nerve. "It seems to me that your inclination to talk is also taking your attention away from your own work. You've made any number of careless errors since you've been here. I think if you said less and concentrated more, you'd get farther."

"Fine," Randy replied, his mouth set in a straight line.

"Also, I have to say that I am dissatisfied with the rate at which you've picked up trading. I don't want to see you playing computer games in your spare time in the future. I think you should be working to improve your understanding of options."

"Peter and Phillip play computer games."

"Peter and Phillip," I emphasized, "have been here a lot longer than you have, and they have already demonstrated their abilities to produce. You haven't. You should be using that time to learn."

"Fine," Randy said, shrugging.

He wasn't taking it very well. This made me angry. Couldn't he see that it was just as hard for me as it was for him? If he didn't listen to me, how were we to get anywhere? I felt I'd gone out of my way to be reasonable.

"The last thing," I said, trying to ignore his attitude, "is that I'm going to change your training around a bit. You've been responsible for overseeing the Swiss franc book up until now. That doesn't appear to be working out. I'll take over that book again. What I'm going to do is to give you a specific amount of money to trade with. You can trade it however you please. Phillip, Peter, and I are all available to help you. You can ask us what we think whenever you wish. But you will be responsible for making the ultimate decision. It's yours to win or lose with as you see fit."

"I see," said Randy.

"I hope that by giving you this responsibility you

213

will learn how difficult it is actually to make decisions in trading. Also, since you often second-guess some of our decisions, this will allow you to put your money where your mouth is."

Randy was silent.

"Well, what do you think?" I asked.

"What difference does it make what I think?" Randy muttered. "You've already made up your mind."

Oh, dear.

I went back to the desk. The market was still quiet. What to do? What to do?

I decided to inform John Anderson of the situation.

"It's important," I warned his secretary.

John's secretary disappeared into his office.

"He can see you now," she said when she re-emerged.

I went into the office. John had just come back from a ten-day ski vacation in northern Italy. He looked terrific: tan, relaxed, fit. The contrast between his appearance and mine is one that I will remember for a long time.

"Well, Nancy," said John smiling. "How are you? Have a seat."

I sat. He was so chipper it was positively disgusting.

"Now, what can I do for you?" he asked, leaning back in his chair expansively.

"Well, I'll tell you, John," I said, leaning forward in mine. "The position is out of control. We need a new, updated computer system. Communications between New York and London are not sufficient to meet our needs. I'm having to get up in the middle of the night and it's affecting my ability to trade. The new trainee I hired in November is not working out. In addition to all of that, I took a large position and we're losing on it. I don't know what to do."

There was a moment of silence. Then John spoke.

"Well," he said, "you do look tired. If you ever want to go on vacation, I can recommend some perfectly charming villas in Italy."

I went back to the desk. There seemed to be no alternative. I took a deep breath, and closed my eyes. Then I picked up the phone and started taking out the position. I sold every option I had bought at a loss.

Three days later the market started to heat up. If I had held that position, I would have indeed made my entire year's projected earnings in one month.

14 Out of the Frying Pan . . .

Thus I entered into a joyless period during which my mood alternated between frustration, discouragement, and outright gloom. By attempting to pull my section together I was unintentionally committing an unforgivable breach of etiquette. I was trying to get something done.

The bank responded to the threat by calling an all-points bulletin and labeling me Public Enemy Number One. My efforts to acquire an updated computer system were viewed as subversive, suspect, and possibly Communist-inspired.

If I had to do it all over again, there is no question that I would have bypassed the existing bureaucratic structure and settled the matter by walking over to the nearest Radio Shack and purchasing the appropriate computer equipment with my bank-issued MasterCard. That simple act of defiance would have saved the bank so much time and money that they could have bought their own Radio Shack outlet with the proceeds, and so gotten themselves into a real business. But I didn't do that. I tried to get my system by working through the bank's normal channels.

Oh, well. Nobody's perfect.

Sam reported his findings about a week later. "It's like this," he said. "You have two basic alternatives."

"Okay," I replied eagerly, pen and paper in hand. "Shoot."

"Alternative one: you can update your present system by purchasing a minicomputer."

"A minicomputer," I repeated, writing it down. "What is a minicomputer?"

"A minicomputer is bigger and more advanced than a personal computer, but not so big as a regular mainframe computer."

"Will it satisfy all of our needs?" I asked. "Will it have enough memory to solve the problem?"

"It will."

"Will it be able to update the position on a moment's notice?"

"It will."

"Will it be able to put together all kinds of sophisticated reports?"

"It will."

"Will it be able to link New York to London?"

"That," said Sam, "is something I can't answer at the moment."

"Okay," I said, writing. "You check that out. Now, you mentioned a second alternative. What is it?"

"Alternative two: link into the bank's mainframe computer."

"Will they let us do that?"

"Well," said Sam slowly, "they should be able to. Basically, what we've got to do is to ask them."

"That doesn't sound too hard."

Out of the mouths of babes.

"Before we ask them, though," I continued. "Will linking into the mainframe satisfy our requirements?"

An expression of pity settled on Sam's features. It's the same look that the TV repairman gives me when I ask if everything's fixed now.

"Nancy," he said, "the mainframe will knock your socks off."

"That's nice," I said. "But will it link New York to London?"

"It will," he said.

Sam went back to further investigate costs and installation. I went back to the desk.

"Anybody want some lunch?" I asked brightly.

"No, thank you," Philip was quick to respond. "But may I offer you some—"

"No, thanks," I said. "Randy?"

Silence.

"Randy?" I repeated, more pointedly. "Would you care for some lunch?"

"No, thanks," he muttered.

There had been quite a change in Randy's attitude since our little chat. And it was all for the worse.

Sam came back after a few days.

"We have to talk," he said.

"Did you find out anything more?" I asked.

"Well," said Sam. "I found out that a minicomputer will be able to link New York to London."

"Terrific," I said.

"And I found out how much it will cost." He named a figure.

"All right," I said, writing it down. "And how long will it take to install?"

"Well," said Sam, "if I order one right now, it will probably be up and running in a month. Two weeks to deliver, two weeks to run tests."

It was then the beginning of February. That would mean I would have an updated system by March.

"Okay," I said, writing. "Now, what about the mainframe?"

"About the mainframe . . ." Sam hesitated.

"Yes?" I said.

"To be honest with you," said Sam, "I'd rather go with the mainframe. It seems silly to buy a brand-new minicomputer when the bank already has a mainframe that will serve the purpose. I mean, we've got the capability right here. It's a waste of money to duplicate effort."

That sounded reasonable.

"Well," I said. "How long would it take to link up?"

"The actual linkup time," said Sam, "is nothing. Two weeks. Just the time it takes to run the tests, same as on the minicomputer."

"That sounds good," I said. "So what's the problem?"

"The problem is getting the approval," said Sam. "That can take serious time."

"Well, before we go to the trouble of getting approval," I said, "will the cost of the mainframe alternative be competitive with that of the minicomputer?"

Sam hesitated.

"It should be," he said finally. "In fact, it should be much cheaper. But . . ."

"But what?" I asked.

"Well," said Sam uncomfortably, "I wasn't able to

219

get an exact number from the people in charge of mainframe time. It seems they can't do anything unless I fill out a number of forms."

"So fill out the forms," I said.

"I already started to," said Sam.

"So what's the problem?"

"Well," said Sam, "they say it can take up to two months to get an answer after the completed forms are received."

"To get an approval?" I asked.

"No. To get an estimate of cost. The approval process can't start until the cost is estimated."

"Oh!" I said. "Not very speedy of them, is it?"

"No," said Sam.

"I assume the problem is not one of literacy?"

"Sorry?" Sam asked.

"They can read, can't they?"

"As far as I know," Sam grinned.

"In that case," I said, "we should be able to speed up the whole process by going right to the top."

"What are you going to do?" asked Sam.

"I'm going to enlist the aid of John Anderson," I announced.

"Oh!" said Sam, not very enthusiastically.

"He is administrative head of the trading floor," I reminded him. "This is his job. It's right up his alley."

"Uh-huh." Sam looked at me.

"It's at least worth a try," I argued.

I made an appointment to see John.

"What can I do for you?" John asked when I got in to see him.

I explained about the new system and the two alternatives. I outlined the problems I was having getting information from the people responsible for the mainframe. As this was a matter of priority, I was wondering if he couldn't be of assistance.

"Glad to help out," said John. "I know just what to do."

"What's that?" I asked.

"We'll set up a meeting and . . ."

The need for the new system was becoming more and more pressing.

As quiet as the market had been in January, when I needed it to be active, that's how active it was in February and March when I needed it to be quiet. The economic forecast for the year was getting worse. Even the Reagan administration was forced to revise downward its estimates of the gross national product.

Recognizing the need for action, Secretary of the Treasury Baker began a concerted policy of talking down the dollar. This apparently fell into the category of: when in doubt, do what's easiest. Even though the dollar had already depreciated by about 25 percent since its high in March 1985 to no appreciable effect, it was certainly simpler to continue this policy than to try to reduce the budget deficit (which many argued was the real culprit), a more formidable task.

But the dollar's slide was a subject for concern by one of the most intelligent and respected members of the financial community: Federal Reserve Chairman Paul Volcker. Volcker, one of the unsung heroes of the last decade (he single-handedly broke the spiral of inflationary expectations that had hurled the country into a recession), understood that too rapid a decline in the value of the dollar would cause more problems than it would prevent. He also seemed to be more familiar with market psychology than the other members of the Reagan administration, and knew that government intervention was likely to provoke extreme price movements that hadn't been intended. Accordingly, he tried to temper Secretary Baker's announcements by addressing himself to all of the problems inherent in a too-rapidly-falling dollar.

The trading community interpreted these actions as a power struggle between Baker and Volcker. They sold the dollar when Baker spoke and bought it back when Volcker replied. Since these verbal tugs of war often came without a moment's notice, and increased in frequency as the participants became more intense, the markets became extremely volatile. The dollar swung like a yo-yo.

Under these circumstances, it was almost impossible for me to calculate my position by hand. As trading was extremely active, my portfolio was growing. I was having to trade off of the barest estimates of what I actually had. As I continued to speak to London at three o'clock every morning before coming into work, I became more and more exhausted. My fatigue was evident in my attire, my face, the very way I walked. I started taking a nap at my desk at about four o'clock every afternoon, in order to prepare myself for the evening's trading.

I couldn't just stop trading, either. I had to protect my existing portfolio, sometimes by putting on new trades. And other bank traders were calling me often to make them prices. Since I needed them to make prices for me, I had to reciprocate. Otherwise when I needed them, they wouldn't be there. It should come as no surprise that I was continuing to lose money.

Although Randy's attitude was unbearable, I waited a week before speaking to him again. When I couldn't stand it anymore, I called him into the empty office again. This time there was no pretense of pleasantry. I simply told him that he was on probation, and that if his attitude didn't change I'd have to let him go.

"Probation?" he squeaked.

"I can't see why you're surprised," I said flatly. "You can't tell me you've tried since our last talk. You've been impossible on the desk. Can't you see that I have enough to worry about without you? Do you really think there's another trader on the Street who would have put up with what I've put up with? How can you sit there and add to my problems? Have you so little conception of what is happening right under your nose?"

There was a moment of silence.

"You're right," he admitted suddenly. "I was angry and I suppose I acted badly. I'm sorry. You have every right to be angry."

"Do you want this job or don't you?" I asked.

"I do. I do." He assured me. "You'll see. I'll change."

In fact, he did try to change. I could see that he was trying, now that he was under the gun.

But did I really want someone who worked hard only when threatened with dismissal? Did I want someone so unsuited to the work and to the rest of the section? Was I being fair to Randy, to myself, to the unit by keeping him on?

The first meeting to discuss my new computer system was called for 3:00 P.M. When I arrived I was surprised to see how many people had already assembled. Besides Sam and myself I recognized Kashir Rameshwar, two assistant administrators, the head of credit for the trading floor, and a couple of unfamiliar faces, including that of an older man, with close-cropped silver hair, who sat ramrod-straight in a hard chair. He was in incredibly good physical condition. His expression was severe. This could only be William Hambrecht, head of the operations department, the infamous Field Marshall.

What's going on here? I thought. Surely all of these people aren't involved in the decision! I started to have a very bad feeling about all of this. By now a veteran meeting-goer, I knew that the larger the crowd, the more difficult it was to get anything accomplished.

John entered and called the room to order. "Let's get started," he said briskly. "We are here to discuss—" he consulted some notes "—Nancy's request for a new computer system."

Murmurs of surprise up and down the table. The two administrative assistants began taking notes.

"I'm going to turn the floor over to Nancy," said John. "Let's all try to get together on this one!"

Everyone looked at me.

"The expansion into London and the corresponding increase in the volume of our options trading business," I began, "has pointed out the inadequacies of our current computer system. We must upgrade. Sam has already done some research on this subject." I explained about the two alternatives and the problems we were having getting answers from the bank's mainframe department.

"I'd like to make this a top priority," I concluded. "That means that someone who is in charge here" (I looked meaningfully at John) "will have to speak to someone in charge there. That's all that's necessary. I'm sorry that most of you had to waste your time attending this meeting. I'm afraid there's very little most of you can do."

For a moment nobody spoke. Then: "Can you explain again why you need the new system?" asked one of the administrative assistants.

"Can you explain again the system you are currently using?" asked the head of the credit department.

"Vot are de choices again?" asked Kashir.

"What is an option?" asked one of the people I couldn't identify.

An hour and a half later, after I had repeated my story at least five times, I tried to make the point again

224

that what was necessary was a high-level conference and a willingness to make my request a top priority.

"I don't see that that's a problem," said John, finally. "I suppose I can speak to someone in charge. What do you think, William?" he asked, turning to look at the Field Marshall.

We all turned to look at the Field Marshall. Obviously relishing the moment for dramatic effect, the Field Marshall frowned at his pencil. Finally, he spoke.

"Let's start over again from the beginning," he said.

The decision to fire Randy was the most agonizing one of my entire career. The night before I fired him, I was miserable. Yet there was no alternative. Randy's employment was a glaring error that needed to be corrected. It was a lesson that I would never have to learn twice.

The conversation with Randy the next morning was brief. I couldn't even look at him. I simply told him that it wasn't working out and that he would have to go. Randy packed up his few belongings and left without saying good-bye to anyone. I went into the ladies' room and cried.

In the midst of all of this, I got a call from Thomas, the investment banker.

"Hi, Nancy. How's it going?"

"Oh, hi, Thomas. Everything's fine. The usual," I lied. My heart sank. Thomas dealt only in large numbers. If he asked me for a price I might end up trading $50 million worth of options that I didn't really want. It would be the icing on today's cake. But I couldn't say no to him. That would be a sign of weakness.

"Glad to hear it."

"What can I do for you, Thomas?" I asked, taking the plunge. Might as well get it over with quickly. "Would you like me to make you a price?"

"Actually, no."

"No?" What luck!

"I'm calling because I'd like to ask you to dinner,' said Thomas.

"Dinner?" I repeated stupidly.

"Yes. It's important. I have something I want to talk to you about."

"Sure. Fine," I said. What could Thomas have to say to me?

I met Thomas at a restaurant frequented by members of the trading community. He didn't waste any time. He got right down to business.

"Nancy, I suppose you've guessed what I wanted to talk to you about," he said.

"Actually not," I replied.

"Well, then, let me tell you. I have an opening on my desk for a trader. I want you to apply."

With everything that had been happening to me, this was the last thing I'd expected. I stared at him with my mouth open. He waited for me to say something, and when I didn't, he continued.

"You'd be working for me. It's an extremely prestigious position. I went to a lot of trouble just to get management to agree to see you."

"Why?" I asked.

"Don't you know why?"

"No."

"You're a woman," he said.

I started to laugh. "You're kidding, right? This is the 1980s."

"I'm not kidding at all. The position I'm offering you is one that involves trading the firm's own capital. They've never had a woman doing that before. It took me two months just to get them to agree to meet you."

Well. Here it was. The kind of job offer that every trader dreams of. A way to get away from the bank and leave the frustration and turmoil of the past two months

226

behind me. Thomas was the best. Whenever I'd spoken with him, I'd always learned something new. His firm had enormous clout in the market.

"No," I said.

"No?" he repeated, astonished. "Wait a minute, before you give me your answer, let me finish. You haven't heard me out. Maybe you don't understand what I'm offering you. You get all the responsibility you can take. You'll trade for larger sums than almost anyone else in the market. I don't have to tell you what kind of power my firm commands."

"I know."

"I haven't even talked about money yet. Don't you want to know what I'm offering? These aren't firm figures, you understand—everything's subject to negotiation—but the compensation is excellent. Your salary is minimal, of course—something over $100,000, just to cover living expenses—but the bonus is substantial. If you perform well and the desk has a good year, we could hand you a check for half a million dollars at the end of the year."

So investment banks did pay that kind of money.

"Take some time to think about it," he urged.

I looked at him.

"I appreciate the offer," I said. "I really do. But I don't need time to think about it. The answer is no."

Larry was waiting up for me when I got home that night. He knew I was having dinner with Thomas.

"What happened?" he asked.

"He offered me a job."

Larry looked at me. "What did you say?"

"I refused."

A look of relief passed over his face. "Why?" he asked.

"I don't know. I just knew it was the right thing to do."

15 . . . and into the Fire

Why didn't I take that job?

On the surface, it seemed the culmination of everything I'd worked for since graduate school. It represented achievement with a capital *A*. Here was power and money on a scale that most people only dream about. I didn't know another trader on the Street who would have turned it down.

But something inside of me said no. It was a purely instinctive reaction. I guess I was beginning to understand at just what price such power is bought. It would be bought at the price of my marriage. It would be bought at the price of all my time and energy. The pressure would have been enormous. Even more than what I was currently experiencing. I would have had to be single-minded in my determination to accumulate wealth. Nothing could interfere with that commitment.

A very expensive trade.

My instinct for self-preservation, however, did not yet extend to my present circumstances. I was at my desk a few days later when Sam approached me.

"I have to talk to you," he said.

"Sure," I said, surprised.

"Not here," he said, looking around.

We went and found an empty office.

"Did we get those cost figures yet?" I asked him.

"Just got them."

"Terrific! Is the mainframe cheaper or more expensive than the minicomputer?"

"Significantly cheaper than the minicomputer. Also, once you go on the mainframe you never have to worry about it again. If you expand to other cities you won't have a problem. With a minicomputer you might have to go through this again as you continue to grow. I strongly suggest that you go with the mainframe alternative. There's absolutely no reason why that couldn't be up and running soon."

"Well," I said, "I'll do what you suggest. You're about the only person around here who knows what he's talking about."

"Thanks," said Sam, looking uncomfortable.

"You're also one of the few people who really works hard and has tried to help. I want to thank you for everything you've done, and let you know how much I appreciate you. I don't know what I'd do without you. Now, what was it you wanted to tell me?"

"I'm resigning."

"You're what?" I could hardly believe my ears.

"I'm resigning. I got a better offer from another

bank. It's for $10,000 more a year. I'm sorry, but I can't turn down an increase like that. It's too much money."

I tried to think. If it was only a matter of money, perhaps I could stop him.

"What are you earning here?" I asked.

"Twenty-five thousand a year," he replied. After a short pause he added: "You can see why $10,000 more a year makes such a big difference. You know, I'm married, and my wife and I have always wanted to buy a house. . . ."

"Yes, yes, I can't say I blame you," I assured him. "You're underpaid at $25,000 a year."

"You're telling me." He grinned.

"Listen," I said urgently, "what if I got the bank to match your increase? Would you stay then?"

"Save your breath," Sam said flatly. "William will never approve the increase. He'll be happy to see me go. He's never liked me."

"But if I did," I persisted. "Would you reconsider?"

"Nancy," said Sam, "I've always liked working with you. I've had my problems working here, but you've never been part of them. In fact, I hope that I have the chance to work with you again sometime. But just accept it. There's no way you're going to keep me here. You'll just be wasting your time."

"Please answer me, Sam. If I get you the extra $10,000, will you reconsider?"

There was a pause. Then Sam smiled at me.

"If the bank matches the offer, I'll reconsider."

The thought of life at the bank without Sam was frightening. I made yet another appointment with John Anderson to see if I could get Sam the $10,000 increase, a small raise, even by the bank's standards. It was getting to be a regular visitation.

"But, Nancy," said John, after I'd explained the

problem, "Sam's not my responsibility. He's in William Hambrecht's department."

"I know," I said, "but you are one of the highest-ranking officers in the whole bank! You are senior to Hambrecht. I know you have no direct authority over operations, but I'm sure that if you talked to him, he'd listen. He'd have to."

"I can try, I suppose," John admitted.

"Please," I urged him. "It's really important. I wouldn't come to you if it wasn't. It's only $10,000. If William's upset about the money, tell him I'll pay it out of my section. We just can't risk losing Sam right now. Even if he only stays until he trains someone else to take his place! Please."

"I'll see what I can do," said John.

After another series of meetings (almost three months since I had initiated the request), a philosophic decision was reached to pursue a link into the bank's mainframe computer. William promised to obtain the necessary approval to perform the actual task as soon as was humanly possible.

In the meantime, the days passed bleakly. Nothing had really changed. Phillip and I were struggling to keep our heads above water in a churning market. This was nothing, however, compared to the quality of my home life.

"Look at you!" Larry exploded in one of our never-ending battles. "You look awful! You're losing weight! The phone rings at three in the morning every night! How can you expect to trade under these conditions? You're not doing your job or your marriage any good. Don't you see how hard it is for me to stand by and watch you destroy yourself?"

"Please try to understand," I moaned.

"What is there to understand? I'm worried about you! You promised me you'd change. Well, you have. You've gotten worse!"

"Have some chow mein," I urged. "You'll feel better after you've eaten."

"I don't want to feel better! I want something done! If you can't handle it, quit!" He paused. His expression changed. "Nancy, is this really the way you want to spend your life?"

"What do you mean?"

"It's just that you don't seem very happy."

"Please," I said. "We'll get that system soon. You'll see. Then things will get better. Just hang on a little longer."

"Oh, Nancy," Larry sighed. "It's not just the system. You're kidding yourself."

"Nancy," said John Anderson, "I'm afraid I have some bad news."

"What is it?" I asked, bracing myself.

"William Hambrecht absolutely refuses to raise Sam's salary by the necessary $10,000. He says your back office can survive perfectly well without him."

"How would he know?" I asked sharply. "He's never even been in my back office."

"He says that no one is irreplaceable. I'm afraid I have to agree with him."

"But, John," I began again, despairingly, "you don't understand all the risks—"

"I do understand," said John. "I understand that you are a highly emotional young lady. I believe you are upset over losing Sam. I'm sorry, but there's nothing I can do."

Highly emotional?

"Look," said John with a grin, "if it makes you feel any better, William has absolutely guaranteed the smooth functioning of your back office. He promised me that you wouldn't even notice that Sam was gone."

Sam left a week later.

"Good luck," I said, kissing him good-bye on the cheek.

"No hard feelings, I hope?" he asked.

"Of course not," I said. "I would have done the same in your place."

"Well, good luck to you, too," he said. Then he paused.

"I guess you'll need it."

For the first week that Sam was gone we did not get one single report produced on time. No reports got to London. The reports that we did get were wrong. I don't remember the exact amount of money that we lost that week. I do remember that it was significantly in excess of the $10,000 it would have cost to keep Sam.

On the Friday afternoon of that memorable week, I went to the back office to check on my reports. I paused at the door and surveyed the scene. The room looked as if it had been hit by a hurricane. There were heaps of paper everywhere. On the desks, on the shelves, on the floor, in and out of the wastepaper baskets, on the window ledge, on top of the computers, on top of the printers. Only the ceiling remained uncluttered.

Buried beneath the mountains of paper were two people, working frantically. There was no sign of William Hambrecht. I wanted to ask when my reports would be ready, but one look inside that room changed my mind. I returned to my desk.

"Phillip," I said.

"Huh?" Phillip looked up from his charts.

"We have to help them back there. They're so disorganized. It's no wonder they're having problems."

"Yes, I know." Phillip looked grave.

"We have an even bigger problem, though," I continued. "Over the weekend the leaders of the industrialized nations are meeting again to plan economic policy."

"I know," said Phillip.

"This could be a big weekend," I remarked. "The dollar could really move depending on what's decided there."

"I know," said Phillip.

"It could be another G-5," I said.

"I know," said Phillip.

"What do you think our chances are of having an up-to-date report on our position by the end of the day?"

"Uh," said Phillip, "I guess not very good."

"I agree," I said. "I'll tell you what. Why don't you go back there and see if you can be of any assistance while I stay here and try to run up the position by hand?"

"Okay."

At 6:00 P.M. I had my reports. They were obviously wrong. Phillip and I found the errors. Phillip went to correct and reprint the reports. I went to see John Anderson.

"Hello, Nancy," said John.

"I just thought I'd let you know that there's a G-5 meeting this weekend," I said coldly.

"I know," said John.

"As of right now," I said, "I want you to know that I don't have a report of my position. If it weren't for hours of manual calculations, I wouldn't even know if I was long or short the dollar. The back office is a shambles. I'm going home now. I'll come in on Sunday. If there are no reports on my desk, I will not take responsibility for what happens Monday morning."

I turned and left. Highly emotional, huh? Let him worry for a change.

▲ ▲ ▲

I got my reports on Sunday. I spent all day in the office preparing for every possible scenario. An on-line computer system could have done everything in five minutes.

The G-5 meeting turned out to be a nonevent. All that work for nothing.

Somehow we got through the next few weeks. Faced with mounting losses, I developed a gambler's mentality. It was impossible to trade conservatively without accurate data. It seemed that my updated computer system was no closer to installation than it had been in January. There was always some new delay.

Hoping against hope for a windfall, I took larger and larger positions on the dollar. I wanted to make it all back quickly and start afresh. This resulted in some truly horrendous trading decisions as my exhausted brain strained to wrestle with a volatile climate. I threw caution to the wind as I threw money at the market.

I was completely, totally, abjectly miserable. I believed that it was all my fault. The losses, the disorganization, the disintegration of my unit, everything. I had invested every particle of my being into this job and I was coming up negative.

Ensnared within the bounds of my own paranoia, I felt my failure in the glances of my associates and superiors. I felt they blamed me for what was happening, and that they looked down on me. That they all knew me for the loser I was. And I believed them. I developed into a person I didn't recognize. I snapped at people for no apparent reason, but actually as a preemptive strike, anticipating their rejection. The marketing desk lived in fear of me. I hated myself. I retreated behind the fortresslike safety of my wall of screens.

I found myself sitting in the conference room again, victim of yet another meeting on the subject of my phantom computer system. I'd lost count of the number of times we'd met to discuss the issue. The same faces, the same questions, the same excuses. I was experiencing an eerie feeling of déjà vu.

The Field Marshall was explaining why the system wouldn't be ready for at least another month. The administrative assistant was wondering aloud whether we shouldn't go back and reconsider the minicomputer alternative. The credit official was asking if the new system would have an impact on credit lines. If so, he was against it.

They were wearing me down. This must be what it feels like to be a political prisoner, I thought; having to repeat the same story over and over again to stony-faced interrogators. The only thing missing was the bright lights shining in my eyes. On the other hand, I had William Hambrecht.

I wearily opened my mouth to reiterate how important this system was to my operation, how I couldn't trade without it, how it couldn't be put off another day, another hour, another minute. I looked from one blank face to the other. Slowly, I closed my mouth.

I'm the kind of person who feels first and thinks second. Suddenly, I had a feeling.

I don't belong here.

This truth freed my thought process. It was so instantaneously obvious that I wondered how I had ever felt different. In that moment, for the first time in months, I was able to look at the situation with some semblance of objectivity. Look at them! I thought. They don't care what's happening. They all know what a problem it is by this time. They all know that it's costing the bank money. I'm the only one who cares. Each of them is caught up in his own little fiefdom. They are actually enjoying watching me suffer. They view passive obstruction as a means of increasing power and influence. It's more important to them that they reaffirm their individual superiority than that they do their jobs in the general interest of the bank.

I don't, I mused, have anything in common with any of them, do I? It's as if I'm from another planet. I actually believe that they resent me for bringing this problem to their attention and making such a fuss about it. They think I'm just making waves.

Look at them! I thought again. Why, they think— they think—

I stopped.

They think *I'm* the problem!

16 Options

To have worked so hard at something and then to be made a mockery of for the very efforts you've made necessarily provokes some self-examination.

The same conditions that had allowed me to become a head trader in just three months were now preventing me from acquiring the support necessary to do the job properly. I had never, I decided, understood the rules of the commercial banking game. If I was having problems with John, William, and all the rest of them, who was really at fault? If the system was protected, nourished, and promoted by those who functioned within its confines, who was to blame, the outsider or the system? Hadn't I really brought all this on myself by ignoring the obvious and trying to change a system that had no reason for changing?

Put another way, if nobody else cared, wasn't I the bigger fool for trying?

"Larry," I announced calmly at dinner that evening, "I'm going to leave the bank."

"Well!" he said, setting down his chopsticks in surprise. "Other than turning down Thomas, that's the first sensible thing you've said in six months." He paused. "Are you sure you're feeling all right?"

"I don't belong there," I continued, ignoring him. "I learned that today."

"Let me feel your forehead," he said, leaning over. "You're going to stop trading? Maybe I should take you to the hospital."

"Cut it out," I snapped. "It's not funny. Besides, I didn't say I was going to quit trading altogether. I said I was going to leave the bank. I'm going to try to get a job at another organization, someplace where I won't feel like a fool for trying to do a good job."

"Oh!" he sighed, starting to eat again.

"So, where do you think I should go?"

"How should I know?" Larry countered. "Trading is the same everywhere. It's all the same breed."

"That can't be true!" I exclaimed, thinking of John, William, and Kashir.

"Oh, I'm not saying you'll find the same level of incompetence at other institutions," said Larry.

"Of course not!" I said, reassured.

"It will probably be worse," he continued.

"Oh."

"But in some places it will be better. Investment banking, for example, is more professional than commercial banking."

"I'm not going to an investment bank," I said. "I've already made that decision."

"Why don't you face facts? It's basically the same everywhere."

"You just want me to stop trading!" I said accusingly.

"I'm not saying that. But I wonder if you really want to keep trading."

"Larry, you're wrong." I was adamant. "I love trading. I don't want to give it up. I just want to move to a place where there are other people like me."

"There is no such place."

"Larry, think of all the money!"

"Forget the money. Money is a false issue. We're not going to starve. Tell me something. You didn't dream about becoming a trader when you were younger, did you?"

"Of course not," I said. "I didn't know what trading was when I was younger."

"Well, what did you want to be when you were growing up?" Larry asked.

"Secretary of state. But I don't think the position's available at the moment."

"Oh, come on. What did you really want to be?"

"Oh, Larry," I sighed. "This isn't getting us anywhere."

"C'mon, this is the first real conversation we've had in months. Indulge me."

"We've had lots of conversations."

"I don't call speculating on the possible outcome of a G-5 meeting a conversation. Let's talk about something interesting for a change."

I thought for a moment. "When I was growing up I wanted to be a writer," I said finally.

"There you go!"

"But, Larry, that was a dream. A dream!"

"What's wrong with dreams?" Larry demanded.

"They're not real, for one thing!"

"You have to make them real."

"Will you stop being so silly?" I sighed.

"What's so silly about it? I think trying to be a writer is an excellent idea. Why did you want to be a writer when you were younger?"

"Why . . . because it's creative, I suppose. And worthwhile. I have a lot of respect for writers."

"Has any of that changed?" Larry asked.

"No."

"Exactly. And do you feel that way about trading? That it's creative and worthwhile?"

"Well . . . not exactly . . . I mean, some parts of it are creative, I suppose, although not on the same level—"

"What about its being worthwhile?" Larry pressed. "Do you think that trading is a worthwhile profession?"

"It certainly pays better."

"That's not an answer."

"Writing's not practical!"

"I'm glad all writers don't feel that way."

"Larry, I am not going to quit trading to write," I said. "It's not an alternative."

"Suit yourself," Larry shrugged.

"Sometime later, perhaps. But not now."

"Just don't wait too long," he said softly.

Leave trading for a career in writing—what was Larry thinking of? I sighed. Did he really think that people were capable of such abrupt turnabouts, and at my age? (I conveniently forgot that I was only twenty-eight.) Why didn't I take up tap dancing as well, while I was at it? Or lion taming? Or nuclear physics?

Sure, I had wanted to write. Everybody has his dreams. But, honestly, I thought, how many people actually pursue them? And of those that try, how many succeed? That was what was important, wasn't it?

Success? I thought so. Hadn't I found that success brings along with it all those lovely intangibles like power, admiration, respect? To say nothing of more tangible rewards—like money? What was the point of trying something if you didn't have a better-than-even chance for success? I mean, what kind of trade was that?

Larry is so forceful, I thought, he makes almost any argument persuasive. It's odd that someone who is normally so intelligent can sprout such idealistic drivel from time to time. He can't actually believe it.

I know! I thought. It must be all those ideas from the sixties. Every now and then he reverts. I'll bet he's been listening to his old Bob Dylan albums again when I'm not around.

I was still determined to quit the bank. I recognized that I'd make a mistake and I needed to correct it. I planned to interview at small, private trading firms until I found one that suited. Options traders were always in demand. I didn't anticipate having any problem finding a new employer.

I started to check around. A little investigation revealed the names of two or three companies that looked promising. One in particular stood out from the rest.

It was a company that had been started by a man named Brad Rubens, who began trading in the early 1970s and was now enormously successful. His firm had started with a couple of million dollars and was now managing hundreds of millions. Brad Rubens was recognized throughout the industry for his achievement. He'd been written up in the newspapers for his brilliant career. He was wealthy beyond my wildest expectations. He owned a number of vacation homes in addition to a fabulous estate, expensive sports cars, a stable of thoroughbred horses, plus several yachts and private planes. The picture of a man who had wrestled with life and won a unanimous decision.

That sounds good, I thought. I'll go there.

The treasurer of the company agreed to meet me right away. He even sounded enthusiastic. We agreed to meet at four o'clock in the bar at the Waldorf-Astoria. The treasurer told me that he would be bringing along Brad Rubens.

I'm going to meet Brad Rubens! I thought. What an honor! Even if he doesn't need an options trader or want to finance an options trading program, at least I'll have a chance to speak with him and maybe I'll learn something. He would be perhaps the most successful man I would ever meet.

I was really worried about that interview. Not so much about getting the job, but about holding my own. This man held a Ph.D. in applied mathematics from a top university. What if I said something stupid? Stop it, I told myself. Anyone with half a brain listens to someone else the first time, and Brad Rubens will be no exception. If he thinks you have nothing to contribute, he simply won't see you again.

The big day arrived. I excused myself from the office at about three-thirty that sunny May afternoon and made my way over to the Waldorf-Astoria.

The bar the treasurer had chosen was very much a man's province: dark, clubby, with massive leather chairs and an enormous, perfectly polished wooden bar. The waiters wore bow ties, black pants, and immaculate white shirts. The atmosphere conjured up visions of a high-class pool hall.

As it was still relatively early in the afternoon, there weren't too many people drinking yet. What patrons there were were portly male figures dressed in dark suits, clutching heavy glasses of scotch and soda or bourbon.

I saw the bartender and one of the waiters exchange an amused glance as I tripped through the artificial gloom in my light spring dress and high heels. I sat down at a table for four.

At least they won't have any trouble spotting me in this crowd, I thought.

A waiter appeared.

"May I get you something to drink, madam?" he asked, addressing the question to the air over my head.

"Ginger ale, please," I replied.

"Ginger . . . ale?"

One good thing about trading. It teaches you how to scare waiters into action.

"Ginger ale," I said, in the voice I used to deal $20 million.

While he didn't seem to recognize the beverage, he was apparently used to the tone of voice.

"Right away, madam."

The ginger ale arrived promptly.

I crossed my legs, sipped my drink, and waited.

I tried to sit up very straight in my chair. This was a problem as the glossy material of my skirt kept slipping against the shiny leather. It would be just my luck to slip right off the chair and under the table during a crucial moment of the interview. I was preoccupied with this unexpected dilemma when two men entered the bar, glanced around, and started in my direction.

That's them, I thought. I stood up when they got to the table.

"I'm Nancy Goldstone," I said, extending my hand.

The taller of the two men shook hands. "I'm Richard Lewis," he said.

This was the treasurer. "Pleased to meet you," I replied.

"And this," continued Richard, "is Brad Rubens."

I held out my hand. Brad shook it limply and grunted something unintelligible at me. We all sat down. "Let's get a waiter over here," Brad growled.

244

The waiter appeared, and while they ordered their drinks I had a chance to study the two men.

Richard had a pleasant, open face, but was obviously nervous. He faced me with a frozen smile. Brad was extremely short and given to chunkiness. When we shook hands, I'd towered over him. His expensive clothes couldn't hide the fact that he was uncomfortable with his own body. He sat with his back to me, preferring to fling his comments over his shoulder, out of the side of his mouth. It must have been an extremely uncomfortable position. My clearest view was of the back of his head. This was an interesting study as Brad was going bald and combed what hair he had left up and around, rather like a turban.

There was an uncomfortable silence.

"I'm very pleased to meet you," I said finally. "I'm glad you could make it."

Richard smiled nervously at me. "Have you been waiting long?" he asked.

"Not very—" I started to answer.

Brad cut me off. "Let's get down to business, shall we?" he demanded curtly, turning his head so I got a quick glimpse of his profile. "I don't have all afternoon." He consulted his watch. "I have a train to catch. Let's make this quick."

I was shocked by his rudeness. Richard, glancing down uncomfortably at his Coke, picked up the slack. Both men had yet to look me straight in the eye, although I think Richard wanted to. "You mentioned that you traded options," he said to encourage me.

"Yes," I said, trying to overlook Brad's strange behavior. "I run the options desk for the bank. I've decided I no longer want to work for a commercial bank. The system is too heavily bureaucratic to be conducive to effective trading. I am going to take my trading program to a smaller, more efficient organization. I thought you might be interested. You said you were."

Brad made a noise rather like a snort. "What's your trading program?" he sneered in my general direction. He made it obvious that he considered it unlikely that I could add, let alone trade.

I started to get angry, but I tried to keep my poise. "Well, it's rather complicated," I hedged.

No trader gives away his program until he's sure that the person he's speaking to isn't simply going to steal it. This was an industry rule, and Mr. Rubens knew it as well as I did. He'd done nothing to inspire the necessary level of confidence.

"What are we doing here then?" he snapped triumphantly. "I expected to see a written proposal of your trading program. Where is it?"

The man suggests a bar for the first meeting, and then expects me to hand over a detailed proposal for his casual perusal?

"I don't have a proposal with me," I said.

"Well, we don't have much to talk about then, do we?" he jeered. "If you want to send over a written proposal, I'll look at it." He got up from the table. "Right now I'm afraid we have to catch a train. Will you excuse us?"

For the first time Richard looked right at me. He was openly embarrassed about his boss's behavior and was trying to offer me an unspoken apology. I think he was as surprised at Brad's reaction to me as I was.

They left me at the table. It took me a moment to realize that a man who was worth in excess of $50 million had just left me with the check.

I walked all the way home from the Waldorf-Astoria to my apartment on the upper West Side. It was a beautiful spring afternoon, but I didn't notice. It was rush hour and the streets were packed with people hurrying home from work. I didn't notice them either. Some of them probably noticed me, however. I was the person having a loud conversation with herself.

The nerve of that man! I fumed. Of all the low-down miserable, slimy little twerps! How rude! How boorish! What a totally vile little worm of a man! Oh, why didn't I throw my ginger ale in his face? I seethed.

But wasn't Brad's behavior just an exaggeration of symptoms I'd already spotted among my peers? Could it be that, instead of growing out of their insecurities as they became more successful, they instead grew more firmly fixed in them.? That trading so catered to an individual's uncertainty that, instead of facing it down and overcoming the problem, the person hid from the truth and let the feeling grow until it was overwhelming? That trading built upon your fears of worthlessness, so that you took refuge in numbers and money, money, money? Look what money had done for Brad Rubens.

Was this the kind of person I wanted to be? Did I belong in trading at all?

It certainly was a very good question. What, I asked myself, did I really like about trading? About the business? In the end, I could find only one thing that I unequivocally liked about trading. I liked telling people that I was a trader. Although most people had no idea what a trader was, they were usually very impressed with the statement and tended to treat me with a mixture of fear and respect. I liked being treated with a mixture of fear and respect.

But it wasn't really me they respected, was it? It was the act of trading, and the money it represented. After all, the people I met at parties didn't know me at all. They couldn't respect me because I was a nice person or a good person or a creative person; they only respected me because they thought I did something difficult and flashy for a living. Most people never looked beyond the reputation of the job.

And that was what was so nice about trading, wasn't it? I never had to show any other side of myself; I could hide behind the business. That's what most people did. That was what Brad Rubens had done.

Over the past year or so, I'd really become a trader in that sense of the word, hadn't I? All other aspects of my life and my personality had become subordinated to the business. Creativity, warmth, energy, even my marriage—all sacrificed to the trader in me.

What if I couldn't tell people, upon being introduced, that I was a trader? What if I took away that category, with all the confidence it implied? What kind of person would be left? Would people still like me or respect me if I wasn't a trader? Would I like and respect myself? What would I have left? Why, at the rate I was going, I'd have nothing left.

On that note, I limped into the apartment. "How'd it go?" asked Larry.

"Terrible. Horrible."

"As bad as all that?" asked Larry.

"Worse," I said gloomily, and went on to describe my meeting with Brad Rubens.

"So where does this guy live?" Larry asked innocently when I had finished.

"I don't know," I said. "Why do you ask?"

"Because I'm going to go beat the living——— out of him," said my husband.

For the first time in ages, I laughed. "Me first," I said.

"I guess this means you're not going to work for Brad Rubens."

"I guess not."

"So what are you going to do?" Larry asked.

"I don't know."

I spent the next two weeks following my old routine, but I couldn't miss the fact that it was getting on toward summer. Summer! Stifling subways and stuffy offices. I dreaded it. It was a time when most people are looking forward to a little relaxation; the sun and the beach. I did not look forward to the inevitable arguments with my spouse over why I was devoting so much time to my work when there was a beautiful summer to enjoy.

Summer! Bah, humbug!

Back at the office one afternoon I was staring fixedly at my Reuters screen, apparently engrossed in the market, but actually wondering idly if the rays from the machine had already permanently damaged my chromosome structure, and those of my children and my children's children. When I was younger my mother had always maintained that the beams from our color television were bad for us, and had insisted that my brother and I sit at least three feet away from the set. All that careful protection—for what? Now I sat not six inches away from the combined rays of six color television sets day after day. I'll probably have little green numbers for children, I thought glumly.

All my life I had been forging ahead like a mechanical stuffed animal that, once wound up, paddles along until it runs into a wall, whereupon it simply changes direction and, in single-minded pursuit of some unquestioned goal, merrily advances until it meets the next obstacle. Thus could my life be depicted, with the possible exception that my batteries never seemed to run out.

If trading, the cream of my chosen career path, was not the answer, what did that say about my choices? Could I have made such a serious mistake? And if I had been wrong, and was finally recognizing my mistake, was there anything I could do about it now, after all this time?

Larry and I spent the Memorial Day weekend at a summer house we'd rented in Connecticut. On the morning of Memorial Day I woke up to the sound of birds chirping. It took me a second to place the sound.

I lay in bed awhile until Larry woke up. Then I rolled over on my side and looked at him.

"I'm going to quit the bank tomorrow," I announced.

17 Cutting Ties

Despite everything that had led up to this moment, my actual decision to quit was strictly spur-of-the-moment. I didn't think about losing the prestige. I didn't think about losing the money. At that moment, I only thought how nice it would be if I didn't have to go into work tomorrow. Who knows how many great decisions are made this way?

"Really?" Larry asked.

"Really."

"Just like that?"

"Just like that."

Larry put his arms around me.

"I think you're making the right decision," he said.

I basked in the glory of this sentiment just long

enough to go into the office and actually quit. In fact, as I reflected on my decision, I had chosen the perfect time to leave. Fully one half of the options in my portfolio (about $750 million worth) expired in June. If I didn't put on any more trades, and made sure that those remaining were properly hedged, I would leave Peter and Phillip with a portfolio that was far easier to manage than the one we'd been working with to date.

In addition to that, it was now June 1. The new system was due to be in place first thing in the morning. I'd be leaving the bank far better equipped for the job of trading options than it had ever been in the past.

Peter could be called back from London to be the new manager. Management and attention to detail were not Phillip's strengths. They'd have to help each other, of course, but Peter would be the boss.

When I walked into the bank on June 1, I did not go directly to the trading desk. I went instead into an empty office and phoned Peter to tell him of my decision. "What?" he gasped, through the three thousand miles of long-distance interference.

"I'm resigning today," I repeated. "I've had it. It's your show."

"You can't do that!" In his panic Peter dropped his customary farm-bred composure. "It's too soon!"

"No, it's not," I said, calmer now than I'd been in months. I was prepared for Peter's reaction. "You can do it. Don't worry. I'll stay until the June options expire. You won't need me after that."

"Please don't do this to me," Peter begged. "Can't you wait a little?"

"Peter, listen to me. You can do this. You can always call me if you need me. I'm not dying. I'm just resigning. You just need to get used to the idea."

"But . . . ," Peter started to argue.

"What's the matter?" I asked. "Don't you want the job?"

"Of course I do," he muttered.

"Then do it," I said.

I hung up with Peter and walked into the trading room. Phillip was already at the desk. I looked around. Nothing had changed. "No system, huh?" I asked Phillip.

"No system," he said, shaking his head.

William Hambrecht happened to be walking through the trading room at that moment. I called him over.

"Weren't we supposed to have a new system today?" I asked innocently.

This simple question unleashed the Field Marshall's wrath.

"I never said that!" he shouted.

"William," I said reasonably, "didn't we sit in a meeting not two weeks ago where you announced that the system would be up and running by June 1?"

"That's a lie!" He was very red in the face. "I never said that! That system won't be ready for another three weeks or so!"

"Okay," I said, shrugging and turning away.

"I never said that!" William continued in a fury. "I don't know how you could possibly think that your system would be in by June 1!"

"I said okay," I returned calmly.

He wasn't prepared for my indifference. He couldn't understand it. He found it maddening that I wouldn't be provoked. "You pull these dates out of thin air!"

"If you say so," I replied. "I'm not going to discuss it further."

"That system won't be ready for three more weeks. At least three more weeks!"

"I said that this conversation is over," I said, in a

253

voice that left him no choice. And then I turned my back once and for all on the Field Marshall.

He stared at me perplexed for a few moments, then stormed out of the trading room.

Well, it was time to quit. But I had a problem. John was out of the office. He was attending a meeting in Washington. I'd have to quit to somebody else. I resigned to Andy, the head spot trader. He was very upset by my decision, and called John in Washington to tell him he'd better fly back to New York that afternoon. John got back in time for lunch.

Once again, we rode the elevator to the executive dining room. Once again, the fawning maître d' led us to a gleaming table for two by the huge, plate-glass windows. It was a beautiful summer day. The sky was a fresh, clear blue. The view was spectacular. This is the last time I'll eat here, I thought with a sudden pang. Have I made the wrong decision? Shall I miss it terribly, after all?

At that moment the food arrived. On second thought, I won't, I decided, looking at the Pâté du Chef (Chopped Liver).

John cleared his voice to speak. Nothing came out.

"I'm sorry you had to miss your meeting," I said, to break the awkward silence.

"That's all right," he replied. "You won't change your mind?"

I shook my head.

"Why are you leaving?" John asked.

A difficult question to answer. "Well . . . all the problems we've been having," I began. "The delay over the computer system. Even today!"

"I know, I know," said John. "I promise you'll get that system as soon as possible. It's almost here. Why don't you wait and give it a chance?"

"Too much water under the bridge," I replied. "I'm sure you'll get your system. But I won't be here when you finally get it. I've had enough."

John sighed.

"Where are you going?" he asked.

Andy had asked me the same question. "I'd rather not say," I hedged.

How explain to this man that I didn't know what I was going to do? That I'd resigned without any clear plan? He'd think I was crazy. I wasn't sure that I wasn't crazy. It was better to let him think I was taking a job elsewhere.

"I wish you'd tell me," he said unhappily.

"I can't."

"I mean," said John, "if you're going to an investment bank I know there's nothing I can do. I know we can't compete with what they pay. But if it's a job at another commercial bank I think we should at least be given a chance to meet the offer."

I was surprised. I thought he'd be glad to be rid of me, but apparently that wasn't the case. He thought he was losing a trader to the competition.

"No," I shook my head. "I'm not going to work here anymore."

"Are we as bad as all that?" he asked. "Should I shut down the unit?"

The question took me by surprise. Nobody had thought to shut down the unit when it was handed over to me after a mere six weeks' experience. Peter and Phillip had over a year's experience apiece. "Heavens, no!" I exclaimed. "Peter can do it."

Word spread quickly throughout the trading floor that I was leaving. People speculated that I was headed for a big job elsewhere. They envied me the money they thought I would be making. Nobody even considered that I might just be leaving. They knew as well as I did

255

that I could get a job elsewhere on the Street for more money than I was currently earning at the bank. Who walks away from that kind of income?

Who indeed?

Most traders who voluntarily resign their posts are asked to leave immediately. Everybody knows that a trader can do a great deal of damage in a very short period of time, so most institutions will not take the risk that the trader no longer has the bank's best interests at heart. I suppose that I should take it as a compliment that when I offered to stay on for two weeks and help smooth the transition, John took me up on it.

They were an uncomfortable two weeks. I was there but I wasn't. I was involved but I wasn't. I performed the same duties that I'd performed for the past fifteen months, but without the responsibility. The two weeks gave me a chance to reflect on what I'd done. I started to panic.

What had I done? Why, I'd given up the best job I would ever have. I'd given up power and prestige. I'd given up my very identity! I wasn't a writer, I was a trader! My God, what had I done? I looked at the people in the trading room. Would any of them have done what I'd done? Of course not! They're not crazy! Just look at their reaction to me; they think I've traded up to a better job!

Is this what they call having second thoughts?

"Larry," I said nervously that night at dinner. "I've been thinking."

"Yes?"

"I think that you and I should trade together. I know you've been trading on your own for some time, but I think we would make a good team."

"Nancy," said Larry, "I thought you were quitting because you wanted something else out of life. I thought you wanted to do something more creative, like write."

"I do, I do," I agreed. "But, well, it seems silly to give up trading. I mean, I've been a trader all this time and . . . well, I'm not sure that I made the right decision."

"What makes you think you made the wrong decision?"

"Well . . . the people at work wouldn't understand just quitting. They'd think I was crazy or something."

"So? Whose opinion is more important to you, theirs or your own?"

"Well, mine, of course, but—"

"But you're embarrassed? You think people will think worse of you when they find out? That they'll tell themselves you just couldn't handle it?"

I nodded.

"Some of them probably will," said Larry. "Do you think you couldn't handle it and that you're a quitter?"

I nodded again.

"That's too bad," Larry said. "I, for one, am quite proud of you. What you did took a lot of guts. Besides, you did a terrific job while you were there. You gave that bank an effective unit, and one that will survive your resignation. Nancy! Think of how much money the bank could have lost when you first started out! They left a junior trader with six weeks' experience to handle a billion-dollar portfolio! And without systems, support, or guidance. By rights they should have had their heads handed to them on a platter! It was only your dedication and commitment that saw them through a very difficult time. You should be extremely proud of what you did."

"Well, maybe . . . but I lost a lot of money, too."

"They came out ahead on the money. That's more than they deserved. Stop trying to win everyone else's approval! Win your own approval for a change. That's the toughest game in town. Trading plays a poor second to that one."

I knew Larry was right. I didn't regret my decision to leave the bank. The bank was like a shallow lover who had overstayed his welcome. That relationship had lost its allure, leaving me to wonder that I had ever found any magic in it at all. But the decision to give up trading in the pursuit of some crazy dream—that was a different story.

My last day at work was the day that half the portfolio expired. I was in the office at 6:00 A.M., making sure that everything went smoothly. That the money that had to be paid got paid. That the options that had to be exercised got exercised. That the three-hundred-plus tickets got written. (I know they got written, because I wrote them.) It took me until 6:30 P.M.

John had dropped by the desk during the day to say good-bye. He had also written me a lovely note, thanking me for what I had done and wishing me well.

At 6:30, being one of the few people still at work, I said good-bye to my staff and walked out into—

Into what?

18 Trading Up

I wish I could tell you that I rode off into the sunset without ever looking back. That I faced my new destiny with all the courage and faith of a character out of *Star Wars* who knows that "the Force" is with him. That I walked in the brilliant light of my own self-awareness from the moment I escaped the gloomy, dungeonlike confines of the bank. However, this was not the case.

Two weeks after leaving the bank, I was a confused muddle of conflicting emotions. I felt a complete failure. I felt I had no identity. I didn't trust my own judgments. Ironically, I felt myself to be somehow less of a person after the experience of high-powered trading than I had before it.

I reacted to the whole thing in the usual way. I took everything out on Larry.

"It's all your fault!" I screamed at him.

"My fault!" Larry exclaimed. "How is it my fault?"

"You made me quit!"

"Nancy!" Larry breathed. "You know that's not true. It was your decision."

"I never would have made it if it wasn't for you."

"What are you talking about? You hated that job! You finally identify the problem, admit you made a mistake, and after two short weeks away from it you are right back where you started again!"

"*No!*" I was furious. "That's not what happened! You badgered me into quitting! I used to look forward to work just to get away from you!"

At last came a day when neither of us could stand it anymore.

It was a beautiful summer day. We were at the house in Connecticut, sitting out in the yard. What a waste of what could be a lovely time together, I thought. Why can't I enjoy myself anymore? What's happened to me?

"Why don't you try and write something today?" Larry suggested.

I started to cry. "I can't write. I've never written anything. It was all just a pipe dream."

"How do you know if you don't try?" Larry asked. "Why are you so averse to trying?"

"Because—because—" I struggled to answer. "Because I'm afraid to try!"

The words came out of nowhere. They were a complete surprise. But the second I said them, I knew they were true.

"Well!" said Larry. "That was a long time in coming."

"That's true, isn't it?" I said. "That's what this is all about, isn't it?"

"Apparently. But why are you afraid to try?"

"Because," I whispered, "I'm afraid to fail."

And that was the truth. I'd always been afraid to try. I set my standards so high that it was impossible to succeed.

But I hadn't been afraid to try to manage a billion-dollar options portfolio after only six weeks. It was so clearly impossible for me to succeed, that if I'd failed, who could fault me? At the same time, once I failed, I could prove to myself once and for all that I wasn't capable. If a person wants badly enough to prove that to herself, she'll eventually succeed.

But I'd surprised even myself. In the face of incredible adversity, I'd succeeded. But had I proved anything to myself by succeeding? Not I. All I concluded from the experience was that the situation hadn't been that difficult to begin with. After all, even I had managed to come out on top.

So how did I react? I raised the stakes. I expanded without systems, without personnel, without guidance. That was a real no-win situation. I'd arranged everything perfectly for my own failure. After all, who but I could have known my own weaknesses so perfectly? And I'd failed, right on schedule.

All to prove that I was no good to begin with.

There is a calm that comes with truth.

"What should I do?"

"Write."

"But won't the same thing happen all over again?" I asked.

"Not if you've really learned something."

"But I'm still afraid to try."

"Listen," said Larry. "Why don't you take it easy

on yourself for a change? Instead of trying to rewrite *War and Peace*, why don't you tell yourself that the first thing you write will probably be terrible? Let yourself off the hook. Don't try for a masterpiece your first time around."

"Well . . ."

"Maybe you'll surprise yourself," he grinned.

Could it really be that simple—that trying for something you believe in is a worthwhile effort in itself? That that is what success is really all about; that it isn't money, or power, or other people's admiration? That believing in yourself is enough?

I took out a pad of paper and a pen.

I stared down at the empty page.

And then I started to write.

Cathy Kelly is a number ~~one bestselling~~
author. She worked as a ~~journalist before becoming a~~
novelist. She is an Ambassa~~dor for UNICEF Ireland and is~~
also a patron of Chernobyl Children's Project International
(CCPI). She lives in Wicklow with her family.

For more information on Cathy Kelly, visit her website at
www.cathykelly.com.

By Cathy Kelly

Woman to Woman
She's the One
Never too Late
Someone Like You
What She Wants
Just Between Us
Best of Friends
Always and Forever
Past Secrets
Lessons in Heartbreak
Once in a Lifetime
Homecoming

Cathy Kelly
Woman *to* Woman

headline
review

First published in the UK in 1998 by HEADLINE PUBLISHING GROUP

This paperback edition first published in 2011 by HEADLINE REVIEW
An imprint of HEADLINE PUBLISHING GROUP

1

Cataloguing in Publication Data is available from the British Library

ISBN 978 0 7553 5634 8

Printed and bound in Great Britain by
Clays Ltd, St Ives plc

Headline's policy is to use papers that are natural, renewable and recyclable
products and made from wood grown in sustainable forests. The logging
and manufacturing processes are expected to conform to the environmental
regulations of the country of origin.

HEADLINE PUBLISHING GROUP
An Hachette UK company
338 Euston Road
London NW1 3BH

www.headline.co.uk
www.hachette.co.uk

To Mum, with all my love

ACKNOWLEDGEMENTS

Thanks.

To John, who told me to stop talking about writing a book and to just do it, and for encouraging me all the way when I actually did. To Lucy, who gave me so much support, made the coffee, poured the gin and brought Tamsin out to meet her boyfriends while I typed. To Mum, who's been saying I could do it ever since we started that ill-fated Mills & Boon, and who has helped me in so many ways, always. To Dad for minding the zuppies, to Francis and Anne for their endless encouragement, and to Laura, my godchild, for being so absolutely adorable and a complete bookworm at the age of two. And of course, to Tamsin, who was here for all of it.

Thanks to Sarah Hamilton for being a wonderful friend and for coming up with the title, thanks to Moira Hannon, Joanne McElgunn and Lisa McDonnell for reading bits and not telling me it was brutal. Thanks to the *Sunday World*'s editor, Colm MacGinty and deputy editor, J. P. Thompson for making this a fantastic time in my life career-wise. And thank you to all my friends and colleagues in the *Sunday World* who are too numerous to name and who encouraged me, asked how it was going, helped me with computer nightmares and never asked if I was writing a sequel to *War and Peace* because it was taking so long. You know who you are. Thanks also to my fellow movie critics for the same thing.

Thanks to Padraig O'Reilly for amazing poster shots and lots of advice for the next book, and to Sobhain McClafferty of Cover Shots and her team for the others.

Last, but by no means least, thanks to everyone at Poolbeg for their enthusiasm, hard work and sheer professionalism.

To Kate Cruise O'Brien for being a marvellous editor, who was endlessly encouraging when I was down in the dumps with brain rot, who helped me learn the difference between writing a book and writing for a newspaper and who gave me lots of wine (thanks, Joe!) to cheer me up. I couldn't have done it without you, Kate. To Philip MacDermott, Paula, Kieran, Sarah, Nicole and everyone else at Poolbeg for their hard work. And thanks to Jilly Cooper whose wonderful novels kept me going through all the dreadful bits.

CHAPTER ONE

Aisling stared at the crumpled-up receipt in her hand and tried desperately not to cry. A credit card counterfoil with smudged writing, it lay forlornly on the palm of her hand with the words 'Lingerie de Paris' plainly printed on the left-hand side.

Her hand trembled slightly as she pulled out a chair and sat down by the kitchen table, blind to the fact that her sleeve was resting on an island of marmalade and toast crumbs left by the boys' usual breakfast commando raid. She closed her eyes and crunched the receipt into a ball, willing the words to have changed when she looked again.

Just moments before, Friday had stretched out in front of her in a comforting and familiar routine. A visit to the dry-cleaner's with Michael's suits, a quick detour to the hairdresser's to get her hair blow-dried for the party and coffee with Fiona in the Merrion Centre for a thoroughly enjoyable gossip over a slightly too-big slice of carrot cake smothered in cream.

No carrot cake, she admonished herself automatically. A brown scone with a tiny bit of Flora and a cup of black coffee with no sugar. Got to stick to the diet. The first week was always the hardest but you've got to stick to it, or so the diet gurus repeated endlessly.

Diet! What am I thinking about bloody diets for, she wailed out loud. What was the point of living on dry toast and two ounces of lean turkey with a mini-Kit Kat treat a day when your entire life had just disintegrated.

Suddenly her regular trip to the dry-cleaner's and the bitching session with Fiona seemed a million miles away.

Michael never remembered to leave his suits out for dry-cleaning and she'd stopped reminding him since it was easier to bring them downstairs herself than listen to him stomp around the bedroom muttering about women with premenstrual tension and complaining about being late for work.

She had also given up telling the twins to put their dirty football jerseys in the laundry basket. They copied their father slavishly in everything and, if he managed to escape from all things domestic, they followed suit. Aisling was used to finding remnants of tissues and receipts glued to every wet item of clothing when she emptied the machine. She had finally realised that she was stuck with two ten-year-old fledgling domestic incompetents along with a card-carrying anti-housework husband. She simply cleaned out the pockets herself.

That morning had been no different.

'Don't forget to bring my navy suit, Aisling, and tell them about the red wine stain on my yellow silk tie, will you?' Michael had shouted downstairs.

'Yes, my lord and master,' she muttered from the depths of the downstairs coat cupboard where she was riffling through duffel coats, soccer boots and the bits of the vacuum cleaner that she never used. She was looking for the boys' tennis rackets. The three-week summer camp in UCD always seemed like a good idea at the time because it certainly kept the boys out of trouble during the too-long holidays. But it meant three times as much organisation as it took to get them off to primary school. The camp timetable was a bit erratic and the boys always forgot to mention that they wanted some vital bit of equipment until five minutes before they were due to go.

Yesterday, it had been swimming goggles. Today, tennis rackets. 'I know I left them there, Mum,' wailed Phillip, hopping from one leg to the other in agitation, his dark eyes huge with anxiety. 'Somebody must have moved them!'

Somebody was responsible for a lot of things in the Moran household, Aisling thought darkly as she rummaged through old papers and a battered plastic toy box she thought she'd thrown out.

Somebody regularly ate all the chocolate biscuits, broke dishes and lost school jumpers. She'd just love to shake somebody.

Michael's voice, even more agitated than Phillip's, broke into her reverie.

'Aisling, where did you put my linen jacket? I want to wear it tonight and I can't see it in the bloody wardrobe! I'm going to be late, for God's sake!'

Triumphantly dragging two battered rackets out of the cupboard, Aisling handed them to a delighted Phillip and shouted back up the stairs, 'I put it in the spare bedroom wardrobe because your wardrobe is so full it would end up totally creased before you'd put it on.'

Two minutes later, Michael rushed the boys out the door to drop them at UCD before driving to work. Peace reigned again. The nine o'clock news blared loudly in the background. She left the breakfast dishes on the table to go upstairs and collect the suits, trousers and ties she was bringing to the cleaner's, scooping up her handbag and keys at the same time. She draped the dry-cleaning pile on the back of a kitchen chair as she had dozens of times before and reached absently into every pocket.

Among the bits of pocket fluff and unused match books Michael always seemed to have stashed in his pockets, she found it. Tucked into the inside pocket of the fine wool navy suit that looked so good with his yellow Paisley tie, was an ordinary credit card receipt, the sort of thing she wouldn't usually look at. But today was different. Something made her smooth it out and look. Fifty pounds' worth of goods from one of Dublin's most exclusive lingerie shops had been purchased with their joint credit card but had somehow never made it into *her* underwear drawer.

Unbelievably, her loving husband had been lying through his capped teeth when he muttered that expensive lunches with his newspaper colleagues and important contacts had sent his Visa card bill sky-high.

The receipt in Aisling's hand made her think that the hefty

bill he'd complained about had nothing to do with lunch at Le Coq Hardi. Instead of buying bottles of pricey Rioja and the best smoked salmon to loosen his political friends' tongues, the deputy editor of the *Sunday News* appeared to have been splashing out on goodies of another kind. Luxurious silky goodies.

Fifty pounds! Aisling marvelled. And in Lingerie de Paris at that. She had never even stood inside the door of the plushest underwear shop on Grafton Street. She'd seen enough adverts for the shop's dainty silk knickers and bras to realise that they were ruinously expensive.

Aisling felt a sliver of anger pierce the gloom in her heart. She'd been brought up to believe that spending money on clothes was practically sinful and she'd never spent more than fifteen pounds on a bra in her life.

Apart from the lacy crimson teddy the girls at work had bought for her honeymoon twelve years ago, and a few frivolous satin bits and pieces which never felt comfortable under her jeans, Aisling's lingerie collection consisted of the type of plain cotton knickers and sensible bras that wouldn't look out of place on a Mother Superior.

If she was knocked down by a bus, nobody was ever going to think she was a sexpot once they'd ripped off her sensible navy cardigan and long, full skirt to reveal underwear about as erotic as suet pudding. It would all match, of course, saggy off-white knickers, saggy off-white bra and saggy off-white body.

No amount of lycra underwear could conceal her spare tyre and cellulite-covered bum. Why waste money looking for sexy lingerie? Anyway, the sort of bras that could contain a well-endowed 38C generally looked as if they could also accommodate a few basketballs at a push and were, therefore, passion-killers of the most effective kind.

Passion-killers, hah! She laughed out loud, a little rasping noise that turned into a sob at the thought of Michael walking into a lingerie shop to buy something for another woman. Had he given the salesgirl a blank look when she asked what

4

size he wanted? Splaying out his hands as though cupping a couple of oranges for the bra measurements?

Men never managed to check their wives' existing under-wear before these shopping expeditions, Aisling had read in a magazine once. Instead, they muttered about small waists, ordinary hips and blushed when they said 'About your size' to shop assistants who'd seen it all before.

Had he asked for the best lingerie money could buy, keen to impress *her*? Or was she with him, smiling as he coughed up for knickers she knew he'd rip off later? Aisling couldn't bear to think about it.

Michael wouldn't cheat on her. He wouldn't, she was sure of that. He barely had time to play with the kids these days, for God's sake. He spent every spare moment working on the newspaper supplement which would '. . . push the circu-lation figures of the paper to the top!' as he was so fond of saying.

She was sick to the teeth of hearing about the last-minute problems, about how he nearly fired the darkroom technician who somehow managed to botch printing an entire roll of film from the fashion spread, shot at great expense in Cannes.

The newspaper had taken over their lives during the past year. Endless meetings and brainstorming sessions resulted in cancelled evenings out and lots of lonely weekends where Michael only appeared for bed and breakfast like a hotel guest who didn't fancy his room that much. He'd even missed the twins' Easter play where they played St Peter and St Paul in matching beige striped robes. Aisling had spent hours sewing the night before.

'I'm afraid I can't leave for another two hours at least,' he said apologetically when he rang moments before Aisling left for the school. 'I'm sorry. Give them my love, though, won't you? Tell them I'll bring them to McDonald's at the weekend, OK?'

'Daddy had to work, darlings,' she comforted her two small apostles when the applause had died down and the cast were being hugged and kissed by proud parents.

Thinking about the boys, two mirror images of their dark-haired father, she began to feel better. Michael loved the boys with all his heart, he wouldn't cheat on them. He wouldn't cheat on her. She just knew it.

There had to be an explanation for the Visa receipt. Yes, of course there was. She felt better now, on firmer ground when she thought about their family and what it meant to him. There was no way he'd risk losing his family for a fling with some floozie. Hell, she couldn't even imagine Michael in a bloody underwear shop. He *hated* shopping.

He'd always urged her to spend money on herself, to splash out on lacy little camisoles and those French knickers she'd bought years ago when her flatmate, Jo, had dragged her into Clerys for a rummage around the bargain bins.

'You never wear anything like that any more, darling,' Michael used to say when he spotted a sexy underwear feature in a magazine or paper. But he'd never gone into a lingerie shop to buy her a present himself in their entire marriage.

'How am I supposed to know you want sexy underwear if you don't tell me?' he demanded one Christmas Day when Aisling laughed out loud as she ripped the wrapping paper off another Delia Smith cookbook. 'For heaven's sake, it takes *you* two hours to buy one bloody shirt! How am I supposed to pick out something you'd like? And *underwear* at that!'

Aisling never pointed out that she knew exactly what he'd like for Christmas because she listened to him and carefully planned her gifts in October. But then she had time to meander around Henry Street, slipping in and out of shop after shop. Michael was always too busy for that.

Instead of turning up with the wrong size blouse or the wrong colour jumper, he simply thrust money into her hand. 'Go on, spoil yourself, Ash, and buy some nice clothes, won't you? Bring Fiona with you; she has great taste.'

Accepting the implied criticism meekly, Aisling duly ventured off on those hateful shopping trips with her svelte and aerobically toned neighbour. She blindly rattled through rails

6

of lovely clothes looking for something that Michael would like and that would actually flatter her figure.

Just when she had steeled up the courage to try it on, a size ten salesgirl with a degree in arrogance would sidle over and ask did she need any help. Aisling was sure that these nasty nymphets waited until there were at least ten other people in the shop before loudly asking the girl at the cash register if they had the pink shirt or whatever in a size sixteen.

Crimson with embarrassment, Aisling would then stand there self-consciously as the assistant looked her up and down with an expression of superiority written all over a face free of crow's feet and laugh lines.

Sometimes Aisling felt like slapping those girls across their insolent little faces and yelling that she had been a sexy size ten herself once. Before two kids and ten years of day-long access to the fridge had changed her figure. But what was the point?

Instead, she kept silent while an enraged and loyal Fiona went into Bitch Shopper overdrive, demanding to see their good stock since she '. . . couldn't possibly wear this sale rubbish'. Fiona could find snagged threads and missing buttons on anything the increasingly harassed assistants produced for her supercilious gaze.

Thank God for Fiona, Aisling thought when the sight of buttons straining reproachfully on tailored trousers and elegant blouses plunged her into gloom and they had to abandon the shopping expedition for a consolatory doughnut in Bewley's.

'Belfast,' announced Fiona, after one depressing afternoon when everything Aisling tried on looked either tent-like or too tight. 'That's where we should go. I love the shops there, they have lots of marvellous shops in the Castle Court centre and you'd love it. We could drive up on Monday, what do you think?'

'Brilliant!' Aisling felt better already. 'I'll start a diet tomorrow,' she vowed with sugar on her top lip and a cup of frothy cappuccino in front of her. But when tomorrow came, and she was serving up Michael's favourite shepherd's pie, she couldn't resist having a bit along with the Weight Watchers baked beans she'd cooked for herself. And well, a bit of Black Forest gateau would hardly hurt.

She'd always loved Black Forest gateau. In fact, she'd insisted on having it as her wedding cake despite her grandmother's outraged disapproval. She could still hear that frail voice grimly prophesying disaster for the young couple who had ignored tradition in favour of modern ideas.

Aisling could have laughed at the irony of it all. Granny Maguire had no doubt been smirking at her granddaughter's predicament from whichever outpost of the dearly departed she'd been sent to. Straight to Hell, Michael always joked after listening to a few minutes of Granny's vicious gossip.

Aisling thought of Michael and the Paul Costelloe silk tie she'd proudly left on his side of the bed for their anniversary the week before. She put the Visa receipt carefully on the table, sank her head onto her hands, and closed her eyes.

Twelve years ago this month, on a glorious sunny morning, Aisling Maguire had carefully dressed in a white lace gown and placed a coronet of white roses on her hair for her marriage to Michael Moran, the ambitious young journalist she'd adored since the first time she set eyes on his handsome face.

It had been a wonderful wedding. Mam had held her tight, tears in her eyes as she whispered, 'I hope you'll be happy, darling.' She and her new husband had run out of the hotel to find Michael's rusty old Renault carefully decorated with toilet rolls and tin cans, courtesy of his pals on the paper's soccer team.

That had been the best day of her life, until the crisp November morning Phillip and Paul had been born after ten difficult hours of labour. Exhausted and drained, she lay back in the bed with her babies in her arms while Michael smiled down at her, an expression of amazement on his face.

When Phillip's tiny hand curled around his father's little finger, Michael had actually cried before sitting down on the

8

bed and putting strong arms around his family, his wet cheek against Aisling's. Babies grasped fingers instinctively. She knew that. She'd read reams of mother-and-child literature. But she didn't say a word and let her husband believe that Phillip was holding his father's hand.

Just a few days before, she had dusted the ornate silver frame holding a group picture of the wedding. Her parents stared stonily at the camera in contrast to Michael's father and mother who had both developed a fit of the giggles during the photographs. Who'd have guessed that the Morans would stick it out for only twelve years instead of "til death us do part'. Yes, death, or another woman.

'I knew you'd make a mess of your marriage,' she could hear her father saying maliciously, his gaze contemptuous as he looked at the daughter who never quite managed to please him. 'You never could do anything right.'

Tears welled up in Aisling's eyes and spilled down her cheeks onto her faded blue sweatshirt. It had belonged to Michael and she could remember him wearing it the summer he laid the patio himself after getting expensive French windows installed. She could see him now, sweat dampening his dark hair, a look of concentration on his face as he lifted another slab into place, expertly tapping it in with a hammer.

Maybe this is all a mistake, she thought helplessly. She got up to clear the breakfast table as she did every morning. Mechanically she wiped the toast crumbs onto a plate and carefully pushed the expanded packet of Rice Krispies back into their box. No matter how hard she tried to convince the boys to eat porridge, they insisted on Coco Pops or Rice Krispies day in, day out. Don't forget to buy cereal, she reminded herself, her mind slipping into housekeeping mode.

Once, she knew more about motor insurance than breakfast cereals, more about the age loading on a ten-year-old Porsche than on the dietary requirements of ten-year-old boys. Thirteen years ago, in the bustling insurance company on O'Connell Street, she had practically run one section of the motor department for months. When the department supervisor left abruptly for a better job, Aisling was asked to take over and she didn't hesitate.

Now, she sometimes wondered how she'd done it all. How she'd run her division calmly and capably, responsible for twelve people and thousands of accounts. She'd actually enjoyed it into the bargain. It had been a challenge for Aisling Maguire, career girl, but a terrifying prospect for Aisling Moran, housewife. She had always planned to go back to work when the twins were old enough but somehow, the longer she stayed at home, the harder it was to think about entering the job market again.

Delighted with his well-run home, beautifully cooked meals and happy, well-turned-out boys clamouring for fatherly attention when he got home from work, Michael never gave Aisling the push she required to get her back at work. As the years went by and their money problems shrank, there was enough money to pay for a childminder should Ash want to get a job. But why bother?

'The boys need you, darling,' he'd said every time she mentioned getting a job. 'Just because they're at school doesn't mean they don't need their mother when they get home, does it? Anyway, my secretary never stops moaning about leaving her three to her mother and every second Monday she's in late because one of them has a temperature or a cold or something. Be grateful you don't *have* to work!' he'd invariably add, obviously not counting running a house as work.

He was probably right, Aisling would sigh, familiar with the problems of working mothers courtesy of the magazines she loved to read. Every second page had a different story about women stuck in the endless cycle of work, kids and housework, with Saturdays spent cooking giant lasagnes to jam into the freezer. Michael was right. She was lucky he earned enough so she didn't need to work.

They only argued about it once, when Aisling's sister Sorcha, unbearably smug thanks to a recent promotion in the

London bank where she worked, asked why Aisling was letting her brain rot by sitting at home every day.

'I can't believe she said that to me,' Aisling said angrily in the car on the way home. 'She treats me like a second-class citizen because I'm not managing a bank or something. How dare she say that! I'd like to see *her* running a home and looking after the boys. I was working when that little bitch was still in primary school!'

'Don't mind her,' Michael said evenly. 'She's just jealous because you've got a husband, two lovely sons and a nice home. She'd kill to be married, not that any man would be stupid enough to take her. Anyway,' he took a hand off the steering wheel to pat Aisling's knee, 'you'd hate to go out to work. Everything's changed since you worked. I mean, where would you start?'

Aisling was incensed. 'What do you mean "where would you start"?' she demanded.

'You couldn't expect to just walk into a good job after seven years of housekeeping,' he said bluntly. 'You haven't any office skills any more, have you? Being able to make a perfect quiche isn't much good when you need a degree to get *any* job these days.'

She didn't speak all the way home, silently fuming. Michael waited until she climbed into bed before attempting to make up.

'Darling, you know the twins would hate a childminder, don't you? Just because they're at school, doesn't mean they don't need their mum.' He nuzzled her neck, planting soft kisses on her collarbone before moving down to kiss the sensitive skin between her breasts. 'You don't *need* to work, darling,' he murmured. 'I'll look after you.'

Aisling resigned herself to being a full-time housewife. When the twins were older, she dedicated herself to a series of gourmet cooking courses until she could whip up salmon *en croûte* with the best of them and make strawberry *millefeuilles* with her eyes closed. When she'd had her fill of cookery, she turned her hand to needlework and, within a year, the dining-room chairs boasted intricate tapestry seat covers of golden sunflowers glowing in a midsummer sun.

By the time she'd finished the decorating techniques course, the house was a riot of rag-rolled walls, sponged radiators and ivy-leaf stencilling. Michael liked to joke that she'd stencil him if he sat still for long enough. Short of doing a brain surgery course, there wasn't much else that the adult education syllabus could offer her.

And here she was, still stuck in the kitchen with a mountain of ironing, the breakfast dishes to do and the knowledge that her husband was cheating imprinted on her brain. Being a dab hand with hollandaise sauce didn't stop your man from straying.

Please let it be a mistake, God. Of course, it could be some silly misunderstanding. I mean, I'd know if he was seeing someone else, wouldn't I?

He could have bought the underwear for *her* as a late anniversary present. He could be planning a surprise and, maybe, he meant her to find the receipt as a teaser. Then she remembered the flowers and the large box of chocolates he'd given her.

Flowers from a garage shop. He'd thrust them into her hands with a quick kiss on the cheek. Those multicoloured bouquets with not enough chrysanthemums or carnations to make a decent arrangement were always stacked outside garages for last-minute gifts. And that's just what her anniversary present had been – a last-minute gift.

Well, she could certainly arrange even the most stingy bouquet beautifully with the help of her last Christmas present, a large book on flower arranging which had obviously been at the top of the Christmas-gift-for-Granny pile in Eason's when Michael had raced in to do his last-minute shopping.

'Flowers! They're lovely,' she said, not even vaguely surprised that her husband had only remembered it was their anniversary when he was filling the car with petrol on the way home from work. He'd never been much of a man for carefully thought-out presents. So how had he overcome this particular blind spot so spectacularly in Dublin's most expensive underwear shop?

It was unbelievable. Aisling shook her head as she thought of Michael with another woman, his naked body in someone else's arms, his mouth kissing another woman's lips, his eyes dark with desire. Did he murmur her name in the same husky voice he used when it was Aisling in his arms?

Who was this other woman? What did she look like? Questions bubbled in her mind as she tried to picture her rival. She was probably slim, beautiful and clever, with a high-profile job and conversational abilities beyond the special offers on bananas in Crazy Prices that week.

How did this happen to them? Never in a million years would she have dreamed that Michael could sleep with another woman, could betray their marriage.

Passionate affairs happened to people in Fiona and Pat Finucane's world where getting divorced and finding another partner was as easy as ordering a bottle of champagne at the most expensive restaurant in town.

But she didn't want to look for another man, a younger version of Michael. She had fallen in love with him thirteen years before and didn't want to replace him. But what if he wanted to replace her?

She squirted washing-up liquid into the sink and let a jet of hot water create a froth of soft bubbles. Plunging her gloveless hands into the sudsy warmth, she rinsed cups, plates and bowls from the boys' breakfast. It was the same routine every weekday; she listened to the Gerry Ryan radio show as she dried the dishes and stacked them away. But today it made her heart sink to the pit of her stomach.

Every part of her life, every mundane task in the family home, was suddenly threatened by the existence of some other woman, someone Michael had gone to bed with.

Aisling stopped clearing up and tried to focus her muddled thoughts. No, this could not be happening. He loved her. They were married! He couldn't go off with someone else, wouldn't

13

go off with someone else. For God's sake, he roared with laughter when she told him Fiona's latest gossip about her cheating acquaintances.

Michael wouldn't betray her. She was jumping to conclusions. That was it. There was probably some perfectly reasonable explanation. Suddenly hopeful again, Aisling realised that there was one way to find out what was going on. If Michael bought anything with his credit card, he filed away the statement. He kept several accordion folders in his wardrobe where he kept bills, bank statements, birth certs and, of course, credit card statements.

Aisling untied the ribbons at the top of the first folder with trembling hands and rifled through the alphabetical sections looking for credit card receipts. At first she found nothing but bank statements and paid gas and electricity bills, neatly filed with a red pen marking 'Paid' on every one.

She tackled the second file, searched quickly through the Cs for credit cards and then onto V for Visa. And there they were, wedged in between a sheaf of medical insurance forms.

Aisling carefully removed the familiar credit card statements and spread them onto the soft beige bedroom carpet. The bloody cat was shedding hair again, she thought absently.

It didn't take long to find the debit for Lingerie de Paris. Unfortunately, it was nestled in between other, equally damning expenses which brought a lump to Aisling's throat.

Silk knickers followed numerous debits for costly meals in Dublin's trendiest restaurants, places she'd never been to. And then she found a debit to Jurys Inns, the plush hotel built near Christ Church Cathedral. The date, two days before their anniversary.

She stared at it blankly. Michael was never any good at remembering dates, but the tenth of June stood out in Aisling's mind. Phillip had picked up some sort of stomach bug and came home from school with a temperature. She had spent most of the afternoon bringing him to the bathroom where he tried to be sick sitting on his mother's lap like a fractious four-year-old. Typically, Michael had been in London. He was meeting bosses of the newspaper group's sister paper for discussions on the supplement. He wasn't due home until the next evening.

By the time the doctor had arrived at the house, Paul had started being sick and Aisling wasn't feeling too good herself. Three Maxalon injections later, the boys were sleeping soundly under their matching Manchester United duvet covers. She was curled up on the settee feeling washed out, miserable and with a sore arm, courtesy of Dr Lynch and his syringe.

'Look on the bright side,' Fiona said encouragingly when she phoned after spotting the doctor's car parked outside the Morans'. 'A twenty-four-hour bug is better than a weekend in a health farm, you're bound to lose a few pounds!'

'Fiona, you're mad, do you know that?' laughed Aisling. 'Only you would think about losing weight when you're staring at the inside of the toilet bowl.'

'But I made you laugh, didn't I?' her friend demanded. 'Laughing is essential for helping people recover from all sorts of illnesses. That's why I always phone up Pat's bitch of a sister when I'm sick. She's a complete hypochondriac. Ten minutes of listening to her blather on about colonic irrigation or the latest disorder she *thinks* she has after reading one of those health magazines has me in stitches.

'It's a psychological thing, it's the thought of sounding like a hypochondriac that does it. I think, "Do I sound like that?" and I feel better immediately!'

'Maybe I should give her a ring,' Aisling remarked. 'The twins aren't terribly talkative tonight and even the cat has gone out scouting for boyfriends.'

'Where's Michael?'

'In London with the editor and the managing director. They're discussing the supplement with the UK paper's MD – in between eating in the sort of restaurants that sends Egon Ronay into spasms of delight. He rang me earlier to say he'd just stopped off in the hotel to change his clothes before they went out to eat.

'He said they were going to that really plus restaurant, San Lorenzo's,' she added.

'Lucky old Michael,' remarked Fiona. 'They're always AWOL for the messy bits of child-rearing, aren't they? Pat practically vanished when Nicole had that awful gastroenteritis a few years ago, in case he might be called upon to do something involving nappies.'

'I know,' Aisling muttered, her mind on Michael's brusque phone call. 'I just wish he'd sounded a bit more sympathetic, though. Here I am stuck at home with the kids sick and he's off having a whale of a time. He couldn't talk to me for more than two minutes on the phone.' She broke off abruptly, suddenly feeling that she was being childish.

'You poor old thing,' Fiona answered, in the soft tone she reserved for her adored six-year-old daughter, Nicole. 'I'm going to pop down to the video shop and get you a nice, slushy, romantic film so you can sit in comfortable misery, all right? And when you're talking to Michael later, tell him you expect a bit of pampering and a huge bottle of perfume from the duty-free to cheer you up!'

'Well, I don't think he'll be ringing because he said I should go to bed early and that he mightn't be in 'til late,' Aisling answered.

'Leave a message for him, Ash. Most of those business hotels have an answering machine for each room. You can tell him you're miserable, make him feel guilty, he'll ring you back.'

'I don't know where he's staying,' Aisling realised. 'I forgot to ask.' Immediately she regretted saying it. She didn't want Fiona to know that Michael could go away without telling her where he was staying. It made it sound as if she and Michael didn't talk. And of course they did.

'Never mind,' Fiona said a little too briskly. 'He'll probably be in so late that he'd just wake you up if he rang. I'll get that video for you. I won't be long.'

An hour later, Aisling was watching *Sleepless in Seattle*. Flossie sat Buddha-like on her lap and a hot whiskey, courtesy

16

of Pat's twelve-year-old Scotch, was in her hand. She didn't sleep much that night, lonely in the big double bed.

She spent a feverish night, tossing and turning, dreaming of mad surgeons racing after her waving syringes the size of hockey sticks. She woke up with the feeling of unease her nightmares always brought. She lay exhausted in bed watching the red digits on the bedside clock-radio tick inexorably towards seven. Why hadn't Michael phoned her from London?

But he didn't phone and, when he returned home that evening, he was so moody and quiet that she simply assumed some calamity had befallen the supplement.

'Everything's fine,' he answered testily when she dared to ask. 'I'm just tired after a day of meetings and a long business dinner.'

The effortless way he had lied hit her now like a punch in the stomach. No stuttering or stumbling. He'd lied with the calm of an accomplished liar. He hadn't even told her what hotel he was staying in and she'd never even thought to ask. Of course, if she *had* asked, he would, no doubt, have pointed out that she shouldn't bother trying to ring him because he was out at a business dinner.

Some dinner, she thought, dropping the credit card statement and scanning the next one. Who had he snuggled up with in Jury's when she was holding their ten-year-old twins' heads over the downstairs toilet? A few entries further down she came across a bill from Interflora which was for enough flowers to fill a stadium if the price was anything to go by.

Then it hit her. Fiona knew. She had to. Why else would she have asked where Michael was staying that night? Why would she have tried to gloss over the whole incident so quickly?

And why else would she have started that strange conversation about a couple of friends who were splitting up, even though Aisling had never met them? It had been the previous week when they had been grocery shopping together after lunch in the Merrion Inn.

They were wheeling their shopping trolleys past the frozen

food department when Fiona started talking about the latest husband she knew who was straying from the marital path.

'I can always tell,' pronounced Fiona. 'That man never did a day's exercise in his life and suddenly he was jogging around the track in UCD three times a week. What does that tell you, Aisling?'

She didn't wait for an answer. 'And the clothes! God, you should have seen him at that party in the Ryans' place last Christmas. He was wearing jeans at a cocktail party, can you believe it? I asked him had he joined Bon Jovi, but he wasn't at all amused.'

Fiona had paused long enough to fling a brace of Lean Cuisines into her trolley before continuing. 'Wives never notice, you see. All that extra grooming, workouts and new bikini underpants go totally unnoticed at home and, before you can say "affair", that's another marriage down the tubes.'

She had given Aisling a long, meaningful look as she spoke, a can't-you-read-between-the-lines look, Aisling realised now.

'Pat would never dream of playing away,' Fiona said once in an unguarded moment. 'He knows which side his bread is buttered,' she added. Fiona knew her husband would never stray in case he risked his partnership in her father's lucrative law firm.

As she smoothed out another statement and searched for yet more proof of her husband's lies, Aisling numbly realised that Michael had always buttered his own bread.

Her father had worked for an accountancy firm for twenty years and retired with just enough money to keep himself and her mother. Even if he had been able to help her husband in his meteoric rise to the top, Michael would never have accepted that help. He was a brilliant young journalist with his eyes firmly set on the top of the ladder and he had never needed family links to give him an entrée into the corridors of power.

Now, at the age of forty, he was deputy editor of one of the most successful Sunday newspapers in the country and, if his star continued to rise, he could soon be editor of one of the paper's sister titles.

But she might not be the woman by his side when he did it. Who would?

She dropped the last of Michael's statements onto the floor and rose to her feet slowly. She picked up the telephone by his side of the bed, not really seeing the empty orange juice glass he'd brought upstairs that morning and left for her to clear away. Under normal circumstances, she would have made the bed by this time and would probably be busy hoovering out the twins' room, tidying the books, comics and toys they carelessly abandoned on the floor.

Right now she didn't care if the whole house fell apart. She simply had to know what was happening, who Michael was seeing. And, maybe, find out that it was all some horrible mistake.

CHAPTER TWO

Fiona answered on the second ring.

'I was just about to phone you,' she exclaimed, 'to see if you fancied a trip into Dun Laoghaire to check out the shops. There's this lovely John Rocha suit I noticed in a magazine at the weekend and I've decided to splash out. We could have our coffee there, couldn't we? Or are you on bread and water for tonight?'

'I can't go shopping now, Fiona.' Aisling's voice quivered. She'd planned to be stoical, but Fiona's warm and friendly voice made her want to sit down and sob.

'I don't know what to do . . . It's about Michael,' she managed to say hoarsely. 'You knew, didn't you?'

Aisling could hear her friend's sharp intake of breath down the phone and for a brief moment she held her breath, hoping there was some reasonable explanation for the hotel bill, the flowers and the underwear.

'Knew what?'

'That he's having an affair.'

'Oh God, Ash. I wish you'd never found out.'

As she looked out the window at Fiona's perfectly manicured garden across the road, Aisling was amazed to see everything looking exactly the way it had the day before. The grass neatly shorn like a barber's number one cut, the petunias spreading out greedily in between the tiny fragrant lavender bushes. How could everything look so damn normal when her life had just suffered a cataclysmic upheaval?

'I'm sorry, so sorry,' repeated Fiona. 'I just didn't know how to tell you, how to find the words. I hoped it would blow over before you found out. That's the best way, he gets it out of his system and you never find out,' she added prosaically. 'I thought it was better not to say anything. But I kept wishing

I'd never seen them, because I felt so disloyal to you.'

'Just tell me who it is,' Aisling interjected, her tone plead-ing. 'Just tell me . . .'

Fiona paused and then spoke again, her voice strong and calm, as though reassuring a small child. 'It doesn't mean anything, Ash, honestly. They all do it, and then they get over it. Remember that, OK?'

'They all do it,' repeated Aisling hysterically. 'Is that sup-posed to make me feel better?'

'No. It's just supposed to make you feel less alone,' Fiona answered. 'You don't know her,' she continued in the same calm vein. 'Her name is Jennifer Carroll and she works in an advertising agency. I only recognised her because she's at every bloody party we go to. You know the type, goes to the opening of an envelope if she thinks she'll get her picture in the social columns. Are you all right, Ash?'

'Yes. Go on.'

'I went out to dinner with the girls from the tennis club when Pat was away last autumn.'

Fiona hesitated for a moment before continuing. 'Michael was in Le Caprice with this dark-haired woman. I thought it was something to do with the paper. Well, he meets so many different people. I didn't think anything of it at first, really.'

'What happened?' Aisling's voice was remarkably steady as she spoke. Fiona couldn't see her digging her nails into the palm of her right hand, clenching her fist as though her life depended on it.

'They were sitting at an out-of-the-way table, but I could still see them,' explained Fiona. 'He kissed her and it just wasn't a platonic type of kiss, you know? When I thought about what she was wearing, I put two and two together. You don't go out for a business dinner wearing a dress with slits practically up to your navel. God, men are all the same, aren't they?'

She paused and Aisling knew she was lighting a cigarette, those long, dark menthol cigarettes that looked faintly ridicu-lous and smelled like burning Polos. Michael always laughed

21

at them, calling them poseurs' cigarettes and asked why she didn't smoke real ones, like the Marlboros he was trying to give up.

'Fiona, why didn't you say something?' Aisling asked.

'I didn't know how to tell you. What could I say?' her friend answered quietly. 'That your bastard of a husband was cheating on you as publicly as he could? That he didn't seem to care who saw him and his bloody girlfriend because he knew that you'd never find out, stuck in your little wifey world?'

Aisling sat with the receiver in one hand as she stared blankly outside.

'I'm coming over,' Fiona said quickly. 'We need a huge cup of tea and a good talk.'

The phone clicked in Aisling's ear and she put it down slowly before turning automatically towards the dressing table to put some lipstick on. As she twisted up the tube of pink lipstick she stopped and looked at herself in the mirror. A pale face with serious eyes stared back, the startling blue irises diminished by pupils enlarged with misery. Her eyes had always been her best feature, but lately she hadn't bothered with make-up. Without mascara to darken her fair lashes, her eyes were undefined and pale in her bare face.

As always nowadays, her unruly light brown, long hair was tied back with a red scrunchie. The combination of no make-up, starkly tied-back hair and a loose sweatshirt, which did nothing to flatter her generous curves, made her look tired and worn. She stared long and hard at herself in the mirror.

She remembered the summer she had first met Michael, when her hair was long and bleached with strands of gold from ten days on an idyllic Greek island and her skin glowed thanks to hours basking in the glorious Mediterranean sun.

He had called her beautiful then and never stopped wanting to touch her skin and kiss her lips, putting his arms possessively around her golden shoulders when they walked through the streets of Corfu town.

As she held her lank hair away from her face, Aisling

wished she could recapture that distant Greek summer and feel young and pretty again. Wouldn't it be wonderful not to feel thirty-five and boring, another frumpy housewife with no prospects, no waistline and a preoccupied husband. God knows, there were plenty of women like her out there. She saw them all the time in the supermarket, listlessly pushing trolleys full of fuel for teenagers and husbands who were never home.

She'd never wanted to become one of them, one of the women who sat on the edge of the sofa at parties trying hard to listen and blend in, trying to think of something funny to say while their more confident sisters fitted in perfectly.

'Hit me if I ever turn out like that, won't you?' she'd told Michael after their engagement party. His matronly cousin had bored her to tears with advice about the right washing machine.

'Don't worry, darling,' he'd laughed, 'you're never going to turn into an Elsie, I promise!'

But she had. Well, sort of. Maybe she didn't discuss the advantages of a Zanussi as opposed to a Whirlpool when they went out, but she certainly didn't fit in the way she used to. And Michael knew it.

That was the hardest thing about going out to parties or dinners these days; being aware of Michael looking at her distantly across the room as if she had failed some secret test. She hated sitting around a dinner table with two or three glamorous career women sparkling around Michael and vying for his attention, while she sat in isolation, too self-conscious to chat to the men placed beside her. No wonder he'd wanted another woman.

She wasn't beautiful, particularly clever or even good at some high-powered job. She was a housewife and, even though that's what he'd wanted her to be a few years ago, that's not what he wanted now.

Maybe if she'd stayed the woman he married, that enthusiastic girl who'd walked blindly through life, hoping for the best instead of settling into domestic bliss like Ma in Little

23

House on the Prairie, maybe then he would have still loved her.

She looked at least ten years older than she really was with her pale, slightly plump face and the beginnings of a double chin. But she had finally decided to do something about it. Without breathing a word to Michael, she had started a diet. Not one of her diet on Monday, stuff your face on Tuesday diets, but a proper diet. She had decided that this was the real diet, the one which would change her life. That, however, was last week.

Sadly, she dropped the lipstick onto the lace-covered dressing table. What was the point, she asked herself? Why bother trying to look better now? He had gone and found someone else anyway.

'Ash, let me in,' Fiona roared up at the open bedroom window. 'I've brought the Hobnobs, darling. What more does a woman need!'

An hour later, Aisling was sitting in the passenger seat of Fiona's sleek black Nissan NX as her friend expertly manoeuvred the car into a parking space in the Frascati Centre.

'Don't back out on me now,' warned Fiona, climbing out of the car and slamming the door with a careless bang. 'You're going to look stunning tonight if it kills both of us!'

It just might do that, thought Aisling to herself as her friend frogmarched her towards the expensive boutique she'd always avoided in the chic Blackrock shopping centre. She had been looking forward to the launch party for months now, eager to meet the team of journalists she had heard so much about from Michael in the past year but had never met.

Michael had been working late more and more. The odd newsroom parties seemed to have dried up along with any chitchat at the Morans' kitchen table. Working late my ass, Aisling growled to herself as she followed her friend into the shop.

'Shopping is the only cure for a broken heart,' Fiona continued gaily, slim brown arms outstretched to rifle through racks of expensive little black numbers.

In a daze thanks to a five-milligram Valium, Aisling moved sedately towards the party dresses, separating the hangers with totally steady fingers. She was beginning to feel quite good, happy almost. Something sexy, she smiled inwardly, fingering the rich brocade and crêpe outfits, looking for a dress to knock the spots off Michael's bloody fancy woman. Aisling knew that the Valium was giving her an unrealistic high, but she simply didn't care and sank into the numb happiness she felt flooding her head.

For a day that had started out in the worst possible way, it was certainly improving, Aisling thought with a giggle as she picked out a totally unsuitable black velvet sheath and waved it at Fiona.

'You should be on Valium more often,' Fiona remarked, putting the black velvet back on the rack and steering Aisling towards the back of the shop.

'The larger sizes, Modom,' Fiona said with a flourish, plucking a subtle grape-coloured jacket off the rack and holding it up against the other woman.

Generously cut on the hanger, the jacket and its matching flowing skirt seemed to have shrunk on Aisling. She peered out of the changing cubicle self-consciously, not wanting anyone but Fiona to see her.

'Maybe something with a better cut . . .' muttered Fiona, eyes narrowed as she stood back examining the outfit.

'Not better cut. Just bigger,' said Aisling flatly, the Valium giggle gone out of her voice. 'I seem to be getting bigger all the time. No wonder Michael went for, what did you say her name was?'

'Don't torture yourself thinking about her, Aisling,' Fiona answered impatiently.

'I can't help it. I can't stop thinking about her, whatever her name is. But I bet she's slim and glamorous. Am I right?'

'OK, she has a good figure and I suppose you'd call her glamorous. To my mind, she's a bit over the top. You know, all red talons, more make-up than Joan Collins and lots of expensive outfits with too much embroidery and huge gold buttons. Like this sort of thing, actually.' Fiona swiped a short denim jacket out from the rails and held it up against her torso with a grimace.

'I wouldn't be seen dead in this,' she announced. 'Denim and sequins, how passé.'

And I wouldn't fit into it even if I wanted to, thought Aisling despondently. She gazed around at the racks of clothes and wondered if they had a generous size sixteen in anything glamorous.

She hated shopping nowadays. But tonight was going to be different. Tonight she had planned to splash out on something which would make her feel good, make her feel a little like the confident woman Michael married.

She had actually managed to lose three pounds in the last week. One main meal a day, as much black tea or coffee as you liked, brown bread or scones for light meals and lots of fruit and vegetables. 'You won't be hungry on our four-week summer diet!' promised the magazine she'd ripped the diet out of. And she hadn't been hungry at all, apart from the sheer longing for a chocolate digestive with her lunchtime coffee.

Now she wondered if there was any point in trying to lose weight. She had planned to look her best tonight, to make Michael proud of her in front of all the new newspaper staff. The supplement was finally being produced after a year of talking about it. Aisling had decided to jump-start her own life to celebrate Michael's hard work.

She'd wasted far too much time while she wallowed in domestic misery, hidden under masses of laundry and dirty dishes.

Plenty of women worked and looked after a family, she knew that. There was no reason why she shouldn't. It could be just what she needed, Fiona had said encouragingly. Now that the boys were older and were walking to school on their own, there was no excuse for Aisling to stay at home. Surely it couldn't be too hard to get a job and climb out of the rut she'd fallen into?

Sometimes, she felt a pang of nostalgia for her old life. Those carefree days living with Jo in Rathmines, when the two single girls had spent every penny of their wages on clothes, make-up and cheap bottles of wine for parties, seemed idyllic. They worked hard all week and played hard at the weekends, always on the move and ready for the next party. Jo never wanted to climb out of her warm bed on Monday morning, but Aisling was up bright and early, raring to go. Plenty of people complained about working in the cramped insurance office in the city centre, but she had loved it.

Every night of the weekend was party night. During the week, they often went to the pictures if they fancied what was showing in the Stella cinema. Afterwards, they'd buy chips and onion rings to eat in the flat's tiny sitting room while discussing the merits of Robert Redford as opposed to hunky young Richard Gere.

Now Aisling went out only to shop or to bring the kids to school or to have a quick cup of coffee in Fiona's before her friend raced off for a game of tennis or an aerobics class. She often spent the entire day on her own, cooking, polishing and waiting for the twins and Michael to come home and liven up her life.

It was a lonely existence, she realised. Was that all she could expect from the rest of her life? She'd planned to hang up her apron and get a job. But what was the point now?

If she couldn't keep her husband, how could she ever keep a job? Who wanted thirty-five-year-old housewives in their office, anyway? And let's face it, her typing skills weren't amazing ten years ago, so how would she cope with a computer?

All she knew about the world of technology was limited to what she'd learned on a speedy tour of the *News* three years previously when they had finally upgraded their system.

Fifteen minutes watching somebody playing hangman on a computer was hardly what you'd call experience.

Thinking of the paper wrenched her mind back to Michael.

Maybe everyone in the bloody office knew. How could she face Michael's colleagues at the supplement launch party tonight knowing what she did, wondering if everyone there was in on the secret? She wouldn't even have the chance to confront Michael before the party either. He'd told her he wasn't coming home beforehand, adding that Aisling should make her own way there.

Charming, she thought, wondering whether he made his girlfriend get to parties on her own or did he sweep up to her house bearing flowers and offers of X-rated antics in the back of a taxi?

'Ash, try this on,' Fiona's voice broke into her daydream and she stared at the dress her friend was holding up in astonishment.

'Red is perfect for your colouring and with a bit of trollopy crimson lipstick and your hair done, you'll knock them all for six!' Fiona said encouragingly.

Aisling took the dress, a low-cut swirl of red crêpe, into the changing room and held it up to her face. Brighter than anything she'd worn for ages, the rich colour made her pale face seem paler than ever.

'Make-up, Ash, you need make-up,' advised Fiona before pulling the changing cubicle curtain over. 'Does Liz Hurley look like that *without* make-up? See what I mean? All you need is half an hour in front of the mirror and you'll look stunning in that dress.'

As she stared at her reflection in the large mirror, Aisling made a decision. Why not, she thought? If I'm going to face all the people who know what's been going on, I might as well do it in style.

CHAPTER THREE

Bending slightly sideways in her grey swivel chair, Jo reached down and slowly slid the chemist's paper bag out of her briefcase. She was trying to remove it with as little rustling as possible, hoping that Brenda, who was sitting at the opposite desk blowing kisses down the phone to her current boyfriend, wouldn't hear anything.

If only she'd stuck the package in her fake crocodile-skin handbag in the first place, she wouldn't have to smuggle it clandestinely out of her briefcase now. She'd been waiting all morning for the right moment to sneak the distinctive blue and white bag into the toilet without someone demanding to know what she'd been buying in the chemist when they had enough make-up around to cover Claudia Schiffer from head to toe.

That was one of the main problems of working in such a small office, and the office of a women's magazine into the bargain, she thought ruefully. Everyone knew everything about you and, being inveterate shoppers, they wanted to know what you'd bought when you came back from the shops at lunchtime.

Personal matters were totally public in the cramped offices of *Style*, where the only privacy to be had was when you locked the door of the tiny toilet and shower cubicle. Everyone who worked in what the interior designer described as a '. . . relaxing contemporary open-plan workspace . . .' could listen to your most intimate phone calls, could hear you talking to the bank about your overdraft, and knew when you'd forgotten your mother's birthday.

What's more, they were all endlessly curious about shopping, shopaholism being the main qualification necessary for working in a women's magazine. Entire lunch-breaks could be

spent oohing and aahing over a sale bargain hat for that
wedding or a new babygro for baby Jessica.

Jo wanted to keep this latest purchase to herself. A pregnancy testing kit was not the sort of thing you could hold up
and scream, 'Look what I got for a tenner in Marks and
Spencer's this morning!' Absolutely not.

It was all so unexpected, such a surprise. Jo was still too
stunned to know what she thought about it. She certainly
didn't want the rest of the office to know anything about it
until she knew whether she was pregnant or not. Or until she
knew how she felt about being pregnant, which was more to
the point. God, it was confusing.

She sighed, jammed the paper bag into her open handbag
and closed her eyes briefly. It wasn't as if she'd had much time
to think about being pregnant. She'd only worked out that her
period was late when she opened the phone bill that morning.

Late for work as usual. She was trying to gulp down a cup
of coffee while opening her post and sticking folders into her
tattered old briefcase when she came upon the phone bill.
Astronomical, what else? All that time ringing Sligo talking to
her mother and the boys. She was about to jam it behind the
coffee jar when she stopped herself.

Write it down, you moron, she muttered, remembering
how very irritating it had been to have to pay the phone
company a reconnection fee the last time she'd filed a bill
behind the coffee and forgotten about it.

Three pens had to be thrown in the bin before she found
one that worked and opened her diary to write, 'Pay phone
bill' in the following week. And then she noticed it. Or rather
didn't notice it.

The capital P which stood for period wasn't there. Details
of her fluctuating bank balance were noted along with
appointments for interviews and a green biro squiggle she
couldn't read. But no mention of her period. She flicked
through the pages rapidly.

'Omigod,' Jo muttered. 'Omigod!' Unless her contact lenses
needed to be replaced, she hadn't had a period since the

second week in April and it was now the beginning of June. She had either stopped menstruating because she was menopausal – unlikely at the age of thirty-four – or she was pregnant. But it couldn't be. They always used condoms *and* spermicide, so how could she be pregnant?

She'd bought the pregnancy testing kit at the chemist across the road from her apartment, but she was running too late to do the test at home.

Which was why she was waiting for the right moment to slip nonchalantly into the office loo without catching anyone's eye. Well, it wasn't the sort of news to broadcast to your colleagues when your brain was still reeling from the shock and your boyfriend was still blissfully unaware of impending fatherhood.

She thought of Richard: clever, witty, good-looking in a boyish way, a talented photographer and an inveterate charmer of women. Of all the words you could use to describe her boyfriend of the last two years, fatherly would have been last on her list. Well, maybe conventional would be last on the list but fatherly wouldn't be far behind.

Three years older than she was, he looked as if he was heading towards thirty, never mind forty, and thought that settling down was something other people did – when they were ten years older than he was.

The thought of being married with 2.5 kids, a semi with a conservatory and an estate car filled him with the dread most men reserved for having their mothers-in-law to stay. At the mention of the word commitment, his eyes glazed over and he would pick up the remote control and switch channels rapidly, searching for something which involved a muddy field, a football or a newscast with in-depth sports coverage.

Of course, when you were a sports photographer you *had* to keep up with current sporting events, but one tiny piece of Jo's mind was beginning to think that the manic channel-hopping which ensued the last time she talked about buying a place together was a ploy to avoid talking about settling down.

She'd known what he was like when she first met him, shortly after he'd given up his secure and pensionable job with one newspaper to set up a sports agency with a couple of other like-minded, risk-taking photographers.

'It was driving me out of my mind working for just one paper.' He told her about his low boredom threshold as they drank red wine and completely ignored the press-photographer awards ceremony going on around them. 'This way, we're our own bosses and we control what we do and what we don't do.'

'Absolutely,' breathed Jo, fascinated by his ambition and his Scandinavian blondness. She thanked God that she'd agreed to make up a party of ten people to cheer on *Style*'s fashion photographer as he accepted his award.

She'd nearly cried off and stayed in to watch *Coronation Street* instead. There is a God after all, she thought happily. She wondered whether she should risk going to the loo to reapply some Crimson Kiss lipstick and adjust her strapless dress in case someone else nabbed the most fascinating man she'd met in years. No, she decided firmly.

Who cared if her boobs were about to spill out of the figure-hugging hot red dress she'd borrowed from the fashion cupboard at work?

Her rippling tortoiseshell hair was piled on top of her head in a haphazard manner, designed to suggest she'd just got out of bed. Mascara emphasised her dark eyes beautifully and only the most observant onlooker would notice the wobbly dark line above her lashes where the hand holding her eyeliner pen had slipped. Jo knew she looked good and she wanted this fair-haired hunk to know it too.

'I can't stand people who just sit still and let life happen to them. I want to *make* it happen, I want that excitement and that energy,' Richard said passionately. 'It's what keeps me going.'

Gazing deeply into his eyes, Jo fell for him like a ton of bricks, low boredom threshold and all. She should have wondered what kind of man would dump a perfectly safe job to run a risky freelance agency. But she hadn't.

She was the sort of individual who woke in the morning with her guts spasming with nerves if she had a difficult interview ahead of her. She found Richard's adventurous spirit intriguing. And frankly, very sexy.

There was something macho about taking such a huge gamble and something equally attractive about realising that his dream had paid off tenfold.

That wasn't enough for Richard, though. Once the agency was making money, he was eager for the next challenge, longing for adventure, while Jo began to yearn for quiet domesticity. He wanted to take up parachuting. She was scared of heights. He signed up for a scuba diving course and gave her a course of diving lessons for her birthday, even though she hated getting water in her eyes. But how could she now complain about the very traits she'd found so exciting in him in the first place?

'Interest rates and conveyancing fees are probably respons- ible for more heart attacks than five pints of Guinness a day, darling,' he'd said only the week before when the most gorgeous cottage in the Wicklow mountains just jumped out of the property pages at her. The picture of the cottage bathed in sunlight made Jo long for the house with twelve-inch-thick stone walls and a box-tree herb garden.

'Darling, you know I love living in the city,' he said, throwing the property pages onto the floor and nuzzling her neck as he breathed in the scent of the vanilla perfume he loved her to wear.

'Anyway, setting up the agency has swallowed up most of my capital and I don't want to take on a mortgage when I can keep renting my flat in Merrion Square for well under the market rate. You'd be mad to sell your apartment so soon after buying it,' he added. 'Let's leave things the way they are.' And they went to bed.

Once Richard had his arms around her, making her feel more turned on and more desirable than any man had been able to do before, she wasn't able to think about anything, never mind buying a house together. All she wanted was his lean body wrapped around hers, his fingers tangled in her hair and his lips gently kissing her skin. When he murmured *exactly* what he was going to do just before he did it, she melted into a quiver of anticipation.

His voice did the most amazing things to her head, not to mention the effect he was having lower down. And when they finally came together in a surge of passion, the intensity of her orgasm made Jo shudder, and wonder how she'd ever thought she'd enjoyed lovemaking with anyone else.

'We're wonderful in bed together,' he said afterwards. It was amazing the way they were perfectly in tune in bed, even though they weren't so in tune out of it, Jo thought to herself.

As she was about to throw a bundle of old papers in the bin a few days later, she looked longingly at the property section and wondered was she mad to think about settling down. Richard was happy the way things were, so why wasn't she? His bachelor pad in the city centre was perfect for a man who liked nothing better than to sway the few short yards from Dublin's trendy hostelries to his front door on a Saturday night.

Trips to Anfield and Wembley where nightclubbing the night away was par for the course, this was Richard's idea of fun. Not getting up for the three a.m. feed.

Would he want their baby, she asked herself? You could go round and round in circles and never figure it out. What was the point in dreaming up problems for the future until she knew for sure?

Ten minutes in the loo would tell her for certain. She looked around at the empty desks abandoned in the lunch-time rush.

The only person in the editorial office was Brenda and she was thankfully otherwise engaged, telling Mark – or was it Kevin – about the lingerie catalogue she'd been perusing that morning, ostensibly for a feature on mail-order underwear.

'You'd really like the black bra with those teeny, weeny knickers,' Brenda purred down the phone, no doubt sending poor Mark/Kevin into a frenzy with the seduction techniques she'd honed after three years of industriously filling in 'How Sexy Are You?' questionnaires in *Cosmopolitan*.

At least Brenda was too busy to listen, thought Jo, as she psyched herself up to do the test. She gave up pretending to study a feature article on the latest tanning creams and had just picked up the small elegant handbag which went with nothing she owned, when she was rudely interrupted. Dropping the bag like a shot, Jo straightened up and smiled broadly at the editor.

'Got a minute, Jo?' inquired Rhona McNamara. She perched one well-upholstered hip on the desk and rearranged the silken folds of her expensive Jaeger skirt.

'Of course. What is it?' With as much nonchalance as she could muster, Jo casually scooped up the magazines from her desk and dropped them on top of the paper bag which was sticking out the top of her handbag in a very noticeable manner. You couldn't do anything personal around here without someone landing on top of you, she cursed inwardly.

'What do you think about changing the format of the new beauty products section? I've been thinking that we should get readers to test certain things and give marks out of ten.'

Rhona's fingers flew about as she spoke, a habit which would make the casual observer think she was using sign language. In fact, she was just trying to keep her hands occupied until they got hold of her next cigarette.

'I think that's a great idea,' Jo answered. Obviously, she couldn't say that she didn't give a damn who tested the bloody make-up when she was faced with this momentous, no *huge* event in her life. When a pregnancy testing kit was burning a hole in her handbag just aching to be used.

'It's a fresh way of looking at products and, since we're all so blasé about lotions and potions, it would be marvellous to get readers to give their opinion about things,' Rhona said in a voice which required some sort of reaction.

'Er . . . I'll include an advert for guinea pigs on the beauty page, although I'll have to drop something to fit it in.' Jo started rooting through the piles of paper on her desk for the dummy or advance pages of the beauty section.

With only two days to go before printing, the July edition of *Style* was nearly totally finished and any changes had to be agreed and inserted within the next twenty-four hours.

Jo still had an entire piece to write about packing for your summer holidays and had managed to leave the ideas she'd jotted down for the article at home.

'D'you know, I haven't been talking to you all week,' Rhona commented, picking up the tanning article and scanning it for mistakes. 'You look a little bit pale, Jo. Are you feeling all right?'

'Fine,' answered Jo as brightly as she could. She raked her dark curls with her fingers and wished she'd bothered with proper make-up on this of all mornings.

'I've had a lot of late nights recently,' she lied, 'and I'm a little tired. Maybe that Elizabeth Arden magic stuff you keep in your desk could give my complexion a bit of a boost?'

Rhona looked at her shrewdly for a moment, taking in her deputy editor's pale, freckled skin, tired brown eyes and un-lipsticked mouth.

Jo took her job as fashion editor very seriously and was nearly always dressed to kill in on-the-knee skirts which showed off her long legs and fitted jewel-coloured jackets which were just perfect for her Monroe-esque curves. She was usually better made-up than Ivana Trump.

Today, she was wearing a fawn-coloured linen ensemble which would have cost an arm and a leg if Jo didn't have a fashion editor's discount at every top shop in Dublin. Chic in the extreme, the effect of the outfit was ruined by the fact that she wasn't wearing more make-up or jewellery and her normally wavy hair had flopped in the June heat. It was very unlike Jo, thought Rhona.

'Come on into my office and we'll have a bitch.' She smiled at Jo, slid off the desk and walked into her tiny office.

It was compact and untidy, with clothes hangers dangling off every nail and magazines, press releases and sticky layout pages covering every available surface. There wasn't enough room to swing a cat in its ten-by-twelve confines.

Rhona's office was, however, blissfully private and a haven for the nicotine-addicted who weren't allowed to smoke anywhere else in the Georgian three-storey house which was home to both *Style* and a tiny secretarial agency.

Jo followed the editor into the untidy room and pushed a clump of plastic-covered dresses to one side of the dusty cream settee which took up at least half of one wall. She plonked herself down tiredly and leaned back into the soft cushions. She levered off her shoes and wondered if this sudden exhaustion was pregnancy or shock.

'Is lover boy wearing you out at home?' Rhona teased, immediately lighting up a cigarette.

Despite herself, Jo blushed. She could feel her face redden and she could also see Rhona looking at her in amazement, cigarette suspended in mid-air as she stared at her deputy with a dumbfounded expression.

How was she going to get out of this one? Jo groaned silently. The woman with whom she'd shared kiss-by-kiss accounts of various lovers over numerous bottles of red wine was not going to believe that just *talking* about sex with Richard would send her blushing to her roots. No way.

Rhona knew her much better than that. Which meant that she was going to have to spill the beans. Only how could she spill anything until she knew for sure?

'Did I say the wrong thing?' Rhona sat down heavily and looked anxiously at her deputy. 'Are you having problems? You know you can always talk to me, Jo, don't you? I don't want to interfere, I just want to help.'

'I don't think you can help me this time,' Jo replied with a small laugh. Here goes, she thought. 'Unless you've been secretly training as an obstetrician and haven't told the rest of us!'

'You're not pregnant, are you?' Rhona squealed. 'Stupid question. Congratulations, Jo! I shouldn't be smoking, should I?' She hastily stubbed out her barely touched Dunhill as though a baby was going to pop out any minute and wail if there was so much as a hint of nicotine in the air.

'Slow down, Rhona. I don't know if I'm pregnant yet. I missed my period this month and it only really hit me this morning so I don't know for sure.' It sounded even stranger actually *saying* it out loud.

'You haven't done a test?' Rhona looked surprised. 'The new ones can tell you if you're pregnant just a day after your period is due.'

'I know, I know.' Jo looked mildly exasperated. 'I was going to do it here, I just didn't want Ms Nosey Parker out there to pick anything up with her radar ears.'

'Fair enough,' Rhona replied. 'I'll send her out for fags and you can pee in privacy . . .'

Rhona stopped mid-sentence and looked Jo straight in the face. 'It is Richard's, isn't it?'

'Of course it bloody is!' Jo said, affronted. 'How many men do you think I'm seeing? One a day and two on Sunday! Come on, Rhona.'

'Sorry, sorry. It's just that you don't seem pleased about it and I just thought, maybe it wasn't his and . . . Forget I said that, please, Jo. I thought you'd be happy if it was Richard's and you seem a little off, you know.'

She leaned over and put her arms around Jo's now tense body, hugging her tightly. 'You know I'm here for you, no matter what happens.'

'Thanks.' Jo stood up, running a ringless hand over her stomach as though she'd be able to tell what lay beneath her linen waistcoat just by touching her belly. What would it be like to feel a baby growing inside her?

Would she feel totally at one with her unborn child, sensitive to every kick and wriggle? If she played her favourite music on the car stereo, would the baby be born liking the same tunes?

Then it came to her with piercing clarity: she wanted this child. She wanted it more than anything she'd ever wanted before, even if Richard didn't. That was the nub of the problem. It was no use wasting time wondering whether he wanted their child, littering her brain with doubts when, all along, she knew what *she* wanted.

She wanted a baby, maybe she had wanted one for years. Trying to be the nineties career woman had meant keeping up the façade of a perfect life, complete with a handsome lover, total independence and a job most women would kill for.

Career women didn't long for babies and a man's pyjamas permanently under the pillows, but suddenly, that's just what Jo wanted.

For once she didn't care if the magazine's publisher demoted her to writing picture captions or gave her job to the horrible, sneaky Emma who was always angling to backstab her way up the career ladder. All she wanted was a beautiful, healthy baby.

'I'm pregnant,' she said aloud, suddenly grinning at Rhona with a smile which lit up her whole face. 'I'm pregnant! I just know it!'

'Well let's send Brenda out for champagne then,' Rhona suggested before hugging Jo to her considerable bosom. 'And for something from the deli. I'm starved.'

'When were you ever not starved?' Jo got up with renewed energy and manoeuvred her feet into her brown suede court shoes.

'I'm going to do the test, to be sure to be sure, if you know what I mean. But I know already. Is that normal?' She looked at Rhona, the mother of three under-tens, for confirmation.

'Absolutely,' answered Rhona. 'I knew I was pregnant the first time because I woke up one morning and couldn't eat a thing, which is not like me, as you know. The day Lynne was born was the happiest day of my life, I always say, mainly because I'd been so sick all the time I was carrying her.'

'I feel fine,' interrupted Jo. 'Hungry actually. I think I need something nutritious to eat, like a Twix.'

'Or a poppy-seed baguette filled with sun-dried tomatoes, Parma ham and chunks of Gruyère washed down with an icy Diet Coke,' said Rhona, who had not been a magazine restaurant reviewer for nothing. 'I'm supposed to be on a diet, but there are only so many things you can do with brown rice and green vegetables,' she added mournfully, thinking of the considerable difference between what she should be eating and what she wanted to eat.

Tall and big-boned, Rhona was always denying herself something in the hope that she'd miraculously turn into a carbon copy of her sleek, younger sister and, more importantly, fit into all the lovely clothes she'd bought for 'when I get thin'.

Sadly, her predilection for all the wrong food meant that she was never going to be anything smaller than a size fourteen. Her 'thin' clothes were getting closer to the second-hand shop every day.

'Brenda,' called Rhona loudly, winking at Jo, 'are you busy? I want you to do something for me.'

Hastily cutting off her steamy conversation, Brenda hurried over to the editor's office with the speed of one hoping to be promoted, while Jo grabbed her handbag and headed for the loo.

By the time she had peed into the tiny tester and put it back into its little plastic case, her heart was thumping along at advanced-aerobics-class level.

She rummaged around for some lipstick in her tiny make-up bag and thought about telling Richard.

She could bring him out to Fitzer's, his favourite restaurant, and tell him the wonderful news over the clam linguini. 'Darling, we're going to have a baby!'

She could see it all in her mind. She would wear the Jasper Conran jacket she'd bought in a discount store in Belfast.

'My darling, that's wonderful!' he'd cry before ordering champagne and toasting their baby. Then they'd go back to her place and plan their future together. A Georgian town house in Dalkey, she daydreamed, with plenty of room for Richard's darkroom and a desk where she could write the novel she was always talking about.

Or maybe an artisan's cottage in Enniskerry, a cross

between *Homes and Gardens* and the Habitat catalogue. Of course, they'd have to get a new bed because Richard's futon wouldn't be suitable for the baby and her ancient double bed was sprouting springs faster than a dodgy biro. There were so many things to buy! She'd better get to Mothercare quickly and get started.

'She's gone. Let me in,' shouted Rhona outside the door.

'Oh Rhona, it's so exciting.' Jo smiled, opened the door and carried the tester into the editor's office as if it was an unexploded bomb. 'I almost can't believe it. Me, a mother! Even saying it sounds strange. What if I'm no good at it,' she asked, suddenly anxious, 'no good at being a mother. Does it just come naturally? I mean, it's not as if I have any real experience of babies or anything. Oh, and what about work? Is it *really* that hard being a working mother?'

Rhona burst out laughing. 'Don't get me started, Jo. You'll learn. I mean, it's not exactly a doddle, I can tell you. First of all,' she started ticking imaginary points off on her fingers, 'you're exhausted and you wonder are you doing everything wrong from feeding to nappy-changing to winding them after their feed.'

'Then, you go to work and leave your precious baby with some woman you're convinced turns into an axe murderer every time you walk out the front door, and then, when your baby walks for the first time, you're not there.

'Ms Axe Murderer is there. You, on the other hand, are listening to some po-faced advertiser telling you that they don't want their anti-wrinkle cream on the opposite page to a feature on how to stop the ravages of time with plastic surgery.' She stopped with a sigh. 'Is there anything else you want to ask?'

'No, just give me a prescription for Prozac and I'll be fine,' said Jo with wide eyes. 'I suppose I never really thought about how difficult it was before. You know me, Rho, I can't walk out the front door without spending half an hour on my hair, throwing at least three outfits on the bed when I'm trying to figure out what look to go for that day and taking another fifteen minutes to do my make-up. It's that liquid eyeliner,' she added. 'It's impossible to get it right.'

'Liquid eyeliner will be the least of your problems, darling, let me tell you. You'll be lucky if you can actually brush your teeth in the morning if your little pet is anything like mine were. And as for leaving three outfits on the bed . . .! Forget it. Five-year-old girls love wearing Mummy's clothes and Mummy's make-up, usually at the same time.

'Believe me, Jo, you won't be long tidying everything you value away from sticky little fingers. It's better now that Susie is finally at school,' she reflected. 'Although she has this thing about Liga biscuits. I still get embarrassed when I think about that time in the Conrad Hotel when I opened my cheque book and it was all glued together with molten Liga.'

'Oh yes, that was a howl and I didn't have any money with me!' Jo started laughing at the memory, and, realising what was in front of her, laughed even harder. 'I can't wait to see Richard when we've got a terrible two-year-old toddling around playing with his Nikons.'

Rhona didn't smile. She'd known Richard from the two years he'd been going out with Jo. She had a rather different vision of his reaction and she didn't find the picture at all amusing.

Without a doubt, Richard would commit murder if he saw any child messing around with any of his possessions. If he stayed around long enough for the child in question to reach the grand old age of two, that was. 'Does he know?' she asked quietly.

'Not yet,' Jo confessed. 'I didn't want to tell him until I was sure. I just wanted it to be between us. But I'm so glad I told you.' She smiled fondly at the other woman.

'Give us a look at the tester then,' demanded Rhona.

Like a magician about to produce a rabbit from a hat, Jo whisked off the plastic lid and gave a whoop of joy.

'Yahoo! I'm pregnant: officially! Just think, Rhona. This is a new life inside me!' She beamed, looking down at her still-slender waist. 'A whole new life in every sense, really.

God, I can't wait to tell Richard.' She sighed. 'He's in Cork today and I know he has the mobile phone with him, but I just can't tell him over the phone.'

'Probably not. Let's go out to lunch, my treat. As you're eating for two officially, you'll need some help in choosing the right foods so you don't end up with a couple of difficult pounds to shift.' Rhona grinned at her slim deputy.

'It must be awful to have to diet,' commiserated Jo. 'I have such a fast metabolism. I mean, I've always been able to eat what I wanted and I never put on weight.'

'Don't remind me. It's not fair to have someone like you on the staff. Able to stuff herself with chocolate and still not have so much as one love handle.'

Rhona picked up her handbag, stuck a pair of sunglasses on her head and held out her hand to haul Jo off the settee. 'Come on, Mummy. Let's toast your wonderful news with some mineral water and something fattening, with cream and chocolate sauce and ooh, I don't know . . .'

'Did I hear you mention food?' Tony, the magazine's chief sub-editor, peered into the office. 'Does anybody ever do anything but talk about food around here any more?' he inquired. 'I was sort of hoping we might work on the magazine this afternoon . . . You know, that A4-sized thing that pays all our wages and currently has a couple of blank pages in it waiting to be filled with gems of wisdom from your pen, Madame Editor?'

'OK.' Rhona took her sunglasses off her head and looked at Jo wryly. 'Back to work, I'm afraid. You and I,' she whispered conspiratorially, 'will celebrate later.'

'Thanks.' Jo smiled as she walked to the door. 'But I just couldn't do any more work today. I'll get one of the girls to finish subbing that article and I'm going home, via the doctor's,' she added with a huge grin. 'Actually, I've got that party at the *News* this evening but I'd love not to go. I want Richard all to myself when I give him the news.'

Rhona couldn't help herself. 'Jo, have you thought about the fact that he mightn't want a baby?' she asked gently.

For a moment Jo's face was blank. Then a broad smile swept over her face, lighting up her eyes and curving her full mouth up in that warm and sexy smile which had been knocking men for six ever since she'd been fifteen. 'Of course he will,' she said confidently. 'He'll be delighted, I promise!'

As she sat in her temperamental Volkswagen trying to exit the Stephen's Green multi-storey car park, Jo was still thinking about what Rhona had said.

OK, so Richard had never been exactly wild about kids. Last Christmas he had refused point blank to go to the all-day party Rhona gave every year where the *Style* staff lounged around their editor's roomy Wicklow farmhouse with glasses of mulled wine, while their offspring watched videos and played on the tiny indoor bouncing castle. That didn't mean he hated children; he just wasn't mad about other people's, that was all.

He told Jo to make his excuses.

'Tell them I'm working, Jo, will you? There's no way I'm going to spend an entire day at a bloody kids' party. I know she's your boss and you have to go, but I don't. You don't really mind, do you, darling?' he wheedled.

Once Richard had decided not to do something, nothing on earth could make him change his mind. Jo went on her own.

The party had been a huge success although somebody had accidentally turned the cooker off and the coq au vin was icy and virtually raw when the guests arrived.

Rhona's husband Ted had returned from a booze-buying session at the local off-licence with five extra people and no diet tonic, but nothing could spoil the day.

After downing a super-strength cocktail Jo had mixed up for her with a bit of just about everything from the drinks cabinet, Rhona relaxed enough to serve beans and sausages. Sick of eating every type of turkey dish possible during Christmas, everyone wolfed down their food and had a whale of a time.

Jo really wished that Richard had come after all. But there

44

wasn't much time for introspection with *Style*'s receptionist, Annette, perched tipsily on the arm of Jo's chair and a hysterical conversation about the rumoured sexual tendencies of the most pious newscaster on the TV going on all around her.

He'd have loved it, Jo thought a little sadly as she gave a corner of cheesy Pringle to Mutt, Rhona's slavering black and white spaniel whose main preoccupation in life was food.

For some reason, that picture stuck in her mind. Her friends and colleagues had let their hair down and enjoyed themselves with their husbands, wives, partners and children.

She'd hated being the only person there on her own although she wouldn't have admitted it for the world. As she told Rhona, she'd enjoyed herself immensely and if the other woman suspected that Richard wasn't actually working, but just hadn't wanted to come, she didn't say so.

The only squabbles were 'You drank the last two times so it's my turn and you have to drive' arguments every time Ted came in with more booze. Everyone had a great time. Nobody complained about the noise coming from the converted garage as boisterous children did their level best to out-bounce each other.

Who'd have guessed that Frederick, the marvellously camp make-up artist who worked on most of *Style*'s fashion shoots, would turn out to be the children's favourite playmate.

'I like children, sweetie. I just don't know if I could eat a whole one!' had been Frederick's favourite phrase, borrowed from W. C. Fields. It never failed to raise a laugh. But after six vodkas and a lethal alcoholic concoction which included peach schnapps and Grand Marnier, Frederick was up on the bouncy castle with the five-year-olds, happily trying to demonstrate the double somersault he claimed to have been able to do in his youth.

How could you not like children, Jo wondered as the parking attendant handed her a fistful of coins and a receipt.

Richard didn't hate children. How could he? He'd been an only child who'd never had anyone to compete with at home.

45

His besotted mother looked after him as if he was the crown prince of Brunei.

That's it, she thought triumphantly. He's never had to compete with a brother or sister for affection and he never learned to deal with children. All he needs is a little time to get used to the idea. We must have at least seven months left for that.

She roared off around the Green, whizzing past taxi-drivers and lumbering buses like a rally-driver. You're not bad, Bessie, when you get going, she told her car. But I may have to trade you in for something more baby-friendly – or at least something with a bit of suspension.

The surgery was full when she got there. Two harassed mothers tried to quieten cross toddlers and an elderly man with a hacking cough occupied two seats. One sulky adolescent mutinously insisted he go in to see the doctor by himself. 'I'm not a child any more,' he hissed at his mother.

'Stop acting like one, then,' she hissed back.

He turned pinker than the outbreak of spots on his hairless face when he noticed Jo looking at him.

Jo grabbed a dog-eared magazine off the centre table and squeezed in between the teenager and one of the mothers. She was in for a long wait, she calculated, judging by the exhausted expressions on everyone's faces. Still, it was only just after three and she had just had the most wonderful news in the world, so she couldn't complain about waiting for the doctor. She couldn't complain about anything.

She wanted to tell Richard so badly it was killing her. She wanted to tell everyone in the waiting room. Instead, she turned her attention to a year-old copy of *Elle* and flicked through the pages with a professional eye.

Jo could no longer look at any publication aimed at women without wondering whether *Style* would look good with a wrap-around calorie counter, three more pages on travel or whatever.

She was just reading an in-depth report about cervical cancer – the sort of article which would have once had her reaching for her edition of *Everywoman* in terror – when a woman walked into the waiting room with a baby cradled papoose-like on her chest.

Jo stared at them, taking in every detail. The baby girl, dressed in pink which matched her soft rounded cheeks, had obviously been sleeping until the noisy surgery waiting room woke her up.

She blinked long dark eyelashes and stared drowsily up at her mother with enormous eyes, smiling a toothless grin when Mum murmured comforting words.

Jo held her breath as she looked at the mother and baby. She had a million questions she wanted to ask, but she didn't say a word. This was what she wanted, thought Jo as the mother gently kissed her baby's downy head, this bond between a mother and her child, a love that was holier than anything she'd ever felt in a church. And now she was going to experience it.

Back to *Elle*. She discovered that shimmery pink was in, black was out and anyone wearing last year's opaque black tights would be arrested by the fashion police. She had just started reading an ancient edition of *Hello!* and was looking at pictures of Michael Jackson's wedding when the doctor called her name. Thank God for that. One more page about Cindy Crawford's workout wardrobe or her marvellous fashion sense, and she'd have gone mad.

The last time she'd been in the clinical-looking surgery, she was in the grip of a particularly virulent stomach bug and had nearly been sick all over the expensive cream floor tiles. Today's visit was definitely an improvement.

'I'm pregnant.' Saying that brought a gleam to her eyes, she just knew it. 'I thought I needed a professional opinion, although I've done a test and it was positive. Are those tests accurate, Dr Daly?' Jo asked in concern.

'Used properly, they're excellent. But I'd prefer to make sure.' Ten minutes and another positive pregnancy test later, the doctor was working out dates and talking about diet and folic acid supplements.

By the time Jo turned her key in her front door lock, it was nearly six. She couldn't wait to make herself a huge cup of sugary tea. She switched the kettle on and peered into the fridge.

Two weepy tomatoes, a soggy courgette, a jar with a scraping of crumb-filled honey at the bottom, a half-full tin of beans and a tub of spreadable cheese covered with green fluff stared back at her dismally.

Only the milk, butter and two yogurt pots looked healthy enough for human consumption. This won't do, she thought. Time to get your act together, Ms Ryan, she told herself as she closed the fridge door. At least she had those potato waffles in the freezer. They were carbohydrates, weren't they? She switched on the answering machine and listened to her messages while she poured boiling water over a tea bag.

Rhona had rung to see how she got on with the doctor. Her sister-in-law had been on to tell her about a surprise birthday party for Shane's fortieth. Could she ring back during the day when he was out? asked Mary against a background noise of a washing machine about to lift into orbit.

Jo was chuckling at the idea of her older brother's face when he realised he'd been duped when she heard Richard's voice: 'Hi, Jo. I'm in Naas on a job for the *Independent*. I'm going to drive straight to the party when I'm finished, OK? William is coming with me and he's bringing his sister along because she's home from Paris. He can't just leave her on her own in the flat. I'm covering the party for the *Herald* as a favour in case the Def Leppard guys or Dennis Hopper turn up. That's it. Sorry I missed you but I'll see you there. Bye.'

Oh no, Jo thought despondently. I wanted to go with you, Richard. Blast you. She plucked the tea bag from her cup and added the last dribble of milk and sugar. A few chocolate digestives, I think, she muttered miserably. She opened the junk cupboard where she kept a bag of mini-Mars bars, biscuits and several bottles of 7-Up for emergencies.

He said he was going to bring me to the bloody party, she muttered as she carried her tea and biscuits into the bedroom.

What the hell is he bringing Will and his stupid sister for? Are they more important to him than I am?

She took a bite of chocolate digestive and washed it down with hot, sweet tea. She turned on the radio and sat down heavily on the bed. How was she going to get the energy to change her clothes?

She looked at the pile of unironed clothes draped on her white cane chair. Last month's 'de-junk your life' feature flashed before her eyes and she thanked God that nobody in the office could see the chaos that was her bedroom.

She was reasonably tidy at work. Losing a vital piece of paper *there* could prove disastrous so she forced herself to dump all the press releases, old newspaper cuttings and scrawled phone messages before they swamped her desk.

At home, however, she flung linen jackets onto the chair only to find them crumpled and requiring half an hour of ironing a week later.

A tangle of tights lay on the flowered blue quilt, silky beige and black skeins abandoned during her frantic attempts that morning to find a ladderless pair of sheer tights to go with her linen outfit.

It was a pretty room, decorated in the blue-sprigged Laura Ashley wallpaper she'd instantly adored when she spotted it in the shop. The white cane dressing table, bookcase and bedside table looked just right with the wallpaper, and matched the long white muslin curtain which hung elegantly from a brass pole.

It all would have been property-supplement-perfect if it hadn't been for the piles of paperbacks and magazines stacked untidily on the bedside table, the sheaf of newspapers dropped casually onto the floor beside her bed and the heap of blouses, T-shirts and trousers on the chair.

The oval dressing table was like a chemist shop's display with bottles of perfume, body lotion and endless old lipsticks she just couldn't bear to throw out. A picture of her and Richard on their last holiday in New York had pride of place beside the walnut jewellery box he'd bought her last year.

What a bloody mess, she thought, remembering Rhona's words of wisdom on small children and their effect on untidy mothers. I'll tidy up tomorrow, she promised. Now what to wear for the party?

Jo glanced briefly at the mirror – could do with a dust, she rebuked herself – and was amazed by what she saw. She *felt* exhausted, but the face that stared back at her positively glowed. Her eyes shone and her skin was healthily flushed with a radiance no expensive face cream would ever be able to match.

Marvellous! I feel like I've been squashed under a cement mixer and I look great! The people who made Oil of Ulay had better learn how to bottle this.

All those articles she'd written about motherhood and the Blooming Pregnancy fashion features came to mind.

She laughed out loud at the thought of pregnant women reading her zero-experience-of-pregnancy claptrap. 'Your skin will bloom and your hair will be shinier than any salon treatment could ever make it . . .' she giggled. And I hadn't a clue what I was talking about.

Let's put that blooming beauty to good use, she decided, as she finished the last bit of biscuit. After a quick shower, an even quicker blast of the hairdryer and ten careful minutes spent applying make-up, she cast a critical eye over herself. The launch of Michael Moran's long-awaited glossy supplement would doubtless be a glitzy, high-profile affair.

Jo had no intention of turning up looking anything but her best, especially as the bosses of two model agencies had told her they were going to be there – with some of their most stunning girls, naturally. The threat of rock star involvement meant that the city's model population would be out in force, an army of perfectly groomed women who were paid to look stunning – and who instantly made other women green with jealousy.

With Richard prowling around, Nikon slung round his neck as he searched for photo opportunities, Jo didn't want to look any less gorgeous than these professional beauties.

Neither did she want to look tired and pale when she told him their wonderful news. Something sexy was definitely required.

She opened the wardrobe door and stood back as her black suede sandals, a fluffy pink slipper and a wire hanger fell out. She searched through jackets, dresses, skirts and trousers, rejecting outfit after outfit until she came upon the perfect one – an elegant midnight blue slip dress which looked deceptively simple unless you knew how much it had cost and realised that only brilliant – and expensive – designers made bias-cut gowns so flattering.

Jo twirled in front of the mirror, twisting and turning to see her figure from every angle. She looked beautiful. A string of glass beads, tiny pearl earrings and high-heeled shoes completed the outfit.

With her tortoiseshell hair cascading down her shoulders in the natural waves she'd never managed to tame, dark eyes shimmering with a faint dusting of Lancôme's silvery grey eyeshadow and the dress swirling around her, she felt like some Thirties movie star. Katharine Hepburn maybe, she thought, remembering rainy Saturday afternoons watching old movies on the TV.

She sprayed her neck and wrists lightly with perfume. Go get 'em, Jo.

CHAPTER FOUR

It was eight o'clock exactly according to the clock on the dashboard. It was time to go in, time to face her husband and the entire staff of the *News* who undoubtedly knew exactly what was going on in her marriage. Or her non-marriage as the case might be, Aisling thought glumly.

The launch party had been going on for at least an hour already, she reckoned. But she had been sitting quietly in the car since she'd arrived, nervously fiddling with her car keys and wondering how to slip in as unobtrusively as possible.

Jo would be there, she reminded herself. Thank God for that. Even though it was over twelve years since she'd shared a matchbox-sized flat in Rathmines with the lively trainee journalist, they'd still remained friends.

Aisling knew that it was largely thanks to Jo's determination that they'd seen each other regularly over the past ten years.

When their lives had diverged – one of them climbing up the career ladder and the other climbing the stairs with piles of laundry – Aisling had begun to wonder whether a high-flyer like Jo would be bothered to keep in touch.

The question became academic when the demands of Jo's job meant she had neither the time nor the energy to socialise outside work. Aisling found that two adorable baby boys required twice as much work as one. Consumed by love for her darlings, she retired from normal non-baby life until the boys reached school-going age and she began to pick up the pieces of her old life again.

Meeting Nuala, an old friend from work, Aisling realised that her world had changed utterly over the past few years while Nuala's was just the same. Nuala talked about flexitime, staffing cutbacks and brokers who irritated her on the phone.

Aisling felt instantly boring, another mother droning on about her lovely children.

She wasn't surprised when Nuala didn't ring back to arrange another lunchtime meeting. That was why Aisling had assumed Jo would be the same. Too busy to squeeze in a hurried sandwich with someone she'd been close to years before. People changed, moved on.

It was a pleasant surprise to find out that she was wrong. Jo was determined to keep in contact, always on the phone or arriving for lunch when she was in the vicinity.

No matter how long an interval between their meetings, they would always slip back into their familiar friendship, laughing at the same things and reminiscing about the days when they hadn't enough money for the gas meter and wrapped themselves up with blankets to keep warm while watching their tiny portable TV.

'I still have this recurring nightmare about not having the rent money and coming back to the flat to find our clothes on the road,' Aisling said, one freezing December morning when Jo had dropped by with Christmas presents for the boys and a beautiful enamelled brooch for Aisling. 'I wake up thinking the landlord is banging on the door and the *relief* to find it's all a nightmare.'

'I know the feeling,' Jo shuddered, even though they were sitting in front of the fire in Aisling's primrose yellow living room. 'God, it was awful not to have enough money, always scraping by.'

'I was buying this gorgeous red jacket the other day and I was just at the cash register with my cheque book when I realised that it cost *more than two months' rent* in Mount Pleasant Avenue! Isn't that unbelievable?' Jo took another sip of coffee. 'I nearly put it back. I mean, *two months' rent*! My mother would be horrified if she saw me spending that much money on clothes.'

'I think, by now, she's figured out that you've expensive tastes in clothes!' laughed Aisling, looking pointedly at the elegant cream crêpe trouser suit Jo was wearing. 'And

53

nobody's likely to think that those shoes were in the £9.99 bargain bin in Penney's.'

'True.' Jo looked down at the cream-coloured soft leather pumps she was wearing. 'It's crazy, really, the money I spend on clothes. But all the fashion correspondents are the same,' she protested.

'If I turned up at a fashion show in my old grey leggings and a sloppy old T-shirt, they'd all wet themselves with glee. So I *have* to spend money on clothes!'

Aisling laughed. No matter what elevated circles Jo moved in, she was always the same – funny, kind and totally lacking in pretension. The same warm-hearted girl who'd lend her less glamorous flatmate anything, even her newest and best-loved dress.

Jo had always been a friend to rely on, the sort of person who'd be there with a box of tissues, a comforting hug and a buoyant speech no matter what happened, Aisling reflected. Unlike her sister, Sorcha, who was so tied up with her job in London that she barely had time to come home for Christmas, Jo genuinely enjoyed Aisling's company. So what if Sorcha thought her older sister has turned into a non-person just because Aisling didn't have a high-powered career by day, and didn't go to management courses at night.

Jo Ryan, deputy and fashion editor of fashionable *Style* magazine, was one of Aisling's best friends and not even Sorcha could call Jo boring. Lively, clever and a little bit wild, maybe. But boring, no.

Funny, warm, and a little too trusting when it came to men – or so Aisling had always thought – Jo had finally met the man of her dreams after years of meeting Mr Wrong after Mr Wrong.

'You'll love him, Ash,' Jo said happily down the phone, one romance-filled week after meeting Richard. 'He's perfect – better than Richard Gere!'

'*That* good?' Aisling chuckled. 'Are you sure he's real, or has he escaped from the pages of GQ?'

54

'He's real all right.' Jo's throaty laugh told Aisling every-thing. The gorgeous photographer had obviously made it to first base. Aisling thought Jo should have waited a bit longer before going to bed with her new boyfriend. Michael had been *her* first and only lover. But, things were different now.

She hoped Richard wasn't like some of the other men Jo had been involved with. Jo always seemed to make huge mistakes when it came to men. She fell for each one passion-ately and wholeheartedly, only waking up to their faults when it was too late. Maybe this time would be different.

Aisling hadn't seen much of her friend since Richard had come on the scene. She briefly wondered if Jo had heard any rumours about Michael's affair.

Surely not, she thought. Jo would have told her if she'd heard anything. Or would she? Aisling's head was spinning thinking about it all. And I'm the one who thinks *Jo* goes around with rose-tinted glasses. How ironic.

Please let Jo be here tonight, Aisling prayed fervently. She and Jo always ended up sitting together at journalistic parties. Aisling was grateful to her more extrovert friend for introduc-ing her to the ever-changing pool of reporters, subs and photographers.

There were always loads of people she didn't know, Aisling reflected, thinking of the occasions she'd tagged along with Jo after Michael had hotfooted it in another direction.

'Come on and meet Lorraine,' Jo would say. 'She reviews books for *The Times* and you'll have loads to talk about.' Instantly, Aisling felt as if she belonged, as if she had some-thing to talk about. Jo never made her feel colourless or uninteresting, the way Michael did.

When she was with Jo, Aisling felt more like her old self again, more like the girl who'd gone to the College of Commerce Christmas party as the blonde from Abba. Jo had been the red-haired one, in sequins and flares. Who cared that it wasn't even fancy dress?

God, she thought, did I ever do that? What did we look like? They hadn't cared what they'd looked like after half a bottle of Malibu drunk in the toilets. She'd never been able to so much as *look* at a bottle of Malibu after that evening. Vodka didn't give you such bad hangovers, Jo pointed out. Gin was even better.

I hope it isn't one of those parties with nothing but wine, Aisling thought. Tonight, of all nights, she needed the buzz from a proper drink, the gentle loosening of inhibitions which made her feel less awkward.

Michael would probably give her one of his reproving looks when he saw her drinking. Once he'd been a great man for a few beers while watching TV, but he'd recently become very anti-booze and patted his now flat stomach smugly as he refused his customary weekend Budweiser.

He wanted to stay lithe for his girlfriend, no doubt, she thought bitterly.

'I'm not drinking beer at home any more,' he'd informed her in January, when she'd just unpacked the shopping all on her own and was stowing two six-packs in the larder. 'It's so unhealthy. And a few glasses of red wine is much better, and more enjoyable. That's what the Italians drink every day and look at how healthy they are.' He looked pointedly at Aisling as she guiltily took a large tub of Bailey's ice cream out of a shopping bag. Ten billion calories at least.

'A friend told me that scientists actually recommend a couple of glasses of red wine a day along with a Mediterranean diet,' he continued. 'I must get one of my students to do a piece on it.'

Aisling wondered if the 'friend' he'd talked about then was the same femme fatale he'd taken to Le Caprice and if the bitch preferred wine connoisseurs to men who drank pints?

Probably. Maybe she was one of those women who delicately sipped two white wine spritzers before loudly proclaiming that she would only drink mineral water for the rest of the night.

How different from me, Aisling thought. Practically under the table after five gin and tonics, she often ended up giggling and silly at parties. Of course, enduring Michael's diatribe in the taxi home was part and parcel of these occasions.

'How could you tell that story tonight?' he thundered the night Aisling told the managing director's wife her hilarious story about the first time she had her diaphragm fitted.

'Jesus, I shouldn't bring you to parties if you're going to embarrass me like this. I don't know what they're going to think.'

There was no point, Aisling decided, in saying that the managing director's wife had obviously loved the story and had burst out laughing as soon as a shocked Michael was out of earshot. No point at all, really.

Who the hell was Michael to tell her she shouldn't have a few drinks at parties? He was screwing some damn woman, breaking his marriage vows as if they weren't worth the paper they were written on. He had no right to tell her what she could or couldn't do. She'd drink what she felt like, especially tonight.

Maybe she did drink too much when she was out. So what? If she felt inadequate in his friends' company, he was responsible. He always kept her at arm's length from his colleagues and made her feel stupid in contrast to the editor's wife, a physics lecturer no less.

Well, Michael certainly couldn't make her feel any worse than she did now. He'd already found another woman, what could top that for humiliation? Blast him! She was going to have the biggest drink she could lay her hands on and she didn't give a damn if Michael saw her do it.

It was time to go in. Aisling checked her make-up in the rear-view mirror and rubbed at a tiny smudge of mascara below her eye. You weren't supposed to rub the delicate skin around your eyes roughly, she knew from those endless magazine articles.

Once she'd hit thirty, she really meant to look after her skin properly. But the new make-up routine fell by the wayside. Before long, Aisling was back to soap and water with a little Oil of Ulay when she remembered it.

Would Michael have stayed in love with her if she had

pampered her skin and spent hours toning, plucking, waxing and beautifying herself? Probably not. If he'd wanted a glamorous career woman to show off to his friends, nothing short of a miracle could have made him stay with his un-careerist wife.

She obliterated the mascara smudge, rubbing away the heavy foundation she'd applied to hide her reddened eyes. Damn, she muttered, rummaging in her meagre make-up bag for a tiny tube of concealer to hide the damage.

Polyfilla was what she needed, Aisling thought miserably as she peered into the mirror. A passing couple looked into her dusty red Starlet as they walked hand in hand through the back gate to the newspaper premises.

Casually dressed in jeans, trendy Timberland boots and matching chunky cord jackets, they strode past quickly. The girl stared straight at Aisling before looking away, flicking long chestnut hair out of her eyes with the confidence of youthful beauty.

Aisling flushed under their scrutiny and imagined that they were thinking, 'Why bother?' Just a boring old housewife trying to tart herself up when all the powder and paint in the world couldn't cover up the beginnings of a double chin.

A drink would be nice, she thought again. Just one large one to give her courage and help her smile at the strange faces. If she could still manage a smile when she'd confronted Michael, of course. Aisling took a deep breath and opened the car door.

She couldn't see anyone else in the corner of the car park where she'd parked. Near the door, a leather-clad figure was parking a motorcycle.

She hadn't been on a motorbike in years and the idea of a spin down the motorway, with the wind in her face and no time to think about her life, was suddenly very appealing.

She'd rented one of those scooters on that brilliant holiday in Greece. Her father had grimly warned her about broken limbs and permanent scars. That did it. Wearing her old denim shorts and T-shirt, she'd sped along the rocky roads with Jo racing along beside her on an equally battered scooter, laughing into the wind with the sheer joy of it all.

'Last one home has to go out with Spiros,' screeched Jo, pumping her foot up and down on the gas pedal. She wasn't going to be the one accompanying the over-hairy owner of their apartment block to dinner in the taverna.

They were probably only going at fifteen miles an hour but it felt like flying as they passed tiny white villas gleaming in the hot Aegean sun, smiling at the local women huddled in their all-encompassing black dresses.

She wouldn't dream of riding on a scooter any more. Scooters and motorbikes were for the slim young girls you saw in tampon adverts, girls with bum-length hair, minuscule white shorts and lots of attitude. They were most definitely not for women who couldn't do up their jeans any more.

The newsroom was probably full of them, she reflected, cute model types drafted in to pose for snaps with the managing director. Maybe she could ask them for hints. She could drag a few of them up to Michael and ask them was he worth fighting for?

For a moment, she savoured a picture of Michael's face, red with anger at his wife calmly telling a group of gorgeous young women that he was a lying, cheating bastard. She'd never be able to do it, though. Fiona would, she'd *love* to do it, if Pat was ever dumb enough to betray her.

Aisling knew she'd only ever dream about slapping Michael. Like she'd dreamed of slapping her father's face every time he made her feel worthless and stupid. Was that all men ever did?

She leaned against the car and closed her eyes for a moment. She was dreading tonight, smiling hello to all Michael's colleagues, wondering what they'd think when they saw her – Michael Moran's once-slim wife transformed into a busty hausfrau with no conversation and zero style. No wonder he'd got himself a mistress when that was what he had to go home to at night, she could almost hear them saying. Damn him!

She slammed the car door shut and smoothed down her dress. No chickening out now.

Aisling was slightly out of breath when she made it to the imposing front doors where a security guard with a clipboard and a self-important expression on his face gazed down at her.

'I'm . . . er . . . expected at the party,' she stammered. 'The supplement . . . My husband works here . . .'

'Name?' queried the guard loftily, pen poised over his list.

'Aisling Moran,' she answered and, as if by magic, the man's stony face lit up.

'Mrs Moran! Grand to meet you at last. Come on in before those news hounds drink the place dry!'

She found herself being bustled over to the stairs where the guard yelled up for Mick '. . . to escort Mrs Moran to the party.'

Aisling had barely put a foot on the bottom step before another, much younger man in a similar navy uniform and a very short haircut materialised and walked with her up the stairs.

Aisling muttered something about not having been escorted anywhere for years.

'Not at all, Ma'am,' the muscular young man smiled cheerily. 'These stairs are a bit steep if you're not used to them and God knows you'd never find your way around the warren upstairs if you didn't know where you were going!'

He couldn't have been more than nine or ten years younger than she was but, from the way he was walking beside her at a snail's pace and the way he called her 'Ma'am', she was obviously a dead ringer for his mother. Marvellous.

'Bye now.' He gave her a good luck sort of grin and walked briskly back the way they had come, leaving her standing outside the newsroom, her heart thumping at the thought of making her entrance alone.

What are you doing here, she asked herself wretchedly? Why aren't you sitting at home with your head buried firmly in the sand as usual?

Because you have to find out what's going on, the voice in

her head pointed out calmly. And if you don't find out now, you never will. It's up to you whether you try and ignore his infidelity or whether you demand that it ends. Get a grip on yourself, Aisling, she said out loud. Go on!

She put one hand tentatively on the door before it swung back on her violently as two men in suits with ties askew pushed their way out of the office giggling hysterically.

'Aisling Moran! How are you?' Suddenly, she was grabbed by one of the revellers and enveloped in a bear hug.

'Tom,' she said with pleasure as she recognised the paper's chief sub-editor, one of Michael's best friends.

'I haven't seen you in an age,' he said warmly. A huge smile lit up his grey-bearded face. A tall man with hunched shoulders, Tom had always been in shape, but now sported a little pot belly under his straining shirt.

Aisling noticed the heavy sprinkling of grey in his hair and beard and realised, with a shock, that she hadn't seen him for well over two years.

But then, I haven't exactly turned the clock backwards myself, she thought wryly.

'How are you?' he roared merrily, sending strong whiskey fumes in her direction.

'This is your husband's big night, eh? You must be so proud. We all are.'

I'm bloody delirious, she thought, grinning back with a saccharine smile.

Tom pushed the swing doors open and led Aisling into a room which buzzed with activity. MTV, RTE, Super and Sky Sports belted out at top volume from the bank of TV screens on one wall. Nobody seemed to notice the cacophony made by Pearl Jam's latest hit, a droning Formula One race and the news in two languages. Instead, they screeched with laughter, talked rapidly and gestured for more drink as two harassed-looking girls wearing black skirts and white shirts circled the room balancing glasses on large trays.

People stood around in little groups of two or three, laughing and shouting at each other, sharing the jokes of colleagues who worked long hours together and knew each other better than their families.

'Are you saying I got that story from another paper?' she heard someone say indignantly.

'You'd swallow a brick, Pat!' said another voice. 'He's only winding you up for a bet. That's another drink you owe me, by the way, Shay.'

'They're all on form tonight,' chuckled Tom.

Aisling thought they all looked glamorous and dynamic. She'd always been in awe of her husband's colleagues, especially the women.

'Here we are,' she heard Tom say, as they pushed their way to the centre of the room where a group of people stood, listening to a tall, dark man.

Michael was holding court, as usual. He had this incredibly irritating habit of pontificating on all sorts of subjects, although politics was his favourite.

At home, he generally started giving Aisling his views on the most recent political crisis when she was ready to turn out her bedside light, or when she was just settling down to watch *ER*. He never realised that she was doing something else and wasn't necessarily interested in what he thought about the Labour Party's conference, or Bill Clinton's speech. But then he never noticed the way her eyes glazed over when he really got going.

Tonight he was on form, preaching about the changing role of newspapers in a world of instant TV news updates. It gave Aisling a glimmer of satisfaction to see one of the not-so-eager listeners raise her eyebrows at a colleague, tacit understanding of the boss's irritating idiosyncracies. Not everyone was as awestruck in his presence as Michael liked to imagine. For a brief moment, that was a very satisfying thought.

She watched silently, trying to look at him like a stranger seeing him for the first time. Tall, dark-eyed and with the type of bone structure the Marlboro man would have died for, he was, as most of his male colleagues complained, almost too bloody good-looking to have any brains at all.

Unfortunately for all the begrudgers, he was a brilliant writer and an even better editor. He had an ego to match. When the yearly influx of journalism students brought eager young women into the office, keen to learn every nuance of the job, they invariably developed crushes on the good-looking deputy editor.

Michael always made this sound funny, telling Aisling how they blushed when they offered to get him a sandwich at lunchtime or asked his advice on their stories instead of talking to the news editor. Despite the way he made these stories amusing, Aisling knew he was flattered by the attention. With Michael, flattery got you everywhere.

Not a quality to make a wife feel secure, Aisling reflected. She watched two of the younger female onlookers gaze longingly at her husband as though he were fillet steak and they'd been starved for a month.

Aisling could have told his admirers that he stared in that intense, Robert Redford sort of manner purely to focus his eyes when he wasn't wearing the stylish designer wire-rimmed glasses he'd bought a couple of years previously.

Of course, she never got the chance to tell anyone and she suspected that they wouldn't believe her anyway. She could imagine these particular admirers privately thinking that the deputy editor's piercing gaze was deeply sexy, something intended for them alone. Big mistake, girls.

'Michael, look who's arrived!' Tom announced cheerily. The entire group turned towards the newcomers. Aisling felt her face flush pinkly as everyone looked at her and hated herself for it. Michael leaned over and took her hand. He led her gently into the centre of the group, almost as if he was pleased to see her. What an actor.

'Aisling, these are most of my team for the supplement. Everyone else, this is Aisling, my wife.' Who was writing his lines, she wondered? Was this his 'caring editor' performance, designed to beguile the gazing students?

Aisling could see the amazement in the women's eyes as they took in her flushed face and less than perfect figure hidden under a loud crimson dress. Gorgeous, clever Michael, one of the most talented journalists in Dublin, married to that! She was used to it now, that look of pity when her husband's admirers realised that their hero was stuck with the least attractive woman in the room.

At least she'd always been sure that *thinking* about her husband was as far as any of his female fans had ever got. She now had devastating proof that one woman had got a lot further than thinking.

As they muttered 'Hello' with varying degrees of enthusiasm, Aisling wondered if *she* was one of them. Maybe that was why Michael hadn't introduced anyone individually.

Perhaps she was standing there as cool as a cucumber, the blonde with the pancake make-up and the Kim Basinger lips, or the tall brunette with tortoiseshell glasses emphasising almond-shaped blue eyes and a thin silk blouse which left nobody in any doubt that she had bypassed the bra drawer when she was getting dressed.

Aisling watched her for a moment and turned her attention to the other women in the group. Would she recognise the other woman from Fiona's description, would she intuitively know who she was?

'Are you all right?' Her husband's voice broke into her thoughts. She raised cool blue eyes to meet his. Strange, she had expected him to look different now that she knew his secret, but he didn't.

He looked exactly the same as ever, a five o'clock shadow darkening his jaw, eyebrows raised in a quizzical expression.

Until today she'd have staked her life that Michael wouldn't dream of doing anything more than talking to another woman. She gazed at her husband, noticing the dark smudges under his eyes from the long nights he'd been working late to put the finishing touches to the supplement. That was what he'd said anyhow.

It was more likely he was exhausted from spending hours with *her*, sharing meals in their favourite restaurant before steaming up the windows of his car; the same car she drove to the supermarket at weekends with the boys squabbling in the back.

God, the betrayal. It hurt so much and it made her so angry. Twelve years of marriage had meant *nothing* to him if he could just forget about her and their sons for a few hot nights with some floozie.

'Are you all right?' he asked again. She turned away. Tom returned with the drink he'd offered to get for her: a large tumbler full of gin and tonic, strong and cool with plenty of ice clinking around the glass.

She smiled thanks at Tom and took a deep reviving slug, feeling the gin hit her system like an injection of adrenaline.

Michael had already moved his attention to the next subject, his personal interpretation of the latest political crisis in Washington.

'We have to talk.' Aisling surprised herself with the calmness of her voice as she reached out and tapped him on the shoulder. Ignoring the look of surprise on his companions' faces, she walked away from the group with him grudgingly following until they were out of earshot.

'What is it?' he asked impatiently. 'Why couldn't you tell me in the first place? Tell me, what's the big fuss?'

She looked steadily up at him. Would he lie or tell the truth? Probably lie.

'The big fuss is about Jennifer Carroll. Does that name sound a bit familiar to you?' She gazed at him expectantly. 'I know you're having an affair, Michael. So I think we need a private talk, don't you? Or do you want everyone on the premises to hear about your sordid secret, if they don't already know, that is,' she spat.

His eyes darkened. He stared at her with the same blank look she'd seen when he was stuck talking to someone he didn't like: cold and indifferent, his face impassive, his eyes saying nothing.

'How did you find out?' he asked, as casually as though she'd mentioned that the car was out of petrol.

'You should be more careful with your credit card receipts,'

65

she answered. 'Didn't you know I'd find out if you left a receipt for Lingerie de bloody Paris in your navy suit pocket? Or did you want me to find out?'

'No.' He stared down at some spot on the grey speckled office carpet, seemingly miles away as though contemplating whether eighty per cent wool was more serviceable than pure wool carpet. 'I didn't want you to find out because it would hurt you and I never meant to do that.'

'Yeah, right.' Aisling laughed harshly, feeling red spots of colour burning on her cheeks. 'You just wanted everyone else to find out that you were cheating on your stupid wife. Let her find out from the neighbours! Was that the way you wanted it? Is there anything else I should know or are you taking out an advert in next week's paper?'

He had stopped looking at the carpet and was looking at her sadly, almost pityingly. Shrewd, dark eyes took in the new dress and the garish bright lipstick.

'Maybe I should have asked Fiona if you have a few other women stashed away somewhere? Or was one enough? Did you have a bet on with that bloody bitch to see how long you could keep me fooled?'

She paused for breath and took a huge drink from her glass. Her hands shook so much that the ice rattled noisily.

'It wasn't like that, Aisling,' he answered slowly. 'I didn't tell anyone and I thought we were discreet, although obviously I was wrong. I never wanted to hurt you.'

'Don't tell me,' she interrupted, 'it didn't mean a thing and you can't even remember her name. Is that your next line? Because I know her name, even if you pretend to have forgotten it. Jennifer Carroll, isn't it?'

She looked at him triumphantly, as though they were playing Trivial Pursuit and she'd just won a piece of pie.

'Just tell me one thing, Michael, why? Why did you do it? Don't you love me any more, don't you care about our marriage and the boys?'

Michael's eyes were still cold.

'I've loved you for thirteen years, Aisling,' he said. 'But I'm

not *in love* with you any more.' The emphasis on 'in love' hit
her like a bullet. Was he really saying what she thought he was
saying?

Michael shrugged and splayed his hands out in a gesture of
apology.

'I'm sorry, but it's not as if you wanted to make our
marriage work, is it? You just wanted to crawl into your shell
and hide from the world.' She stared at him, disbelieving
what she was hearing.

'You, the boys and your damned house, that's all that
mattered to you. Not me.'

'You never wanted to be a part of my life, you never asked
me anything about *my* day, what *I* did. It was always the boys.
Did you ever remember that *we* got married, not you, me and
two kids, but *us*?' As he warmed to what was obviously a
familiar theme, his voice sounded harsher than she'd ever
heard it before.

'No, you don't remember, do you?' he snarled. 'You cut me
out of your cosy little life and I couldn't deal with that.'

He stopped, but his words hung in the air like icicles, cold
and deadly. He could have stabbed her with them and it
wouldn't have hurt as much as the look on his face hurt her.

She didn't want the marriage to work? For God's sake, she
desperately wanted it to work but he hadn't given her any
choice in the matter. He'd just run after some woman and
now he wanted to make it all her fault!

'You've made it pretty clear that you don't want to be part
of my life,' he continued, 'so I wanted someone who did want
to be with me.'

His voice was calm. Maddeningly calm. She'd just confronted him with the biggest crisis a marriage could face and
he was looking at her with calm indifference. He spoke about
their marriage as if it was already dead as a dodo.

'Don't give me that rubbish!' she screamed. 'Lingerie de
Paris and nights in Jurys isn't about our marriage not working.
It's about sex – you and some other woman having sex.

'You just couldn't stop yourself, could you? Everything we

67

had just wasn't enough for you. So don't try and blame me. Don't tell me it's my fault!'

She stopped abruptly, aware that people nearby had stopped talking.

Normally, she'd have been embarrassed, but tonight she didn't give a damn who heard her. 'How dare you . . .'

'I'm not trying to blame you,' Michael interrupted. 'It's just that . . .' He sighed heavily. 'Look, we can't talk about this here with everyone watching and listening. Let's wait 'til we get home, OK?'

'Home! Let's wait 'til we get home!' she repeated shrilly. 'You conveniently forgot about home when you were shacked up with that bitch in a Dublin hotel, lying that you were in London! So you can forget about coming home with me! Your home is with your bloody girlfriend and I don't want to see you until you've dumped her!'

'Aisling.' He tried to grab her but she managed to shrug his arm off. The door. Where was the door? She couldn't see through her tears. She just pushed past the double doors before he caught up with her.

'Stop,' he commanded. And she did. Turning her round to face him, Michael looked her in the eyes, his pupils boring into hers intently.

'I never wanted to hurt you, Aisling,' he repeated. 'You have to believe that. But you've changed. I don't know what's happened to you, but you're different. It's as if you shut yourself off from me and I can't live like that. I'm sorry.

'You're right about me not coming home,' he added. 'It wouldn't work. It's better if I don't come home tonight. I wanted to tell you everything a long time ago, but I could never find the right time. I didn't want to hurt the kids but there's no time that's right for kids in the middle of a marriage break-up.'

She could feel the blood pumping through her body, keeping her alive when all she wanted to do was die.

She'd given him the chance, the chance to say he loved her and that it had all been an awful mistake. But he hadn't used it. He had turned her own words against her.

God, if only she hadn't said he shouldn't come home, if only she'd kept her mouth shut and let him explain, let him beg forgiveness, surely everything would have been all right?

She'd given him a cast-iron excuse to leave. Aisling had never quite understood the expression 'time stood still', until that moment.

He was standing just a few feet away from her wearing a pale blue shirt with the top buttons open to reveal a few inches of tanned neck, a neck she had snuggled into when they sat on the couch watching TV late at night. His after-shave permeated the air and, if she reached out, she could touch him, hold him in her arms and be safe for ever.

Perhaps if she wished hard enough, she could turn back the clock and keep her mouth shut. Then he'd stay with her. Then he wouldn't need anyone else.

But it was too late. He didn't want her. He wanted another woman in his arms and in his life. Blindly, she took another huge gulp of her drink, wanting to blot out what had just happened.

'I'll stay in Tom's tonight and I'll be over to pick up some stuff in the morning.' Michael looked at her coolly, his eyes raking in the new dress and her flushed face, red from downing too much gin too rapidly.

'I better go back in. The MD is going to launch the supplement in a few minutes.'

Aisling looked at him mutely.

'Don't have any more to drink, Aisling,' he added coldly. 'I'm not going to drive you home if you get drunk, so you're on your own.'

With that he was gone, back to his besotted students and the whispering of colleagues who had seen everything.

Aisling slowly drained her glass and turned towards the stairs. So this is what heartache feels like, she thought numbly, walking slowly down the stairs, her beautiful new dress billowing out behind her.

The security guard at the door saw her walking towards him like a sleepwalker, her expression vacant and her eyes dull. He wanted to ask if she was all right, but he wasn't sure how to do it.

CHAPTER FIVE

Jo parked the car and got out quickly, noticing Aisling's car parked several spaces away. Great, she thought. She slammed the door shut and slipped her keys into her bag. We'll be able to catch up on all the gossip.

Jo hadn't walked more than five steps before she saw Aisling emerge from the front entrance. Even from a distance, Jo could see that her friend's complexion was ashen, an expression of sheer pain on her face.

Jesus, Jo thought, shocked. What could have happened? She ran towards Aisling, feeling the silk of her dress shimmer loosely around her body as she moved and realising that dainty heels and no bra were not ideal for running on gravel.

'What's wrong, Aisling? What's wrong?' Catching Aisling's hand in hers, Jo looked at her friend anxiously, her eyes seeking some reason for this terrible pallor, this frightening look of despair. 'Talk to me, Ash, please,' she pleaded.

'He's left me. He's in love with someone else,' Aisling said flatly, gazing into the middle distance with grief-stricken eyes.

Jo couldn't believe what she was hearing; Michael had left her? How ridiculous! Michael adored Aisling, worshipped the ground she walked on, didn't he?

Surely Aisling had got it wrong ... or had she? Jo was dumbstruck. She simply didn't know what to say. Aisling stood there silently, the lines around her eyes and mouth set in hard, unyielding creases.

'He's not in love with me, you see,' said Aisling, like a child reciting a poem learned by rote. 'He's in love with her and it's all my fault.' She started to cry properly, great big heaving sobs which shook her body, as if she was coughing her last breath.

'Oh Ash.'

'I found out today,' Aisling wept. 'Fiona told me, she'd known for ages but she couldn't tell me. I know she couldn't tell me. And I was going to confront him, get him to say he was sorry and it would be all right. Everything would stay the same. But he won't, he won't . . .'

Aisling buried her head in Jo's shoulder, sobbing onto the silver knitted wrap Jo had worn to cover her slip dress in case she felt chilly.

What could Jo do but hold Aisling, trying to ease the hurt with a friend's arms when all Aisling wanted was her husband's arms, and his voice telling her it was over, that he loved her and no one else. But Jo suspected that Michael wouldn't be saying that. Not ever again, maybe. Who could have guessed, who'd have known, that this seemingly devoted couple were on their way to splitting up? Maybe she'd have seen it coming if she hadn't buried herself in Richard's life, neglecting her old friends for him.

'Come and sit in my car,' she cajoled. 'Please, Aisling, please.'

'Can't. I have to go home to the boys. I told the baby-sitter I wouldn't be long.'

Aisling sniffled and found a scrunched-up piece of tissue in her bag among the shopping lists and Saturday morning under-elevens' soccer timetables. She took a deep breath and looked at Jo.

'Don't be silly, Ash. Just sit with me for a few moments and stop crying. You can't drive home like this.'

She steered Aisling over to her car, opened the passenger door and helped her in as if she was an invalid.

'I'm so sorry, so sorry,' sobbed Aisling. 'I just don't know what to do. How could this happen, I just don't know?'

'Oh, you poor thing.' Jo leaned over the handbrake and hugged Aisling warmly, wishing she knew what to say. She tried to remember the sort of advice the magazine's agony aunt would give, but found herself remembering the medical advice for first-time mothers over the age of thirty.

Aisling hiccuped. 'I knew things were different lately, but I thought it was me. I thought I'd got into a rut and that I had to sort myself out. But I never even thought of this. How could I?

'Was I the only person who didn't know or should I have realised something was wrong? I don't know.' She broke off suddenly, staring out the windscreen at nothing in particular.

'Look Ash, there's no point torturing yourself now. Maybe it was just a short-term thing, maybe he's sorry but he's not able to admit it.'

'No, it's not just a fling. It's serious. He said our marriage was over.'

Jo stared silently at her friend, knowing that there was no quick solution to this problem. She opened the glove compartment, found a pack of travel tissues and handed Aisling one to replace the soggy, twisted one which was crumbling in her hands.

Just moments ago, she had felt like someone living a glorious dream life of motherhood, with a fairytale wedding and contented family life just waiting in the wings. Now she felt about a hundred years old and very weary. Aisling and Michael had always epitomised the perfect couple to her: what hope was there if *they* couldn't make it?

It wasn't as if Jo hadn't witnessed enough relationship and marriage break-ups already. She knew plenty of people who'd fought tooth and nail over every stick of furniture in their soon-to-be-sold house and automatically hissed 'that *bitch*' or 'what a *bastard*' when anyone mentioned their ex-partners' names.

She'd learned to be careful when she bumped into people she hadn't seen for a while – you just never knew what a simple question like 'How's Gerry?' could provoke.

'Burning in Hell, I hope!' snarled one bitter friend the previous Christmas, when Jo had innocently inquired after the other woman's once-adored husband.

She knew it was silly, but she'd always had this rose-coloured view of the Morans' marriage. Maybe it was because she'd been so close to Aisling all those years ago and so thrilled when she'd fallen in love with Michael, but Jo really believed that they were perfect for one another. How blind had she been? A perfect house, two lovely children, a wife delighted to play housekeeper-cum-nanny and a handsome husband didn't necessarily make an ideal marriage.

'I have to go home, Jo.' Aisling straightened up. 'The boys are with the baby-sitter and I must go home to them, honestly.' She smiled briefly, the professional-mother smile dusted off and brought down from the attic for an emergency. 'You go on, I'll be fine.'

'I can't leave you like this.' Jo was horrified. 'Don't be ridiculous, Ash . . .'

'You're here to go to the party. They expect you.' Aisling shrugged, checking her blotchy face in the mirror. 'I'll talk to you tomorrow.' She managed a grim smile.

'I'm sorry, Jo. I shouldn't have told you this, it's not your problem.'

'Of course, it's . . . well, OK, it's not my problem,' Jo stammered, 'but you're my friend, Ash, and you shouldn't be on your own tonight. I just have to see Richard for a moment . . .' She broke off, desperate to tell Richard her news and knowing that Aisling wouldn't want to wait there a moment longer. 'There's something I *have* to tell him.'

'Don't worry,' replied Aisling brusquely. 'I'll ring Fiona when I get home. She'll come in.' Aisling opened the car door and got out with Jo following her.

God, this was awful, Jo thought in distress. What was she going to do? Damn Richard for not picking her up earlier. She'd have told him about the baby by now and she could've driven Aisling home, instead of having to leave her in this condition. What the hell was she to do?

Aisling made the decision for her.

'Thank you, Jo.' Aisling reached over and took Jo's hand. 'I'll phone you tomorrow. You go on in.'

'Don't go . . . Ash,' begged Jo. 'Hang on for a couple of minutes, please. I can't let you drive home on your own in this state.'

'I'm fine,' Aisling insisted. 'Fiona will be at home this evening. She wants me to ring her as soon as I get in.'

'You can't drive like this,' protested Jo.

'I'm fine, really. I'll be home in half an hour.'

'You promise you'll ring Fiona?' Jo demanded, feeling torn.

'Yes. I promise, I promise on my granny's life.' The corner of Aisling's mouth lifted into a slight smile at the words, an old joke shared by two flatmates many years ago. Aisling had always hated her grandmother with a vengeance.

But how was the landlord supposed to know that when the demure insurance clerk from the basement flat innocently promised not to have any parties, 'On my granny's life.'

Then Aisling was gone, hurrying towards her car before Jo had a chance to stop her. She watched Aisling drive slowly out the front gate with misgivings, praying that she'd get home safely, hoping she would have the sense to ring her neighbour for help. Mind you, what could anyone do?

Suddenly she didn't feel like going to a party after all. Poor Aisling, she thought, and what about Phillip and Paul? They were too young to deal with their parents splitting up. How could a couple of ten-year-olds understand the notion of separation or divorce? Jo's hand slipped to rest on her stomach. I'll never let anyone hurt you, my darling, she murmured. Nobody will hurt you.

She walked slowly towards the entrance, the jaunty spring in her step gone. When she pushed open the heavy newsroom doors, she was greeted with cries of hello as her ex-colleagues waved celebratory bottles of beer and glasses. The usual suspects were out in force, she noticed, making her way expertly through the throng, waving hello here, shaking hands there, without stopping at all. It was a trick she'd learned early in her journalistic career and was very useful for avoiding people you couldn't stand or people who'd talk all night once they'd started.

Jo skirted the groups of merrymakers, smiling and waving to all comers. She needed a party like she needed a hole in the head but there was no escaping this one. Half an hour with

Janice would undoubtedly cheer her up.

Janice O'Brien was talking nineteen to the dozen as per usual at a makeshift bar at the back of the newsroom. Janice and her companions *appeared* to be testing different types of lager and seeing who could tell the difference between Smirnoff, Stolichnaya and Absolut.

Jo knew better. With someone else paying the bar bill, the *News* team could pile up empty bottles faster than women queuing to see the Chippendales. Ridiculously large numbers of bottles were already empty, lined up against the wall awaiting disposal.

'Where have you been, sexy?' Nick Cullen slid an arm around her and planted a hot, beery kiss on her cheek. Tall, muscular and able to hold his beer better than any barrel, Nick was a brilliant reporter and a dreadful flirt, always keen to bring the female reporters off to the pub.

'You can't be pissed already,' Jo asked as she pushed him away.

'In an act of selflessness,' Brian Reddin interrupted, 'we started earlier on our own so we wouldn't drink this bar dry.'

'Thank God you've come!' said Janice gratefully, pulling her friend over to lean against a photocopier. 'This pair of lushes have been keeping me prisoner here, making me get them drinks all evening.'

'All that exercise must be great training for the marathon, then,' Jo commented. 'I still can't believe you're drunk already,' she added, poking Nick in the chest.

'Is Richard coming tonight?' Janice inquired, reaching back to the bar as she poured a stiff gin and tonic for her friend.

'Yes. I thought he'd be here already but I couldn't see his car,' said Jo, scanning the room for a sight of her boyfriend's short blond hair.

'He's supposed to be working tonight and didn't have time to pick me up before he got here, so where in the hell could he be? Unless he was in earlier and decided to wait until the party was really going. Did he?' she looked at the others.

'We haven't seen your Viking at all this evening,' inter-jected Nick, using the nickname which irritated the hell out of Richard, 'so you're mine for the night,' gorgeous. Love the dress.' His bleary eyes lit up appreciatively as he took in Jo's curves accentuated by her clinging silken dress.

'Thanks, Nick, I wore it specially for you, of course.'

'Oh really . . . D'you fancy you and I taking a stroll to the photocopier to see if you really *can* photocopy your bum and bonk at the same time?'

'Since I don't fancy seeing my derrière in full blown-up glory all over the newsroom next time I come here, I think I'll pass, if it's all the same to you,' she replied tartly.

Jo took the drink Janice had poured for her, knowing that refusing alcohol would automatically start Janice's mind tick-ing furiously. She waited until Janice was mixing up a drink for herself, then she reached back and swopped her gin and tonic for a glass of mineral water.

Then she hoisted herself onto one of the desks and sat back as Janice filled her in on the latest gossip. Everyone was asking who would get the fashion editor's job when Anita Brady left the following month to edit a new woman's magazine.

'They'll never get anyone as good,' remarked Janice, reach-ing out to spear a cocktail sausage from a passing waitress. 'Oh, these are lovely,' she squealed as she bit into the succulent flesh. 'Come back here immediately!'

'Anita's hell to work for,' she added, taking four more sausages from the waitress. 'But she's good at her job, so you have to learn to live with the temper tantrums. It's the husband I feel sorry for. You can't blame him for seeking solace in the arms of another woman when he's married to the sort of cow who could put Mike Tyson in hospital.'

Jo looked up sharply, searching Janice's face for a hint of ambiguity. Did she know about Michael and Aisling? But Janice had moved on from infidelity to incompetence.

'That nauseous Denise Keogh from features. She obviously thinks she's a dead cert for the job even though she has as much fashion sense as a lobotomised gorilla.'

'Don't mock, Janice,' interrupted Brian. 'The odds are two to one that she gets the job and you've a tenner on her to win!'

'Only because her uncle owns shares in the bloody paper,' said Janice caustically, 'and because I like to bet on dead certs. If she *does* get the job, I'll bet you twenty quid that her first fashion spread is on leg warmers, tank tops and frizzy hair. Oh yeah, and blue eyeliner.'

She broke off as they spotted Richard pushing his way through the partygoers. A tall willowy blonde in a slinky black mini-dress followed close behind like a puppy on a lead.

'Nice dress she's nearly wearing,' remarked the columnist with a flash of the bitchiness for which she was renowned. 'I've got scarves bigger than that.'

'Miaow, miaow.' Nick wagged a finger in Janice's direction. 'I think it's a lovely dress.'

'You would,' she replied smartly. 'That's because when you think at all, you think from below the belt.'

Nick sniggered into his beer again and nearly lost his balance as a result, but Jo didn't notice even when he grabbed her to steady himself. She watched her boyfriend, the father of her unborn baby, talking animatedly with his beautiful companion as he strolled round the room sizing up photographic opportunities.

The blonde simpered and giggled every few steps, licking her lips in what she obviously thought was a very sexy manner.

'Hello, darling.' Richard smiled at Jo when he and the blonde reached her corner of the room. 'This is Sascha, Will's sister. She's just started freelancing in Paris with *Now* magazine and she's doing a piece on Dublin social life.'

'I thought she was working undercover on a prostitution story,' Janice muttered under her breath.

Nobody heard. They were all staring at the blonde apparition in front of them. Sascha smiled at the group from sleepy green eyes, seemingly unconcerned that she'd forgotten either a reporter's notebook or tape recorder and had been gazing only at the handsome photographer instead of keeping her eyes peeled for material.

'I'm sure I know you from somewhere, don't I?' asked Janice, eyes narrowed as she tried to remember where she'd seen the other woman before.

'Didn't you do some modelling for one of the British catalogues?' she asked. 'Next, was it?'

'Yeah,' Sascha smiled again, displaying perfect white teeth and the self-confidence of a woman who knows she'd look fabulous wearing a bin-liner.

'I was with the Première agency for a couple of years and I did a lot of work in Japan.' She paused, giving the three men the benefit of another practised hundred-watt smile.

'I've left modelling. I'm just getting into writing now. I feel I'm a natural writer, y'know, it comes from in here.' She touched her tanned cleavage. Richard's gaze slid down to the spot in question as if mesmerised by her model-girl 32A chest. 'So I'm going to try reporting and then go home and get on with a book or something.'

The two female journalists stared silently at her beautiful blank face, wondering what besotted commissioning editor had given Sascha the job of writing about one of the world's literary capitals, when it was clear that any word longer than two syllables would involve a lengthy consultation with the dictionary.

'When did you start writing?' Jo asked kindly.

'Last month,' said Sascha happily. 'I've just done an article on modelling and some of the girls said I wouldn't be able to do it, but I think writing comes from the heart, doesn't it? I know I can do it.'

Sascha smiled at everyone broadly. 'I've been doing this personal development course and when I focus my energy on something, I can make it happen. That's what my counsellor says anyway. You're all writers, huh?'

'You could say that,' Janice answered, sarcasm dripping from every syllable. 'We just dabble, you understand. I'm still not sure whether I should stick with writing or focus on brain surgery, perhaps. Decisions, decisions.'

Jo smiled nervously up at Richard, hoping that he'd read her mind and leave Sascha to her life story so they could talk quietly together. 'Would you like a drink, darling?' she murmured. But he had other ideas.

'No, duty first. I better take a few pictures.'

Jo moved closer to him, breathing in the lemony smell of Eau Sauvage and the faint fragrance of fabric conditioner from his pristine cotton shirt. God, she loved the way he smelled, the way his skin tasted, the way he always looked.

Tonight, dressed in a plain charcoal grey suit which she knew had cost about a month's salary, he oozed style and elegance. Compared to Brian and Nick in their casual chain-store chic, *he* looked like a model from the Next catalogue.

And he was all hers. She couldn't help feeling a little self-satisfied as she pulled his head down and whispered into his ear. 'I've something really, really special to tell you. Follow me.'

With an apologetic glance at Sascha, Richard followed Jo into one of the glass-fronted offices which opened onto the newsroom. He leaned up against a steel grey filing cabinet and Jo wrapped her arms around his waist, leaning her head against the comforting bulk of his chest.

'You know you said that you never expected to settle down with anyone in the way you have with me,' she began. 'Well, I think we're going to become really settled soon. In about seven months,' she added with a little laugh.

'We're going to have a baby!' Looking up excitedly, Jo waited to see Richard's reaction. He was going to be thrilled, she was sure.

'Well,' she whispered, 'what do you think? You're pleased, aren't you?' He was speechless.

Of course, it was a shock, a *huge* shock, she knew that. And it would take a moment to sink in. But he'd be so pleased, wouldn't he?'

'Say something,' she said nervously.

'Oh, I just don't know what . . .' He stopped mid-sentence,

an expression of mounting shock on his face.

'How could it happen?' he stuttered. 'This is unbelievable, I don't believe it.'

'I know it's a shock, darling,' she said swiftly, wanting him to take her in his arms. 'I'm having our baby, Richard,' she said softly. 'Aren't you pleased?'

She stared up at him, willing him to smile and kiss her. She wanted to feel strong arms around her and his voice telling her it would be all right. But he stared at her with the sort of expression she had only ever seen on his face when Ireland was thrashed at Landsdowne Road or when an entire roll of film had been overexposed.

Jo felt nausea quiver in the pit of her stomach. She couldn't believe this was happening. This was the moment when Richard should kiss her and hug her as if she was Belleek china. If she was china, he obviously didn't like the pattern. What the hell was going on?

'B-b-but how?' he asked incredulously.

Jo's temper suddenly snapped. 'Jesus, Richard, what do you want, a biology lesson? How the bloody hell do you think it happened?'

She knew she sounded shrewish and she didn't care. Richard was supposed to love her and she had just told him the most wonderful news in the world. And all he could do was stammer and stutter and ask how it happened!

'This is our baby!' she cried. 'Don't you care? Aren't you happy? We're going to be parents in seven months, Richard!'

'I don't believe this,' he said hoarsely, 'how could you be pregnant?'

'Well I suppose it must have something to do with making love, which we do all the time, and the fact that condoms aren't one hundred per cent safe. Look, I only found out this morning,' she said, suddenly weary.

'I know we didn't plan it . . .'

'You can say that again,' he snapped.

'Look, it just happened, right? I'm as surprised as you are, Richard.' Jo rubbed one hand over her left temple, feeling the

81

familiar throbbing migraine build up.

'What was I supposed to do? Shut up and pray it would go away, like a terrified sixteen-year-old girl? I thought you'd be happy and that you wanted to settle down finally,' she hesitated for a moment. 'The baby's due in January.'

'What do you mean it's due in January?' he asked. 'Jesus, we're not ready for a baby, I mean, why didn't you tell me?' he said incredulously.

'I *am* telling you,' she answered.

'I do not believe this is happening, I just don't believe it,' he repeated, running a hand jerkily through his hair. 'OK, let's think about this. Who else have you told? Not that bloody Janice I hope, otherwise it'll be all over the place like a rash. You know what she's like,' he spat.

'I didn't want to tell anyone until I told you,' she faltered.

'Look Jo, this is an awful mess, can't you see? I don't want children, not now anyway. I'm not ready for all that stuff yet, you know that. What made you think differently?'

Jo stepped away from him. For the second time that day, her pulse was racing and she could feel the blood racing in her veins.

All she wanted to do was sink into her bed at home and close her eyes, or start reading her latest book, curled up under the duvet. And not think, not think about anything.

'Let me get this straight. You don't want this child,' Jo said quietly, 'and you don't want to settle down with me. Have I got that right?'

Her face was pale as she looked at him, wanting the truth, hoping that his answering smile would abruptly banish any doubts. She could hear sounds of merriment coming from the newsroom. Corks were popping. Jo guessed that the paper's managing director was about to launch the supplement with a champagne toast.

At the sound, Richard unconsciously reached for the camera slung around his neck on a fraying Canon strap and looked longingly in the direction of the party.

Jo was close to tears but she had to get an answer from him.

'Talk to me, Richard. What do you want to do?'

'Oh God, Jo, why did you get pregnant, now of all times?' He ran a hand through his hair and for a brief moment she remembered lying in the Egyptian cotton sheets on his bed, running her fingers through his hair while he lay sexually sated in her arms. They were so close, that was why she could never have imagined this.

'Why now, of all times? In a few years, yes, but not now.' He looked at her beseechingly, like a naughty boy who's just sent his football through the neighbour's kitchen window.

'Will can look after the agency for a few years and I planned to go to London to work with one of the sports papers there. It's a brilliant opportunity, darling. I was going to ask you to come with me.' He was pleading now.

'It'll be marvellous. Just a few more years and then we can settle down and maybe have kids if you really want them . . .'

His voice rose excitedly as he looked eagerly at Jo, waiting for her to agree, waiting for her to smile and say what she'd always said, 'Whatever you want.'

Memories came flooding back to her, memories of the times she'd asked him about his previous relationships. Among the litany of model girlfriends, there had been one long-lasting relationship with a German girl who had left Dublin when she and Richard broke up.

'Beate wanted to settle down and I just wasn't ready for that.' Richard shrugged. 'We were too young.' She'd believed his simple explanation, grateful that he hadn't wanted to marry any of her predecessors, and that he'd been too young to settle down with the only one who sounded like a true love.

Richard Fitzgerald had once been the Don Juan of the photographic world, but she had tamed him. He'd given up a lifetime of bimbos to be with her, or so she'd thought.

He wasn't too young to settle down any more: he was thirty-seven to her thirty-four. Surely it was time for him to stop running away from responsibility and start a family? Obviously not.

83

Commitment-phobic, Janice had called him the first time she had seen him. Perhaps her friend had been right.

Richard gently stroked her palm, tracing delicate circles and kneading the fleshy base of her thumb. People with lots of soft flesh in that precise spot were supposed to be very sensual he had always said, joking that she must be the sexiest woman in the world because of her soft, caressing hands.

Before, when he'd murmured endearments into her ear and stroked her skin, her heart leapt with love for this funny and talented man. Not tonight.

'Darling, don't be upset, please.' He was all charm again. He'd always been able to charm his way out of any trouble. He just smiled that boyish smile and wheedled until she gave in and forgave him.

Like that time he'd promised to pick her up from the office Christmas party and simply never showed up. It had taken two hours to get a taxi that night because the streets were black with ice and half the city had left the car at home so they could get drunk.

He'd been so contrite, so full of remorse at having forgotten all about the party, that she'd forgiven him by lunchtime the next day. It was funny the way he never forgot any professional commitments, only personal ones.

'We can have children later, my darling,' he said pleadingly. 'We're not ready for this yet, are we?' he murmured, reaching out to stroke her cheek, waiting for her to give in. She always gave in, Jo realised suddenly. For all his relaxed charm and boyishness, Richard always got his own way. In everything. It didn't matter whether they'd argued over where to go for dinner or what film to see, somehow Richard always got what he wanted. For once, he was out of luck.

'What are you suggesting?' she asked, her voice dangerously low.

'Well,' he looked around as if to check that nobody could hear them, 'you know, get rid of it.'

She snatched her hand away as though his fingers were burning her, staring him in the face angrily.

'And if I don't "get rid of it" as you so euphemistically call it, what then?'

'Jo, you're being unreasonable. All I'm saying is that this is the wrong time in my life for a baby.' Richard's face was fast losing its engaging smile. 'I'm not ready for it. *We're* not ready for it.'

'No, *you're* not ready. You're so bloody selfish,' she hissed. 'You just couldn't bear to have to think about someone else besides yourself. We can't have a defenceless baby interrupting your plans, or getting in the way of your life, can we?'

'There's no need to be insulting.' Richard gave her one of his superior looks and tried another tack. 'We should talk about this tomorrow when you're less hysterical.'

'Hysterical!' Jo hadn't felt so close to hitting anyone in years. 'That's typical! Just because I'm pregnant, I've suddenly turned into a neurotic, moody brood mare with no brain whatsoever,' she shouted.

'Shush, someone will hear,' Richard hissed.

'Oh, we can't have that, can we?' she snarled. 'Listen, I don't care who hears me. In fact, I want everyone to hear me so I can find out what they think about the wonderful photographer everyone adores begging his girlfriend to have an abortion because it's ". . . not the right time in my life". When will it be the right time, Richard? Because you're running out of time, you're nearly forty, don't forget.

'It's not as if we were two scared teenagers or didn't have any money either,' she glared at him. 'We can certainly afford another mouth to feed and let's face it, the world will hardly be scandalised by us having a baby and not being married, Richard. So what's wrong with me having our baby?'

If someone had told her that her feelings for him could be reversed in a matter of moments, she'd have laughed at the idea. Nothing could wipe out the love she felt for Richard, the bond which tied them to each other, she would have said. But that was before he had looked her in the eye and suggested that she abort the child she wanted with all her soul.

'I'm no good with children,' Richard said helplessly. His

85

fingers played nervously with the frayed camera strap in a way that she found suddenly irritating.

'If you want it, it's your decision. I'll give you the money if you change your mind.'

'Keep your money. I don't want it or any part of you,' Jo said coldly. 'I'm having this baby, Richard, and that's final. You can go off with Sascha and play at being adults. She's just about the right IQ level for you and she's unlikely to ask you to do anything more taxing than teach her to read!'

Furious, Richard turned and stormed back into the newsroom while Jo walked slowly over to an open window and breathed in deeply. Gradually her pulse slowed down and she opened her eyes to stare out at the city silhouetted in the dusk.

In the middle of the towering spires and office blocks, she could see the minty-green-domed roof of Rathmines church, the one she and Aisling had gone to when they lived a stone's throw around the corner. Well, the one Aisling had gone to.

She remembered the thrill of Sunday mornings in the flat when there was nobody there to tell you to get up and get ready for Mass. Luxuriating in her comfy single bed, Jo always snuggled in deeper, resisting Aisling's attempts to get her to come to eleven Mass.

Aisling had loved sitting in the huge dark church. She said that Sunday Mass in the huge church was the only time that the various people of Dublin's flatland came together, until Jo remarked that not everyone in Rathmines was Catholic.

'You know what I mean,' Aisling said in exasperation. 'It doesn't matter to me what religion people are, it's just that sense of being together for a while. It would feel the same in any church or mosque or whatever,' she added passionately.

Sometimes she managed to drag Jo out of bed and hurried her along with the other, more eager churchgoers. And Jo had enjoyed Mass. The anonymity of this church made a change from Mass in her small home town where you knew everyone's great-granny's uncle, what they did for a living and why young P. J. had turned out bad.

In Innisbhail, she'd explained to Aisling, all you had to do was ask the chemist for some throat lozenges and half an hour later every second person on the street would ask you how you were feeling.

She'd had so many plans when she left her home town in Sligo to go to journalism college. Journalistically, she was going to change the world and if she didn't win a Pulitzer prize for her ruthless exposés of injustice, she was damn well going to win the Booker for her novels.

So much for literature, she thought wryly, when you can't even find yourself a decent man who'll stand by you. Her hands involuntarily slid down towards her stomach, caressing the tiny bulge which was probably more Twix bars than baby.

That other girl, the one with all those crazy dreams, was long gone. In her place was a strong woman who was determined to be the best mother she could for her baby, her fatherless baby.

She'd certainly written enough articles about single parents, now she was going to find out what it really felt like. When she'd interviewed women who'd been left holding the baby, she'd wondered how they got by on their own. Now that her own selfish boyfriend had run for the hills, she was going to find out about single motherhood the hard way.

CHAPTER SIX

Warm breath fanned her cheek. Aisling stretched her limbs under the duvet. She knew she had to get up. But . . . Just another few minutes on the warm, soft sheets, just a bit longer . . .

Hold on a moment. Her brain switched on weakly. It's Saturday. Why was Michael trying to wake her early on a Saturday morning, she wondered sleepily? And why did she have this leaden feeling in her head?

A waft of hot, fishy breath made her open gluey eyelids to gaze up at Flossie who was standing on Michael's pillow. Push off, Aisling groaned, wishing Flossie would go away and let her have just a few more hours in bed. Why hadn't Michael let the cat out? Couldn't he do anything around the house?

She moved into a more comfortable position and pretended to be asleep, hoping the cat would be fooled and leave. Flossie didn't budge and started up her secret weapon, a peculiar bad-tempered miaow which was simply impossible to ignore.

'All right, all right! I swear I'm getting you a cat-flap today!'

Aisling struggled up on the pillow. It felt as if an army band was rehearsing some horrible marching song, using her skull for drums. She squinted at the clock-radio – 8.17 a.m. and Saturday. Where the hell was Michael? He couldn't have gone to the office already, could he?

Then her brain made the unwelcome connection.

Michael hadn't let the cat out because Michael wasn't there. He had left her. Their marriage was over and she had a hangover roughly the size of France. She'd only just woken up and immediately she wanted to go right back to sleep, maybe for a hundred years.

Rolling over onto her stomach and abruptly dislodging Flossie, Aisling laid her head heavily on the pillow and felt miserable. Sober and sick, she began to remember the day before with horrible clarity.

Underwear, expensive underwear. Oh God, she remembered. She could dimly remember shopping with Fiona, her mind befuddled with Valium. And of course that slice of banoffi in the coffee shop which must have been at least 400 calories. Forget the bloody banoffi.

She could even recall arriving at Michael's office, even though the picture in her head was Technicolor high drama, very *Gone with the Wind* and utterly removed from reality. But after that . . . It was all hazy, like she had been utterly drunk and had blacked out.

Only she hadn't got drunk until much later. She hadn't got drunk until she arrived home and proceeded to drink everything in the house with an anguished Jo begging her to stop.

'You don't know what he's done,' she remembered saying as she sat at the kitchen table with the brandy bottle in one hand and a tissue in the other.

Of course Jo knew damn well what had happened. Aisling had explained everything in lurid detail, over and over again as she sank deeper into depression. And deeper into the brandy bottle. They'd discussed the whole sordid thing endlessly, from the 'men stray, so what?' theory put forward by Jo when she still thought it would all blow over, to the 'OK, he's a bastard – *all* men are bastards' conclusion.

She remembered Jo telling her about the baby, and about Richard's reaction.

'I couldn't believe it, Ash,' Jo had said, staring into the depths of the mug of tea she was cradling in her hands. 'I just never thought he'd react like that.'

'The funny thing is,' Jo continued, 'I wasn't really sure what I wanted myself at first. I kept wondering was I ready for motherhood and stuff like that. And then I did the test and I just knew, I knew I wanted the baby so badly.'

She paused and looked at Aisling, dark eyes brimming with unshed tears. 'You know what I mean, you felt that way about the twins, I remember. When you got pregnant, I really envied you. You were so happy, so content. Look at me,' she gave a sad little laugh, 'I'm a bloody wreck.'

Swept up in her own misery and with three large brandies inside her to numb the pain, Aisling hadn't really registered the awful state Jo was in.

'He'll change his mind,' she'd declared confidently. What a stupid thing to say. Poor Jo, alone except for a drunken friend wallowing in self-pity. She must have been so drunk. She couldn't even remember Jo leaving and she had no idea how she got into bed. Did she get into bed herself or did Jo help her? How horrible. And what sort of a mother did that make her?

Too damn drunk to notice if the poor twins had been sick or needed her in the middle of the night. Who knew what terrible thing could have happened and she wouldn't have been able to pull herself out of the bed to help them. She was just a useless, fat cow. No wonder Michael hadn't wanted her.

Staring at the sulky lump which Flossie had curled herself into on the end of the bed, Aisling remembered the confrontation with the man she loved and she wanted to curl up catlike herself and die.

What had she done? Why had she given him the chance to leave? She should have said nothing and maybe everything would have been all right. As each moment passed, another agonising moment of the night before came back to her, little spiteful daggers shooting into her heart.

She remembered confronting Michael in front of everyone, screaming like a fishwife in her eye-catching red dress, baring her soul and her dirty laundry in public. And she remembered hearing his cold response.

He didn't love her, he couldn't bear to be in the same house as her, for God's sake. She had been discarded like an old pair of shoes, used and dumped when they started letting rain in and were no longer fashionable. His horrible cutting words came flooding back into her mind and she finally stopped fighting the misery. Hot, hopeless tears soaked into the pillow as her predicament became clear: she was alone, alone for always.

The thought made her cry harder, so she didn't hear Paul run into the bedroom, shouting: 'Mum, Mum. Look what Phillip did! Mum? Mum?'

Despite her misery, Aisling's mummy autopilot cranked into action and she buried her swollen eyes in the pillow so that he wouldn't see how wretched she looked.

'I'm sick, darling. I think I've got that awful cold Aunt Fiona had and my eyes hurt. But you can help, Paul. Would you let Flossie out and . . . get me some milk?'

It was a calculated move. Phillip would have demanded to know why. *Why* was she sick, why wasn't Daddy there, why did he have to get the milk, why couldn't he have the money for rollerblades? Luckily, Paul was less cerebral. Not as clever at school as his twin, he was much easier to handle and could be told what to do, as long as Phillip wasn't with him.

Getting milk was a mission from Mum and he was a special agent, ready to spring into action. Full of delighted self-importance and with his brother's misdemeanour forgotten, Paul was already swinging down the banisters, eager to prove himself manly enough to look after his mother.

God, the lies adultery generated, Aisling thought morosely. Well, I can't tell two ten-year-olds that their father has run off with another woman and that their mother is on the verge of a nervous breakdown. Hah! There was a film about that: *Women on the Edge of a Nervous Breakdown.*

She'd seen it in the video shop although she'd never got it out. Perhaps now was the time to watch it. Maybe it had hints on how to get a life. Like 'lose two stone, get a great job, get yourself a toy boy and murder your cheating husband'. Easier said than done, of course.

Grimacing at the dull ache in her head, Aisling hauled herself out of bed and stood in front of the mirror, not exactly delighted with what she saw. Her eyelids were swollen and pink like pigs' trotters, her face was an unbecoming shade of beige with grey highlights and her hair was greasy after a night of sweating out more gin and brandy than was good for your liver.

Even the cute Honey Bunny picture on her nightie was faded and misshapen after years in the sixty-degree hot wash. Just like me, she mouthed silently. Wonderful. How come Danielle Steel's heroines never looked like they'd spent the night under a bush in the park when their lovers walked out on them, she thought miserably, picking up her brush.

They always looked even more fragile and doll-like than ever, with every bit of Estée Lauder still in its rightful place and not a hair escaping from the artful chignon they'd been taught to do in their Swiss finishing school.

They didn't let themselves go, reach for the gin and scrub their skin raw from using kitchen roll to wipe away the tears. Deep in dreamland, she nearly jumped out of her skin when the phone rang, its blistering peal assaulting her already painful head. She let out a deep breath, wondering whether she'd be able to face answering it. What would she say if it was her mother ringing up for a chat?

Hi, Mum. Yes, I'm fine. I've had a pretty normal week, y'know. The twins love summer camp, I've finished redecorating the downstairs toilet and Michael has left me, that's all really. How about you?

The phone continued to ring. Go on, do it, she muttered. You can't hide for ever. Her hands were shaking as she picked up the receiver and she didn't know whether she was shaking with delayed shock or hangover.

'I was nearly going to hang up,' exclaimed Jo, sounding worried. 'How do you feel?'

'Delirious. Except for the fact that my head is about to explode with a hangover and my life is in pieces.'

'Join the club,' Jo said mournfully. 'I've been going over everything in my head and wondering what I've done wrong.' She sniffled. 'Sorry. I didn't mean to moan at you. It's not your fault that my bloody lover has abandoned me and my bump.'

'It's not your fault either, Jo. I've been thinking about you and how useless I was last night. I'm sorry. All I could do was cry about my problems. You must be in bits, you poor thing.' Back in her familiar role as comforter, Aisling began to feel marginally better all of a sudden. Someone else's troubles made her momentarily forget her own and she could wallow in Jo's misery instead.

After all, she was married to Michael and nobody could take that away from her, whereas Jo was left with nothing but an extra toothbrush in her bathroom and an unborn child whose feckless father had disowned him/her. What could be worse than having one of the most wonderful times of your life ruined when you were left to go through it all on your own. Then again, what help had being married been to her? Damn all. Married or unmarried, no commitment was worth the paper it was written on unless the other person meant it.

'I was awake half the night thinking just that: that it was *all* my fault,' Jo was saying. 'My fault for getting pregnant and my fault for blithely assuming that Richard would want to be a father, as opposed to being just a sperm donor, of course.' Her voice was bitter and harsh.

'Not that he minded being a sperm donor from the fun point of view . . .'

'None of them do,' interrupted Aisling drily.

'Too bloody true. But at least most men can accept their responsibilities. Richard certainly doesn't want to. Oh damn. There's my doorbell.' Jo sounded flustered. 'Hold on a minute, will you.'

Poor, poor Jo, Aisling reflected, automatically starting to pull up the duvet and plump the pillows with the phone wedged in the crook of her neck.

Remembering her own pregnancy made her smile to herself as she worked: that magic moment when she told Michael they were having a baby – that was before she knew she was carrying twins, of course. Buying the cots and the double buggy, reading Penelope Leach as they sat together in front of the fire, stroking her rounded belly proudly and waiting for baby kicks.

Whatever happened, she'd had that togetherness. But Jo didn't. From believing that she was one half of an expectant couple, Jo had abruptly become a one-parent family. That's what I am too, she realised.

A deserted wife with two kids, no career prospects and a washing machine on the verge of packing it in. Another bloody statistic. Add one to the deserted wives' register, one to the single mothers' register and one to the womanising bastard list, she thought bitterly.

Tears stung her eyes. Don't be such a wimp. You don't know that for sure. You don't know what'll happen, so don't think about it. He'll change his mind, you know he will, he has to. He can't give up on us after all we've been through and he won't give up the twins, will he?

Would another woman give him enough to make him forget everything he'd once treasured? She thought of the woman Fiona had described to her, a glamorous career woman who was doubtless much more interesting to talk to than a harassed housewife.

Was it her fault for making that seduction too easy? Should she have abandoned the ironing, hoovering and cooking to read the Karma Sutra, picking up hints to spice up their sex life and waxing, painting and oiling herself in an effort to turn into a siren who could keep any man glued to the bedroom?

What was it model Jerry Hall had said about keeping Mick Jagger by her side: be a cook in the kitchen, a maid in the dining room and a whore in the bedroom.

Why wasn't it enough to be an ordinary wife and mother? Oh God, it all seemed so hopeless.

She swallowed hard and ran a harsh hand over her eyes, trying to obliterate the tears and the misery which was about to creep up on her again. Reaching into her bedside drawer, her fingers found the small plastic jar of pills Fiona had given her the day before. Years of dosing herself on vitamin pills meant she could just put two of the tiny tablets in her mouth and swallow without water. Screwing up her face at the acrid taste, she covered the mouthpiece with one hand, and yelled.

'Paul, love, are you coming with that milk?'

Her answer was the sound of feet pounding up the stairs as

her black-haired first-born – Phillip arrived ten minutes later – raced upstairs, across the landing and into her room bearing a plastic tumbler of milk. It was one of the green plastic tumblers the twins drank out of when they were small. Paul had always loved his one and the way it gave everything a special, plastic taste.

'I spilled a bit,' he said unnecessarily, handing her the tumbler with two inches of milk sloshing around in the bottom and milk splashes clinging to the side. 'But I cleaned it up.'

'Thank you,' Aisling said gravely, wondering what item of clothing her untidy son had ripped off the radiator to clean up with. Still, cleaning up at all was a start.

'Have you got a headache, Mum?' he asked, spotting the tablets with eagle-eyed ten-year-old's eyes. 'Why were you crying?'

'I didn't sleep, darling, and I've got a dreadful headache. But the milk will help.' She rumpled his hair affectionately and he grinned at her, his eyes crinkling up just like his father's. Other mothers had talked about their sons hitting twelve and suddenly shrugging off each affectionate gesture, furious if their mothers hugged them the way they'd been doing for years. Thank God she still had a few years of night-time cuddles before the twins became too grown-up for hair-rumpling and tickling sessions.

'Mum, can we have money for McDonald's today?' Paul asked. 'Mr Breslin is bringing us all to Stillorgan after the match and we can go into McDonald's if you let us.'

'Yes. But no milkshakes. You know how sick they make you.'

'I promise.'

He was out the door and yelling for his brother in a flash and Aisling felt the tension leave her body as another normal day in the Moran family home began to unfold. Everything was going to be fine, she just knew it. Last night was just a glitch, a bad patch that had to come out into the open. They shared so much: the boys, their life, their home. How could

Michael give all that up? The man who had cried in her arms when the boys were born wouldn't be able to leave them for some floozie. He'd come back. It was just a matter of time.

'Sorry about that,' Jo said. 'My next-door neighbour's alarm went off and she couldn't remember the code, so we had to ring her son and . . . oh, it took ages.'

'What are you doing today?' Aisling asked briskly, her new-found optimism giving her strength.

'I don't know.' Jo sounded forlorn. 'I had planned to hit Mothercare and look at baby clothes before buying some books on pregnancy . . . But I don't know if I'd be able to face it now.'

'Well, that's just what we're going to do,' Aisling said firmly. 'Lounging around crying won't solve anything. I've got to get the boys ready for soccer and then I'll meet you in the Ilac Centre outside Dunnes at . . .' she glanced at her watch, 'half ten and we can start shopping. Oh, and I'll bring some of my pregnancy books – it's not as if Michael and I are going to decide to have another child right now.'

Jo said nothing, mainly because she didn't know what to say to such a bizarrely blinkered idea.

'That's settled,' Aisling declared. 'I'll see you then.'

Hanging up, Jo sat for a moment on the couch in her small living room, thinking about her friend's sudden change of mood. Last night she had been scared that Aisling would drink herself into unconsciousness; now it seemed as if the previous day's events had never happened.

Was Aisling blotting everything out or was she really as well as she sounded? Leaning back against a cushion, Jo contemplated the whole messy situation. Which of us is worse off, she asked herself.

Gratefully sitting down on a bench in the centre of the busy shopping centre at twenty-five minutes past ten, Jo was still thinking about Aisling's predicament. Leaning back against the wooden bench, she looped her handbag strap around her wrist and tried to relax. Casually dressed in jeans and a cream cotton cricket sweater with her hair curling around her shoulders and a smattering of freckles on her face, Jo was the picture of health and casual chic. That was on the outside, of course.

On the inside, her stomach was gurgling away volcanically, considering whether to send her second breakfast up the way it came or not. Nausea came over her in waves and she wondered how long she could last without having to race for the loo which was, naturally, at the other end of the centre.

Please don't let me be sick, she prayed silently. I promise never to eat muesli ever again. She closed her eyes and willed her stomach away from the notion of morning sickness. Just let me be OK long enough to meet Aisling and then you can be as sick as you want, right?

Amazingly, her stomach obeyed and the nausea subsided. It must be all those stomach-toning classes, she thought proudly, opening her eyes with relief. Now I can even control the insides as well as the outsides!

Six minutes later, she watched Aisling emerge from the car-park exit, her well-rounded figure hidden in a long navy and cream striped shirt worn over navy ski pants.

'Sorry I'm late,' she gasped, sitting down on a corner of the bench, her face flushed from rushing down six flights of stairs. 'Everyone and their granny were ahead of me looking for parking spaces so I had to keep going up and up. You look lovely,' she finished.

'Make-up is a wonderful thing,' Jo remarked. 'You should have seen me an hour ago. This morning sickness thing is not funny, not bloody funny at all.'

'You poor thing,' Aisling said comfortingly. 'It is horrible. But you're looking all right now, aren't you?'

'I think so,' Jo stood up gingerly, took a deep breath and found that she didn't feel sick any more. 'Right. Let's shop.'

Twenty pounds' worth of pregnancy books and a pair of elastic-waisted trousers later, both women were tired of shopping. They'd been in what felt like every shop in Dublin and the Eason's bag was growing heavier with every step.

Deciding that she was now ravenously hungry, Jo suggested an early pub lunch.

'They make the most amazing toasted sandwiches in here,' she said, leading the way into a small pub on Mary Street. Like an oasis in the middle of one of the city's busiest shopping districts, the inside of the quaint, atmospheric pub was cool and welcoming. The pub's trademark dark wooden chairs and stools were already occupied by regulars who knew better than to saunter into Keating's during the lunchtime rush if they wanted a seat.

Aromatic smells of barbequed chicken, toasted cheese and garlicky potatoes filled the air and, by the time she led Aisling upstairs to sit in two huge armchairs in the tiny gallery, Jo was hungry enough to eat for three, never mind two.

'Listen to this,' she murmured, scouring the handwritten menu hungrily. 'Toasted BLTs on garlic bread or cajun chicken with sautéed mushrooms . . . mmm. The food is just amazing here. I could eat two of everything right now! But I'll have . . . the chicken. Yes, chicken.'

'The cheese salad sandwich sounds nice,' said Aisling, wondering why she didn't feel hungrier. 'Cheese salad on brown,' she smiled at the casually dressed young waiter who'd appeared pen in hand beside them.

'And a little bottle of white wine, if you have icy-cold ones, thanks.' She smiled at him again, but he was already gazing warmly at Jo, eager to please the attractive brunette who was biting her full lips tentatively as she considered what to have.

Wouldn't it be nice to have that effect on men, Aisling mused, watching the waiter watching Jo. She was used to being ignored when she was out with Jo, although she had never been jealous of her friend's ability to attract men effortlessly. Aisling had simply never considered herself attractive enough to compete with Jo's potent sex appeal.

It had been exactly the same when they shared the flat. No matter how long Aisling had spent curling her eyelashes with the horrible metal curler or applying judicious amounts of blusher to where her cheekbones *should* have been, she always felt a little dowdy beside Jo.

Even in those awful second-hand dungarees of hers with her hair tumbling around her shoulders like she'd just been standing in a wind tunnel, Jo still looked good. Men flocked to her as though hypnotised or, as Jo liked to joke, 'like slugs drawn to begonias'.

'Chicken with garlic potatoes,' Jo said firmly. 'And a cup of coffee. Do you have decaffeinated?'

'Of course,' murmured the waiter. 'Do you want anything else?'

'No.'

'I'm surprised he didn't offer you a full massage and champagne,' Aisling remarked when he'd gone, full of twenty-something unfulfilled lust.

'Young guys are all the same,' Jo said dismissively, settling back into her armchair. 'Give them one smile and they're already imagining you with your clothes off.'

'Not in my experience, they aren't. The last time I smiled at a young man he was packing my shopping in Dunnes and he looked at me like I was on day release from John of God's.' Aisling sighed heavily.

'But how can I expect strangers to fancy me if my husband doesn't.' Now the Valium was wearing off, she felt miserable again, miserable and hopeless.

'Come on, Ash,' soothed Jo, patting her on the knee. 'There's no point torturing yourself. It's not your fault.'

'But it is,' she wailed. 'It is. It's all my fault. I pushed him away. No wonder he wanted someone else.' She started to cry silently, her body shaking as the tears started rolling down her face.

Jo could do nothing except clasp Aisling's hand between her own. That bastard, thought Jo vehemently.

'Salad sandwich and wine,' announced the waiter, planting a small plate, a wine glass and a small green bottle on the table in front of Aisling without looking at her, 'and chicken.' The timbre of his voice changed as he gently placed a large heaped dinner plate before Jo. 'Your coffee is coming,' he added, gazing at her hopefully.

Jo ignored him. 'Ash, you can't go to pieces, you can't,' she said gently. 'He's gone, but the boys aren't. They need you now and you can't let them down.'

She grabbed the paper napkin the waiter had laid reverently in front of her and handed it to Aisling. 'Blow,' she commanded. Aisling blew.

'Listen, I wish it was different, but it isn't. We've both been dumped, nothing's going to change that, Ash. So we've got two choices: we could both go to pieces, cry all day, beg them to come back and bawl in front of anyone who'll listen.' Jo took a deep breath.

'We could decide to be victims. My baby would be born totally screwed up because I'd be totally screwed up having her, and the twins would turn into little brats from being dragged back and forth between you and Michael.

'We can't do that to them, can we, Ash?'

Aisling shook her head silently.

'Or we can fight back, survive on our own,' Jo emphasised the words heavily, determined to get her message past the wall of misery Aisling was erecting around herself.

'Maybe Michael *will* come running back to you, but you can't rely on that. You have to be strong on your own and so do I. Who knows,' she added wryly, 'Richard could be frantically speaking to my answering machine as we speak, begging forgiveness . . .' She broke off with a sarcastic chuckle.

She could just picture his face the night before, furious that he wasn't getting his own way for once. The chances of him changing his mind about the baby were slimmer than her chances of fitting into her jeans in about six months' time.

'You're right, you're absolutely right.' Aisling opened her eyes abruptly and rubbed the napkin over her cheeks. Then she sat up in her chair and picked up the wine bottle. She poured most of the contents into her glass and took a deep draught.

'I know he's not coming back, you know.' Her voice shook

as she said it. 'I just don't want to think about it. I don't want
to believe it. I want to exist in the happy place in my head
where everything's all right, where he's just at work and
where he'll be home tonight.'

'I know.' Jo stared back at Aisling. Picking up her fork, Jo
stuck it into a steaming pile of slivered golden potatoes oozing
with garlic.

'Despite everything, despite what Richard said about the
baby, I'd still take him back,' she said quietly. 'But he's not
coming back though, is he? So it's up to me now. It's up to us.
We have to get on with it, Ash,' she urged. 'You've got to get
some sort of a life for yourself, get a job and . . .'

'Get a job *now*! I can barely think straight, never mind
actually do something I've been terrified of for years!' Almost
crying again, Aisling stared at her friend in horror.

Jo went on eating.

'You can't be serious?' Aisling demanded.

'Of course I am,' the other woman answered with her
mouth full. 'Realistically, you're now a one-parent family and,
even if Michael is so wracked with guilt that he pays you huge
amounts of maintenance for the boys for the next couple of
months, it will inevitably change.' She knew she was being
brutal, but Aisling had to face facts. 'You don't know what
he's going to do now, and he could, well *they* could, have a
family and . . .' she paused to fork up more chicken, spearing
a delicious-looking bit of potato as well.

Aisling stared dully at her untouched sandwich, her eyes
red-rimmed and sad. God this was difficult, Jo thought. 'I'm
sorry, Ash. I'm trying to help, but I'm not making a very good
job of it, am I?'

Aisling took another large slug of wine and prodded her
sandwich listlessly. She wasn't even vaguely hungry now,
although Jo's chicken was disappearing faster than 99p
knickers in a sale.

She knew Jo was speaking the truth. Hideous to imagine
Michael setting up another home with that woman and
having more children.

101

'I suppose you're right,' she said slowly, twisting her wine glass around by its thin stem. 'There's one slight problem. What am I going to do?'

'Work in an office, of course. What you did before.'

'That was eleven years ago. Everything's computerised now and I haven't a clue how to work a computer. Anyway, who's going to employ me?' Aisling asked. 'There are three hundred thousand unemployed people in this country, so who the hell is going to take on a housewife with two kids, no experience, no skills and no confidence?'

Jo stirred three packets of sugar into her coffee, poured in milk and took a sip. 'When Michael met you, you were virtually running the entire motor department, not to mention studying for your Insurance Institute exams at night. You did all that when you were just twenty-two and you're trying to tell me that you couldn't do it now, when you're older and more experienced?'

'It's *because* I'm older that it seems impossible,' said Aisling weakly. 'We thought we could do anything when we were twenty-two, for God's sake. It's all totally different now, Jo. You don't understand!'

'Understand what?'

'Just because you've a brilliant job at the magazine and buckets of confidence, doesn't mean that everyone else is the same. Look at you,' Aisling cried. 'You're a successful journalist, you've got your own car, your own apartment, your own bank account and independence.

'Maybe you think that's nothing because most of your friends are journalists. But not everyone is talented and clever and able to walk into any job anywhere. I'm not afraid to work, Jo, but I'm afraid of looking for work and being told I'm too old or unskilled or useless.' She stopped miserably.

'Ash, when we met, what is it . . . fourteen, no, fifteen years ago, you were the one who was going to make something of her life,' said Jo passionately.

'I was absolutely terrified of being in Dublin, of going to college, of having no one to go home to at night and talk about what went wrong that day. It was awful, you know what I was like.' She gulped down some more coffee. '*You* gave me the confidence to stick it out in college when I really wanted to run home to my mother, and you kept me from falling for every asshole who asked me out. You were so strong,' Jo added gently. 'You still are. It's just that you've forgotten.'

Had she forgotten, or was Jo just being kind, Aisling wondered? Had she ever been sure of herself, ready to stick her neck out because she knew she could do anything?

For a moment she remembered sitting in the kitchen at home, all dressed up in clothes from her first proper pay-packet and telling a fascinated Sorcha what the department head had said to her that evening. Mum had been cooking dinner, eyes on the soup she was stirring on the spotless cooker but listening to every word about the motor department and how Margaret Synnott thought Aisling should start studying for the Insurance Institute exams as soon as possible.

'She said loads of people *say* they're going to do them, but most of them don't actually bother. But you get a bonus for each part of the exams you pass and she said if I want to get on, it would be worth it,' Aisling said, basking in Sorcha's admiration of her new black leather boots.

'I know I said I was never going to study again in my whole life after the Leaving, but I don't mind this. What do you think, Mum?'

Her mother stopped stirring and turned around, a warm smile on her face. Eithne Maguire had never been to a beauty parlour in her life, she got her hair inexpertly cut at the tiny hairdressing salon over the butcher's shop and never spent money on her wardrobe when she could buy something for her children. But when she smiled, her whole face lit up and her blue eyes shone.

'I'm so proud of you, Aisling. I've always known you could do anything you put your mind to. Where did I get such a bright daughter,' she said fondly, hugging her first-born. 'We're all so proud of you.'

This wasn't strictly true and they both knew it. Nothing Aisling could do would ever be enough for her father but, for a few hours, that didn't matter. Her mother, the one who'd always protected her from her strict and puritanical father and from his mother's constant sniping, was proud of her daughter. That was enough.

There were tears in Aisling's eyes as she leaned over and hugged Jo, but they weren't sad tears.

'Thank you. Nobody but Mum has said anything like that to me in years.'

'Well they should have,' replied Jo, forking up another mouthful of food. 'Since your bloody control freak of a father ripped every shred of confidence out of you when you were a kid, I'm not surprised that you still feel that way. Michael ought to have given you a pep talk every day to make sure you didn't sink back into the mire of insecurity, but,' she shrugged expressively, 'he's a man, so why would he bother? Ash, you can do it without him, I know you can.'

'I'm still hungry,' she added, scooping up the last bits of chicken off her plate.

'Here.' Aisling pushed her untouched sandwich over to her friend and waved to the waiter.

'Another coffee and another bottle of wine,' she said sharply. She wasn't going to waste her time smiling at him this time. Career women didn't have time to worry about rude waiters.

It was nearly half one by the time they'd walked back to the Ilac Centre and said goodbye beside the lifts to the car park. Jo wanted to go home via the office and pick up some work she had to finish before Monday, Aisling needed to get some groceries before the boys got home from football at three. She only needed bread and milk and she could get that at the newsagent's.

She'd spent her last tenner on lunch so she walked back towards the Ilac's cash dispenser and slid her card in. She was just punching in her PIN number when a thought struck her – how much money did they have in the cashsave account?

Michael topped up their current account with his salary, but he put anything left over in the cashsave account.

'If we put everything in the current account, we'll just keep writing cheques,' he said. 'We've got to save something. You never know when you're going to need a lump sum, Aisling.'

Aisling never pointed out that she was anything but reckless when it came to money. Years of listening to her grandmother drone on about wasting money had instilled in her a sense of economy. When they were first married, she bought her fruit and vegetables from a tiny greengrocer, bought meat cheaply from a small, family-run butcher and wouldn't have dreamed of buying bread when she could bake it herself.

Now that Michael was earning a good salary, she'd stopped the time-consuming trekking around buying cheap fruit and vegetables and bought everything in the supermarket. But she still carefully cut out money-off coupons, turned her old T-shirts into dusters and made her own soup, bread and marmalade. Nobody could accuse *her* of frittering away the family's money.

She pressed the 'account inquiry' button, chose the cashsave account and waited. There'd been at least three thousand pounds in there the last time she'd looked. Michael kept saying he was going to transfer it into the building society account, their 'holiday' fund.

But when she'd asked him about taking a holiday the previous month, Michael had been very vague about when he could take time off. The supplement had changed everything, he muttered, he couldn't just leave the country a month after getting it off the ground.

No wonder he hadn't been keen to look at the brochures she'd picked up from the travel agency, Aisling thought grimly. Three weeks camping in France with the family obviously paled beside the thought of a scorching week in the sun rubbing Ambre Solaire into that bitch!

She scowled as she looked at the small green numbers on the cash dispenser screen. Jesus! What was wrong? Three hundred and thirty pounds was all that was left in the cashsave account. Aisling stared at the figures intently. That couldn't be right.

She was sure he hadn't moved the money, or maybe he had and just hadn't told her? Flustered, she pushed the button to check the current account. They were nearly two hundred pounds overdrawn. Aisling looked at the little 'dr' beside the total and felt weak. What the hell was going on? Why were they overdrawn? She hadn't spent very much lately, apart from the dress she'd bought yesterday.

'Do you want more time?' demanded the little green letters on the screen. Just more money, thought Aisling, feeling the faint stirrings of temper. She quickly withdrew two hundred pounds, as much as she could take out in one day. Snatching her money from the machine, she stuffed it into her purse and turned round rapidly, cannoning into a young man waiting behind her.

'Watch out, missus!' he said to her departing back. Aisling didn't even hear him. She was already halfway to the lifts, her growing rage giving her a fierce, angry energy. All the lifts were on the upper floors and a small crowd of shoppers waited for them, idling away the time examining their shopping bags and chatting.

Normally, Aisling would have waited for the lift, not keen on panting up endless flights of stairs. Today, she ran up the stairs, her heart pumping and her temper boiling. How *dare* he take everything out of the account! How dare he!

What sort of a bastard was he to leave her and the boys, and then take all their bloody money into the bargain! What the hell were she and the twins supposed to live on? How were they going to pay the mortgage or buy food without any money? What a bastard! She could kill him, *would* kill him.

Wait until I get my hands on you, Michael Moran, she growled under her breath as she marched towards her car. You'll be sorry you ever heard of bloody Jennifer Carroll, I'll see to that! Aisling dragged open the car door and threw her handbag in. I never thought he'd stoop so low as to take money from his kids' mouths, she thought, grinding the gearshift into first.

She'd never driven out of the city centre so fast. Barely noticing amber lights, she wove in and out of different lanes, gritting her teeth and swearing at other drivers.

No matter how terrible the previous day had been, no matter how devastated she'd felt when Michael told her he didn't love her, she'd had one consolation. The boys. If Michael wanted some high-flying career woman with legs up to her armpits and a wardrobe full of basques and suspender belts, then he could have her.

But Aisling would always have the boys, their beloved boys. And if Michael ever got bored with Ms Carroll, he could always come home for Phillip and Paul's sakes. And for hers. She wouldn't turn him away, couldn't turn him away. She loved him, despite everything.

That thought had consoled her, knowing that Michael would find it hard to be apart from his children and that he'd *have* to come home. Eventually.

Or so she'd thought. Obviously, she'd been wrong. If he could callously strip their bank account, knowing that Aisling had no other means to support the twins, then he'd gone too far. He could discard her, but not Phillip and Paul. Damn him, but she'd fight him tooth and nail for every penny the boys needed!

What sort of man would get up early the morning after leaving his wife, and drain their bank account? Suddenly it all made sense. Aisling, you fool! If you could only withdraw two hundred pounds with your bank card in one day, that's all he could take out too. Which meant that he hadn't just grabbed the money this morning, he'd been siphoning it out for a few weeks! What a pig!

She'd never forgive him. If he thought she was going to be a pushover, crying every time she saw him and begging him to come back, he was wrong. She was going to be as hard as nails and every bit as cunning as he had been to protect her children. Watch out you bastard, she hissed.

When she opened the front door, she immediately knew he'd been there. Flyers for a pizza company were thrown casually on the hall table, the way only Michael left them. That always drove her mad. Why couldn't he bring them into the kitchen and either stick them in the basket where she put the bills or put them in the bin? Because tidying up was *her* job, of course.

She didn't even bother to pick up the flyers, but ran upstairs to their bedroom. His side of the wardrobe was open, a couple of metal hangers lay on the bottom shelf where Michael usually kept his shoes.

He'd taken everything, suits, trousers, and the shirts she ironed so carefully, leaving nothing but a forgotten belt hanging forlornly from the tie rack inside the door. She checked the drawers and their en suite bathroom. Everything of Michael's was gone. Only a damp ring remained beside the sink as proof that his aftershave had stood there, the big bottle of Eternity for Men she'd bought him for Christmas, thinking that forty quid a bottle was a bit pricey.

He'd even remembered to take his shower gel, the tangy lemon-scented one he preferred to her coconut version.

He'd remembered everything, she thought bitterly. He'd never managed to do that during their twelve years of marriage. Packing for holidays had always been a nightmare, as she had to remember everything Michael and the boys needed. If she didn't stick his shaving kit in the suitcase, he was quite likely to forget it. Not so today. This time Michael wasn't coming back after two weeks.

Good. She didn't want him back. But she damn well wanted to know where their money was. In the bedroom, she picked up the phone and dialled the *News*.

'The deputy editor's office,' she snapped.

'Hello.' His voice sounded the same as it had the night before. Calm and relaxed. She was going to knock that out of him, that was for sure.

'What the hell have you done with the money from the cashsave account?' she demanded.

'Aisling?'

'No, it's Cindy-bloody-Crawford. Of course it's me, your poor bewildered wife, the one who never noticed you taking all our money from our joint account. How did you do it, huh? Take out two hundred with your card every day in anticipation of dumping me?'

'Stop screaming down the phone, Aisling,' he said coldly. 'And stop making wild accusations. I didn't *steal* anything.'

'Where's the money then?'

'In a separate account, your account.'

'What account?' she demanded.

'Didn't you read my note?'

'No, I didn't.'

'It's on the bed, on your side.'

It was all her side now.

'Listen,' Michael said wearily, 'I opened an account for you last month. I knew this would all come to a head and I wanted to sort out things financially. I'm not going to let the kids starve just because we've split up, so I talked to a solicitor about the best way to handle things, and he advised me to open an account for you.'

Aisling was dumbstruck. He'd talked to a solicitor over a month ago. He must have been planning this for months. What a bastard.

'Are you listening, Aisling?' His voice interrupted her thoughts. 'There's one thousand five hundred in the account. I left the details on the dressing table. I'm going to close the current and cashsave accounts. We don't need joint accounts any more.'

She sat down on the bed, only half listening. He'd consulted a solicitor over a month ago, that was how sure he was that their marriage was over.

'I can't believe you've been cold-bloodedly planning this without telling me,' she said slowly.

'I haven't time to discuss it,' he said harshly. 'I'll look after the boys financially, but I'm not keeping you in luxury for the rest of your life. I'm not a bottomless pit, Aisling. You'll have to get a job. You've always said you wanted one, anyway.'

'And you never wanted me to get one,' she screamed. 'You absolute bastard! I'd like to kill you!'

'I don't have time to listen to your insults,' Michael said coldly. 'I've a job to do. Unlike you.' With that, he hung up, leaving Aisling mouthing furiously at the dialling tone.

The note was on her pillow, a page ripped from a notebook and covered with Michael's distinctive scrawl. A small, blue lodgement receipt was under it.

'Aisling, I'm sorry you aren't here. I wanted to talk to you about money and about the boys. I've opened an account for you and put half of the holiday money in it. I'd like to talk to the boys myself, it's important that they hear it from both of us. I'll ring you later about coming over this evening.'

That was it. No 'love, Michael'. Well, he didn't, did he? Damn him. He even expected her to wait patiently for him to turn up in the evening so they could tell the boys together. He could bloody well stuff his idea of dropping in when he wanted. He'd have to consult her before he set foot in the house. If Michael wanted to fight, she'd fight back!

CHAPTER SEVEN

Fiona thought it was a brilliant idea.

'Of course Pat can help you get a job! He's always moaning about hiring twenty-year-old office juniors and having them leave as soon as they're trained to work the computers properly.'

Fiona sat down on one of the Morans' pine kitchen chairs, scarred from endless Dinky toy games, and crossed long, sleek legs encased in black lycra sports leggings. 'He'd jump at the chance to hire someone like you.'

'Do you really think so?' Fiona was as generous as she was eccentric. Aisling didn't want her to badger poor Pat into hiring their suddenly single neighbour as a huge favour. If she was going back to work, she certainly needed a leg up, but not charity.

'I'm very rusty, Fiona, and I'd be eager to learn, but only if Pat thinks it would work,' she said earnestly.

'Don't be ridiculous, Aisling. If you can whip up a four course meal in two hours without becoming hysterical when the freezer packs in and defrosts your home-made ice cream into slop, then you'll have no trouble answering a few phones.'

'And Daddy adores you, you know,' Fiona added with a smile. 'He always wants to sit beside you at dinner parties and you'll probably have to fight him off once he sees you sitting all secretarial behind the reception desk!'

Despite herself, Aisling burst out laughing, thinking of Fiona's imposing and steely-eyed barrister father trying to inveigle her into his office for a passionate session on an antique desk strewn with legal tomes and writs.

'I just can't see that happening.' She grinned.

'Well I certainly can,' replied Fiona. 'Since Mother left him, he's like a fourteen-year-old who's just discovered what sex is all about and is anxious to try it out as often as possible. I told you that he almost ended up in bed with one of the bridesmaids at my cousin's wedding?'

'Really?'

'You have no idea what he's like. Mad as a March hare and twice as randy. The thing is, women just love him, they always have,' Fiona paused to light up a cigarette.

'I know,' she muttered, 'I don't know why I keep smoking these things if I'm so keen on being fit. Pat gives me the same bloody lecture every day, but a girl's got to have some vices.'

'I wasn't going to say anything,' protested Aisling. 'I can hardly talk about being fit under the circumstances. My thighs haven't seen the inside of a pair of lycra leggings for years and if my stomach gets any bigger, I'll need those horrible roll-on things Granny wore.'

'Over my dead body,' Fiona said firmly. 'The only roll-on product modern girls use is deodorant, my dear. Aisling Moran, career woman, is going to be sleek, healthy and devastatingly sexy, even if I have to personally drag you to the gym three times a week.'

She got up and stuck her cigarette under the tap for a moment. 'I'll talk to Pat when I get back from my step class and find out what's the story workwise. There's always someone away and hiring temps from the agencies costs a fortune. He'll be thrilled to get his hands on you. Well, Daddy certainly would.'

Aisling giggled again. No matter what disaster hung over life like a dark cloud, a few moments in Fiona's company listening to her spiky and bitchy comments on life in general could raise anyone's spirits.

Through Fiona's eyes, Aisling was changing her life for the better, going back to work as a confident and mature woman. Not for a moment would Fiona see Aisling as a terrified and lonely wife, suddenly single and unsure of what life held for her and her two sons.

That was part of her charm, Aisling realised. Fiona viewed

life through tinted glasses and if they weren't always rose-tinted, they certainly made everything in life look more interesting.

If her husband of ten years decided to leave his fun-loving, tennis-mad wife, Aisling knew that Fiona would take a deep breath and start again, searching for a better life and a faithful mate without being destroyed by the break-up.

She watched her friend pull on a pink sweatshirt over the tiny hot pink lycra leotard which Aisling reckoned wouldn't fit one of her thighs. Tanned from frequent trips to the Finucanes' villa in Spain and a perfect size ten thanks to aerobics every second day, Fiona looked fantastic.

When she was dressed in the exquisite clothes she adored shopping for, with her long nails beautifully manicured, her gold Cartier watch catching the light and her rich chestnut hair shimmering from endless salon treatments, she looked every inch a rich bitch. Thank God she wasn't.

Aisling remember the day the Finucanes had moved into the huge red-brick house across the road, a fleet of removal vans lined up outside full of expensive-looking pieces of furniture. At least ten harassed men in overalls spent the afternoon carrying furniture into the house, struggling with huge pine wardrobes, enormous squashy sofas and a gleaming dining-room table which looked big enough for at least twenty people.

Aisling couldn't help peering out of her bedroom window, fascinated to see what sort of furniture the new neighbours had. A tall, immaculately dressed brunette roared up in her sporty black car and marched into the house with a small fluffy dog in tow. Aisling decided that her new neighbour was obviously some high-powered career woman and wasn't the sort who'd be interested in coming over for morning coffee.

So she got quite a shock when Fiona arrived on the doorstep two days later, introduced herself and asked were the people two doors away totally mad or just mildly insane?

'All I said was that my husband and I had moved in across the road and that we wanted to say hello to everyone when the poor dear turned white as a sheet, told me she didn't want to buy anything and slammed the door in my face,' Fiona complained.

'She's deaf,' explained Aisling, 'and probably a little bit mad into the bargain. If you think she's bad you should meet her brother. He stills thinks it's 1944 and he's working undercover as a spy in France.'

'Isn't there anyone normal living around here?' demanded Fiona.

'We're pretty normal,' Aisling replied. 'Most of the time, anyway. Do you want to come in for coffee?'

'I'd love to. If I don't get at least four doses of caffeine into my system before eleven in the morning, it goes into shock. I could go home and bring some disgustingly sweet biscuits if you want any?' she offered.

Aisling laughed. 'Believe me, I've got loads of disgustingly sweet things here. Too many in fact.'

They'd been friends ever since. Sometimes they did their shopping together, chatting volubly while they waited impatiently in the supermarket queue or wandering through clothes shops while Fiona shopped and Aisling vowed to diet.

She'd always urged Aisling to join her in the gym or come playing tennis with her friends. Now she gave Aisling a determined look as she picked up her keys.

'You've got to get out and you've got to start looking after yourself, darling. I've seen enough girls fall to pieces when their marriages go sour and I don't want to see it happen to you. Tomorrow you and I are going shopping for trainers and I don't want any arguments, right?' She grinned and poked Aisling in the arm.

When Fiona had gone, Aisling went into the sitting room where Phillip was sitting cross-legged on the floor, eating Rice Krispies and watching some spiky-haired DJ counting down the Top Ten hits. There were comics and football cards strewn all over the carpet, along with two empty crisp packets and Phillip's discarded socks.

'Phillip, this place is a mess! Tidy it up.'

'Why? Who's coming?' he answered back smartly. 'Dad?'

Aisling felt that knot in her stomach again, the one which sprang into action when she thought of the effect Michael's departure would have on the twins.

The night before, she'd told them their father was going to be away for a week. She didn't know what to say and decided that she'd break the news to them gently.

Paul had simply looked surprised. 'I thought Dad was coming to watch us play soccer on Saturday,' he said slowly. 'Will he be back in time?'

'I don't know, darling.' Feeling guilty for lying and even guiltier for stopping Michael coming home to tell them himself, Aisling gave Paul a kiss on the cheek and turned to say goodnight to Phillip. Dressed in his favourite Manchester United pyjamas with a comic propped up in front of him, he gazed at her steadily but didn't say anything.

Aisling kissed him and gently stroked the purple bruise on his left arm he insisted he'd got from banging into the goalposts at school.

'Goodnight, Giggs, or is it Cantona tonight?' she asked.

'None of them,' he answered dully.

She forced herself to smile and left the door ajar on her way out so the boys would have the glow of the landing light for comfort. She switched off their light and headed downstairs. She went straight for the drinks cabinet and a stiff gin and tonic.

Phillip knew something was wrong. Of course he did. Children detected every nuance of their parents' relationship, she'd read in a magazine once. Phillip certainly did. Michael always said that Phillip was a budding investigative reporter – inquisitive, pushy and as unstoppable as a freight train. 'Why?' was his favourite word.

This time, Phillip, I don't know *why*, Aisling thought morosely. She stared blankly at the comics and crisp wrappers scattered on the rug. The place needed hoovering as usual. She had to tell the boys. She should have told them last night. There was no point pretending everything was OK. They'd

115

find out sometime. Phillip looked up at her, the TV forgotten and anxiety in his big, sad eyes.

'Is Dad coming home today?'

Phillip's question didn't surprise her. She looked at his earnest, questioning face, those dark eyes reminding her so painfully of his father. Decision time. Don't be a coward, Aisling. Tell them now, you have to.

'Where's Paul?' she asked resolutely.

'Upstairs,' he answered.

Aisling went to the bottom of the stairs.

'Paul,' she called. 'Come downstairs. I want to talk to you.'

He ran down the stairs noisily, jumped the bottom two steps and landed heavily on both feet. Sockless of course. If Phillip wasn't wearing his socks, Paul wasn't either.

Running into the sitting room, he skidded to a halt and thumped down on the floor beside his twin. He picked up one of the crisp wrappers and looked inside.

'You've eaten mine!' he said accusingly, glaring at Phillip.

'I didn't!'

'You did . . .'

'Quiet!' shouted Aisling. Damn, she hadn't meant to shout. 'Boys, there's something I've got to tell you,' she began in a softer tone. 'It's about your father and I . . .'

She stopped, aware of the enormity of what she was about to tell them. What words could you use to say 'your father's left me', she asked herself? They were still looking at her, mini versions of Michael, the same features, the same colouring.

For a brief moment, she remembered the day she'd told him she was pregnant. Wrapped up in their own private world as they walked through Bushy Park on a freezing March day, they'd gone through names they liked and tried to imagine what their baby would look like.

'Like you, I hope,' she'd smiled, wanting their child to have Michael's dark looks instead of her own pale skin and mousey hair.

'No, you,' he'd murmured, pushing aside her parka hood to kiss the soft curve of her neck.

116

Phillip and Paul were still staring at her, waiting much too patiently. Poor kids, she thought, they knew something was wrong. All she could do was soften the blow, make it as friendly as possible.

Even though her heart was full of rage at what Michael had done, she couldn't use the boys like Exocet missiles, turning them against their father as ammunition in a marital war. She shouldn't have told Michael to get stuffed when he'd rung the night before.

She tried again. 'Dad and I have been fighting lately, and . . .'

Jesus, what could she say? He's gone, he doesn't live here any more? It all sounded so horrible, so final. If they were only a few years older they could understand. But at ten, how could they be expected to?

'Dad has moved out for a while, boys. He hasn't been happy . . .'

'Why, why wasn't he happy?' asked Phillip anxiously. 'Was it my fault? I didn't mean to keep asking for rollerblades.'

'No, no, darling. It's nothing to do with you. Dad loves both of you, he's just . . . he needs to be on his own for a while. He wants you to be strong and understand that he loves you very much.'

'But why's he gone then?' Paul was looking at her with so much confusion in his eyes, that she didn't know whether to hug him or cry herself.

'Dad and I don't always get on,' she said slowly. 'Sometimes adults fight and need some time on their own, and that's what Dad wants. Time on his own. You'll still see him,' she added, trying to sound reassuring.

'Why, Mum?'

For once, Paul was asking all the questions. Phillip just stood there, head bent, his thick, dark hair falling over his forehead. Aisling reached out to stroke it, but he wrenched away from her hand.

'I'll tell you what, let's go to McDonald's for lunch. Does that sound like a good idea?'

'OK.' Paul looked as if he might cry.

'We went to McDonald's yesterday. I thought we weren't supposed to eat burgers all the time?' said Phillip sullenly.

'Not all the time, no,' answered Aisling. 'Sometimes we can break the rules, can't we? Where are your socks, boys? I'll give you five minutes to be ready to go, OK?'

Paul sprinted up the stairs in search of his missing socks, while Phillip stared at the floor. Aisling put her arms around him and hugged him tightly, feeling the tension and misery in his body.

'Darling, I'm so sorry about this. It's not your fault, it had nothing to do with you or rollerblades, or anything like that. This is between Dad and me . . .'

'It doesn't matter,' he said suddenly. He pulled away from her and picked his socks up off the floor. 'I'm not hungry.'

Aisling sat on the edge of the bed, talking quietly on the phone so the boys wouldn't hear her and wake up. It was nearly half nine but it was still bright outside. A man and woman were walking a dog on the other side of the road, holding hands as their brown and white terrier ran eagerly in and out of gardens.

'It's so unfair. The boys are so upset. I feel as if it's my fault, as if *I'm* ruining their childhood.'

'Don't be silly, you're doing all you can,' Fiona answered. 'What else can you do?'

'Oh, I don't know.' Aisling sighed heavily, thinking about the day's events. Lunch had been a disaster. Phillip refused to eat anything. Paul had followed suit, leaving a half-eaten quarter-pounder and most of his chips to Aisling. Normally, she'd have wolfed them down. But today she didn't feel remotely hungry.

'What do you think about the temping job Pat suggested?' Fiona asked.

'Bloody terrified, that's what I think. I don't know what scares me most, actually going back to work or finding out that I can't remember anything after twelve years. I'd hate to let Pat down when he's been so good giving me this chance.'

'Rubbish, of course you'll be fine. It's nothing demanding, honestly. You've got a week to think about it, anyway,' Fiona pointed out. 'Elizabeth isn't going on maternity leave for another three weeks, so you've lots of time to get used to the job. It'll be a doddle for you.'

'Thank you, Fiona. Thanks for everything, cheering me up, getting me a job and oh . . . just for being there,' Aisling said gratefully. 'I don't know what I'd have done without you or Jo.'

'How is she?'

'Actually, she's doing pretty well. I was talking to her earlier and she'd just come in from a long walk in Portmarnock. Said she wanted to tire herself out so she'd sleep tonight. Poor thing.'

'What was the boyfriend like?' Fiona asked.

'I don't really know, I only met him a couple of times and we didn't exactly talk. Michael wasn't too keen on him, but then,' Aisling gave a little hollow laugh, 'Michael's judgement has been a little faulty lately. Or maybe it's *my* judgement that's been faulty.'

She paused for a moment.

'Stop moping,' ordered Fiona, 'and give me the low-down on this horrible man. Is he gorgeous or a complete scumbag?'

'He's very handsome, all blond hair, blue eyes and white teeth. He could advertise toothpaste.'

'But still a scumbag?'

'I think so. Actually, most of Jo's boyfriends have had some fatal flaw or another, like not wanting to settle down. Which is odd, really,' Aisling said reflectively. 'I've read that women who've been abused or hurt as children automatically go for the type of men who'll abuse their kids, it's a vicious circle.'

'She wasn't abused, was she?' Fiona asked in amazement.

'Lord no. But her father died when she was young and I often think she unconsciously picks men who are going to leave eventually, sort of like her father left,' added Aisling. 'Strangers meeting Jo would probably think she has everything, a great

119

CATHY KELLY

career and great looks. In reality, she has as many problems as
anyone else, more maybe.'

'I know what that's like,' remarked Fiona. 'Before my
mother and father split up, they were always fighting, at each
other's throats like pit bulls. But because we had the big
house, the Jag, the housekeeper, etc., everyone assumed we
had the life of Riley. Everything looked so different from the
inside,' she added.

'We all pretended everything was perfect, but I never
brought girls home from school in case they witnessed one of
Mummy's rages. Daddy had given her these china figurines
over the years and when she got really vexed she'd fling them
at him. By the time she left, there wasn't a china ornament in
the house, she'd smashed them all.' Fiona gave a little laugh.
'So I know all about covering up, I'm an expert at it.'

'I'm sorry, Fiona,' said Aisling sympathetically. 'I never
knew.'

'Oh, I just don't talk about it any more. It took me ages to
get it out of my system, but I'm fine now. The point is,' Fiona
said emphatically, 'that things would have been a lot better if
they'd just split up, instead of carrying on a bloody charade for
years.'

'What went wrong?' asked Aisling, unable to conceal her
curiosity. She'd never heard Fiona talk about her mother
before, except to say that they rarely met up because her
mother lived in Arizona.

'Drink,' Fiona said abruptly. 'She drank like a fish, all her
family did. That's why you'll never see me drinking too much,
I'm too bloody terrified to. It runs in families and I don't want
it to run in mine any more.'

Christ, thought Aisling, remembering the nearly empty
bottle of gin in the drinks cupboard. She'd been drinking far
too much all weekend.

'I'd better be going, Ash,' Fiona said. 'Pat was off playing
snooker all afternoon and wants to have a cosy family night in
to make up for it. I'll be over tomorrow to discuss your
working wardrobe,' she added. 'We'll have to find something

120

drop-dead gorgeous to give you confidence on the first day.'

'Something drop-dead gorgeous from *my* wardrobe?' exclaimed Aisling.

'If we can't find something, we'll just have to go shopping,' continued Fiona gleefully. 'Fun, fun, fun!'

'Goodbye, you irrepressible shopper,' laughed Aisling, hanging up.

Right, she decided. No gin tonight. Just think of Fiona's mother.

The next morning she brought the boys to school and waved them in like she did every other Monday morning.

It just didn't feel like every other Monday. Last week, she'd been a reasonably contented, well, not totally *dis*contented woman. Now she was separated and broke.

With her finances very much in mind, she headed for Roches Stores in the Frascati Centre and took a basket instead of a trolley. Walking around aisles scented with the delicious smell of freshly baked bread, Aisling shopped carefully, adding up the prices in her head.

Twenty pounds seemed so much to pay for such a small amount of shopping. That expensive conditioner would have to go back, there was a much cheaper generic one. And one-fifty for those little pots of fromage frais? Ridiculous.

At home, she put everything away and sat down with a cup of coffee and a pen and paper. She listed the various household bills, working out how much money she needed every week. The total seemed huge, especially compared to the money she had in the bank. One and a half thousand wouldn't go very far. What would Michael pay for the boys' keep, she wondered?

The phone rang as she was hanging out the washing. Damn. She raced in, nearly tripping over a raised slab on the patio in the process.

'Hello,' she said breathlessly.

'Hello, Aisling,' said her mother. 'I've been wondering if you were all sick or something since I haven't heard from you all weekend. Are the boys OK?'

Only a mother knew how to ask questions that were loaded with meaning, thought Aisling, wondering where to start. She had been expecting the call. Or rather, dreading it.

It was a rare weekend when Aisling didn't ring her mother at some point or another. She usually waited until Sunday afternoon to ring because her father was invariably having a little nap over the newspapers and wouldn't answer the phone.

There was always something for Seán Maguire to complain about. These days, twenty-two-year-old Nicola was the bane of his life, constantly on the phone talking to 'that boyfriend of hers' or going out in unsuitable clothes. Enduring one of his five-minute moans was a waste of her time, Aisling thought. It didn't surprise her that Nicola's twin brother, Nicholas, was never in trouble with his father. Seán had always wanted a son, something he'd never let Aisling forget.

'I was worried, Aisling,' her mother was saying.

'The boys are fine, Mum.' It was time to bite the bullet. 'I'm afraid the problem is Michael . . .'

'Oh Lord, what's wrong with him? I just *knew* there was something wrong!'

'There's nothing wrong with him, Mum,' Aisling said. Nothing a slap on the face wouldn't cure, anyway. 'He's . . . er, we've split up.'

'What! I can't believe it, Aisling, that's terrible, just terrible.'

Aisling had never heard her mother so shocked. This was so difficult. Please God don't let Mum figure out everything. I couldn't face discussing the whole bloody thing again.

Aisling could hear her mother pulling up a kitchen chair to sit down on. The phone in the Maguire home was in the kitchen, making it impossible to have any sort of private conversation at all, Nicola constantly complained to her older sister. Eithne Maguire's voice quavered as she spoke again.

'But why, Aisling? What happened? Have you been having problems and why didn't you tell me? And what about the boys, poor lambs?'

Aisling felt a lump in her throat. Why did all this have to be so hard? Why didn't stationary companies print separation cards, like the change of address ones. It would be so much easier. 'Mrs and Mrs Moran have split up and henceforth Mr Moran will be residing at Number 10 Primrose Avenue with a Cindy Crawford lookalike while Mrs soon-to-be-ex Moran will be remaining in the family pad fielding telephone calls from curious relatives.'

'The boys are doing all right, Mum. Michael and I haven't been getting on and we had a fight. He's moved out for a while, that's all.'

'*That's all?*' demanded her mother. 'What do you mean, "that's all"? Is this serious? Is he gone for good, Aisling? Tell me.'

Aisling gave up. There was no point trying to pretend that she and Michael were in the middle of an amicable separation. She might as well tell the truth even though it hurt like hell.

'Listen Mum, I'll tell you the truth, but I don't want Father to know, right?' she said fiercely. 'You can tell him that we've grown apart and are perfectly happy with the situation, I just don't want him knowing.'

'All right, love,' Mum said softly. 'Just tell me everything.'

Everything took three-quarters of an hour and two cups of tea. Father would undoubtedly have a seizure when he got the itemised phone bill – itemised so that Nicola '. . . couldn't ruin me ringing that lout . . .'

While her mother was making the second cup of tea, Aisling idly mused that Telecom Eireann should have a special 'disaster' phone-call rate, a once-a-month reduction so that people with problems could ring their relatives and receive family counselling. They'd make a fortune.

'Are you not having a cup yourself, love?' Her mother asked in concern when she picked up the receiver again.

'No. I've gone off tea and coffee. Weird, isn't it? And I haven't so much as looked at a chocolate biscuit all weekend!'

'Well, that's good, darling,' answered her mother, sounding

unsure as to the benefits of a chocolate biscuit aversion in the middle of a crisis.

'It's just that I've always tried so hard to stop myself eating biscuits,' explained Aisling. 'I wanted to be slim and a size ten, like the woman Michael married. But I couldn't help myself, I kept eating and kept hating myself for eating. It was a vicious circle I couldn't escape. And now I'm not hungry at all and he isn't here to see it . . .' Her voice broke for the first time since they'd started talking. 'Oh Mum, what's going to happen? What went wrong?'

'I don't know, love,' her mother answered. 'I don't think it's that simple or that black and white. When your father and I were married, we knew it was for keeps, no matter what happened. And Lord knows, I've felt like getting a divorce myself more often than I'd care to admit. Your father hasn't been easy, you know that,' she added. 'But it's different now. Everyone expects more from life, everyone wants to be happy. They demand it. Nobody wants to try any more.'

'I wanted to try,' sobbed Aisling. 'He didn't. He's a bastard, isn't he?'

Her mother said nothing.

'Well he is, isn't he? Don't you think so? Or is it all my fault?'

'It's not your fault, Aisling. I just don't want to start criticising Michael. I made that mistake once with your father when he and your grandmother had a big row. By the time they were great pals again, he'd remembered the things I'd said about her and I don't think he ever forgave me for it.'

'You mean that Michael and I might get back together,' whispered Aisling hopefully.

'Nobody knows what's going to happen,' her mother said diplomatically. 'I just can't see the two of you split up for very long. Michael isn't stupid. He'll miss the boys and his life with you. He won't be able to forget all about the last twelve years just like that.'

'You think so?'

Aisling was ten once again, with a big tear in her new green striped dress from climbing over the fence at the back of the park and getting stuck on the barbed wire. She was waiting for her mother to fix it, to fix everything. Mam always knew the right thing to say. Her gentle and kind voice softened the harshest blow. She could mend any rip with her tiny, almost invisible stitches, dry the bitterest tears with the right words, and straighten out Aisling's world when everything seemed awry.

Now Aisling wanted her to fix something that had been battered radically out of shape. It wasn't fair, was it?

'I'm sorry, Mam,' she said quickly. 'I shouldn't have asked that. Jesus, if I don't know what's going to happen or how he's going to think, I can hardly ask you.'

'Aisling, I'd love to tell you it'll all work out between you and Michael, but I can't. It may not work out the way you want. And you'll have to face that. I do wish things were different, though,' sighed her mother. 'I know you're putting on a brave face, darling, but it's not going to be easy. I'd love if there was something I could say to make you feel better, but I don't know what to say.'

'As long as you don't tell Dad what's really happened,' begged Aisling, 'that's the best thing you could do.'

'Your father isn't that bad . . .' began Eithne loyally.

'Mam,' interrupted Aisling, 'he'd be disgusted we're splitting up and it would be all my fault. You know what he'd say. I can just do without that sort of disapproval right now. I mean, I have to psych myself up to get a job for a start. That's going to take about ten times more self-confidence than I've got as it is. I mean,' she said tiredly, 'I've been waking up in the middle of the night just *thinking* about it all in terror. What if I'm useless?'

'Don't be daft, Aisling.' Her mother's voice was firm. 'You've been running that house like clockwork for ten years, and you've never been afraid to get your hands dirty. Don't tell me you're afraid of working in an office, because you shouldn't be.'

There it was again. *Another* person who believed she was superwoman. Had she been incredibly successful at deceiving people into thinking she could do anything? Or, and this had to be wrong, did they actually believe that she *could* do anything? What a pity Michael hadn't felt the same.

CHAPTER EIGHT

Jo leaned weakly against the bath, ignoring the freezing tiles hard against her knees. She felt cold in just a T-shirt and knickers, but when the nausea hit her, she hadn't time to grab her dressing-gown. She barely had time to reach the bathroom before she retched.

She knelt by the toilet in exhaustion as the spasms in her stomach ceased. Maybe if she breathed deeply, she could calm the nausea with relaxing breaths. But even deep breathing felt too strenuous.

Instead, she just stayed where she was, closed her eyes and wished she could crawl back to bed until she felt better. Bed always seemed more appealing when you couldn't sleep late. This morning, the soft sky-blue sheets and cosy duvet were positively irresistible, simply because she had to leave them.

Rhona was already halfway to France, complete with the car, kids and enough books to last for three glorious weeks travelling around the Loire Valley. Jo had to edit the August edition of *Style* on her own. Usually, she loved the challenge of doing two jobs at once, planning the magazine and setting up fashion shoots in between chasing up articles and dealing with endless phone calls. Inevitably someone forgot to get a photo of this new designer or that TV chat show host at home, and the entire office would collapse into panic before Jo took charge and sorted whatever mini-disaster out.

Today she felt incapable of organising her underwear drawer, never mind Ireland's biggest-selling glossy magazine. It was ten past eight, she realised tiredly. Time to have breakfast. The very thought of eating made her feel ill.

She closed her eyes for a couple of blissful minutes, and steeled herself to get up and face the day.

Why did something so utterly wonderful as having a baby include one of the most horrible side effects imaginable? And why did she have to be one of the fifty per cent of expectant mothers who suffered from it? She hated the other fifty per cent.

Jo had read all about hormonal surges and gastric juices ganging up on you to make you sick as a pig. But the paragraph about overcoming morning sickness in her ancient edition of *Everywoman* had been the last straw.

Reading that having a small carbohydrate-rich breakfast '. . . brought to the wife by the husband as soon as possible after waking . . .' had made her feel even sicker, if that was possible. What she wouldn't have given to have Richard hovering over her in the morning, bringing sweet tea and sympathy along with toast and marmalade. Stop moping, Ryan, and get on with it.

She got up off the bathroom floor and washed her teeth. Her face was still deathly pale and she looked tired and drawn. Who cares, she said aloud. Nobody's going to be looking at me today. They'll just have to put up with a pale and interesting fashion editor for once.

It was only when Jo was gingerly sipping a cup of coffee that she remembered the lunchtime fashion show, a preview of the Autumn and Winter range from one of the country's most famous – and expensive – designers.

Jo had been invited weeks ago and would have to turn up, nausea or no nausea. It was going to be a glamorous, high-profile affair with every fashion editor in the country on full make-up alert, wearing the most expensive outfits from their wardrobes. An A-list fashion show, definitely. Designer Maxine was showing her collection in Stark's, a chic and over-priced restaurant where the price of one bottle of good wine would feed a family of five for a week.

Not that any of the fashion pack would actually *eat* very much. Eating and being a fashion journalist were mutually exclusive – you couldn't do both. Everyone would just pick at their food.

Jo nibbled the corner of a piece of cream cracker wearily. Why did the show have to be today? Instead of slopping into the office in a sweatshirt and comfortable jeans, she'd have to dress up and, for once, she just didn't have the energy for it. Damn, damn, damn, she muttered. She opened the wardrobe and stared at the crammed rails of clothes. She plucked a fitted red jacket from the middle of the rail and held it up to herself. Too bright, she decided, jamming it back into the wardrobe.

She mulled over a clinging navy shift dress with a matching short jacket. With the right sunglasses and pearls, it looked very Jackie O. But Jo wasn't in a Jackie O mood. She looked more like Jack Charlton.

It would have to be the hand-painted silk dress she'd got in the Design Centre. Pale gold with rich, burnt umber brush-strokes, the clinging dress always made her look like something from a medieval tapestry with her hair falling in curls around her bare shoulders. Perfect.

But it wasn't. Instead of highlighting her curves, the dress simply highlighted her belly. Flat just the week before, it had turned into a little mound overnight and the gold dress stretched across it unbecomingly.

The grey pinstripe trouser suit was just as bad. The ultra-expensive black lycra dress, which was guaranteed to vacuum-pack even the flabbiest tummy, was even worse. She wasn't in the mood to wear the navy crêpe trousers and matching mandarin shirt, even if it was loose enough to look good.

Baby, what am I going to do with you? Jo asked her bump. Poor Mummy can't go to Maxine's fashion show looking like a bag lady. What am I going to wear? You're going to have to get used to being asked this question, you know.

She stroked her belly softly, sure that the baby was listening to every word. You're going to be the most fashion-conscious baby the world has ever known, all right, darling?

If only Rhona wasn't on holidays. Jo could have rung up and asked if she could take the day off. And just blobbed around all day, watching the afternoon soaps and drinking tea.

129

Instead, she had to find some bloody thing which would fit her *and* look nice.

An hour later, she strode into the office looking as if she'd just spent the morning having the works done at the beauty parlour. Her glossy dark hair was coiled into an elegant knot held in place with tortoiseshell pins. She wore a slim-fitting navy jacket unbuttoned over a biscuit-coloured silk dress. Sheer tights and beige high-heeled mules completed the effect. Jo looked marvellous. Nobody would notice that her open jacket hid a softly rounded stomach.

'Thank God you're here,' gushed Emma Lynch, who rushed into Rhona's office just moments after Jo had arrived and put her briefcase down on the editor's desk.

'Why? What's happened?' Jo didn't look up as she opened the briefcase, and took out her diary and a computer disk. She couldn't stand Emma but she had to keep it to herself.

A twenty-six-year-old rich girl with delusions of brilliance and a penchant for tantrums, Emma was one of the most irritating people Jo had ever met. Unfortunately, she was also the publisher's niece and had recently been appointed to the position of junior features writer, despite her inability to write an entire paragraph without a grammatical error.

No talent and good connections make a winning combination, Rhona said drily. She had agreed to take Emma on for two years when she'd finished her one-year public relations course. Everyone else had regretted it ever since.

Emma's job was to rewrite press releases, get quotes from celebrities about their beauty hints and do general dogsbody work. Naturally, this wasn't good enough for Emma.

She moaned about not getting anything enjoyable to write and had started wheedling her uncle for promotion. She wanted to do 'proper' interviews, she'd been telling anyone who'd listen. Not just rewrite boring press releases or answer the phones. But something juicy. Today she'd found just what she was looking for.

'You won't *believe* what's happened!' Emma said dramatically. She said everything dramatically. It drove Jo mad.

'Poor Mary has got the most awful flu and can't go to London to do that interview with Helen Mirren. She rang in earlier and, because you weren't here, I took the liberty of ringing Uncle Mark and asking him what he thought . . .' Emma smiled a self-satisfied little smile. 'Well, to see if he thought I should go, actually. Because we couldn't keep them waiting just because you weren't in . . .'

'Hold on a minute, Emma,' Jo interrupted coolly. 'When did Mary ring in?'

'At ten past nine, and . . .'

Jo interrupted again. 'And what time was Mary's interview scheduled?'

'Half six in the Mayfair.'

'This evening?'

'Yes, but the flight was booked and everything . . .'

'Emma, why did you decide to ring Mark with something like this when you knew I was going to be in this morning, and when you also knew we had plenty of time to get someone else to interview Helen Mirren? Can you tell me that?' Jo's tone was sharp.

Normally she was able to ignore Emma's manipulative behaviour and constant running to 'Uncle Mark', but not today.

'Well, I just thought it would be . . .' stuttered Emma, going an ugly shade of pink.

'Better if *you* went, Emma? Or better to organise something without consulting me?'

Jo sat down in Rhona's big swivel chair and steepled her hands in front of her. She knew exactly what Emma had been up to. She'd made Jo look bad in front of Mark Denton, *Style*'s publisher, and netted a major interview for herself into the bargain.

Denton was a man famous for his lack of patience and his business skills, in that order. He was also unaccountably fond of his niece.

'I thought it would be helpful if I went.' Emma sniffed. Jo eyed her warily, realising that the younger woman was ready to go into tantrum overdrive. Big mistake, Emma, she thought.

'Shut the door, Emma, and sit down,' Jo commanded.

Startled, Emma obeyed.

'Now you listen to me. Don't you dare go over my head ever again, do you understand? I'm the deputy editor and when Rhona is away, I'm acting editor. I will not stand for some little madam trying to tell me how to run this magazine, do you understand?' Jo hissed.

'If you want to learn *anything*, you've got to work *with* me, not against me, Emma. You got this job because of who you are, but if you ever want to get *any* job on merit,' she yelled, 'you'd better stop playing games and learn. And that means taking orders. You're not going to London for that interview.'

Emma was open-mouthed with shock, but Jo didn't stop.

'I'm rescheduling the interview so Mary can do it. You haven't the experience for this type of interview. Now cancel those plane tickets.'

With that, Jo picked up the phone and dialled Mary's number.

'You can't do that, I've got it all arranged!' shrieked Emma.

'I can and I will,' answered Jo icily. 'I presume you have some work to do, so do it!'

Emma flounced out of the room, slamming the door childishly. Straight off to ring Uncle Mark, no doubt, Jo thought wearily. With a great start to the morning.

She'd just finished talking to Helen Mirren's publicity consultant when Annette, the receptionist, came in with a cup of tea and a message from Mark Denton.

'He's in the car and wants you to ring him back pronto,' said Annette. 'I'm sure you can guess what it's about. I heard that little bitch phoning him as soon as she left your office.'

'That girl will be the death of me,' Jo said.

'Pity she couldn't be the death of herself,' Annette said.

Jo waited until she'd drunk most of her tea before phoning the boss. She'd need every spare ounce of self-control not to scream back at him once he got started.

Mark was one of those people capable of sending her into a frenzy of temper, something he regularly managed at the weekly editorial meetings. He remained calm, no matter what, while she was left open-mouthed with temper. How Rhona managed to get on with him so well was a complete mystery to Jo.

'What the hell is going on over there?' Mark demanded. 'I've just had Emma crying at me over the phone about some stupid bloody interview and wasting money on plane tickets. Jesus, don't tell me you can't run the place when bloody Rhona's away!'

Jo could feel her blood pressure rise along with her temper. Relax, she said to herself, don't lose your cool.

'There's no problem, Mark,' she replied calmly. 'Unfortunately, Mary is sick and can't fly to London for an interview she'd set up with Helen Mirren. Emma seems to have got the idea that *she* should go and had it all arranged until I got here.' She paused before the lie.

'It would be marvellous if Emma could have gone, but I happen to know that Helen is, er . . . very particular about interviewers, she prefers more experienced journalists.' She crossed her fingers at the lie. 'Emma just doesn't fit the bill. If she's that keen to interview someone, I can set up something less challenging for her, but she's not ready for big interviews yet.'

'What the hell's the problem, then?' Denton's voice was a fraction less aggressive. 'Why's she ringing me in floods? Rhona doesn't have this effect on her.'

Suddenly Jo snapped. If he wanted to know what the problem was, she was damn well going to tell him!

'The problem is that Emma finds it very difficult to take orders or to be told what to do, Mark,' Jo said candidly. 'She doesn't want to be a team player, she wants to be out on her own.

'We've had some great journalism students in the office and they've been eager to learn, willing to do any job to gain experience.' Her voice was raised and she just didn't care.

'Emma has never been like that. She thinks she knows it all

and she never wants to do what she's asked. She just doesn't understand that there's a lot more to journalism than interviewing someone famous. Emma thinks she's too good for the day-to-day jobs in a magazine. And to make matters worse,' Jo paused for breath, 'she does everything she can to create friction in the office. Ringing you this morning before I got in is a prime example of what I mean. That's Emma trying to make trouble and abusing her relationship with you,' she spat. 'I won't stand for it.

'If you want her to be the editor of *Style*, Mark, then make her editor. But until you do, don't expect me to kowtow to her just because she's your niece, right!'

There was a silence at the other end of the phone. Jo was wondering whether she'd gone too far when he spoke.

'At least I can rely on you for straight-talking, Jo,' Denton said flatly. 'And that certainly was straight-talking. I didn't know Emma was such a problem, Rhona never mentioned it before.'

'Emma is in awe of Rhona, so she never puts a foot out of place when she's around. She doesn't feel the same about *me*,' Jo admitted. 'That's the problem. She thinks she can use you to sideline me. I don't dislike Emma,' she lied. 'But I won't have some twenty-six-year-old with zero experience trying to tell me how to run this magazine.'

'Point taken,' he said coolly. 'I'll tell Emma not to run to me when something disagrees with her, but I want you to work with her, Jo. She's got her heart set on journalism and I promised her parents I'd give her a good start.' His voice softened. 'She's a sweet kid at heart, you just don't know her. That tough exterior is all a front.'

Yeah, thought Jo. She's just a cuddly little thing, like a bloody piranha. Still, you've got enough opinions off your chest for one day, Ryan. Keep your mouth shut if you want to keep working.

'I know what you mean,' she answered warmly. What an Oscar-winning performance.

'She's probably insecure. I never spotted it until now. I was

134

quite taken in by that tough act. Don't worry, Mark, I'll work with her. But she's got to learn to work under me, she'll never get on in this business if she automatically puts up her fists to the boss.'

'Yeah, you're right, Jo. Help her out, she's a good kid,' Mark said earnestly.

'Of course. I'll bring her in later and get this sorted out.'

'That's great, Jo. Talk to you tomorrow.'

With that, he was gone. Jo hung up with relief and leaned back in her chair. It was still only eleven o'clock, but she felt as if she'd been in the office all day. This isn't good for you, my darling, she addressed her bump.

By the time Jo had discussed the beauty pages and the lucrative suncream advertisement supplement with the beauty writer, Nikki, chief sub Tony and Aidan from advertising, it was nearly time to leave for the lunch. After redoing her lipstick and anchoring a few stray hairs back into the knot at the nape of her neck, she grabbed her handbag and marched out of Rhona's office.

Nikki was standing up beside the reception desk, talking rapidly on the phone and attempting to open her mascara at the same time.

Annette was unwrapping a sandwich covered in clingfilm and talking to Brenda, who was eating a rice cake and eyeing the mayonnaise squelching out of Annette's tuna sandwich hungrily.

Emma was nowhere to be seen.

'She went off to lunch half an hour ago,' Annette informed Jo. 'She said she wouldn't be back.'

'OK,' said Jo. 'Brenda, will you talk to Nikki about writing the suncream supplement. I was hoping to get Emma working on it, but if she's not back today, I want you to take over. How's the diet going?' she added, as Brenda spread a meagre amount of diet cottage cheese on another rice cake.

'Fine,' answered Brenda glumly. 'I've lost nearly a stone. I've only another ten pounds to go.'

'When's the wedding, anyway?' Jo asked.

'The end of July. My sister's lost all her weight and she's bought a size twelve wedding dress. I'm not going if I can't get into a size twelve.'

'Don't be daft, Brenda,' interjected Nikki, sliding tanned skinny arms into a slinky little pale gold cardigan. 'You'll look marvellous whatever size you are. I'll give you some of that wonderful Lancôme face tanner and you'll look sexy and sunkissed.'

'Nikki, you're starting to *sound* like a cosmetics press release,' laughed Jo.

'I sleep with make-up brochures under my pillow and *absorb* it all.' Nikki took a brush out of her handbag and ran it through her straight blonde bob. 'I don't put milk under my cornflakes any more, I replenish their lost moisture with a vital enriching fluid!'

'Don't mock it,' Jo said. 'Think how handy all that "replenishing moisture" jargon comes in when you're writing ad features!'

'That's this afternoon's work,' Nikki smiled on her way out the door. 'Now, I'm going to stuff my face in Bewley's with my beloved husband and he'll kill me if I'm late. Bye.'

'I'm going to be late myself,' Jo said, looking at her watch. 'Annette, I'm going to Stark's for Maxine's fashion show. God only knows when I'll be back. These damn things always start late. When Emma comes in, tell her she's not to leave this evening until she's seen me, right?'

'No problem,' said Annette.

The four o'clock news was blasting out of Annette's radio when Jo finally walked into the office, clutching a hand-painted silk scarf from Maxine's beautiful, albeit overpriced, new collection.

'Emma's gone home, Nikki had to leave early but left the beauty feature on your desk and you're to ring Anna from Models Inc. about who you're going to pick for the wedding dress feature.' Efficient as ever, Annette handed over a sheaf of pale yellow phone messages along with some post.

'I thought Emma was to stay until I'd talked to her,' said Jo crossly.

'Wouldn't listen, just marched off about five minutes after she got back from lunch,' Annette explained.

Jo sighed and walked into Rhona's office, wishing she'd had the chance to tackle Emma before the little bitch went home to Mummy with tales of woe about the horrible deputy editor. Would Denton sack her *before* or *after* her maternity leave?

'Oh, Jo,' called Annette. 'I nearly forgot. Richard rang and said he'd see you tonight at your place.'

Jo felt her heart quicken. Richard wanted to see her, he'd changed his mind, he *must* have! Oh, thank you, God, thank you, she whispered fervently. He wants me to give him another chance, I just know it.

Emma instantly forgotten, Jo rushed to the loo to see how she looked. Her carefully applied foundation had almost vanished in the summer heat and there were little smudges of mascara under her eyes. No problem. She whisked out her make-up bag and started the repair job.

How like Richard not to say *when* he was coming, she thought happily, blotting up excess lipstick with a tissue. But who cared what time he arrived? He was coming to see her, that was enough.

She was squirting another blast of Trésor onto her wrists when the doorbell rang.

Richard looked better than ever, blond hair gleaming against faintly tanned skin. A broad smile showed off the perfectly white teeth he brushed religiously.

'Jo, my darling,' he murmured, sliding one arm around her waist as he pulled her close for a slow, sensuous kiss.

'Oh, Richard,' she said softly. 'I've missed you so much.'

'I know, my darling, I know. These,' he produced a huge bouquet of pink roses from behind his back, 'are for you.'

Jo felt tears prickle behind her eyes. Pink roses. 'They're so beautiful,' she said tearfully. 'Thank you.'

'Don't cry,' Richard said quickly. 'Let's put these on ice.'

He bent down and picked up two bottles of white wine from the doorstep.

'It's your favourite, darling, German Riesling. Now, have you got anything to eat? I'm starved.'

'Er, no.' She'd spent the whole weekend planning to shop properly and had still only made it to the corner shop for milk, bread, cheese and ice cream. Chocolate-chip Häagen Dazs. Sinful but glorious.

Anyway, why didn't he bring something to eat if he was hungry? In fact, why had he brought wine when he *knew* she couldn't drink any? Oh well, he was just being Richard – thoughtful and thoughtless at the same time.

At least he was making an effort. He never remembered practical things, but he was trying. She'd just have to get used to his foibles when they were living together. So what if he always drank the last of the milk and then expected more to materialise magically, that was Richard for you. She could live with it. Thank God he was back. She loved him so much, she couldn't let her damn hormones screw their reunion up.

In the kitchen he'd found the corkscrew and was expertly opening the first bottle. She stared lovingly at the back of his neck, admiring the way the denim blue shirt clung to his strong shoulders.

'Glasses, darling?' he inquired. Jo opened a cupboard and handed him a wine glass.

'I can't drink, Richard, because of the baby.'

'Have a sip,' he said persuasively. 'Half a glass won't kill you.'

They sat on the big three-seater settee, the way they always had. He lounged at one end, the glass of wine beside him on a small table. Jo sat curled up beside him.

Sky Sports blared out of the TV, but Jo didn't mind. He paid the subscription so he never missed an important match and usually she sat and read while he watched, bored with the endless discussions of players and tactics.

Now, she sat peacefully, watching him watching TV, content just to be close to him.

Maybe it was the weekend without him, a weekend without his touch, that made her so needy. She'd missed him, missed his touch, missed his arms around her.

After two years with Richard, she'd almost forgotten all those times when she'd felt desperate for a man's touch, felt alone and unloved when her current man wrote himself out of her life. She certainly should have remembered what it felt like, it had happened often enough. But that was all in the past. Thankfully.

Her fingers spread out on Richard's chest as he watched the TV, luxuriating in the feeling of soft denim warmed by his skin. He didn't respond, totally absorbed in the game. Nothing changes, she thought happily, delighted at his presence and determined not to freak about the things which had always irritated her before. The poor man needed time to get used to pregnancy mood swings.

She felt perfectly happy. Serene, almost. This was bliss. He'd changed his mind, he'd come back to her and the baby. They had a future again. They were going to be parents. She was going to have the most beautiful, most adored baby in the whole world. It was all so perfect.

When the match was over, Richard was still hungry. 'Let's get pizza,' he said, stroking her cheek gently before kissing her on the forehead. 'A twelve-inch pepperoni with garlic bread. My wallet's in my jacket.' Jo felt hungry herself, despite the large lunch she'd wolfed down in Stark's.

He was opening the second bottle of wine when the pizza arrived. The quarter of a glass of wine that Jo had drunk was rattling acidly around her stomach, but she was still starving. They ate enthusiastically straight from the box, strings of mozzarella dripping juicily from the slices of pizza they pulled apart with their hands.

'Delicious,' Jo mumbled, her mouth full.

'Like you,' Richard grinned back.

They never got to see the Liverpool match. Instead, they

139

ended up on the carpet, kissing garlic butter off each other's mouths and pulling at clothes with greasy fingers.

When they finally made it into the bedroom, Richard finished undressing her, carefully unclasped her bra and buried his face between her breasts, fuller now than they'd ever been before. He licked each nipple eagerly before sucking them, making Jo arch her back with pleasure.

'Oh, darling,' she moaned, 'that's wonderful.' She ran her fingers through his hair as he kissed her breasts, sending quivering bolts of desire through her body.

'How's this?' he asked, sliding his hand down her belly until he was stroking the soft skin of her thighs, making her purr with pleasure. His fingers stroked the soft silk of her skin, gently roaming under the elastic of her silk panties to touch her softly, fingers tantalising and questing.

God she wanted him, she was ready for him, so ready. Who needed foreplay after a weekend apart?

'I've missed you, Richard,' she said, moving out from under him, straddling him and leaning down to kiss his lips gently. She nuzzled his neck while one hand fumbled with his belt, trying to open it without looking.

When she turned to look, her breasts, heavy and ripe, swung low and his lips moved to catch a nipple in his mouth. It was amazing, simply amazing what he could do to her. She felt sexier than ever before, as though being pregnant made everything make sense. Pregnant, she was utterly womanly and feminine, ripe and blooming, thanks to this man who was burning her skin with his touch.

'And I've missed you,' he groaned, his hands pulling her hips down hard onto his, grinding his hard body under hers. 'I want you now, Jo.'

Quickly, he slid her panties off and ripped off his boxer shorts. Pulling her on top of him again, he slid inside her, feeling her soft, welcoming and wet.

'Oh, Jo,' he moaned, burying himself in her as deep as he could. 'That's so good.'

It was, it was wonderful. She clung to him, sweat beading

on her upper lip as he thrust into her, again and again. She wanted him so much, she was so excited. She was nearly there, nearly coming.

'Oh, Jo,' he shouted, 'oh God!'

His body spasmed, as he thrust deep inside her before he collapsed on top of her body, breathing shallowly and quickly in post-orgasmic exhaustion.

Her own excitement dipped instantly, needing his friction to bring her to orgasm. Damn. As he lay on her heavily, she breathed more evenly and wrapped her arms around his body.

She wouldn't come now, the moment had passed.

'That was amazing, Jo,' he murmured.

Gently stroking his cheek, she felt a rush of emotions well up inside her. She loved him, but he was so selfish. Just because he was as horny as hell after a sex-free weekend didn't mean he had to completely forget about her satisfaction and make love like a chauvinist pig. She'd been so turned on and she'd missed him so much, she'd been crazy for him. And he hadn't cared that she hadn't come.

Damn him! Richard never changed, did he?

He shifted beside her, reached one hand up and caressed her face.

'I love you, Jo, you know that?'

Of course, she melted. He'd always had the power to do that to her, to make her forget his behaviour with just a few words. It didn't matter that she hadn't come. They were together, together with their baby. That was all that mattered.

Her fingers smoothed his hair, moved down to massage his shoulders. His skin was damp with sweat.

Together they'd made a baby, a precious life. Yes, they'd had their fights and they'd argued bitterly a few days ago, but that was natural. People fought and argued. Now Richard had accepted their baby and he wanted to be with her. OK, so he hadn't said it in so many words. But he meant it. He didn't have to *say* it. She knew.

'Darling, I'm so tired,' Richard said sleepily. He slid one arm under his head like a pillow. 'That was great, I'm just so tired. 'Night,' he muttered.

She watched him, sexy, handsome and thoughtless. But he was her man, the father of her unborn baby. Maybe fatherhood would knock some of the thoughtlessness out of him.

Moving gently so she wouldn't wake him, Jo untangled her limbs from his and climbed out of the bed, padding silently into the bathroom to wash her teeth. Almost too tired to take off her make-up, she forced herself to go through her usual beauty routine.

She splashed cleanser on her face, wiped away the grime of make-up and pollution with cotton wool, and brushed her teeth carefully. She quickly applied a film of moisturiser, then rubbed body lotion into her breasts, to keep pregnancy stretch marks at bay. That'd do.

She switched off the bathroom light and wandered into the sitting room and turned off the TV. Richard's jacket and jeans were flung on the settee and the huge pizza box sat opened on the glass coffee table. Grease-marked kitchen paper and two crumpled sections of tinfoil lay on the ground. The smell of garlic bread permeated the air. She'd tidy it up in the morning.

The sun didn't wake her, even when it shone in through a crack in the curtains at dawn, a shaft of light cutting through the dark of the bedroom like a floodlight. It was the morning sickness that did it, waking her up just after seven with bile rising in her throat. She knew she was going to be sick right now.

She got to the loo just in time, retching painfully as her sleepy body tried to come to terms with another bout of pregnancy nausea.

'Baby, how can you be *doing* this to me?' Jo groaned wretchedly, hanging over the toilet bowl for the nth morning in a row. 'Why can't I be one of those lucky cows who don't suffer from morning sickness?'

After ten minutes waiting to get worse, she began to feel

marginally better. Thank God. Jo got up shakily and reached for the Bathroom Duck. What a stupid bloody name, she thought, squirting a blast of lemon goo around the rim of the toilet. Doesn't look anything like a bloody duck.

Her mouth felt like the inside of a binman's wellie, she thought. That's daft too. Who the hell knows what a binman's wellie tastes like?

She couldn't face brushing her teeth so she stumbled into the kitchen and turned on the kettle. A cup of sweet tea would be the business. She was absolutely exhausted, but there was nothing like a session of puking to make you totally and undeniably awake.

One empty wine bottle stood on the counter and she jammed it head-first into the bin. Bloody ironic to feel like she was incredibly hung-over every day when she hadn't drunk more than half a glass of wine since getting pregnant.

The other bottle stood on the coffee table. By rights, Richard should have the most appalling hangover since he'd drunk most of the two bottles. But he'd probably be fine, all that training to be a sports photographer had made him immune to hangovers.

Sky News was chirpy and irritating. Jo watched it for half an hour and then decided to tidy up. What was the point in spending all morning groaning about being sick? Since she was up that early and since Richard would lie in bed for hours, she might as well take advantage of the fact and clean the flat.

It didn't take long to bin the remains of the pizza, but it would take a bit longer to get rid of the smell of garlic bread left hardening overnight on the coffee table. When she'd dumped everything and put down carpet freshener for when she could hoover, she picked up Richard's discarded clothes and folded them neatly.

His wallet lay on the hall table with the change from the pizza beside it. Jo smiled at the wallet, remembering buying it for him in Bloomingdale's in New York.

It had been made by Gucci and was miles cheaper than it

would have been in Dublin. 'So you'll think of me whenever you open your wallet,' she'd joked at the time. It was an old Dublin gag they'd both known and laughed at – how did you find your girlfriend? I opened my wallet and there she was.

Jo put the change into the wallet and tried to slide it into the inside pocket of his jacket. It wouldn't fit. Something bulky was blocking it. Puzzled, Jo pulled an envelope out of the pocket, smoothing it out to reveal a Ryanair travel folder. Something clicked inside her head and she opened it quickly. It couldn't be, no way. It just *couldn't* be.

The ticket was open-ended, executive class to London the following Monday morning. Jo stared at it for a moment. London. He was still going to London.

Her mind sped back over the previous night's events. Richard had never said anything to make her think he'd changed his mind. She'd just *assumed* that he had, assumed that his very presence was proof that he'd acquiesced. That he wanted her and their baby. The flowers, the wine, *everything*.

But he hadn't. What had he come for, a quick fuck? she thought bitterly. Why hadn't he *said* anything? Because that would be too difficult, too confrontational, of course.

'I hate rows,' he claimed from time to time, usually when they were in the middle of one. He preferred to walk away from the argument, get into his car and drive off for the day. Then he'd ring her the next day, say sorry and arrange dinner. By then, Jo's temper would have cooled and the fight would be shelved, if not forgotten.

Damn him, she wasn't going to let him run away this time. He wasn't going to breeze back into her life for a few hours and just breeze out again. This was serious. She was pregnant and he was going to run away again? No way.

'Richard,' she said loudly, shaking his shoulder. 'Wakey, wakey.'

He blinked tiredly, screwing up his eyes at the harsh sunlight streaming into the bedroom. 'What time is it?' he mumbled hoarsely.

'Ten past eight,' she snapped.

'Jesus, Jo, why did you wake me?' he groaned. 'I'm shattered.'

'*You're* shattered?' she screeched. 'What about me? When were you going to tell me about London, Richard? When? Were you going to ring from the airport? Or from your hotel in London?'

'Oh for God's sake,' he muttered, turning away from her in the bed. 'It's no big deal. I'm just going for a couple of weeks to see what it would be like working there. I'm not emigrating.'

'Not yet, maybe, but you will. Ireland's too bloody boring for you, isn't it, Richard?' she demanded. 'You want *excitement*, don't you? The world would end if Richard Kennedy actually had to settle down for more than five minutes! All I want to know is where I fit into all of this? Or have you forgotten that I'm carrying our baby?'

'Don't be ridiculous, Jo!' He sat up in the bed, raked his hair out of his eyes and looked at her warily. 'I haven't forgotten. I just thought you might have given the subject some more thought. You know, what it'll mean to your career or whatever, and maybe even changed your mind. We don't have to do this now.'

Jo stared at him angrily. She couldn't believe what he was saying. If she hadn't wanted an abortion on Friday, she damn well wasn't going to want one now.

Richard pushed the duvet back abruptly and got out of bed. He strode into the bathroom and slammed the door behind him.

'I'm afraid we *do* have to do this now,' she shouted through the door. 'The baby isn't going to go away, Richard, I'm still having it.'

The toilet flushed. Richard marched out of the bathroom, wiping his face on a towel. He didn't speak.

'When you turned up last night, I thought *you'd* changed your mind,' Jo said fiercely. 'How can you do this to me? Is this your party piece, running away from women when you get them pregnant?'

It was as if she'd flicked a switch. His face changed in an instant, becoming dark like thunder. Jo had never seen him like this and she was stunned, afraid almost.

'I didn't do anything,' he snarled. 'You wanted to trap me, didn't you? Well it's not going to work.'

Almost absently, Jo took her old pink fluffy dressing-gown off the hook on the bedroom door and wrapped it around her. It was sunny outside. The weather forecast on Sky had promised balmy weather, but Jo still felt cold. She stood beside the bed and stared blankly at the dressing-table mirror, not seeing her reflection at all.

He picked up his watch from the dressing table and strapped it onto his wrist. She followed him into the sitting room where he picked up his clothes and dressed silently, barely contained rage in every movement.

'Richard,' she said tentatively. 'We have to talk . . .'

'No, we don't. You've made your bed, you lie on it,' he spat.

That did it. 'Don't talk to me like that, you arrogant pig!' she yelled. 'We both did it, do you think I got pregnant on my own?' She faced him angrily.

'Yeah, well I don't want it,' Richard said, venom in every syllable. 'I'm leaving.'

'You can't,' Jo said. 'How dare you talk to me like that, you're all the same, bloody men terrified of commitment!'

'And *you're* all the bloody same,' he answered harshly, 'getting pregnant at the drop of a hat because it's the only way to get a ring on your finger. Well it's been tried before, sweetie, and I didn't bite the bullet that time either!'

'What do you mean?' asked Jo, stunned.

He said nothing, just continued buttoning his jeans calmly.

Jesus, he couldn't be saying what she thought he was saying. 'Beate. She got pregnant, didn't she?'

'So?'

'Why did you never tell me?'

'There was nothing to tell,' he said flatly.

'Did she have the baby?' Jo asked.

'What is this?' he demanded. 'Twenty fucking questions?'

She hesitated at the anger in his voice. 'I just wanted to know.'

'Yes, all right? She had the baby and I have never seen it and she probably wouldn't let me, even if I wanted to, which I don't!' he slid his feet into his Italian suede slip-ons and picked up his jacket.

'Oh, Richard, why?'

'Look, just because you've always played happy families doesn't mean that everyone else does, right? You don't know what it's like to have a father who couldn't give a shit whether you lived or died, a father who'd kick you rather than say a kind word. I do,' he hissed. 'I know *just* what that's like and I'll tell you something, it turns you off the idea of having kids. I don't want any fucking kids. I decided that a long time ago. That's my choice. If you're so fired up about a woman's right to choose, why don't you ever think about a man's right to choose, eh?'

Jo said nothing, silent in the face of Richard's fury and anger, an anger which had lived inside him for thirty-seven long years.

'All that feminist stuff about a woman's body being her own, that all sounds great when it's about women,' he continued angrily, 'but let a man say what *he* really wants, and that's different! I don't want kids. Simple as that. That's my decision,' he hissed. 'I gave you the chance and you didn't take it. So you do what you want. You will anyway.'

With that, he picked up his jacket and car keys and walked to the door.

'Call me a bastard or whatever you want, I'm sorry. It's over.'

The front door slammed. She was alone.

CHAPTER NINE

Her shoes pinched. Why was she wearing those bloody shoes in the first place? Aisling realised they looked wrong about fifteen minutes after she left the house. By then, it was too late to turn back. They were too high, shoes bought for a wedding outfit that had languished in the wardrobe for three years after that one July day when the sun had thwarted the bridal party and stayed firmly behind the clouds.

They'd been too high then, sinking heavily into the grass outside the church. And they were still too high. Aisling did her best to walk quickly along Leeson Street, feeling totally self-conscious in her navy blazer, long cream skirt and cream court shoes.

The people sitting in motionless cars were probably office veterans, no doubt. Seasoned workers who knew what to wear to work and how to do more than switch on a computer. Could they see pure ignorance written all over her face? And pure fear, come to that?

Streams of people passed her by, walking quickly along the pavement, listening to Walkmans and staring straight ahead as they bypassed slow walkers and parking meters.

From open car windows, she could hear snippets of radio talk shows and the thumping bass of loud music. Aisling sneaked the odd sideways glance into the cars beside her. One attractive woman was peering into her rear-view mirror, mascara wand held aloft as she finished her morning make-up. Another driver was reading, a newspaper spread out on the steering wheel. Others just gazed vacantly out of their windscreens, probably praying for the car ahead to move.

It was all so hectic, Aisling thought in surprise. She hadn't seen Leeson Street this busy for years, nearly twelve years to be exact. Since she'd given up work, she was never there

148

during the early morning rush. If she brought the boys into the city centre during the school holidays, she waited until the traffic jams were gone.

Now, in common with all the people walking purposefully towards offices, banks and shops, it was where she worked. Work. She had a job. Oh God. Those words hadn't seemed petrifying when she was twenty-two, confident in her ability to deal with any problems in the motor department. Had she really run that place or had she imagined it all? Right now, Aisling wasn't sure her former career hadn't been a dream. If she'd been as good as Mum and Jo were trying to convince her she was, why the hell was she scared out of her mind at the prospect of starting a much easier job when she was older?

Dodging the cars, like everyone else did, she crossed Leeson Street and turned right onto Pembroke Street Upper. She was sweating from the hasty walk and panicked that she hadn't put enough perfume on.

A subtle squirt of Chloé had seemed like the right idea at ten past seven. But after the long walk from Haddington Road where she'd decided to leave the car, she was hot and sticky, and wished she'd splashed on more perfume.

She hadn't wanted to overdo it. She wanted to appear like a working woman, someone who left the house at seven-fifty every morning like clockwork, with the kids fed, the kitchen tidy and a casserole defrosting for the evening. Not like a terrified ex-housewife overdoing it with gallons of perfume, high heels and an outfit which looked perfect in Quinnsworth and totally wrong behind a desk. Now she wished she'd had the presence of mind to put some deodorant in her bag.

Number seventeen. There it was, a rich dark green door with brass fittings and a gleaming brass plate beside it proclaiming that this was the office of Richardson, Reid and Finucane, Solicitors. A magnificent Georgian house in a line of magnificent houses, like something out of *Homes and Gardens*.

What she wouldn't give to be sitting at home right now, with a copy of the magazine spread on the kitchen table as she contemplated another spurt of decorating. Anything, even stripping the wallpaper off the back bedroom, would be preferable to this sheer terror. Calm down, Aisling, she told herself. It's your first day, nobody is going to expect too much from you. Hopefully.

She walked carefully up the pristine stone steps and admired the two elegant bay trees in wooden tubs on either side of the door. To the right was an intercom and she pushed it slowly.

'Good morning,' said a clear voice. 'Can I help you?'

'Aisling Moran to see Ms Hogan,' Aisling answered, more calmly than she felt.

The voice said nothing, but a buzzing sound emanated from the side of the door. Feeling like a truant about to face the head nun, Aisling pushed and found herself in a formal, pale green lobby where a red-headed girl sat behind a low desk.

'Hello,' smiled the girl. 'Go up the stairs to the first landing and take the first door on your left.'

She could have been speaking in Swahili. With a fixed grin on her face, Aisling moved mechanically up the stairs, her brain trying to figure out the words 'first door on your left'.

Left, which was left? Was this it? She tentatively pushed open a green panelled door and walked into an airy, high-ceilinged room.

A petite woman in a grey skirt suit with a sweep of ash blonde hair to her shoulders stood before Aisling, a china cup and saucer in one hand and a beige folder in the other. Beautifully made-up grey eyes stared at Aisling for a moment before the woman smiled glacially.

'I'm Aisling Moran,' said Aisling nervously. This blonde vision looked at her as if she had just walked dog mess into the carpet.

'I know,' said the blonde coolly. 'I'm Vivienne Hogan, personal assistant to Mr Richardson and the personnel director. Welcome to Richardson, Reid and Finucane.'

Her expression was about as welcoming as a blizzard, but Aisling smiled back anyway.

'I'm afraid something's come up and I won't be able to bring you around the office and introduce you. Caroline Dennis will look after you. She'll be here in a moment,' Vivienne said, walking gracefully to the door. 'Sit down and make yourself comfortable.' She gestured towards a grey office chair.

'Thanks.'

The door shut silently. Aisling felt as if she could breathe again. Was she imagining it or had the other woman really been cold? And if so, what in the hell had she done to deserve such a frosty welcome? She tried to remember what she'd been like to newcomers to the motor department. Had she ever looked at them the way Vivienne had at her? God, she hoped not.

She sank into the chair and tried to take a few deep breaths. It didn't help. Focus on the room, Aisling. Relax.

The room looked like the drawing room it probably had been. It was papered with subtle embossed cream paper. A gilt-framed oil painting of a weary-looking horse hung on one wall.

Under normal circumstances, she'd have been fascinated by the ceiling mouldings which had vine leaves beautifully picked out in gold paint. Today she was too preoccupied to do much more than notice them.

As offices go, she thought, it was very nice.

Several metal filing cabinets filled one wall and there were two desks positioned opposite each other, both with computer keyboards and VDUs. A wire basket and a large pile of beige folders covered one desk, along with a very healthy plant and a large silver frame with a photo of a smiling little girl in a school uniform.

A tiny brown Koala bear clung to a pen in the red plastic pen holder and a rainbow-coloured mug proclaiming 'World's Greatest Mum' sat beside what looked like a very high-tech phone.

By contrast, the other desk was like something from an office manual, 'the perfect desk'. Not one stray piece of paper spoiled the highly polished wood. White metal baskets were half empty and only a pen and a yellow Post-It pad beside the phone gave the impression that anyone had been using the desk at all. Obviously Ms Snotty Hogan's desk, Aisling decided bitchily.

A coffee percolator bubbled away in one corner of the room and the rich scent of freshly brewed coffee made her long for a cup. Should she help herself, Aisling wondered? Why not? She was an employee after all, even if not a very welcomed one.

She chose a bright red mug and was just starting to pour when the door opened again. Jumping guiltily, Aisling nearly spilled the coffee onto the pale carpet.

'Did I give you a fright?' inquired the intruder, a plump woman with a cluster of dark curls and a voluminous, bright floral dress.

'Sorry. Viv told me you were here and asked me to show you around. I'm Caroline, Pat's secretary.' She proffered a hand and Aisling shook it, grateful to meet at least one person who seemed pleased to see her.

'I'm Aisling and I hope it's OK to get some coffee but it just smelled so nice . . .'

'Oh, Viv should have offered you one but she'd madly busy this morning and obviously forgot. Your office is on the next floor but you'll have to come down here for coffee anyhow because Elizabeth's percolator has gone kaput.'

Caroline dropped a bulging brown handbag onto the chair beside the perfect desk and slung a white cotton cardigan over the armrests. Aisling was amazed. In her long, flowing dress and hippie-ish bead necklace, Caroline looked as if she'd be more at home behind the other desk.

So where did Vivienne sit? Not at the messy desk, that was for sure. And why was poor Caroline making excuses for Viv's rudeness? Aisling doubted that 'Viv would have offered' her a cup of coffee. Unless Aisling's throat was on fire, she reckoned.

'Elizabeth isn't going to be in today, she's feeling a bit

under the weather.' Caroline poured herself a mug of coffee and stirred in three sugars. Opening a square tin of assorted biscuits, she selected two chocolate biscuits and a pink wafer one.

'Want one?' she offered before taking a large bite of chocolate-covered digestive.

'No thanks,' answered Aisling, who hadn't even managed to finish her Special K.

'You'll *love* Elizabeth's office,' mumbled Caroline with her mouth full of biscuit. 'Well, *your* office! It's quite the nicest of all the assistants' ones. Of course, it's a bit isolated up there at the top,' she added. She took her coffee and led Aisling out onto the landing and up the stairs. 'But the view is wonderful! You're above Leo's office, Leo Murphy, that is. He's your boss. He's in court this morning according to Elizabeth, but he'll be back at one.'

Caroline stopped talking, breathless after the first flight of stairs. They climbed another two flights, past panelled green doors and sedately framed prints of Georgian Dublin in feathery ink and watercolours.

'This,' Caroline opened a door and showed Aisling another bright high-ceilinged room, 'is Leo's office.'

'Very nice,' said Aisling.

'You want to see Mr Richardson's office,' Caroline continued. 'It's beautiful. He collects antiques, you know. His office is like Sotheby's and his house is the same. Although I expect you know that.'

'Er, yes,' answered Aisling, although she didn't.

Why would she know that Edward Richardson collected antiques? She'd only met him a few times at Fiona's house and even then they'd talked about Fiona more than anything else. And about Nicole, of course, the apple of her grandfather's eye.

Obviously Caroline thought she was on intimate terms with Pat Finucane and, therefore, with his father-in-law. She followed Caroline up another flight of stairs to a small landing at the top of the building.

'I know it's small,' said Caroline, ushering Aisling into a tiny office dominated by a large window, 'but just look at the view.'

Aisling looked, and was impressed. Five huge filing cabinets took up a lot of the office space and there wasn't enough room to swing a cat, but the spectacular view the window afforded over Dublin's rooftops more than made up for the lack of space.

'It's wonderful,' breathed Aisling, squeezing between the desk and the cabinets to look out the window.

'I knew you'd like it,' smiled Caroline smugly, as though she'd designed the entire place herself. 'You may as well make yourself at home since Elizabeth isn't going to be in today. I'll get her calls transferred to my phone until you've got the hang of everything. You could start doing some typing, though, couldn't you? I'll give you some letters to look at so you can see the format.'

Aisling felt herself blanch. How the hell was she going to be able to type letters when she didn't know how to use the computer?

She gazed at the complicated-looking keyboard and knew she'd have to confess. Sort of.

'I don't know how to use this type of computer,' she said nervously.

'Oh,' said Caroline in surprise. 'This is an Apple Performa, it's a doddle, really. What have you worked on before?'

Aisling racked her brains for the name of the computer system the motor department had been buying before she'd left.

ICBM. That was it. 'An ICBM,' she lied confidently. 'No, an IBM. Sorry.' Moron, she told herself. You've just said you can use an inter-continental ballistic missile.

'I'd really prefer to be thoroughly acquainted with this system before I start typing,' she added quickly, hoping Caroline hadn't noticed her gaffe. 'Perhaps I can do something else until Elizabeth can brief me properly.' That sounded great, she thought. Very professional.

Caroline's eyebrows were furrowed as she considered this.

'You could do some filing,' she ventured. 'I know Elizabeth has been letting the filing slide a little because she hates going up and down the stairs all the time. There's a file room downstairs, two cabinets in Leo's office and the ones here. It's quite a trip up and down those stairs.'

'Of course I'll file,' Aisling said, relieved. 'Just show me where to start.'

She was leaning over a cabinet in the file room looking for Ms Sandra Burke's file when Vivienne walked in at a quarter past one.

'You're not at lunch?'

Aisling looked flustered. 'I didn't know when lunch was,' she said. 'There's so much filing to do, I just thought I'd keep working.'

'You'll be working through lunch often enough without starting on your first day,' Vivienne commented. 'Caroline was supposed to bring you to the canteen but she obviously forgot, I'm sorry.'

Amazing, thought Aisling, Ms Ice Queen is actually apologising for something. She was even more amazed when Vivienne told her to take a break and get a cup of coffee from the percolator in her office.

'Leave this until after lunch,' she added. 'The canteen is in the basement, although it's not precisely a canteen, more a badly equipped kitchen. There's a kettle, a fridge and a microwave in case you want to have something hot. Go down the corridor and take the second left, OK?'

'Fine,' said Aisling.

'I'm going to Baggot Street. Do you want anything from the shops?'

'No thanks, really. I'll just get a cup of coffee and I've brought a sandwich.'

'Well, get some proper coffee from my office, won't you,' Vivienne added. 'And I'll see you later this afternoon to see how you're getting on.' She smiled briefly, then opened a filing cabinet near the door, selected a file and left as quietly as she'd come in.

Marginally cheered up, Aisling left the file room and thought briefly about going down to the canteen for lunch.

If Caroline had accompanied her, she would have been delighted to meet the rest of the staff. But she just didn't feel up to marching in on her own, explaining who she was and what she was doing here to a bunch of curious strangers. Instead, she knocked gently on Vivienne and Caroline's office door and, when nobody answered, went in for some coffee.

She took a biscuit as well and looked at the desks with renewed interest. So *Vivienne* was the World's Greatest Mum, she thought. Presumably, she wasn't such a tough career woman at home. Maybe they'd just got off on the wrong foot. Some people were naturally prickly and needed time to get comfortable with others, she decided charitably.

At her desk, she ate her tuna fish sandwich hungrily and drank a Diet Coke. She'd found a recent copy of *Style* in one of Elizabeth's wire baskets and she flicked through the pages, only half concentrating on an article about summer camps as she wondered how the boys were getting on at theirs.

She hadn't planned on sending them to the day camp for the whole summer, but she'd no option now that she was working. Thank God that Fiona had offered to pick them up at three the first week.

'Only until I get sorted out,' Aisling said firmly when Fiona offered to help. 'You can't spend your whole summer minding them.'

Brave words. She was finding it hard enough to cope with her first day at work without feeling like an idiot.

She'd just taken another bite of her sandwich when her door opened suddenly and a very tall and very dark man walked in. He was heavily built, with the sort of tan which spoke of lots of outdoor pursuits. He had a shock of jet black hair and a suit to match.

'Aisling, isn't it?' he said in a deep voice.

'Yes,' she answered. 'Hello.'

'I'm Leo Murphy.'

He advanced with one large hand held out and leaned over

the desk. The way his eyes roamed over her made Aisling feel uneasy.

She didn't know whether it was his intense gaze or the way he was smiling like an alligator who had spotted his lunch, but she felt, well . . . uncomfortable.

Since he was still holding out his hand, she reached out her left hand, the one without tuna stuck to it, and awkwardly shook hands. He held her fingers for much longer than was necessary and, when he released it, he smiled, a very self-satisfied smile.

'Aisling, I'm delighted you're going to be with me when Liz is away.'

Nobody else had called the other woman Liz, but Aisling instinctively knew that Leo Murphy would enjoy shortening his secretary's name, turning the elegant Elizabeth into the snappy Liz.

'Liz, bring your notebook in here now.' She could just imagine him saying it. She hoped he wouldn't start calling her Ash, only her closest friends and family called her that.

'I hope you've been made to feel at home.' He pushed aside a pile of files and sat on the side of her desk, his big body dwarfing Aisling as he leaned over her.

'Tuna, mmm. Health-conscious, are we?' he didn't wait for her to reply. 'I'm pretty health-conscious myself. Rugby, you know.' He patted his bulky chest proudly. 'A man's got to work out, don't you agree?'

'Absolutely,' she answered.

'I can see we're going to get on very well,' he continued. 'Come on down to my office when you've finished lunch. I'll go over what I want from you.'

'Yes, Mr Murphy.'

He slid off the desk and headed for the door.

'And Aisling,' he turned to give her the benefit of another feral grin. 'It's Leo, not Mr Murphy. We don't stand on ceremony here.'

She rinsed her hands in the tiny bathroom on the third floor and knocked on Leo's door.

157

'Come in, Aisling. Have a seat.'

He sat behind the desk and stared at her. God, there was something about him she didn't like. She didn't know what it was, but there was definitely *something* odd about him.

'You haven't worked for some time, I believe. Pat's been very good to take you on, I'm sure you appreciate that.'

Aisling felt sick. The way he made it sound, Pat had given her the job for services rendered, the sort of services you wore a French maid's outfit and stockings for.

'Of course, I understand that you're going through a rough time,' Leo added. 'It can't be easy. We'll make this as pleasurable as possible, of course. We run a tight ship here and I need to know you're behind me one hundred per cent. Liz will fill you in on the day-to-day details of the job.'

He paused and Aisling wondered if she was supposed to say something.

'That's great, Mr . . . er, Leo,' she said. 'I want to work. I know I'm a bit rusty but I'm a hard worker. Elizabeth will be here for the next two weeks, won't she?'

'Yes. But when she's gone, don't hesitate to ask me anything. Anything,' he repeated in a syrupy voice. 'That's all for now.'

He picked up his phone and started dialling a number. Aisling got up to leave, anxious to get back to the solitude of her little office.

'Can you get me the Law Directory?' he asked suddenly. 'It's on top of the cabinet over there.'

He held the phone to his ear but his eyes were on her again.

She turned around and was suddenly struck by the thought that her cream skirt really needed a slip underneath it. Was he watching her, eyes taking in her VPL, she thought, horrified. She blushed furiously.

'Thanks.' He took the book and she left the room rapidly. Outside, she took a long, deep breath and wondered what was wrong with her. He hadn't said anything awful, had he? So why was she so spooked?

When Caroline popped her head around the door at five to two, Aisling was delighted to see her.

'Sorry I didn't get to see you for lunch. I had to race up to Grafton Street to look for a present for my husband. It's his birthday on Wednesday and they have shirts in Arnott's that he'd love. Did you find the canteen?'

'Vivienne told me where it was,' answered Aisling, 'but I had a sandwich here. I didn't know anyone and I thought I'd wait until I met everyone, you know,' she finished lamely.

'That's awful!' declared Caroline. 'I'll kill the girls for not coming and getting you. We've got two juniors who are so scatty that they'd forget their heads if they weren't screwed on. And I bet you never had any coffee, either, did you?'

'Yes, I did. Vivienne told me to get some from your office,' Aisling said.

'Come on down and get another one now and I'll send the motorbike courier off with your percolator this minute. Leo will go mad if he doesn't get his coffee in the morning, you know!'

She laughed at this and Aisling decided not to ask about Leo's decidedly odd behaviour. She could have picked him up the wrong way. It was only her first day after all. No doubt things would look different the next day with Elizabeth to guide her through the maze of office politics.

'I don't want mash. I want chips!' declared Paul crossly, pushing his plate away from him.

'You can't have chips,' snapped Aisling. 'You're not leaving this table without eating your dinner, mash and all.'

She scraped the last bit of mashed potato out of the saucepan onto her plate and dumped the saucepan noisily in the sink. Granted, the dinner wasn't one of her better efforts. But mashed potato, fish fingers and beans were all she'd felt up to cooking after her first day at work.

They *should* have been eating a delicious lasagne she'd made on Saturday. But she'd forgotten to time the oven to cook the damn thing.

Phillip said nothing. He stuck his fork in the small hillock of mash he'd made in the centre of his plate and slowly mixed the beans into it until he'd made a pale orange mess. Since the boys had come over from Fiona's at half six, just ten minutes after Aisling had got home, Phillip had been stonily silent.

Feeling guilty at being away all day and for snapping at Paul, Aisling tried again.

'Please eat your dinner, boys,' she begged. 'There's ice cream for dessert and we can go to the video shop afterwards for a treat, all right?'

'Do I have to eat this, Mum?' wailed Paul. 'I'm not hungry.'

Count to ten, Aisling. She tried the honest approach.

'Paul, I'm very tired because I've been working all day. I'm sorry that dinner isn't very nice but it's the best I can do. Please eat it.'

For once, it worked. Taken aback by such candour, Paul stuck his fork into a fish finger and ate a bit. And another bit. Seeing his twin eating, Phillip stopped making fork tracks across his mash and actually ate some.

Thank you God, Aisling said silently. She didn't care what she'd promised the previous night, she just *had* to have a drink tonight.

Back from the video shop, she left the boys watching *Flipper* for the millionth time and went upstairs to have a bath.

She stripped off her work clothes with relief and put on the peach-coloured satin dressing-gown she'd treated herself to the Christmas before. Soft and silky to the touch, it had always made her feel faintly glamorous. But not tonight. Only a two-week stay in a health farm and four hours under a beautician's expert care would make her feel anything other than a harassed working mother with smudged mascara, aching feet and limp hair from her hurried walk to the car after work.

Aisling added a liberal dose of Body Shop Neroli essential oil to the steaming, foamy bath. Five drops were enough to relax you, the instructions said. Five wouldn't have a chance, she thought, counting out ten. With a glass of icy white wine

160

– the last bottle from Michael's precious wine rack – by her side, she lay back into the bubbles and let the day wash away from her.

The sensation of warm water gently taking the aches and pains away was pure bliss. She took a big sip of wine and wriggled her toes with relief. High-heeled shoes were definitely the wrong thing for work.

What she needed was a pair of low-heeled ones like Vivienne had worn. She had a black pair which would fit the bill perfectly, even if they were a bit old. They'd look fine if she polished them up. There just wasn't enough money in the kitty for a new pair.

As the water cooled, she reached up with her left foot and twisted the hot tap on again. Heaven.

For the first time since Michael had left her, she wasn't thinking about him or crying over him. Worrying about how she was going to cope when Elizabeth was on maternity leave, not to mention dreading working for the distinctly seedy Leo Murphy, was occupying too much of her mind to think about her absent husband. He'd got her into this mess, she thought venomously, but she had to get herself out of it. And she would, damn him.

'Fine, it was fine,' she said airily, when Fiona rang full of inquiries about her first day at Richardson, Reid and Finucane. After all Pat had done about getting her the job, Aisling couldn't very well say she felt like she'd just run a marathon and was dreading the next day, could she?

'Pat was in court all day or he'd have been in to see how you were getting on,' Fiona explained. 'But he said Vivienne and Caroline were going to explain everything to you. How did you get on with them? Caroline's very nice but Vivienne always sounds like a bit of a workaholic to me.'

'Caroline's lovely,' Aisling was able to say truthfully. 'I didn't see much of Vivienne, really. Elizabeth, the girl I'm replacing, was out so I did the filing all day. It was simple enough, but pretty tiring. You see, I didn't want to admit that I couldn't use the word processor so that's why I volunteered to file. And I met Leo Murphy. He's a bit different,' she ventured.

'Yeah, Pat says he's an acquired taste,' Fiona answered. 'He's only been there a year or so, but he's great at conveyancing apparently. I've never met him. What's he look like?'

Picture Jack Nicholson in *The Shining*, Aisling thought.

'Very dark haired and well built,' was what she said. 'He prides himself on being muscular,' she couldn't resist throwing that in. 'He plays rugby and believes men should work out.'

'Gosh, you sound very well acquainted already!' chuckled Fiona. 'Is he a bit of a hunk?'

'Not really, no.' If only she knew.

'Do you think you'll enjoy working there?' Fiona asked seriously. 'I was on edge all day wondering how you were getting on.'

You and me both, Aisling said to herself.

'I really want it to work out for you,' Fiona added.

'Oh Fee, it's wonderful,' Aisling said warmly. She had to lie so she hoped she was doing it convincingly. 'It was a bit tough at first, but the girls are so nice, I know it'll work out fine.'

'That's great,' said Fiona in relieved tones. 'You need something to keep your mind off Michael. I was so worried about you last week, you know.'

'I do feel a lot better now,' Aisling admitted. 'Maybe it's just coping with all the practical things, feeding the boys, paying the bills, that kind of thing. I haven't let myself descend into total misery. And work will certainly help,' she said with a laugh. 'I didn't have much time to think about Michael today! Which is all thanks to you and Pat for getting me this job. You've both been wonderful.'

'What are friends for?' demanded Fiona.

'Not all friends are as good as you,' Aisling pointed out. 'I've had a few calls from friends of ours and they just don't know what to say. Poor Angela Dunn just stuttered and stammered and finally said she'd ring me in a few months, like I was going into mourning! Nobody from Michael's office has rung, although I suppose it must be awkward for them.'

She didn't say that this had hurt her deeply. All she'd wanted was a friendly voice on the phone, telling her that even though she and Michael weren't together, the friends they had known for the past ten years were still there. Break-ups certainly made you realise the value of true friends, like Fiona and Jo.

'Mum has been great,' Aisling added. 'She arrived on Tuesday with a freezer full of pies and stews for us. I said Michael had left, he hadn't died! Luckily, she saw the funny side of it.'

'Ash! You're dreadful!' laughed Fiona. 'What must your poor mother have thought? You're dreadful for joking about serious things. Anyway, your mum's generation aren't used to the idea of people splitting up and the poor woman must be in shock.'

'Oh, Mum knows my sense of humour by now. I think living with Dad has knocked her own sense of humour out of her, though. He wouldn't recognise a joke if it bit him on the bum. Mum put him on the phone the other night and it was like talking to the sideboard. He was on the verge of doing his "I'd hoped for more from you, Aisling" routine but he stopped. I think Mum must have grabbed the phone off him.'

'Don't mind him,' Fiona said indignantly. 'You've done so well with your life. What did he want, Einstein for a daughter?'

'Someone smarter than Einstein, I think,' Aisling said drily. 'Luckily Sorcha's achievements have made up for the shame of me being a mere housewife. I swear that his chest swells when he tells people she's working in a bank in London. Mind you,' she added, 'if Sorcha lived here, he wouldn't be so delighted with her because they fight like cats and dogs. Distance is a wonderful thing.'

'Has she heard?' Fiona inquired.

'She rang on Saturday and told me I was a fool to have stayed at home cleaning the toilet. She has a great way with words, that one. I did point out that there was more to my life than sticking my head under the rim to see what germs were lurking, but I stopped myself. It was easier to say nothing.'

'Wait until *she* has a family and a home,' said Fiona sounding vexed. 'She'll find out it isn't so easy to be mother and chief bottle-washer after all.'

'Sorcha isn't going to have any children, my dear,' pointed out Aisling. 'She wants to have her tubes tied.'

'Around her neck, I hope,' muttered the other woman.

'She has that effect on me too, Fee. She completely ruined my ideas of what a little sister was supposed to be like. Thank God Nicola came along or I'd have always thought that little sisters were like some sort of biblical curse. You know, "And the Lord said, a little sister will be born, to ravage your bedroom, destroy your toys and keep you in eternal trouble until you leave home." '

'Was she really that bad?'

'Worse. And talking of kids, thanks for picking up the boys this afternoon, although Phillip has been like a briar since he came home.'

'He was a bit moody,' Fiona agreed. 'I thought he'd cheer up when he saw you . . .'

'No chance!' said Aisling. 'I think I've just crossed the line from Good Stay at Home Mummy to Bad Working Mummy. You should have seen the look on his face when he got beans, mash and fish fingers for dinner!'

'You've ruined all three of them with your gourmet cooking,' started Fiona, stopping abruptly when she realised what she'd said. 'Sorry.'

'You're right,' Aisling replied matter-of-factly. 'I did spoil them, Michael particularly. Home-made bread for breakfast, smoked salmon pâté at the weekends because he loved it, chicken *en croûte* or fresh pasta for his dinner and he never had to so much as wash up a cup or throw a towel in the laundry basket. I wonder is he allowed to get away with that type of behaviour with *her*? I don't think career women have much time for very old-fashioned men,' she added sarcastically.

★ ★ ★

164

Lying on her own in their big double bed later, she thought about what Fiona had said. She was right. Aisling had totally spoiled the three men in her life. She'd become obsessed with being the best housewife possible.

The house could have won prizes for cleanliness, her interior decoration was the same. She'd prided herself on her cooking, as though being a wizard with a food processor made up for her lack of abilities outside the home. And somewhere along the way, Aisling Moran had disappeared. That's what Michael had said. Had he been right?

He'd married her because he loved her, her vitality and her sense of humour. When she'd slowly lost her self-assurance, her belief in herself, she'd panicked. And thought that becoming the perfect homemaker was the answer. Only it hadn't been.

Michael had wanted Aisling, the woman he married. But she'd turned into Super Housewife, handy in the kitchen, but out of water anywhere else. Would a job have changed all that, she asked herself? A day in Richardson, Reid and Finucane had certainly given her lots to talk about.

She'd have enjoyed telling Michael about the different characters in the office and with his support behind her she probably wouldn't have been so uncomfortable in Leo Murphy's presence. But if Michael had still been with her, Leo would never have been so lecherous, she was sure of that. Being separated suddenly made her fair game for the likes of Leo. How the hell was she going to face him on her own?

Aisling sat up in bed and switched on her bedside light. It was ten past twelve, she had to be up in six and three-quarter hours and she didn't feel even vaguely like sleeping.

She plumped up her two pale yellow pillows behind her, then suddenly reached over and grabbed Michael's. For the past week, she'd made the bed every morning as if he was coming home that night, arranged his pillows just the way he liked them. She still slept on her side of the bed.

Why the hell was she doing that, she asked herself crossly? He wasn't coming back. In fact, even if he wanted to, he wasn't coming back. So there! He could stuff his pillows! She laughed at her own joke. Now, what to read? Something fluffy and romantic or something wonderfully scary?

Leaning down to her bedside table, Aisling found the book she wanted. It was funny how she'd got out of the habit of reading when she couldn't sleep at night, she thought. Michael always slept soundly and solidly, seven or eight hours no matter what. She'd never been so lucky but had rarely turned on her light to read at night in case it woke him. Not any more. She could read until dawn, steal all the duvet and all the pillows, and paint the entire bedroom whorehouse pink if she felt like it! So what if it was after twelve, she'd go to bed early tomorrow night. Satisfied with herself, Aisling settled back against her comfortable back rest. Perfect.

Tuesday was a good day. Elizabeth turned out to be a funny and warm woman in her early thirties who was delighted to be pregnant after four years of trying for a baby. Under her relaxed and expert tutelage, Aisling quickly learned how to use the word processor once she'd admitted that she had never used one before.

'I can't believe it's so easy,' Aisling exclaimed, after she'd managed to open files, save documents, print letters and keep file copies on floppy disks.

'Technology is the Emperor's New Clothes of the nineties,' said Elizabeth. 'Everyone's so scared of it that lots of people are terrified to touch a keyboard and the people who are good with computers try and lord it over everyone who isn't. Look how easily you've picked it up.'

'As long as I can do it when you're gone,' Aisling answered.

'I'm not going far,' laughed Elizabeth, patting her enormous bump. 'I'll probably spend the next few weeks stretched out on the couch at home watching reruns of *Knots Landing*, so just pick up the phone if you've got a problem.'

'Thanks. It's great to know that,' Aisling replied. 'I just hope I can handle Leo as easily,' she added guardedly. She was desperate to know what Elizabeth thought of her boss, but wasn't sure how to broach the subject. Perhaps Leo and Elizabeth got on like a house on fire. It might be a terrible blunder to ask if he made *her* feel as uncomfortable as he made Aisling.

'Oh, don't mind Leo,' the other woman said dismissively. 'His bark is much worse than his bite. He's moodier than any premenstrual woman *I've* ever known! Just ignore his moods. As long as you keep the office running efficiently and don't overbook him, he's a lamb, really.'

A lamb, huh? More like a wolf in sheep's clothing, Aisling reckoned. However, he'd been pretty harmless all day, acting the part of the busy boss. Aisling wished he'd always be like that. Unfortunately, she suspected that Elizabeth's presence had a lot to do with it. Who knew what he'd be like when she was gone and he could stare insolently at Aisling again?

Pat Finucane dropped into her office at lunchtime and apologised for not welcoming her in person the day before.

'How are you getting on?' he asked kindly.

'Brilliant,' said Elizabeth. 'She'll be running the whole place in a month. I just hope there's a job for me when I'm finished my maternity leave!'

Buoyed by Elizabeth's confidence in her, and by her improved relationship with Vivienne, Aisling left for home a much happier woman than she'd been the day before.

Her good mood wasn't to last.

'Hi, Aisling.' Michael's cold and distant voice on the phone hit her like a punch in the stomach.

'How are the boys?'

'Fine,' she replied, just as tersely.

'Now that I'm settled, I'd like to see them at the weekends. They can stay with me on Saturday and go home on Sunday evening, what do you think?'

She didn't know what to say. They were talking like a divorced couple already.

'I suppose that's all right,' she answered grudgingly. 'Where will they be staying?'

He hesitated for a moment. Could he be trying not to hurt her, she wondered?

'I'm living with Jennifer.'

God, it was like an ice pick in her guts. How could she have thought she was all right, she wondered blankly. Don't cry, don't let him see how upset you are.

'Where is that?' she asked in what she hoped was a nonchalant voice.

'Sandymount. It's just off Sandymount village.'

'How nice,' she replied. They were like two strangers talking, discussing property. They'd be talking about auctioneers' fees and stamp duty next.

'I don't want the boys to think that they don't have a father any more,' Michael said, suddenly intense. 'I want them to have *two* homes. That's so important.'

'It might be a bit of a shock to them to find you're living with someone else, Michael,' she interrupted caustically. 'This has all been rather sudden.'

'I know, I know,' he said worriedly. From the tone of his voice, she knew exactly what he was doing, running his fingers through his dark hair until it stood up in glossy peaks. She'd always smoothed it down, well, she *used* to smooth it down, a long, long time ago.

Neither of them spoke for a moment. The silence was almost worse than the stilted conversation.

'We have to talk about money,' she said finally.

'I hear you've got a job,' he put in.

'How did you know?'

'I rang Pat to find out how you were. I knew Fiona would have been talking to you.'

'Oh, give me a break, Michael,' she said angrily. 'If you wanted to know how I was, why couldn't you ring *me*! I was wondering why you were so silent, couldn't face talking to me, was that it?'

He sighed tiredly. 'I didn't ring up to fight, Aisling.'

'We're not fighting, Michael,' she snapped. 'I just want you to be up front with me. I'm not going to fall on my knees every time you ring and beg you to come back, OK! I've got over the begging wife stage.'

Damn him! He made her so angry. Why was he still playing games, weren't they over that?

'Don't be afraid to ring me, Michael. I want to talk about money, about the house, about all the practical things. And I want to know where you are so that if there's a problem with the boys, I can reach you.'

'That's fair enough,' he answered. 'I'm sorry, I should have rung. I don't know what to say to the boys.'

She was amazed. What an admission from Mr Know It All! At least she'd faced up to the realities of the situation and told the boys what was happening. He was scared to. Suddenly, Aisling felt a lot better. *She* was the strong one, she was the one who'd taken it on the chin. *She* was fighting back! What a nice feeling that was.

'You could try the truth,' she said smartly.

'You think so?'

'Well, they're ten years old, Michael, not ten *months*. I think they're going to put two and two together if they spend the night with you and *her*.' Aisling couldn't bear to say "Jennifer".

'You're right.'

Wow, it was a long time since she'd heard *that*. A slight smile lifted the corners of her mouth.

'Pick them up at one on Saturday,' she said decisively. 'They'll just be back from soccer and they'll be ravenous. You could always bring them to McDonald's, give them lunch and then tell them.'

This was hilarious. *She* was advising him on the best way to tell the boys that he now lived with another woman. Ironic wasn't the word for it.

'That's a great idea, Aisling,' he said sounding grateful. 'Thank you for making this easier.'

'I'm only doing this because I'm up for the Nobel Peace Prize,' she answered sarcastically. 'And because I want to protect the twins as much as possible. It won't do them any good to have us screaming at each other.'

'You're great,' Michael said. 'Thanks. I'll see you on Saturday, then?'

He hung up and Aisling did the same with relief. At least they'd talked. They had actually conversed like two adults. That had to be good, surely? She'd been dreading hearing from Michael and yearning for it in equal amounts. One part of her wanted to scream abuse at him, the other wanted him to come back, to hear him beg forgiveness and tell her he adored her still.

But there was no point harbouring secret hopes of a reunion when it was obvious Michael wanted her back like he wanted a hole in the head. This way, she was forced to meet reality face on.

'Mum, can we go out to play with Greg?' demanded Phillip, appearing in the kitchen with a football in his hands.

'All right, but stay in his garden if you're playing football. Don't play on the road, OK?'

'Yeah.'

Phillip was gone in a flash.

'Be back by eight,' Aisling shouted after him.

The front door slammed loudly. It was nearly seven, time for *Emmerdale*. The dinner dishes were still on the kitchen table but she didn't feel like tidying up. She quickly put the milk, butter and the cheese back in the fridge and left everything else. Time enough to do it later. Two weeks ago she wouldn't have been able to leave the mess without tidying up. Every dish would have been washed, dried and put away in fifteen minutes and she'd have then swept the kitchen floor and hoovered up the crumbs.

Not any more, she thought. There were no prizes for faultless housekeeping in the real world.

By Thursday evening, she was exhausted. Too exhausted to join Fiona at aerobics.

'Come on, you'll love it!' wheedled Fiona on the phone. 'Nicole's got her friends in and if you send the boys over, Pat will look after them all. You can do the beginners' class.'

'Oh, Fee, I really don't feel up to prancing around in my awful old leggings and spare tyre. It's so long since I did anything like that, I'd be *hopeless*,' Aisling answered. 'I'd really prefer it if you lent me one of your library of exercise tapes. I can start at home and that way I won't feel so flabby and unfit when I finally go with you.'

'OK. But you're definitely coming with me next week, aren't you?'

Aisling laughed. 'You never give up, do you? Let me get semi-fit before I go to the gym, Fee. I don't know if my self-confidence could face jumping up and down like an elephant in the middle of a group of Cindy Crawford look-alikes.'

'There won't be anyone like that in the beginners' class,' Fiona pointed out. 'The Cindy Crawford types all go to the advanced step class and make me feel like a heifer.'

'I'm *never* going near that place if there are women who can make *you* look fat!' Aisling was horrified at the thought. 'I'll come over and pick up Mr Motivator or Jane Fonda now and go for the burn later.'

'Nobody "goes for the burn" any more,' Fiona rebuked her. 'Even Jane admits she was wrong about the "no pain, no gain" motto. Anyway, she's had plastic surgery so I've lost my faith in her. She's too old-fashioned and I hate Mr Motivator. I've got a couple of step videos that are easier when you don't have a step; you could try them. You should also try Callanetics. It's not fat-burning but it's great for streamlining your shape.'

'That sounds painful,' said Aisling. 'Does it hurt?'

'Not a bit,' Fiona answered cheerfully.

Callan Pinckney's soothing American voice was telling Aisling how to stand with feet hip-distance apart, with one hand on her hip and the other reaching upwards. Painfully upwards. The video had only been on five minutes and Aisling already felt tired.

She didn't think she could reach a little bit more than she thought she could, as Callan kept saying encouragingly to a

171

class of very flexible-looking people.

Her arm was going to wrench itself out of her shoulder if she reached over any further. Thank God. She'd done it.

'Do one hundred,' Callan said crushingly.

'One hundred!' shrieked Aisling out loud, already wondering if she had ruptured something vital. You must be mad. But Callan wasn't listening. She was leaning over like a gymnast, gently moving her body back and forth, seemingly without excruciating pain.

I'll be in agony tomorrow, Aisling muttered to herself as she leaned, watching the counter on the screen clock up every little movement. She had to give up at 54 but Callan and her class stuck it out to 100. Masochists. Then it was time for the other side.

CHAPTER TEN

'It must be good for you if it hurts that much, mustn't it?' Aisling eased herself gingerly onto a bar stool in Larry Murphy's on Baggot Street.

'Current exercising wisdom doesn't recommend pain,' Jo said, as she picked up the bar food menu. 'I've never done Callanetics myself, but I've heard it's brilliant for toning you up. I suppose it's hard at first because your muscles aren't used to the movements. What do you want to eat?'

'A cheese sandwich on brown bread and a cup of tea,' Aisling answered.

'That sounds good,' Jo replied, and proceeded to order a sandwich for Aisling and fisherman's pie and chips for herself.

Aisling was going to say something about how that eating for two stuff was all old hat and just made you chubby as well as pregnant, but she thought better of it.

'You look good, anyway, even if your muscles are in agony,' Jo commented, taking in Aisling's definitely less bulky shape. In a long navy skirt and slim-fitting pink silk blouse, Aisling was looking better than she had for years, the long-hidden fine bone structure beginning to show on her face.

After years of wearing only the barest hint of make-up, she had started putting foundation, eyeliner and mascara on in the mornings as well as the usual eyeshadow and lipstick. Seeing Vivienne so smartly dressed and perfectly made-up every day made Aisling realise that the bare-faced look she'd worn for trips to the supermarket wasn't suitable for the office.

Her indigo-blue eyes were fringed by darkened lashes, a careful smudge of eyeliner highlighting what had always been her best feature. The coral lipstick she'd always favoured had been thrown in the bin by a disgusted Fiona who'd produced

173

a pinkish-mauve one instead and insisted on painting it on with a brush.

'Fiona, I'll never get to work in the morning if I have to use a brush to put my lipstick on,' protested Aisling during the mini make-up session on Wednesday night.

'You don't *have* to paint it, but it does stay on longer that way,' Fiona said firmly, as she rooted through Aisling's top drawer. 'I can't believe you have silver eyeliner, Ash!'

'Jo and I bought loads of it in a discount shop when we were going through our Abba phase,' Aisling attempted to explain. 'It was supposed to make your eyes look bigger if you put it on the inside lower rim . . .'

'Give me strength! You'd look like a reject from a Seventies Top of the Pops Special if you wore that,' said Fiona. 'Why are you keeping it?'

'I can't bear to throw anything out.'

Fiona held up a bottle of congealed bronze nail polish. 'Darling, I think this has to go. In fact, let me throw all of this out.' She poked around in the drawer with flawless oyster-coloured nails, dislodging two Mary Quant eyeshadows in what looked suspiciously like glittering purple and sky blue.

'Very Charlie's Angels, but not so good for anyone over seventeen, despite what they've been wearing on the catwalk lately. Dump this junk, Aisling, and I'll bring over some decent stuff for you. I do tend to overspend at the cosmetics counter and you may as well get some use out of my binges.'

Aisling laughed. '*Tend to overspend!*' she said. 'Famous last words, Mrs Finucane!'

She was glad of Fiona's expert advice though. Her own attempts to look made-up hadn't been precisely successful. Pumping the brush in and out of her elderly mascara tube had left her with lashes like tarantula legs. With the right materials, however – what she reckoned was around thirty pounds' worth of Fiona's expensive Lancôme stuff – she was getting much better at applying subtle amounts of cosmetics and with excellent results.

'Fiona gave me this self-tanning stuff and I put some on last night,' Aisling revealed, as she poured a few drops of milk into her tea. 'It really does perk your complexion up.'

'Whatever it is, you look great,' complimented Jo. 'Maybe you should market the Dump Your Husband Diet.'

Aisling giggled into her tea. You could never stay maudlin for long around the irrepressible Jo.

'I think it's too much of a *crash* diet,' Aisling pointed out. 'A bit too shocking to the system.'

'I'm on the Seafood Diet,' announced Jo, taking a bite out of a fat-glistening chip. 'I see food and I eat it.'

She ate another chip, put her head to one side and stared at her friend with narrowed eyes.

'Your hair,' she announced after a moment. 'You should do something with your hair.'

'Like what?' asked Aisling self-consciously, smoothing back the escaping tendrils from her pony tail. Her wavy curtain of light brown hair reached to about four inches below her shoulders and was too long and unruly to leave it loose when she typed. She never coloured it and rarely used the hairdryer, but Aisling knew her hair would have been nicer in something more elegant than a pony tail.

'James, my hairdresser, could do wonders with your hair,' Jo said enthusiastically. 'You need a little lift, a better shape or *something*. But it needs to be cut.'

'I've had it this length for years,' Aisling said defensively. 'It's handy. I can tie it back.'

'Ash, you need something career-womanish now, not handy. Anyway, tying it back is the only thing you can really do with it at that length. It would take years off you if you cut it. You don't need to do anything radical, you know.'

Aisling still wasn't convinced. 'Like what?' she asked.

'Softer, shorter, more feathery.' Jo was getting into her stride now. 'With highlights!'

'I'm a bit old for highlights,' said Aisling morosely, remembering the Greek summer when she'd first met Michael. Her hair was longer then, longer and bleached gold in the sun. She was never going to look like that again.

175

'Do you want some more tea?' asked Jo. 'I'm so thirsty, I just have to have another pot. I'm off coffee for the baby's sake.'

'No thanks.' Aisling could feel the tears coming. Damn, she'd been doing so well. She hadn't cried since Wednesday when she'd opened her bedside drawer and found the snapshot of the family outside Kilkenny Castle two summers before.

Michael had been shading his eyes from the sun and an eager eight-year-old Phillip had moved away to talk to the friendly American woman who'd offered to take the picture for them. They'd looked such a family then, a unit. Staring at her own smiling round face as she held Michael's hand and tried to hold onto Paul's T-shirt, Aisling wondered if they really *had* been a happy family at all. Or if she had believed in the perfect family, while Michael had been planning his affair? She'd cried. Bawled her eyes out in fact, and woke up with red, puffy eyes which didn't go terribly well with the red blouse she'd carefully ironed the night before.

'I haven't cried since Wednesday,' she said wetly, searching in her handbag for a tissue.

'Sometimes I feel so strong and determined to succeed, and sometimes I just cry.'

'That's allowed,' Jo sighed. 'I feel like sobbing my eyes out half the time, in between those moments when I dream of strangling Richard with his camera strap.'

'I'm sorry,' sniffled Aisling. 'I didn't mean to whinge. Has Richard not got in touch with you yet?'

'Yes and no,' answered Jo flatly. 'Yes, he got in touch and no, I won't be seeing him again. Ever. Unless I'm called up to identify him on a slab in the morgue, that is. A girl can dream.'

Shocked out of her tears, Aisling stared anxiously at her friend. Had pregnancy scrambled her mind?

'Richard is a little shit,' announced Jo after a moment. 'Correction, he's a *big* shit. Another pot of tea, please.'

'He did come and see me,' she explained to Aisling. 'Bearing gifts and begging forgiveness. Or so I thought. That big shit let me take him to bed. He let me think everything was wonderful, fine, hunky dory until I found out that he's *still* going to London. With Sascha, the rocket scientist, I have no doubt,' she added. 'I have my suspicions about that bitch and my ex-beloved.'

'The pig!' Aisling was outraged.

'Oh I did better than "pig", I can tell you that,' said Jo with satisfaction. 'That bastard had better keep away from me for the rest of his life or he'll be getting dentures fitted!'

'Jo, you're priceless! Tell me, what really happened?'

'You wouldn't believe it if I told you. Do you know, my life is turning into one of those mini-series things from the States. You know the sort of thing – *She loved him, but he had a deep, dark secret that rocked her to the very core of her being* – in a deeper voice than I can do, of course. I quite fancy Jaclyn Smyth in my part or should that be Jane Seymour? It needs one of those dark, sultry and depressed heroines anyway. I can't imagine who should play scumbag himself.'

Jo took the tea from the barman. 'It's nearly half one,' she said. 'When do you have to be back?'

'Two. But it'll only take me five minutes from here.'

'OK. Here goes. The story of my life: part twenty-six.'

Aisling only made it back to the office in time by the skin of her teeth. She'd thought things were bad for *her*. Poor, poor Jo. Imagine having the father of your baby dump you like a Christmas kitten that had grown bigger and less chocolate-box-cute in January? Then, to add insult to injury, imagine finding out that he'd done it all before, that he'd already dumped another unwanted Christmas cat *plus* an unborn kitten. What a complete asshole.

'Thank God you're back,' said Elizabeth gratefully when Aisling walked into their tiny top-floor office. 'I feel awful. I've just got to go home and lie down or I swear I'll pass out!'

'Of course you've got to go,' Aisling said automatically. 'Are you able to drive? Should I ring Pete and get him to collect you?' Pete was Elizabeth's husband, an accountant who sounded as though he cherished the ground she walked on.

'No, I'll be fine. It's only to Stoneybatter. I'm just sorry for you, Aisling.' Elizabeth raised apologetic brown eyes to Aisling's. 'I think I'm going to have to take my maternity leave from today. I don't know if I could manage another week. I know there's still loads I haven't shown you . . .'

'Don't be silly,' chided Aisling, trying not to think of what it would be like to have the horrible Leo all to herself from this moment on. 'You need to get home and look after yourself. Richardson, Reid and Finucane will keep going even if I do forget to bring Leo his morning coffee and lose half his letters! Don't worry.'

By the time she'd walked Elizabeth slowly to her red Panda parked on Fitzwilliam Square and made sure that she was in a fit state to drive home, Aisling's mind was in overdrive.

Not only was she terrified of losing vital documents on the bloody Apple, but she didn't know if she'd be able to cope with Leo's abrupt and demanding requests.

'Where's the bloody Reilly file?' he'd screamed only that morning, forgetting that he hadn't actually asked for it.

That wasn't even *mentioning* his ability to make her stomach turn inside out when he got her alone in either office and asked her how she was getting on.

'Any problems?' he'd breathed the day before when she'd brought him his mid-afternoon coffee. ('Black and no sugar. I'm sweet enough!')

'Fine, Leo,' she'd said breezily. 'Elizabeth is being great and I hope I make as good a secretary when she's gone.'

Secretary, you big sleazeball, she thought to herself. Not a piece of meat in a skirt.

It did occur to her that she'd envied Jo for her ability to make men stare at her, dumbstruck by her sexy, totally natural charm. But there was a big difference between ogling and admiring. If any man ever dared to give Jo the same sort of insolent and undressing stare that Leo Murphy gave *her*, Jo would have cut him down to size in a moment.

No, Leo didn't look – he slavered and made her feel more

uncomfortable than she'd ever have imagined possible. But what could she do?

This was the only job she was likely to get. She couldn't leave just because of Leo. Women with two kids, an absent husband and no skills, bar the ability to make a perfect cheese soufflé, couldn't afford to be picky jobwise. She'd have to get used to Leo, his slimy looks, little grins and vaguely suggestive comments.

He was in subdued form all afternoon.

He barely registered the fact that Elizabeth had decided to go on maternity leave early, muttering 'Hmm' indifferently when Aisling told him. So much for loyalty.

'Get me the Wilkinson files,' he said finally. 'There must be at least three of them. And get Tom Wilkinson on the phone afterwards. By the way, I won't be in on Monday, so cancel my appointments and leave my diary free on Tuesday afternoon. That's all.'

He wasn't even looking at her, Aisling realised delightedly. Yahoo. She hurried down to the file room with a light heart. Maybe she'd been imagining him as a big bad wolf when he was just a bored boss who amused himself between cases by eyeing up the office temps.

When she went back into Leo's office with the bulky Wilkinson files, he was on the phone. Obviously a private call, since he made her or Elizabeth call everyone for him, even his dentist.

'Don't give me that!'

His strong fingers, covered with coarse black hair, played fiercely with one of the red office pencils, twisting it around and around rapidly, nearly breaking it. Snap! It broke.

Aisling dropped the files on his desk and almost ran to the door. If he was ringing Mrs Murphy, God help her. For a brief moment, Aisling relished the fact that *she* didn't have to endure any more of those cross phone calls from a husband irritated by work and determined to take it out on *someone*.

Safe in her office again, Aisling wished she could lock the door for the rest of the afternoon. She decided to start

179

working on the letters Elizabeth had been doing before lunch and prayed that he wouldn't want her again. No such luck.

'Aisling, come down here.'

His voice on the intercom at a quarter to four made her heart sink. She'd been kept busy getting Elizabeth's unfinished work in order and cancelling Leo's appointments for Monday.

He hadn't even told her where he was going to be so she'd tried to sound both firm and mysterious on the phone.

'Mr Murphy has been called away on urgent business and won't be able to keep your appointment,' she'd said several times in her best posh voice.

Aisling didn't know why, but she firmly suspected that she was lying for Leo. Instinct told her that his sudden change of plans had nothing to do with a crucial conveyancing case.

Leo's face was still like thunder.

'Have you finished my dictation?' he snapped.

'Er, yes. Well, nearly.'

'How nearly?' he asked sarcastically.

Aisling could feel herself getting red in the face and wished she was anywhere except in this office right now. Cleaning out the garden shed in the company of several spiders and a few wasps would be nice by comparison.

'I've done six letters and I've got two left,' she stammered.

'Is that all?' Leo's heavy eyebrows were raised at least an inch as he stared contemptuously at her.

Aisling thought that doing six letters in an hour and a half as well as cancelling loads of appointments was pretty good for a novice. But she kept her mouth shut.

'You're not going to be much use to me if you can't keep up,' he said nastily.

'I'm sorry, Leo. I'll get faster, honestly.' She was begging and she knew it. She couldn't afford to lose this job. Please don't let him sack me, she prayed.

'Mmm. I hope so. Can you do shorthand? I've a letter to go out this evening.'

'Yes.' She'd have said yes if he'd asked could she parachute

180

out the top window. Shorthand had never been a requirement in the motor department, but dealing with lengthy phone calls from irate customers had taught her how to scribble at high speed.

This particular skill had not deserted her and after two attempts to decipher what turned out to be 'contemporaneous' – which Aisling would have dearly loved to have changed to the more sensible and more suitable 'at the same time' – she finished Leo's letter in fifteen minutes.

He was long-winded, but maybe that was simply his legal training. If he could say something in ten words instead of two, Leo went for the ten words every time. Nobody in Leo's world just *did* anything – they gave it due consideration, previous problems notwithstanding, deliberated at length and finally reached conclusions, without prejudice, of course.

Once the letter was signed and in the post, Leo was a different man, charming, chatty. All glinting, admiring eyes. After sprinting noisily up the stairs, he casually dropped a few files onto Aisling's desk and settled himself comfortably against its side.

'So, what have you planned for the weekend?' he asked cosily, as though he hadn't been bawling her out just half an hour previously. Aisling smiled nervously as she opened another document on her computer just to give her something to do other than look at him.

Had he been snorting some sort of recreational pharmaceut-
~~al~~ down in his office? Or was his type of two-facedness just
~~parcel~~ of office life? She was damned if she knew.

~~he~~ said cheerily, hoping the conversation

~~Leo~~ loosened his red
~~m~~ shirt.

lied with as much sincerity as she could muster, thinking of the previous evening when Phillip and Paul had been so glued to a Power Rangers video in Fiona's that they hadn't wanted to come home at all.

'Pity.' Leo got up abruptly. 'We must have a drink some evening. I can't have a new member of staff without bringing her out for a drink, now can I?' He smiled, baring a set of wolfish canines.

She kept typing, wishing she could pull on her cinnamon-coloured cotton cardigan and do up all the buttons. The pale pink silk blouse she'd had for years had been washed to that comfortable softness she loved but, precisely because it *had* been washed to death, it was a bit on the see-through side.

She had that uncomfortable feeling that her white bra was visible through the pink silk. Guess who'd be looking.

She concentrated fiercely on her typing. Her fingers were clumsy.

'Gotta go,' he said after what seemed like an eternity. 'Be good.'

'Bye, Leo.' She smiled at him as he left. Please let him be gone for good. Please.

As she walked out the front door, Aisling felt like those military cadets she'd seen in movies, the ones who threw their caps into the sky with delight once they'd graduated despite the despotic sergeant who'd made their lives a misery.

The week was over. Finally. Thank you God! Suddenly fearful that Leo was lurking near the front door waiting to drag her off for a drink somewhere, she hurried to her car.

She was dog-tired, had a ladder creeping up her tights, knew she had to stop and get milk, and had promised the boys she'd pick up a video for them. But she didn't care. It was Friday. She could crash out in front of the TV because the week was over.

Aisling felt tired but good. hampton Road.

one of them, bunions, paper cuts and all. The week had been hell but she'd got through it.

She picked up a bottle of wine for herself in Superquinn and crisps for the boys along with two litres of milk. Hell, she needed a treat. In an ideal world, they'd never eat crisps, she wouldn't drink wine and cellulite would only affect supermodels. But it wasn't an ideal world. If the boys were happy watching TV and stuffing their faces with crisps while she crashed out with a book and a bottle of £4.99 plonk from somewhere unpronounceable in Spain, then the evening would be going pretty well.

Phillip and Paul were like two athletes on performance-enhancing drugs on Saturday morning.

'You're only going for one night,' exclaimed Aisling, taking Paul's swimming togs and three squashed-up T-shirts out of his bag.

'I might need them.' He tried to stuff it all back in along with his Independence Day alien spaceship and the dog-eared Paddington book he'd loved since he was four.

'You won't, darling,' Aisling said again. 'Let me do it. Daddy will forget to pack all this stuff back again tomorrow morning and you'll go mad if you leave anything behind.'

'I can go back and get it the next day,' Paul pointed out.

'I suppose you can.'

Aisling wondered how Ms Carroll would cope with two energetic ten-year-olds spreading muck through pale carpets and squabbling over the remote control.

For a few gleeful minutes, she thought how thoroughly enjoyable it would be to sabotage the trip. She could almost hear herself telling the boys that Daddy would want them to make themselves at home in his new house, that they should behave exactly the way they did here.

'Daddy would be upset if he thought you weren't having fun, boys, and I'm sure Jennifer wouldn't mind you bringing your soccer ball, your Oasis tapes and your Power Rangers videos.'

Stop it, she warned herself. The only damage you'd do

would be to the twins. Don't turn into one of those bitter women who use the children as ammunition.

'Behave yourselves, won't you?' she said as she packed their toothbrushes and the peppermint toothpaste they liked into a small spongebag.

'Yeah,' muttered Paul from the depths of the bottom of the wardrobe. He was rooting around among the books, toys and plastic cars he insisted on keeping.

'I'll miss you, you know,' she said quietly. He didn't hear.

It was five past one when she drove up to the house after picking the boys up from their soccer match. Michael had parked his car on the road, not in the driveway. It was at once both frighteningly familiar and terribly strange to see the silver gleaming Saab outside the house again.

'Dad's home!' yelled the twins in unison from the back seat.

Aisling felt a prickle behind her eyes at the sight of the car, a painful memory of those days when it had belonged there.

He climbed out of the driver's side when she drove in, tall and rangy in chinos and a cream and blue striped casual shirt she didn't recognise.

'Paul, Phillip, come here!' he yelled unnecessarily as the boys launched themselves at him.

'Dad, Dad, we missed you!'

'We won at soccer!'

'I got a medal in judo in summer camp!'

Michael picked Paul up and swung him around rapidly, releasing him suddenly into a giggling heap on the drive before grabbing Phillip in the same way.

They tussled for a few moments and then Michael picked up the soccer ball Phillip had dropped and ran onto the grass with it.

Whooping with joy at playing with Dad again, they followed him happily, tackling clumsily, tripping up and shouting at each other.

Aisling left them to it. They didn't need her. It wasn't right to think of the boys as her private property, but that's what she'd been doing. She had to face the fact that they didn't belong to either her or Michael. They were their children, not their possessions.

She walked into the kitchen, flicked on the kettle automatically and opened the washing-machine door.

Might as well get the clothes dry.

'How are you?'

Michael leaned against the jamb of the kitchen door, hands in his pockets, a relaxed look on his dark face. He stared at her, dark eyes blank. Blast him! Here she was hyped up and nervous about seeing him for the first time since that horrible Friday and he was looking at her as if he hadn't a care in the world. The shirt was definitely new. Obviously expensive. *He* hadn't been sitting home trawling through his wardrobe looking for suitable things to wear. He'd been shopping with Bitch.

'Fine,' she answered curtly.

'You're looking well, anyway. Have you lost some weight?'

She allowed herself to smile at him.

'I don't know. I've just been so busy. Maybe I have.'

'It suits you.'

His voice was admiring. What was he up to? Flattery wasn't going to get him anywhere.

'I hope you've figured out what to tell the boys,' she said, determined to burst his bubble.

'I have.' A wary look appeared on his face. 'I'm sorry you've had to deal with everything. I didn't want it to work out this way, you must understand that, Aisling.'

Oh God, she was going to cry. She'd been fine until he started this.

'I don't want to talk about it, Michael,' she said, turning away and bending down to drag the washing out of the machine. 'Make sure nobody gives them Coke before they go to bed, all right?' She couldn't bring herself to say *Jennifer*. 'When will you bring them back?'

'Is six OK?' he asked.

'Fine.'

185

She didn't turn around, she couldn't. She just wished he'd go out to the car and let her say goodbye to the boys on her own.

'We have to talk sometime, Aisling.'

'I know, I know. Just not now.'

'See you tomorrow then. I'll leave my phone number on the pad in case you need to contact me.'

She heard him searching through the jamjar where she kept odds and ends, looking for a pen that worked. 'I'll wait outside, Aisling. Bye.'

She slammed the door of the washing machine viciously and straightened up. The boys waved at her from the back seat, not a shred of sadness on their happy, laughing faces. She waved just as happily, a grin superglued onto her face.

When they were gone, she felt her entire body sag miserably. Whatever would she do until Sunday at six?

'Have dinner with us,' begged Fiona on the phone five minutes later.

'I'd love to,' said Aisling tearfully, glad that Fiona hadn't dropped over to witness her sobbing into a tea towel. She couldn't imagine being even vaguely hungry and the last time she'd had dinner with the Finucanes, Michael had been by her side. But anything was better than an evening on her own, an evening of remembering.

Dinner turned out to be Fiona's favourite menu, the simplest and quickest thing she could cook – or reheat. Smoked salmon and brown bread – 'No cooking,' she said triumphantly – followed by chicken Kiev straight from Marks and Spencer's with a few wilting bits of broccoli and baked potatoes cooked by herself.

'That was lovely, darling,' Pat told his wife afterwards, before sinking into an armchair, exhausted after an energetic round of golf.

The two women sat at the dining-room table picking at the chocolate mousse which had turned out miles lumpier than it had looked on the packet.

'I wish you'd teach me how to cook.' Fiona lit up a cigarette and inhaled deeply.

'You *can* cook, Fee,' Aisling pointed out. 'You know you can follow a recipe book as well as anyone else can, you just get bored in the middle and forget about it all until it's too late. Anyway, there's just no point killing yourself cooking gourmet dinners to the exclusion of all else. I can vouch for that,' she added somewhat bitterly. 'Sorry, I didn't mean to moan.'

'You're allowed,' the other woman answered.

'Shirley Conran said something about life being too short to stuff a mushroom. I wish I'd realised that long ago,' Aisling sighed.

'She also said that she'd prefer to lie on a bed than hoover under it,' laughed Fiona. 'I like that one!'

'After this last week, I'm a convert to that way of thinking,' Aisling said with a smile. 'Life is certainly too short to stuff mushrooms when you're working and looking after two kids. I finally tidied up the twins' room this afternoon and you'd swear it hadn't been done for a month. I've no idea how they can make the place that messy in such a short length of time.'

They chatted, drank coffee and retired to Fiona's Scandinavian white kitchen to stow the dinner dishes in the dishwasher.

By eleven, Pat was snoring in front of the TV and Aisling said her goodbyes.

'Thanks, Fee,' she said sincerely. 'I'm not sure I could have faced an evening of unadulterated aloneness.'

'Well, you got an evening of unadulterated excitement!' laughed Fiona. 'Plus an haute cuisine microwave-in-three-minutes dinner and a sleeping host. What more could you ask for?'

That night Aisling slept fitfully. She awoke in a cold sweat at five past seven and knew she'd never get back to sleep. Punching the pillows didn't help.

Tomorrow, she'd doubtless sleep through the alarm. Today, when she *could* stay in bed for hours, she was wide awake.

Plenty of time to clean, polish and hoover meant that the house was spotless when the doorbell rang a little after six that evening. You *could* have licked your dinner off the floor, Aisling decided, if you felt that way inclined, that was.

She opened the door gratefully and the boys exploded into the house, dragging their luggage after them like dead bodies.

Michael hadn't come in, he just waved at her from the car. 'Darlings, I missed you so much,' she said tearfully, hugging them both tightly.

Paul shrugged her off and headed for the kitchen. At least Phillip gave her another hug before he followed his twin.

'How did you get on?' she asked as brightly as she could. Please say she was a hideous old cow and the house was like a pit, she prayed unfairly.

'Jennifer is really nice,' announced Paul with all the tact of a traffic warden. 'She's got this great car, a Nissan 100X T-bar,' he added. 'Black. And she's brilliant at Quasar.'

Aisling felt about two feet tall. Two feet tall and stupid. And ugly. Not content with taking her husband, this bloody woman had managed to charm her boys as well. What a pity she hadn't taught them to hate the cow!

'She can't cook, Mum,' said Phillip loyally.

'Yeah, we're hungry.' Paul threw open the fridge door and peered inside anxiously.

Bread and water for you, Aisling wanted to say angrily, but she couldn't. It wasn't their fault.

'I'll make you something,' she said. 'Tell me . . .' she hesitated, 'what was she like? What's the house like?'

The How to Split Up Nicely books probably didn't recommend pumping your ten-year-old sons for information on their father's new girlfriend but she just had to find out something.

'She's got this great garage door that opens when you press this thing in the car,' Paul said enthusiastically.

Yeah, it's called somebody else's husband, thought Aisling sourly.

'But is the house nice?'

'It's OK. She's got a big telly.'

Great. What do you expect from kids who wouldn't notice dry rot if they saw it. Aisling wanted hard facts, modernist or romantic, all muslin curtains and brass headboards or Philippe

Starck lemon juicers and icy white sofas?

'She's got a conservatory,' volunteered Phillip. 'And lights in the back garden.'

For candlelit dinner parties, no doubt. Aisling ripped the plastic off a frozen pizza and jammed it under the grill.

'You can't have chips. Will you eat baked beans?'

'Yeah,' they choroused.

God, the food must have been awful. Beans were not high on the dinner excitement-ometer. Aisling cursed the rusty tin opener for the millionth time and reminded herself to get a new one. She slopped the entire can into a saucepan and stirred it angrily with a wooden spoon. She should have shares in Heinz by now.

'How's Daddy?'

'He brought us to McDonald's and got us a new video. I said I missed him, but he won't come home.' Phillip carefully poured orange juice into a glass and drank the contents in one gulp.

Aisling's spoon stopped stirring.

'What did you ask him?'

'I said we wanted him back and he said you and he had rowed and decided to be away from each other for a time,' Phillip said quickly, obviously repeating what he'd been told verbatim. 'He said you didn't love each other any more.'

He looked up at her, big dark eyes welling up with tears. Aisling cursed Michael and his truthfulness. How the hell did he expect two ten-year-olds to understand what she couldn't?

Beans forgotten, she pulled Phillip to her and held him tightly. His green sweatshirt smelled of Michael's aftershave and another scent she couldn't identify. Something heavy and cloying. *Her* perfume.

'Why can't he come home, Mum?' Phillip asked.

There was no answer to that one.

'Daddy needs to be away for a while. Not away from you boys,' she added hastily. 'Away from me. Mums and dads who've been married a long time sometimes need to have a

189

break, you know. Lots of people do it. It can be good for everyone.' She faltered. 'People get very bored stuck together for ever. You wouldn't want to be friends with just Greg and no one else, now would you?'

'No.' Paul had stopped poking around in the fridge and was looking mutinous. 'But that's different!'

'Why?'

'We're boys. Boys don't stay with boys. They're just friends. Not like girls and boys.'

Oh well, thought Aisling. She wondered how to explain that boys sometimes ended up with boys, and girls with girls. But that particular version of the birds and the bees would have to wait until they'd got a grasp on the whole concept of mummies and daddies breaking up.

'It's not that simple, boys,' she said.

Phillip gave her a hard, inquisitive stare so like Michael's that she felt her jaw drop.

'Why not?'

Ask your bloody father, she wanted to yell. The beans began to bubble.

'Get plates, Phillip,' she commanded in a voice that left no room for arguments. 'Paul, lay the table.'

For once, they just did what they were told. She waited until they'd washed their hands and were sitting quietly at the table, cutlery at the ready, before she said anything.

'Boys, it's not easy for any of us. But your dad and I have split up for a while. It's very difficult for me, I miss Dad too. But he's gone for a while and we're just going to have to live with that. It's not your fault. He loves you both just as much as ever. So do I,' she added.

'This is a grown-up thing and we've got to get on with life. I don't want you getting miserable thinking he's never coming back or that he doesn't want to see you. Of course he does. That's why he brought you to see Jennifer today.' Even saying her name hurt.

'For the moment, you've got *two* homes. Isn't that great?' she added brightly.

190

'Yeah,' said Paul, 'and three cars. I want Jennifer to pick me up from camp in her car!'

'Great idea,' said Aisling from behind gritted teeth. Little turncoat. 'Here's your beans.'

She slopped a puddle of beans onto his plate and wondered was it too late to stick her head in the oven. The prospect of Leo Murphy, two irritable children and a glamorous rival turning up with a size eight bum and a sports car to pick up the kids was just too much for one woman to bear.

CHAPTER ELEVEN

Jo climbed out of the car slowly, grateful for the chance to stretch her legs after so long in the driving seat. Her back ached and her shoulders were stiff from continually crunching gears as she passed trundling juggernauts and carloads of tourists meandering along the road west. It had taken two weary hours to reach Longford, the half way point between Dublin and Jo's home town in the West. Holidaymakers enjoying the June sunshine had dawdled along the road all the way from the Naas Road, admiring cows, lamb-filled fields and the lush green countryside.

Fifteen years of travelling from Dublin to Sligo had made Jo immune to the charms of the N4. She didn't want to gaze at cows, so once she left the outskirts of the city, she just put her foot down and drove, eager to get the four-hour journey to Innisbhail over with.

By lunchtime, the rumbling in her stomach meant she just had to stop somewhere for something to eat and a break.

How do you expect to grow if you won't let Mummy eat properly? she addressed her tiny bump as she walked into the Longford Arms from the car park, massaging her aching neck with one hand. Proper lunch or just a sandwich? she wondered when she reached the reception area.

A handsome man standing at the desk followed her with his eyes, openly admiring the tall, leggy brunette in the flowing saffron-coloured dress.

Out of the corner of her eye, Jo saw him look and couldn't resist giving him a come-hitherish little smile. Then she casually flicked back her curls with one hand and walked into the dining room, her dress swirling around slender tanned ankles. She couldn't be bothered with men right now, but it was still nice to know that she hadn't lost her touch.

Fortified by a huge chicken salad, cheesecake and a Lucozade for energy, she was back in the car by two and overtaking tourists' cars at five past.

As she drove past the villages and hamlets which had signposted every journey home since she'd been nineteen, Jo felt a growing sense of excitement.

She couldn't count the number of times she'd travelled down this road, dying to see her mother, Shane and Tom, full of news and eager to hear theirs. She certainly had some amazing news for them this time. But Jo had decided not to tell anyone until after Shane's birthday party. You're only forty once, she thought and it wouldn't be fair to disrupt the surprise party her sister-in-law, Mary, had been painstakingly planning for weeks by announcing the existence of another addition to the Ryan family.

She'd tell her mother, Jo decided. She'd have to. Her mother could detect something out of the ordinary in about two seconds, which was why Jo had only made a few hurried phone calls from the office since she'd found out she was pregnant. It wasn't that Laura Ryan would pass out at the news that her only daughter was pregnant *before* they'd gone through the big church wedding shenanigans. Her mother had never been one of those people who gossiped disapprovingly at the back of the church before Mass, the ones who tut-tutted over any poor girl who was pregnant and unmarried.

But Jo knew what her mother had gone through. It had been a huge struggle to raise three kids on her own when their father died. She had been both parent and sole breadwinner for four-year-old Jo, seven-year-old Tom and ten-year-old Shane. While Laura was able to run the small dairy farm her husband had left her, she was determined that her children never wanted for anything.

When times were lean she sold eggs from her Rhode Island Reds and the rich yellow butter she churned every week. Jo loved her job of collecting the eggs in the morning and evening, leaving one in each nest to confuse the hens into laying there again the next day. By the time they were teenagers, the three Ryan kids could drive the tractor with ease, knew how to help a cow give birth and could milk in their sleep. When Tom decided to study to be a vet, Laura knitted Aran jumpers for sale in Innisbhail's craft shop to help pay his fees. Now that Shane ran the farm and had turned it into a much larger business, the bad times were over. Laura still kept her hens and made her own butter, but she'd handed over the farm to her elder son and was finally able to relax after twenty years of difficult single parenthood.

So much had changed since Jo had first talked to her mother about settling down and having a family. She'd been seventeen then, in the first flush of what she thought was the love of her life, dreaming of a fairytale wedding, exquisite children, a bungalow beside the sea with a tennis court out the back and a garden big enough for ten kids.

Seventeen years later, she could laugh at her teenage dreams. At least she could afford a baby now. Then, her entire fortune had consisted of a collection of much loved second-hand books, four David Bowie albums and thirty pounds in her post office account. Not exactly enough to keep a small child in nappies, never mind puréed vegetables.

She'd planned to rely on Steve, of course, her well-off, clever boyfriend. Would he have been a better father than Richard, she wondered?

She passed a bus bound for Dublin, ready to pick up scores of weary office workers and students and bring them back home for the weekend.

That particular journey was burned into her head like a cattle brand, hours of endlessly winding wet roads interspersed with mind-numbingly boring stops in rush-hour traffic and only one longed-for break in Mullingar for steaming tea. Four hours in a rackety bus had never been her ideal way to spend Friday evenings.

She remembered that freezing January night the bus had broken down outside Foxford and she and the other passengers had been stranded there for two hours before another bus arrived. Three squares of chocolate and a sip of tea from

194

someone else's flask were not enough to keep hypothermia at bay when the wind whistled wickedly outside and the heating didn't work inside.

Her mother had been quite frantic when Jo finally reached home, convinced that there'd been some dreadful accident. Jo could understand how she'd felt. Just a few miles down the road from where the bus had broken down, the tiny white cross was still there, tucked neatly into the ditch at a deceptively gentle-looking bend. A few plastic flowers were jammed up close to the cross, just under the letters 'RIP'.

She'd thought those little grottoes were pretty when she'd been a child, always full of flowers, the small Virgin Marys in their sky-blue cloaks brightening the roadsides.

The road widened just before she reached Ballina. Jo remembered driving out that way with Steve, going to a party in his mother's precious Mercedes. Banana yellow with cream leather seats and an opulent interior smell Jo would never forget. It was Mrs Kavanagh's pride and joy.

Being Steve, he'd taken the corner badly and the car had nearly ended up in the ditch. Jo didn't know which thought had terrified him most – being injured or facing Mummy's wrath if he dented her car.

That had been Steve all over, but she hadn't seen it at the time. Of course, she hadn't seen it this time either. She'd screwed up exactly the same way seventeen years down the line. Awful though it was to face it, Richard and Steve seemed to share some awful genetic code, Bastards' DNA, which helped them forget responsibilities and promises as soon as something or someone more interesting appeared on the horizon.

You'd think I'd have copped on by now, Jo thought all of a sudden. What if I have a baby boy and he turns out to be a mini-Richard?

Don't be ridiculous. She patted her belly and turned up the volume. Mariah Carey's clear, piercing voice filled the car singing 'Always Be My Baby'. Mariah's man wanted to leave her but she knew he'd be back. Lucky girl. Jo was beginning to wonder if she could keep any man.

The car crested the hill and Innisbhail lay before her, a small town nestling in a shallow valley, facing a remarkably sedate Atlantic on the fourth side. On bad days, the sea was a murky grey, surf crashing violently against the rocky shore. Today it was calm and the couple of small fishing boats far out to sea bobbed serenely on the water.

In the distance, she could see the remains of the old abbey beside her mother's home and the small wood where she'd played as a child.

The view always brought a lump to Jo's throat. Today was no different. This is where your mummy comes from, she told the baby tremulously, wishing she didn't feel so emotionally precarious all the time.

Just last week, she'd cried when the owner of a health farm had rung up to say thanks for the lovely piece they'd written in the June issue. And on Wednesday, when she'd stupidly pulled out of a parking space in front of another driver on Capel Street and he'd responded with angry gestures and lots of honking, she'd felt like dissolving into tears.

Cop on, Jo, she commanded. Don't wimp out now.

She drove down the familiar winding road and into the town, past the convent where she'd gone to school and along the main street where she and Marie Brennan had spent five years walking their bikes wearily up the hill before the long cycle home. Everything looked exactly the same, apart from the bright orange plastic burger bar sign hanging over the old post office, jarring with the sedate black and white shop fronts on the left side of the road.

The seats outside O'Reilly's Bar had been repainted and someone had finally replaced the tired-looking hanging baskets with new wire ones from which rampant nasturtiums hung in wild clumps.

The Birkenstock twins were walking along past Dillon's, the butchers, their once-auburn hair tied back into greying sensible plaits as they marched steadily up the hill, nattering non-stop in German, no doubt. They'd tried to teach Jo once but she'd never got beyond the 'How are you? I'm fine' stage. She was sorry now that she hadn't made the effort to learn German. Then again, she was sorry she'd never learned how to play the piano, how to knit Aran and how to change her own spark plugs.

Well, there'd be plenty of time for that when she was the size of a house and could spend hours reclining on the settee, reading educational books and waiting for baby to make an appearance.

A man on the footpath was waving energetically at her. She jerked back to reality and stopped the car, opening the window all the way down.

'Hello!' roared Billy Gallagher enthusiastically, dragging two small cross-looking boys over to Jo's car.

'How are you?' His sunburned face was warm with greeting, as friendly as it had been when they'd been in high infants together and she'd stuck up for him when the big boys bullied him because he was the teacher's son.

'I'm fine, Billy. How are you? God, the boys are getting so big now, I can't believe the size of them!'

'Say hello to your auntie Jo, Connell and Michael,' he demanded, pulling the boys closer to the car.

No joy.

'Ah sure, they take after me.' He grinned. 'Shy.'

'You were never shy, Billy, don't give me that!' Jo laughed.

'A slow developer, then . . .'

'How's Marie?'

'Bringing her granny into Ballina to get her glasses changed. She'd have been here if she knew you were coming today,' he said, mildly reproachful. Jo knew that Marie would be vexed if she found her old friend was coming home for Shane's fortieth birthday party a day early and hadn't told her.

'It's so busy in the office now that I didn't know if I'd be able to get away a day early,' she said, not quite truthfully. It was difficult to pacify everyone when you lived a long way from home. Everyone thought they should be first on your visiting list.

She didn't want to upset Marie, but once she'd told her exactly what was going on, the other woman would definitely understand why she had come home early without mentioning it.

'Will I get her to ring you when she gets home?' asked Billy, as three-year-old Connell started to pull in the direction of an ice cream van.

'Do that. Bye boys, bye Billy.'

After that, she waved at people but didn't stop. You could be stopping all day, saying hello to this one and that, giving potted histories on what you'd done or where you'd been. Jo loved the friendliness of Innisbhail, the sensation of being enveloped in a warm, welcoming blanket. But it could be a bit overwhelming, especially when you were in a rush.

Two miles out of town, she took a left turn at the abbey and drove a quarter of a mile before turning left again, past the old green gates and over the cattle grid to park beside her mother's Mini.

The Albertine climbing rose was out in force, covering the front of the small, whitewashed cottage in a wreath of baby-pink flowers. She could smell its rich, heady scent on the afternoon air as Prince, the old sheepdog, stumbled sleepily out into the sunshine and started wagging his tail as soon as he saw her.

'Hello, old boy,' she said delightedly, rumpling his fur. Prince panted and wagged, gazing up with rheumy eyes, happy to have someone new to pet him.

'Darling, how wonderful to see you!' Laura Ryan stood at the porch, her hands covered in flour and more than a bit of it on her dark curly hair.

'Mum.' Jo ran up and hugged her mother, breathing in the smell of lemon soap she always used along with the scent of Charlie Red she'd worn ever since her seven-year-old grandson, Ben, had bought it for her for Christmas.

'You look good,' her mother said slowly, standing back and taking in her daughter's ever-so-slightly fuller figure which was admittedly well hidden by her flowing dress.

'Have you been baking or bathing in flour?' Jo demanded, laughing as she brushed flour from her mother's hair.

'Baking until Flo Doyle rang me to say she'd seen your car in the town. It's impossible to answer the phone when your hands are covered in flour.'

'Good to see the old bush telegraph is still working as reliably as ever!' Jo said.

'That woman has nothing better to do but look out her front window and use the phone all day long,' her mother answered, heading back into the kitchen to put the pastry lid on her apple tart. 'She rang "so I'd be prepared for you" to put it in her words. What does she think I'd be doing that I wouldn't want you to see? Having it off with the postman?'

Jo laughed and automatically went to the black iron range to move the heavy metal kettle onto the hottest plate. Prince followed her, his nose snuffling her dress in the hope that she had a couple of Mixed Ovals hidden somewhere. The kettle hissed satisfactorily, already nearly boiled.

'Just give me a moment to finish this one and I'm all yours,' her mother said, putting the finishing touches to the tart. 'There's coffee in the cupboard if you want it,' she added.

'No, I've given up coffee.' It had been nearly two weeks since Jo had tasted a drop of coffee.

'You've what?' Tart forgotten, Laura turned around and stared at her daughter. Dark brown eyes met dark brown eyes as her mother's quizzical gaze bored into Jo's head.

'Given up coffee, that's all,' Jo answered. Then she laughed out loud. She should have known better than to try and hide the news from her mother for even one millisecond. She should have just announced it as soon as she'd got out of the car.

'It's not good for babies, is it?' she said simply.

'Oh Jo!' Her mother's face crumpled into tears and she threw her arms around Jo, clinging to her as if for dear life.

'Oh my darling, that's wonderful news. I'm so happy for you, so happy. Now sit down,' she said, leading Jo to the old faded green armchair which had been in the kitchen as long as

199

Jo could remember. 'Sit down and tell me everything.'

Jo sank gratefully into the chair, feeling immeasurably comforted by her mother's love and affection. The small kitchen, with its flowery wallpaper, lace curtains and gallery of Seánie, Dan and Ben's finger paintings, was so familiar. So what if Richard had left her. She still had her family. Her mother pulled up a small stool and sat down beside Jo.

'When did you find out? And why are you only telling me now?' she demanded. 'If you told Richard's ratbag of a mother before me, I'll murder the pair of you!' She was only half joking. Although Laura Ryan had never actually met Richard's mother, she'd heard enough about her from Jo to loathe the other woman.

'That's the problem,' said Jo, wondering how best to broach the subject. Head on, she decided. 'Richard doesn't want to know. He's baby-phobic or commitment-phobic or something like that . . .'

Her mother's freckled face paled visibly. 'What do you mean, he doesn't want to know? It's his baby, what is there to know?'

'I mean that he didn't want me to have it, Mum. It was an accident, we didn't plan it or anything. But I thought he'd be happy, it's my fault really.' She sighed.

'Don't be ridiculous!' Laura said angrily. 'It's not just your fault. It takes two people to make a baby and he's old enough to know the consequences of sex. What did he expect?'

Jo barely registered that her mother was talking about sex in such a nonchalant manner.

'He expected me to be the sort of career woman who wouldn't want a baby messing up her perfect life,' said Jo in a wobbly voice. 'He wanted me to have an abortion, but I wouldn't.'

She broke down finally and sobbed. Her mother wrapped her arms around Jo, holding her close and whispering the same soft nothings she'd whispered thirty years before to comfort a little girl frightened of shadows in the bedroom after her father's funeral.

'There, there my love. Don't worry, Jo. We're all here for you, I promise. Anyway, I've always wanted to be there for the birth of a grandchild and this is the perfect opportunity.'

They sat like that for a while. Prince lay on the floor beside them, knowing something was up and waiting with his nose between his paws in an expectant manner.

'I'm OK, Mum, honestly.' Jo felt around for her handbag and got a tissue. 'I'm used to the idea, thinking about the baby is giving me some kind of strength.'

'Are you eating properly?' demanded her mother, getting up to make tea.

'Yes, Mum.' Jo laughed. 'Like a horse, in fact. I'm going to end up like the Michelin Man if I'm not careful. I've had the most dreadful morning sickness and I can't keep anything down before twelve. After that,' she said, 'I eat everything I can get my hands on!'

'You'll have some fruit cake, then, won't you?'

'Definitely.'

Jo laid out the china cups and saucers her mother always insisted on using and settled herself at the kitchen table. Hot sweet tea and mouthfuls of soft, crumbling cake gave her an energy boost and she started her story.

The scent of perfectly cooked apple tart filled the kitchen by the time she was finished.

'What's the plan for Shane's birthday anyway?' she asked.

'For a start, he'd better not see you or he'll know something's up,' her mother said, carefully laying four perfectly golden tarts on the table. 'He's gone to Killalla to look at some cows and he won't be back until late. Mary's coming over here with the boys and we're going to finish the cooking. We've got a hundred coming so that's a lot of sausage rolls.'

'Don't tell her, will you?' begged Jo. 'I don't want to ruin Shane's night. It's *his* party.'

'It's more Mary's, the amount of work she's done,' Laura said. 'She's made enough cakes and quiches to feed the five thousand, so if nobody's hungry we'll all have full freezers for the next month. I've said I'm going into Ballina shopping tomorrow so I won't be over to them for lunch,' her mother added, carrying the tarts away to the tiny pantry.

'It was the only excuse I could come up with. Mary's telling him she's going with me, but we plan to make up the salads here and bring everything down to O'Reilly's. She bought banners and balloons and everything, God bless her.'

'Shane is going to get quite a shock,' commented Jo.

'Shock isn't the word for it. Mary's been telling him he shouldn't let being forty bother him and that she's not going to make a fuss. I told him I'd get him a nice pullover and some socks and bring the pair of them out to the pub tomorrow evening before I go to bingo. Poor Shane. He hasn't a clue.'

They laughed together.

'He hates the thought of being forty, but I think he's a little upset that Mary and he aren't doing anything special tomorrow night. I can't wait to see his face when he realises he's been had,' Laura said with a grin.

'How are Tom and Karen?' asked Jo.

'It's been hard for them now Karen's back at work,' said Laura. 'Oisín is some handful and Anna, the girl who runs the crèche, is driven demented with him. Karen hates leaving him in the morning and I wouldn't be at all surprised if she gives up work to mind him herself.'

Lord, thought Jo to herself when her mother had gone outside to make up the hens' feed. If Karen couldn't cope with six-month-old Oisín despite having the back-up of a husband, two unmarried sisters living round the corner and a helpful mother-in-law, how the hell was *she* going to manage totally on her own? She knew that her extrovert sister-in-law loved her job as a beautician. The idea that *Karen*, of all people, wasn't able to combine motherhood and career gave Jo a headache thinking about it.

'I'm not giving up my job for any baby,' Karen had said defiantly when she was pregnant and an elderly neighbour commented that she'd better stop working before she began looking pregnant.

Mary had coped with two small children and her job as a

202

nurse, Jo reminded herself. Mary had worked four days a week in the local hospital even when Ben was going through the terrible twos and made valiant efforts to demolish any room he was left alone in for more than three minutes.

When Mary arrived at half seven, honking her horn excitedly and sprinting into the house to see her sister-in-law, Jo was desperate to ask her how she coped with both a new baby and a job. But she couldn't. She'd never really been interested in Karen and Mary's pregnancies, but now she was fairly bursting to ask questions.

Instead, she rolled out layer after layer of flaky pastry, leaving her mother and the nimble-fingered Mary to handle the lumps of sticky sausage meat. Prince sat glued to Mary's side, knowing she was soft-hearted enough to slip him the odd bit of sausage meat, something his mistress, who was watching his weight, never did.

'How's that gorgeous man of yours?' asked Mary with the smile she hadn't been able to take off her face all evening.

It would have been cruel to ruin Mary's evening by telling her the truth. She was so excited at the thought of the surprise birthday party that she was running on pure adrenalin.

'He's fine.' Jo didn't dare look at her mother.

'How's his back?' Mary inquired, her professional interest sparked by Richard's constant lower-disc problem.

'Fine,' Jo answered tautly, wondering whether he was getting a soothing massage from that Sascha bitch. A nice kick in the backside, that's the sort of treatment she'd like to give him now. She thought of all those evenings when she'd worn herself out gently rubbing massage oil into his aching muscles.

'He'd really want to watch his back, you know. He could have a lot of problems later in life,' Mary continued seriously, blithely unaware of the looks being passed between Laura and Jo.

'Tell us, love, what should we be wearing for autumn?' asked Laura, as though she actually gave a hoot for fashion.

'Oh yes!' said Mary eagerly. 'I was going to wear my velvet

dress tomorrow night, but if you think I should try something else, Jo?'

'What else have you got?' Jo asked, delighted to change the subject. 'I love that amber two-piece you wore for Oisín's christening. What about that?'

'Do you think that would be nice? I've gone off it because my tummy's sticking out,' sighed Mary.

'Get out of here! What tummy?' demanded Jo, thinking of her own expanding belly.

'Do I look all right?' begged Mary, adjusting her bra strap in the toilet mirror in O'Reilly's the following evening. 'Shane hasn't said I look nice at all.'

'He's shell-shocked, Mary,' Jo pointed out practically. 'The poor man still hasn't got over how you managed to set up this entire party without him hearing a whisper. He certainly hasn't got his brain sorted out enough to tell you that you look beautiful. And you do,' she added.

'Oh, I don't know,' said Mary tearfully, fiddling with her lustrous red curls.

'You look lovely,' Jo said firmly. 'Now come on out and get the dancing started. It's like a wedding out there, everyone's waiting for you two to start dancing!'

After several duty dances with old family friends, Jo was about to head outside for a breath of fresh air when a hand on her shoulder made her whirl around.

'Hello, Jo.' She'd have known that husky voice anywhere. Steve Kavanagh hadn't changed a bit.

He was still good-looking although he certainly hadn't got any younger. The gleaming blue eyes that used to dazzle her now had a generous scattering of tiny lines around them.

'How are you?'

For a moment, Jo couldn't think of anything to say. Her social smile deserted her and she just looked at him blankly. What did you say to the first man who'd ever broken your heart?

Get a grip, Jo, she told herself sharply. What have you been doing for the last seventeen years, if it wasn't learning how to get one up on this sneaky, two-timing pig?

'Wonderful, Steve, I'm wonderful,' she breathed in her best sexy voice.

'And how are you?'

Was it her imagination, or did his eyes light up at the tone of her voice?

'Fine. But you look fantastic,' he said, a hint of awe in his voice. Thank God she'd worn the Lainey Keogh dress that moulded her figure like a second skin.

'Thank you, Steve.' She smiled like a cat who'd just found a cat-flap in the cream bun factory door. 'Isn't Miriam with you tonight?'

'Yes, she's over by the bar. We were on our way back after dinner and thought we'd drop in.'

Thought you'd crash the party because you can't bear to miss anything, Jo thought nastily. There's no way you and your horrible wife were invited to this party.

'It's been a long time, Jo,' he said.

'Gosh, I suppose it has, she replied. 'Ten years at least, she added, knowing well it was fifteen.

'I think about you, about us, sometimes.' Steve stared at her, giving her the benefit of the lethal Kavanagh smile she'd never been able to resist when she was a teenager.

'Do you?' Jo smiled at him indulgently. 'Weren't we the mad things, convinced we were in love at seventeen?' She laughed, as though she hadn't spent months crying when she heard he was going to marry Miriam Timmons.

'Sometimes I see your picture in the magazine and wonder what it would have been like if we'd stayed together . . .'

'Goodness, Steve, you old romantic. We'd have killed each other if we'd stayed together. I couldn't imagine it!' it gave her a dart of pleasure to see him flinch as the barb struck home. Serves you right, you bastard, she thought. He wasn't ageing well.

Funny, thought Jo, eyeing him up surreptitiously. She used to think he dressed so well. Now she was a fashion editor and

Steve Kavanagh was standing before her wearing a red polo shirt which didn't go with his red cheeks and a pair of cream jeans which did nothing for his beer belly.

'Joanne, nice to see you.' Jo swivelled around to face her old-time enemy, the only person who'd ever called her by her full name since she'd insisted on being called Jo at the tomboyish age of ten.

'Miriam, what a surprise!' The chubby Miriam Timmons she'd known had grown up into a very thin woman, with a short helmet of frosted blonde hair and the sort of mahogany tan which would have cancer specialists shaking their heads in disbelief.

She was dressed beautifully, in a coffee-coloured suede skirt and a silk blouse, but the clothes hung on her bony frame like laundry on a clothes-horse. A cluster of gold bangles and gold necklaces rattled as she moved and she made sure that her ostentatious engagement diamond, in a setting as big as a knuckleduster, caught the light as she waved her hand.

'Well, Joanne, you're looking well. Are you here on your own?' Miriam looked around the room pointedly as though trying to seek out Jo's boyfriend. Jo would have bet a year's salary that Miriam knew damn well she was here on her own and wanted to rub it in. Boyfriend couldn't be bothered to come with you, huh? Jo could almost hear the words.

Miriam's heavily made-up eyes dropped to Jo's bare ring-finger. Two can play at that game, thought Jo.

'I didn't expect to see you two here,' she said. 'Mary didn't mention inviting you.' Take that, you gatecrashing cow, she thought venomously.

Miriam blinked nervously. She'd done that in French class when she tried to pretend she'd mislaid her grammar copy-book.

'We, we were . . . just passing and thought we'd drop in!' she faltered.

Score one to me. Jo smiled to herself.

'Steve was telling me you buy *Style*,' she added. 'It's lovely to know that the people at home follow your career. Although

I should point out, Steve,' she said, 'that the photo they've been using on my bylines recently is at least a year old. It was taken when I was at the Paris fashion shows last spring and it's ancient!'

Miriam was simmering.

'Duty calls,' sighed Jo regretfully. She slipped an arm around Steve's waist and gave him a peck on the cheek. 'So nice to see you, Steve,' she added warmly. 'Bye, Miriam.'

Jo turned and walked away, aware that two pairs of eyes were glued to her back. A little sexy sway wouldn't go amiss, she decided. What wouldn't she give to hear the conversation between Steve and Miriam now.

Maybe it had been plain old bitchy to vamp it up so much and kiss Steve goodbye, but she didn't care. Miriam deserved it. And the wonderful thing was, she hadn't felt a thing when she'd kissed Steve. Not a smidgen of regret at what might have been. She'd shed quite enough tears over him. Thank God she was cured. All she needed to do now was cure herself of Richard.

'It's so wonderful to be back!' Rhona stood at the office door, a huge smile on her tanned face and bags hanging off her arms. 'Did you miss me, darlings?' she trilled, dropping the bags to hug Jo warmly.

'Sorry I didn't ring last night, pet,' she whispered. 'We didn't get in until after eleven and I didn't want to interrupt your and baby's beauty sleep. And how has this place been while I've been away?' she added more loudly for the benefit of the rest of the staff.

'Great,' said Jo. 'We had a ball and it looks as if you did too.'

'I want to make loads of money and retire to France.' Rhona retrieved her bag and dragged out a batch of tiny tissue-paper-wrapped packages. 'Now these,' she said, doling them out to everyone, 'are only small pressies, but don't say I ever forget you.'

'Oooh lovely,' squealed Brenda, who'd found a pair of shell earrings in her package.

On the phone as ever, Nikki waved a hand-painted pottery candle-holder at Rhona and mouthed 'thank you'.

'I didn't know what to get you, Tony,' said Rhona, as the chief sub-editor emerged from the advertising office with a pile of papers in his hands. 'I knew you wouldn't like anything but booze, darling, but this lot would complain if I gave you any and not them, so I got you this.'

She produced a tiny bottle. Tony took it and peered through his glasses to see what the label said.

'Aphrodisiac oil!' he exclaimed.

'I just thought you might need some,' Rhona said innocently, batting eyelids sooty with mascara.

'You didn't complain the last time we went to bed, Rho Rho,' he countered. 'She said I was a tiger,' he told everyone with a dramatic sigh. 'Women . . .'

'What about them?' A deep voice behind them made everyone hop guiltily.

Standing outside Rhona's office, holding a heavy black briefcase, was Mark Denton. He did not look terribly amused. But then, Jo decided, he rarely did these days.

If Jo had been asked to describe Mark Denton, she would never have said that he was handsome. Some women said he was attractive, sexy even, although she could never see it. She had to admit that he was well built with rugby player's shoulders topping a lean, tall frame. But his Roman nose was crooked, his jaw could have broken rocks and the only sign that his chin had ever yielded against anything was the off-centre dent in it. Short, greying dark hair was raked back over a lined forehead. And his shrewd and piercing eyes looked as if they'd never shone with delight over anything – apart from a successful deal. Everything about Mark screamed money, power and taste. If you liked that sort of thing.

Today, he was dressed in a beautifully cut grey suit with a subtle yellow silk tie and polished shoes.

'I'm here for the sales meeting,' he announced.

Jo could have hit herself. She'd completely forgotten about the meeting and she should have reminded Rhona the moment the other woman came in. Mark Denton was invariably early, 'to catch people out' Rhona always said cheerfully and correctly.

He wouldn't be pleased to see the entire office having a whale of a time at half ten on a Monday morning when the publication of the August issue was only a week away.

He strode into his large office and slammed the briefcase onto the highly polished conference table.

'Coffee, Brenda,' hissed Jo. Brenda scurried off like a rat let out of the lab to make the rich Colombian coffee the boss preferred to instant.

Presents completely forgotten, the staff dropped everything and rooted around their desks for folders, sheets of ideas, notebooks and pens. Mark Denton had that effect on people.

Jo knew she had those papers about the advertisement feature on safe tanning, but she was damned if she could find them. Even the usually unflappable Nikki was frantically trawling through her briefcase, muttering curses as she went.

Only Rhona remained calm and cool. She picked up her bags, sailed into her office, sat back in her chair and lit a cigarette with relish.

'God, I miss this place when I'm away for longer than two weeks,' she shouted out the door.

'Maybe I wouldn't be happy in a French château after all. I really do get itchy feet after too long simply lolling around in the sun, drinking wine and reading novels.'

'Don't torture me,' moaned Jo, who was longing to lie down in the sun and read novels even if she couldn't have kept more than a teaspoon of wine down. 'That sounds like sheer bliss. I'd kill to be doing that right now, to be *anywhere* rather than here,' she added in a quieter tone so Mark wouldn't hear.

'I don't know how you deal with him, Rhona, he's so difficult.'

'That's because you spark off each other, darling.' Rhona put out her cigarette and picked up a fresh notepad from her desk. 'You two are like bullfrogs in a pond, each one determined to be in the right and boss of the pond.'

209

'I am not!' Jo was shocked. 'You never said that to me before. You said *he* was difficult!'

'Don't mind me.' The editor got up and slipped her arm around Jo. 'I'm still woozy from the journey and probably saying things I'll regret when I calm down. You're just the sweetest creature imaginable when Mark is on the premises, honestly.'

Jo sat back in her chair at the conference table while Nikki and Tony discussed ideas for the Autumn beauty supplement and mulled over what Rhona had said. There was no way she sparked off Mark, she decided crossly. It was all his fault. He irritated her beyond belief. Look at that meeting two weeks ago when he'd deliberately annoyed her by mentioning the poster campaign. All right, she should have noticed that the designers had spelt three words wrong on the mock-up, but at least she'd caught it in time. Lord knows what it would have cost to reprint two hundred posters because of a few careless spelling mistakes. But they didn't have to reprint so why did he have to bring it up at all?

'What do you think, Jo?'

Startled, she looked up to find them all looking at her expectantly, a distinctly quizzical look on Mark's face. Damn. She hated to be caught out by him of all people. There was no way she could brazen it out and pretend she knew what they'd been talking about.

'Sorry, I was miles away.'

'Obviously.'

Was she imagining it or was there a slight smile on his face? Probably a smirk, the pig.

'I've a lot of things on my mind,' she started hotly but got no further.

'I know the feeling,' Mark interrupted gently. 'Are you OK, you look a little pale? Would you like someone to get you some water?'

'No, no thanks,' answered Jo weakly. What was going on? Was Mark Denton, tough guy *extraordinaire* getting soft in his old age – or did she look absolutely dreadful, so dreadful that even he'd noticed?

'Mark's got a great idea for the September issue, but we've really got to get working on it immediately,' said Rhona briskly. She poured some Ballygowan into a glass and sent it down the conference table to Jo. 'He wants us to do a big fashion feature from New York, linked with an advertising supplement centred around the Mademoiselle chain of shops. It's pretty hush-hush right now, but they're opening two shops here, and four in the UK in November.

'Linking up with them would be a brilliant chance for us to push the readership figures up, especially if we could do some sort of competition with them,' Rhona continued. 'It would mean a higher profile for *Style* and lots of ads.'

'And lots of money,' said Aidan, the advertising manager, excitedly.

'I've made tentative inquiries and what we need to do next is to go to New York and try and put things in motion.' Mark paused for a moment and slowly took a sip of coffee from his cup. 'The thing is,' he began, 'I'd like you to get involved right now, Jo. I need you to come to New York with me. You'll know the right way to talk to these people and it'll be useful for setting up fashion shoots later, when we send a model and photographer out.'

'Oh.' Now she *was* stunned. Mark wanted her help in setting the deal up? Amazing. Jo's mind turned somersaults thinking about it all. A month ago she'd have hated the idea because it would have meant being separated from Richard. Not a problem she had now.

And it meant she could spend hours in Bloomingdale's, wandering through miles of beautiful designer clothes with her credit card at the ready. Of course, travelling with Mark would hardly be a thrill, but at least it would be a break.

'Do you think you could manage it?' Mark was looking at her very strangely now, heavy eyebrows knitted together in consternation. Was he actually *asking* her and not ordering? What was happening to him?

'I'd love to, of course,' she replied in a businesslike manner. 'When do we go?'

'Saturday?'

Saturday! She'd hardly be packed by Saturday. It took her at least a month of planning and thinking about her wardrobe to go away for a weekend, never mind a business trip to New York. She just nodded her head and said 'Right.'

'I'll set up meetings for Tuesday and Wednesday, which gives us Monday to recover from jet-lag,' Mark was saying. 'We should be finished by Thursday, Friday at the latest.'

'Lucky old you,' said Nikki enviously. 'I love New York and I adore the Village. Weren't you there only last year with Richard?'

Jo felt her stomach lurch at the mention of his name. She hadn't told the other girls in the office that she and Richard had broken up. She hadn't heard a word from the bastard since that horrible morning in her flat so it was pretty obvious that he was out of her life for good. She knew she had to tell people, but she kept putting it off. How could she tell them she was single again and pregnant all in the one fell swoop? It was so embarrassing, so humiliating.

'Nikki, do you have the pictures for the perfume ad feature?' said Rhona loudly. She knew that Jo was on the verge of tears and guessed the reason why.

For the next half an hour, the conversation around the conference table ranged from advertisement features to production problems. Jo sat quietly, answering questions and trying to join in. But she didn't feel up to it. Damn Richard.

Under the table, her hands caressed her tiny bump, gaining solace from the thought of the life inside her. Baby, baby, you make me strong, she said to herself.

When the meeting was over, Mark dismissed everybody curtly but asked Jo to stay. Instead of remaining at his seat at the top of the table, he moved into the chair beside her.

'I got the feeling that you're not keen on going to New York,' he began, splaying his hands onto the table as he spoke. He had strong fingers, more suited to a builder than a man who made deals on his mobile phone and drove a Porsche. There was no wedding ring on his left hand, something which never ceased to amaze the entire office.

Why wasn't Mark Denton married? There were always plenty of women hanging around him, Jo knew that. Quite a few of Jo's journalistic pals had expressed an interest in him and told Jo she was a lucky bitch to work for such an attractive man. She couldn't see it herself.

Rhona knew more about him than she let on, Jo knew that for sure. Whenever there were rumours about Mark and a mystery companion, Rhona pretended to know nothing. That was why she was such a good person to confide in. No secret would ever pass Rhona's lips once she'd sworn to keep it. He certainly wasn't gay. Definitely not.

'If there are personal reasons why you can't be away, I'll understand,' Mark said slowly. 'But I'd really like to have you with me. I know you'd make an excellent impression on these people, you talk their language and understand their ideas. I'm good on the business end but hopeless in that respect.' He laughed. 'I don't know the difference between one designer and another, but I know you do.'

Charmed by his frankness and complimentary manner, Jo relaxed.

'I'd love to go,' she replied. 'It was a surprise, that's all.'

'I've been thinking about it for a few days,' Mark said. 'I'd hate one of the other magazines to steal a march on us which is why I want to get this sorted out immediately. I hope this isn't disrupting your calendar too much, I hope you've nothing planned with Richard or anything . . .' His voice trailed off.

Was he pumping her for information about Richard? Jo wondered for a second. No, he couldn't be. How could he know?

'I've nothing planned,' she said brightly. 'Where are we going to stay?'

'The Manhattan Fitzpatrick. It's a beautiful hotel and it really is a home away from home. Sitting in the bar you'd think you were in Dublin because the place is packed with Irish people.'

'Lovely,' said Jo, meaning it. When she and Richard had gone to New York the previous summer, they'd stayed with one of his friends in a small apartment in Queens, an apartment with dodgy air-conditioning at that.

'By the way, thanks for putting me wise to Emma,' Mark added. 'I really had no idea what she was up to. I suppose I'm the doting uncle who sees her through rose-coloured glasses. She was always a handful as a child, so I don't know why I thought she'd change that much when she grew up. But she really is a good kid. She just needs to mature a bit, that's all.'

'I understand,' answered Jo automatically.

'Do you have any plans for lunch?' he asked. 'I'll be away all week so I won't have a chance to talk to you about the trip. If you're not doing anything, we could go to Dobbin's.'

'I'd love to have lunch,' she said truthfully. Might as well be hung for a sheep as for a lamb and anyway, she was starved. Dobbin's was a fantastic place for lunch even if it was too expensive for her purse. Mark Denton could certainly afford it.

She stood up and smiled at him.

'I've just got to finish an article and make a few phone calls,' she said. She didn't want him to think she'd drop her responsibilities like a shot at the mention of a free lunch.

'Fine. We'll go at half twelve.'

Back at her desk, Jo returned to the article she was writing on autumn's essential fashion buys and the ten wardrobe staples every woman needed. She flicked through an album of pictures from the top designers' autumn/winter collections and chewed the top of her pen. She hated following fashion blindly, telling ordinary women with ordinary curves that over-the-top Seventies stripes or snakeskin jeans were going to look as good on them as they did on skinny little Kate Moss.

Jo's idea of fashion was the sort of outfit which suited each individual wearer. 'Tailored black trousers are a must-have,' she wrote, as she had for the past three years.

'I'm glad to know I'm in fashion,' said Rhona, peering over Jo's shoulder at her VDU. 'Are elasticated waists allowed?' she asked, smoothing down her black tailored trousers.

'Of course,' replied Jo. 'Where did you get those trousers?' she demanded. 'The way my waist is going, I need elasticated ones myself.'

'Welcome to the club,' said Rhona. 'All you need is a belt to hide the elastic bit and you can breathe in comfort. Tell me,' she asked innocently, 'what did Mark want to talk to you about all on your ownio?'

Jo looked up suspiciously but Rhona's expression was serious.

'We're going to lunch to discuss the trip,' she said, knowing she sounded defensive and wondering why.

'Oh,' Rhona said. 'That's nice. Don't forget to come back to the office afterwards, will you? No sloping off for indiscreet drinkies in O'Dwyer's and ending up in Joy's nightclub at four in the morning.'

'Rhona!' Jo was scandalised and shocked. 'Are you mad?' Realising she was almost shouting, she whispered, 'Just because we manage to talk for the first time without coming to blows, doesn't mean we're engaged you know. For God's sake Rhona, I know I'm single, I'm not desperate!'

'You don't have to be desperate to fancy Mark,' Rhona answered mildly. 'Just because you're blind to his charms doesn't mean that lots of other women wouldn't rip out your contact lenses to be in your place, Jo.'

'Well, I'm not one of them,' hissed Jo. 'For a start, I won't be drinking and there's as much chance of him fancying me as there is of you winning the 3.30 at Leopardstown!'

'Fine,' grinned Rhona. 'I'll expect you back at two with a doggy bag and a bottle containing the two glasses of wine you couldn't drink.' She waggled one finger at Jo. 'Don't have fun, whatever else you do!'

At half twelve on the dot, Mark appeared beside Jo's desk, briefcase in hand.

'Are you ready?' he asked.

'Yes,' replied Jo nonchalantly. 'See you later,' she called in to Rhona's office on the way out.

Rhona's response was a wicked wink.

Knowing that Mark was behind her and couldn't see, Jo stuck her tongue out at Rhona. Fun with Mark Denton? Honestly, all that Chardonnay and the French sun must have scrambled Rhona's brain.

'Nice car,' she said as she settled herself into the low-slung passenger seat of the Porsche. 'It must cost a bomb to insure.'

'It does,' Mark answered wryly. 'But she's worth it,' he added, patting the steering wheel lovingly.

Here we go, thought Jo, another man in love with his car. She waited for the spiel – 'it goes from nought to sixty miles an hour in half a second and has triple cylinders and buckets of horse power . . .' Boring, boring, boring.

But he didn't say anything like that.

'I always dreamed of having a car like this,' he said instead. 'My father loved cars but he never had the money to buy anything but old wrecks. I remember him bringing me to a car show once, and we spent hours looking at all these beautiful sports cars. He said he'd love to drive one of them, just once before he died.' He paused, concentrating on turning right down Fitzwilliam Place.

Jo sneaked a sideways glance at him, amazed at this sudden softening of the hard-as-nails image. For once, his jaw wasn't as firmly set and he looked younger than his forty-three years, more approachable somehow.

'He died before I got my first business off the ground,' Mark explained, 'so he never got the chance to ride in a sports car. When I bought my first BMW, I drove to the graveyard in it. It was as if I was showing him that I'd done what he'd always dreamed of doing. I suppose that sounds very senti-mental to you, does it?' He turned to look at Jo.

She shook her head, still seeing a younger version of Mark standing beside his father's grave with tears in his eyes.

'I understand completely,' she said finally. 'I never really knew my father. He died when I was four and I can't remember him at all. But I like to think he looks down on me sometimes. I'd like to think that he could see me and be glad that I'm doing well,' she said quietly.

'He has a lot to be proud of,' Mark said. 'You *have* done well.'

Jo flushed and then laughed to hide her embarrassment.

'I wouldn't say that,' she started.

'Why wouldn't you say that?' demanded Mark, braking at traffic lights and turning to look her straight in the face.

'Things aren't always what they seem, Mark,' she explained hesitantly. 'We all look at other people, see that they have X, Y and Z and think, "They're happy, they've got everything." But we don't see the other side of things at all, the problems people hide.' She shrugged. 'If you put up a good enough façade, you can fool everyone. Even yourself.' Yeah, she'd managed to fool herself all right, fool herself that Richard cared for her.

The car purred to a halt outside Dobbin's and Mark switched off the ignition.

'Do you want to talk about it?' he asked.

'Not really,' Jo replied, amazed that this man could be intuitive enough to know that she was talking about her own problems. 'Let's have lunch and talk about business.'

'That's fine by me,' he answered.

Seated in a booth up beside the wall, they stared at the menu silently. Everything sounded so beautiful, thought Jo hungrily. Tarragon vinaigrette, deep-fried brie on a redcurrant sauce . . .

'I love the way they describe food,' she said to break the silence. 'You couldn't imagine how it could taste any better than it sounds!'

He chuckled. 'That reminds me of an awful joke,' he said.

'Tell me,' she commanded.

'OK. This American guy goes into a restaurant in Ireland and says to the waitress that he wants a chicken smothered in gravy and she says, 'If you want it killed in that cruel way, sir, you better do it yourself!' I know, it's a dreadful joke.'

Jo broke out laughing and crumbs of the bread roll she'd just bitten into spewed out onto the table.

'Sorry,' she mumbled, her mouth still full. She swallowed and grinned over at him. 'That's daft but it's still funny. I used to love silly jokes like that, especially the elephant ones.'

'Elephant jokes?' he asked.

'Oh, they're totally silly but I love them,' she said. 'Here's one. Why do elephants paint the soles of their feet yellow? So they can hide upside down in bowls of custard.'

He laughed and said, 'You're right, that's silly.'

Just then the waiter appeared.

'We better pick something to eat,' Mark said, serious again, 'or we'll never get back to the office.'

'I'll have the avocado salad,' Jo said straight-faced, 'and chicken smothered in gravy!'

Mark burst out laughing while the waiter stood there with a bemused expression on his face.

'Sorry,' Jo grinned up at the waiter. 'I'll have the avocado salad, the monkfish and some water, not the sparkling stuff.'

She looked at Mark as he scanned the menu. He was a strange man and no mistake. He'd never been anything other than abrupt and businesslike with her during the three years she'd worked for him.

Today was startlingly different. He was still the boss, no doubt about that. If his dinner arrived with a single flaw, it would be dispatched back to the kitchen like a shot, she knew. Yet it was as if he'd suddenly decided to open up to her, to let the tough businessman façade drop a little. Wait until she told Rhona.

'I'll have the brie and the monkfish,' Mark announced, 'and a bottle of number 33.'

He hadn't even looked at the wine list, Jo realised. He obviously visited Dobbin's so often that he knew exactly what he wanted.

'I'm not drinking anything,' she said quickly before the waiter left.

'I'm sorry. I should have asked. Make that a glass of red

wine, will you?' he asked the waiter.

Jo was waiting for him to ask why she didn't want wine, but he didn't. He leaned back in the wooden bench seat and smiled at her over the small vase of carnations, a warm smile that lit up his face. He was almost handsome when he smiled. Maybe that was what made other women fancy him, his smile, something he rarely produced when he was in the office.

'So tell me, Ms Ryan, what spurred you on to become a journalist and a fashion journalist at that?'

She looked at him curiously. 'What's brought this on?' she asked bluntly.

'I suppose I don't know that much about you, other than what you've done for *Style* over the past three years, which has been excellent,' he added. 'And seeing as we're going to be travelling together, I thought it would be nice to know each other a bit better.'

His face was serious as he spoke and she found herself noticing that his eyes were a beautiful cool grey colour. Jo was suddenly glad she had washed her hair that morning and worn her navy silk dress even though she'd felt so weak when she woke up that she'd felt like wearing her dressing-gown into the office. And was it her imagination, or was he gazing at her in a distinctly un-bosslike way? Stop that, Jo, she reprimanded herself. He hasn't been interested in you in three years, he's hardly going to start now. There's got to be some ulterior motive for this 'tell me about yourself' stuff.

'Don't you have my CV in your files?' she asked smartly.

'Yes,' he admitted. 'But CVs are limited. They tell you when and where a person is born, what they got in Leaving Cert English and whether they like hang-gliding or knitting, all useless when it comes to getting to know someone.'

Amazing. He wanted to know about her. Maybe he was interested in her after all! How weird. Was she interested in him, she wondered? No, she couldn't be. She was pregnant with another man's child, a man who'd dumped her. She couldn't possibly fancy any man.

219

'Fair enough, I'll spill the beans, on one condition,' she said firmly.

'What's that?' he grinned.

'You tell me the same about you.'

'I'm afraid I'm very boring, Jo.'

'That doesn't matter. You don't talk, I don't talk!' She smiled triumphantly at him.

'You drive a hard bargain.'

'I thought that's why you were bringing me to New York with you,' she said cheekily.

'Of course, of course. For that, and because you understand the world of clothes. I've never been able to understand how they can make two yards of fabric into a dress and charge two grand for it,' he said. 'It's a complete rip-off.'

'I'd keep that particular sentiment to yourself when we're in New York,' Jo laughed, 'or we'll be going home empty-handed. The secret of understanding the fashion world is to tell all designers that they're either the new Coco Chanel or the most innovative designer you've ever seen, not that they're rip-off merchants!'

Their first courses arrived and Jo attacked her salad with gusto.

'No breakfast,' she explained between mouthfuls of avocado.

'Want some brie?' he said, holding out a piece on his fork, the sort of intimate gesture lovers make. She felt that ache in her chest again.

'No thanks,' she said, remembering all she'd read about avoiding soft cheeses during pregnancy for fear of listeria. She stared down into her plate, shuffling pieces of radicchio around in the oily dressing, terrified that the tears would start. What the hell was she doing wondering whether Mark Denton fancied her or not when the man she'd loved had walked out on her?

If Mark noticed her sudden change of face, he didn't mention it. 'Were you always interested in fashion?' he asked blandly.

Fashion, yes, she could talk about that for hours. Grabbing the lifebelt he'd thrown her, Jo started talking. She was still at it by the time Mark had paid the bill.

'That was lovely, I really enjoyed it,' she said truthfully as they left the restaurant.

'I'm glad,' Mark said, opening the passenger door for her. 'Actually, I brought you out because I wanted to talk to you about something.'

'Of course,' Jo replied. What would she do if he asked her out to dinner? Say yes? She'd have to say yes. Anyway, it would be fun. He was a very entertaining companion when he wanted to be.

He opened his door and slid into the driver's seat.

'It's Emma. After what you said to me when Rhona was away, I've been worrying about her. She really needs a firm hand and some guidance. I'd love it if you could take her under your wing, Jo.'

Jo felt herself deflate like a burst balloon. So that was what it was all about. He wasn't even vaguely interested in her. He'd simply been softening her up before asking her to look after his bloody niece. What a fool she'd been to even imagine that Mark Denton would be interested in someone like her. You're a complete moron, Jo Ryan.

'What would you like me to do?' she asked tersely.

'Take her on like a student. Train her how to write, how to interview people, you know the sort of thing. If you agree, I'd be delighted and so would Emma.'

It wouldn't kill me to be nice to the scheming little bitch, Jo decided. But she wasn't going to take any cheek from her.

'I'll take her on, Mark,' Jo said coolly. 'However, I want her to understand what I'm doing for her. She better be prepared to work hard and not whinge or run to you every five minutes if she wants my help.'

'I'll talk to her,' he said quickly. 'Thanks, Jo, this means a lot to me.'

She sat in stony silence until the car stopped outside the office.

'I'll see you at the airport at ten on Saturday morning, OK?' he said.

'Right. Thanks for lunch,' she said quickly before slamming the car door.

'How did you get on?' Rhona asked eagerly when Jo stalked into her office.

'Bloody awful,' Jo snapped. 'That man drives me insane.'

'Oh.' Rhona looked pensive. 'Maybe he'll grow on you when you're away.'

'I doubt it.'

CHAPTER TWELVE

Jo's fingers tightened their grip on the seat's armrests and she swallowed deeply. For the tenth time in five minutes she wished she'd never watched that bloody movie about the plane crash in the Andes.

She hated take-off, hated flying full stop. But taking off was the worst. At least when you were flying, you had no idea what was going on. The air-stewardesses smiled and passed out booze and the clouds were usually so thick that you hadn't a clue how far away the ground was. Taking off, however, was so immediate and fraught with danger. You could see *everything*.

If she looked out the window, Jo knew, she'd see the runway and Dublin airport and lots of housing estates growing smaller by the minute. She couldn't help herself, she had to see. Big mistake. The sprawling airport had turned into a matchbox-sized arrangement and the fields were beginning to develop that patchwork look.

The plane banked slightly and Jo wondered if you were allowed to leave your seat and sprint to the toilet when the seat belt sign was still on. Her old friend, nausea, was back. She'd have to climb over Mark Denton and the person in the aisle seat to get out, but she could do it. Or could she? Maybe she'd just breathe deeply and pray.

'Are you all right?' asked Mark, putting one large hand on her clenched left one.

'No.' She was too scared to lie. 'I hate flying,' she muttered. 'And I hate the window seat.'

'Let's talk about something to take your mind off it, then,' he said comfortingly.

'Did I ever tell you how Rhona and I met?' he asked, settling himself sideways in his seat, and keeping her hand firmly gripped in his large one.

'No.' Jo didn't feel like being humoured. She wanted to behave like a spoiled child and ignore him, make him suffer for bringing her out to lunch purely to talk about his horrible niece. She'd practically ignored him since they'd met in the airport. She'd given him a cool little smile when he'd brought her into the Aer Lingus business-class lounge where there was free tea, coffee, booze and newspapers – and lots of comfy armchairs to sink into.

Mark had managed to ignore the fact that she was ignoring *him* and had been consistently pleasant to her, as though he was humouring a spoiled child. She *hated* that.

'After that, I had to give her the job,' he was saying. 'You know Rhona.'

Yes, she did. She remembered Rhona's parting words to her which had been along the lines of, 'If you fall desperately in love with Mark when you're living the high life in New York, don't forget that I want to know all about it when you come home.'

Some bloody hope. A – why would anyone fall in love with a man when they were nearly three months pregnant with the child of another man who'd done a runner?

B – how could anyone feel even vaguely romantic squashed into a jumbo on a never-ending flight to New York?

And C – why would anyone be stupid enough to fall in love with Mark Denton? Rhona was mad sometimes, Jo decided.

Mark had stopped talking and was patting her hand.

'Better now?' he asked.

'Fine,' she muttered.

He ignored her cross expression and started talking again, obviously under the misapprehension that he was somehow being helpful. He kept the conversation going through the meal – roast chicken and rice, with a brown-bread scone, some sort of cheesecake thing and a foil-wrapped mint chocolate which he handed to Jo – only stopping while they watched the in-flight movie.

'I hate Julia Roberts,' grumbled Jo sleepily, wondering how

in the hell she could be tired when it was only lunchtime. True to form, she'd slept badly the night before, waking up in a cold sweat at three a.m. after dreaming that she'd arrived at Dublin airport for the eleven a.m. flight minus her passport, suitcase and, worst of all, her handbag.

A few minutes dozing would make her feel better. She wriggled around in the small seat, rolled up her sloppy grey sweatshirt into a makeshift pillow and closed her eyes. She woke two hours later, shocked to find that she was leaning comfortably against Mark's shoulder, snuggled up to him cosily.

'Sorry,' she said abruptly, sitting bolt upright. She hoped she hadn't snored or something equally awful. Richard used to say she snored in her sleep; it would be too embarrassing to snore on the boss's shoulder.

'You missed the coffee,' Mark said, stretching his arms and massaging the shoulder she'd been leaning against. Oh no, she groaned inwardly. He obviously hadn't been able to move for hours because she'd been glued to his side. He probably thought she'd done it on purpose, that she fancied him. How awful.

'I didn't wake you because I thought you needed the rest,' he said. 'You look very pale. Anyway, the coffee wasn't very nice. Nothing like the stuff in the office. Are you all right, Jo?'

Mark looked at her with concern in his eyes. Nice eyes, she decided. Kind eyes. It was time she stopped ignoring him and started behaving like an adult again.

'I'm fine,' she answered. As fine as you could be when you felt like a complete moron. 'Sorry about squashing your arm for so long.'

He grinned. 'That's OK. Would you like some water or orange juice?'

'Water would be lovely.' She was desperately thirsty all of a sudden. Since she always wrote that drinking lots of water on the plane and keeping your moisturiser handy were vital for flying, she might as well practise what she preached.

Mark waved in the direction of the air-stewardess. An

attractive redhead appeared at their seats a moment later.

'Can I help you?' she asked, giving Mark what Jo considered a very warm, come-hitherish smile. The stewardess's eyes took in Mark's cream polo shirt with the Ralph Lauren designer logo, his expensive Tiffany watch and the absence of a wedding ring on his strong left hand. Her smile deepened.

Mark certainly had his own quiet charm, Jo realised with a jolt. It was just as well he wasn't her type.

She'd always gone for handsome men, the sort of smooth, chiselled-featured boys who could model Armani suits. Mark was tall, well built and there wasn't an ounce of fat on him, but he was a million miles away from Richard Kennedy. Richard was movie-star gorgeous while Mark was rugged, a hard-working self-made man to Richard's model-boy look.

'Could we have some water?' Mark asked the stewardess before turning to Jo. 'Or do you want juice, Jo?'

'Water, thank you,' Jo said, watching the stewardess's smile shift from admiring to professional once she realised that Mark wasn't on his own.

You're welcome to him, Jo felt like saying. He's not mine. Of course, she didn't say anything of the sort. She sipped her water and eyed Mark surreptitiously. He was attractive really, very attractive in fact. Would it look bad if she got out her powder compact and put on some lipstick?

Kennedy airport was hot, sticky and crowded. Exhausted from the flight, Jo was glad when Mark took charge of the luggage, especially since her suitcase was crammed with at least a quarter of her wardrobe. He lifted her case and his leather suit-carrier effortlessly onto a trolley – without demanding to know why hers was so heavy and what had she brought, the way Richard always did – and led the way through the crowds out to the noisy arrivals hall. It was bedlam.

People of every skin colour imaginable pushed up against the barriers like a human rainbow, anxiously watching passengers emerge and shrieking loudly in different languages when they spotted their visitors. It was like being in Marks and

Spencer's on the first day of the January sales.

Jo was poked in the back by a child with a tennis racket and had her ankles bashed by someone else's trolley as she followed Mark through the throng. The blissful air-conditioned cool of the plane seemed miles away from the humid New York air.

Her white cotton T-shirt and jeans were pasted to her body. What she wanted most in the world was to lie down in a cool room and rest, then stand under a cool shower.

She was considering flinging herself on the trolley and letting Mark push her to the hotel, when she spotted him – a uniformed man in his twenties holding a sign that read, 'Fitzpatrick Manhattan Hotel, Mr Mark Denton'. Mark waved at the driver who immediately hurried over and took control of the trolley.

'Welcome to New York,' he said in a strong Cork accent. 'I'm Seán. Nice to meet you.' Jo could have kissed him. Seán loaded the cases in the back of the stretch Cadillac limo the hotel had provided while Jo slid onto the cool leather seats and sighed with relief.

She didn't care if her luggage ended up in Hong Kong, as long as she didn't have to look after it – or anything else for that matter.

As Seán wove through the heavy airport traffic, Jo stretched out her legs and wondered why she'd never travelled in a limo before. Was this what movie stars felt like when they eased from airport to airport in the comfort of a luxury car, distanced from the world behind darkened windows?

There was what looked like a tiny drinks cabinet fixed into the back of the driver's seat and she'd have loved to open it, just to see what was in it. But that would probably be as gauche as hell and she didn't want Mark to think she was overawed by sitting in a limo. She adopted her best 'I do this all the time' expression and stared out the window. Huge American cars raced past, gleaming Cadillacs and Buicks which would dwarf her own Golf.

Mark and Seán talked, discussing the quickest route into

Manhattan with many of the city's roads under repair. Half listening to them talk about parkways, expressways and toll roads, Jo stared at a skyline dominated by shining skyscrapers. It was like looking at the opening credits of *Dallas*.

This was her third trip to New York, but she knew that no matter how many times she visited, she'd still feel that special buzz from visiting the city she'd dreamed about when she was a kid. She loved it. The sprawling city buzzed with vitality, it was alive like nowhere else she'd ever been.

She was also amazed by how much Mark appeared to know about New York judging from his conversation with Seán. He'd never mentioned living there, but he seemed to know it so well. He talked about watching a Yankees game in Yankee Stadium – was that football or baseball, she wondered? Then again, she hardly knew anything about him other than what he did for a living, how he met Rhona, why he liked fast cars and that he had an unbelievably soft spot for his niece. Oh yeah, that he could talk the hind legs off a donkey to comfort someone with air-sickness.

When the limo pulled up at the hotel on Lexington Avenue, Jo clambered out of the back gratefully. Inside, the Fitzpatrick Manhattan was an oasis of calm, away from the buzz of traffic, screaming police sirens and the ever-present blaring taxi-drivers' horns. More European than American, the hotel was quiet and elegant, with Irish accents of all varieties mingling with American ones. From the bar to the right, the sound of Christy Moore's gentle singing drifted out on the air along with the sound of laughter.

'Do you like it?' asked Mark, who'd been watching her reaction from the moment they'd stepped inside.

'It's wonderful, a brilliant choice.' Jo's smile was genuine. The idea of staying in a glorious and sophisticated slice of Ireland in the middle of New York was just perfect.

Registration was speedy and, within minutes, Jo was being shown her suite, an airy sitting room furnished with beautiful reproduction furniture, two large settees, a writing desk and a massive TV concealed in a huge armoire.

228

The bedroom was nearly as big, with another TV and enough drawers to hold four times the contents of her suitcase. Even more importantly, it was perfectly cool, thanks to the magic of air-conditioning.

'You need a rest,' advised Mark, looking at her pale face and tired eyes. He stood awkwardly in the sitting room while she admired the bedroom and peeked into the bathroom. 'I'll go. If you want to have dinner with me, I'll ring you about eight and we can go out to eat. But you might have friends you want to meet,' he added hesitantly.

'No, I'd love dinner,' she answered. 'Just let me crash out first.'

'We're only here five minutes and you're already talking American!' he grinned down at her. She'd never noticed how tall he was before, he must be six foot, nearly as tall as Tom, her brother. 'I'll call you at eight,' he said and was gone.

Ten minutes later she lay up to her neck in bubbles in the black and white tiled bathroom. The bath, an old-fashioned deep enamelled one, had just cried out to be used and since every muscle in Jo's body ached, she'd given in and filled it.

So what if she was lying in a warm bubble bath in the middle of a sweltering July afternoon? Outside, New York buzzed in the heat. But inside, it was calm, serene and, since she'd turned the air-conditioning up, almost chilly. *The Four Seasons* rippled through the air from the New York classical radio station Jo had found on the radio after much knob-twiddling. She had turned the music up loud but she was amused by the idea that she'd still hear the phone if it rang because there was one in the bathroom. What a howl, she thought, picking it up with soapy fingers. Who would you ring from a bathroom phone? Hi, Mom, I'm having a pee, how are you? She just loved hotels.

When the phone rang at eight, Jo had dozed for an hour, ordered a pot of decaff from room service and dressed in her navy crêpe Mandarin shirt and trousers.

'I'll meet you downstairs,' said Mark.

He was waiting for her when she arrived, lounging in a wing

armchair, dressed in an expensive-looking charcoal-grey jacket, pale grey polo shirt and jeans. Jo nearly did a double take. Mark Denton in *jeans*!

'I even wear T-shirts sometimes,' he said drily, noticing her amazement. 'I expect that *you* sometimes wear a tracksuit, no make-up and stick your hair in a pony tail,' he added with a grin. 'Nothing like the elegant Ms Ryan we're used to in *Style*.'

'Touché,' she replied. 'And yes, I do sometimes forget to apply my make-up with a trowel. But a *tracksuit*?' she asked in mock horror. 'Never. I have jogging pants though, have occasionally worn odd socks because they've got separated in the wash, and I've got a pair of rather tattered leggings. Does that count?'

'Of course.' He slid an arm under her elbow and they walked to the door. It felt nice to be accompanied, to have a man escorting her out, even if it was only for show. Richard's absence made her feel so alone most of the time, as if she'd never have someone to hug and kiss again.

They walked slowly south along Lexington Avenue and Jo tried to forget her troubles and savour the sense of being somewhere totally different from home. The traffic jams of the afternoon were a thing of the past and now the streets were almost quiet by comparison, large sedans cruising along sedately with only the bright yellow cabs roaring up and down the streets at high speed.

The Fitzpatrick Manhattan was in an affluent area of Manhattan. Park Avenue was just one block over while Fifth Avenue was only another two blocks away. Well-dressed people walked along the streets, rushing the way all New Yorkers did. But they avoided eye contact as they walked. That was the big difference between many American big cities and Dublin, Jo felt.

On Jo's last visit, Rhona had filled her so full of warnings on being mugged or staring people in the eye in case they turned out to be complete weirdos, that Jo had been in a constant state of anxiety. She'd even carried the ubiquitous 'mugger's wallet', a purse containing a few dollars to give to any prospective muggers until she'd relaxed and stopped worrying. Now, walking at a leisurely pace with Mark – she'd swear he was walking particularly slow for her, as if he *knew* she didn't have the energy to walk quickly – she wasn't even slightly nervous. He knew New York, she felt safe with him.

'Here we are,' Mark announced, stopping at a brightly coloured café on a street corner. The Starlite Xpress Diner. He peered in the window at the board behind the chrome bar and read out the menu: 'Arnold Schwarzenegger Burger, Dolly Parton Sandwich . . . Oh look, Jo. You can have a Cindy Crawford hot dog!'

'Probably lettuce and a minuscule bun.' Jo laughed, taking in the customers sitting at small tables with paper cups, cans of Coke and styrofoam burger boxes.

'I just thought you'd like to experience dinner in a genuine New York diner,' Mark said with a deadpan expression. 'And it's only six dollars each.'

Jo eyed him speculatively. Was he kidding? Or was he serious? She didn't know. If he wasn't joking, he could have told her they were going casual and she'd have dressed accordingly. She certainly wouldn't have wasted her lovely – and very comfortable – navy outfit on the Starlite Xpress Diner.

'Right,' she said, with a firmness she didn't feel. Men. She'd never understand them. Mind you, Mark was so well off it was probably a thrill for him to eat in a diner instead of a ten-pounds-a-starter restaurant. 'Let's eat.'

He took pity on her.

'Jo, you are so gullible. I'm joking.'

'Pig!' she declared, giving him a light slap on the arm.

He laughed and grabbed the hand that had slapped him. Jo felt a shock of electricity shoot through her at the touch of his hand. She would have pulled her hand away, but his grip was so firm, firm and warm.

'I'm sorry. Forgive me.' His grey eyes glittered and the corners of his mouth turned up into a disarming smile. Silhouetted against the lights of the diner, he looked like a great big bear of a man. Jo had the strangest desire to feel those big arms wrapped around her. Get a grip, Ryan!

'You looked so lovely and dressed up, I just couldn't resist teasing you,' explained Mark with a grin. 'I've actually had the Bill Clinton Burger here, and it was lovely but, like all his meals are reputed to be, absolutely huge. I couldn't finish it. We're going somewhere much nicer than this.'

'What could be nicer than this?' demanded Jo in mock amazement. 'I'm mad for a Dolly Parton Sandwich but I hope they've got curried chips on the menu.'

'Curried chips! You can't be serious!'

Jo tried to look offended. 'I love them, especially with onion rings and battered sausages. Oh yeah, and mushy peas.'

'There was me thinking you were one of those types who live off crispbreads,' remarked Mark.

'I've never had to diet,' explained Jo. 'Never used to, anyway,' she added ruefully, thinking of how she'd been eating for three, never mind two, most afternoons when the morning sickness wore off.

'Come on, then,' said Mark. 'I'm starving.'

He tucked her arm under his and they walked on.

Jo felt a spark of excitement ripple through her body at his touch. She didn't know why, but she wanted to slip one arm around his waist and feel him pull her in close as they walked.

This could not be happening, she thought. She was three months pregnant with one man's child, an absent man at that, and here she was getting all lovestruck over another one. Her boss into the bargain. Had jet-lag completely scrambled her brain?

'You'll love the restaurant we're going to,' Mark promised. 'It's like stepping into a scene from *Wall Street*. The whole place is full of business types in button-down shirts and braces and women with those hard-looking hairdos. All they do is talk about shares, stocks and deals.'

'You're kidding?'

'No, the men really do wear braces. And bow ties sometimes. If you were into stock-market espionage, you could learn something here. Well, probably not,' he conceded. 'The tables are so close together that all the business types know that what you say in Smith and Wollensky's at half nine at night will be around the city by the time the Dow Jones opens the next morning. So they probably talk in code.'

'It sounds marvellously high-powered,' said Jo in delight.

'It is.'

Smith and Wollensky's was jam-packed by the time they walked in the door, but an advance call from the Fitzpatrick's concierge meant that they'd skipped the queue. A table would be ready by nine, the maître d' assured them. Jo and Mark squeezed through the people crowded up against the long bar, managed to grab one bar stool for Jo, and ordered drinks.

'I always forget that they don't measure spirits in this place,' said Mark with regret, looking at the massive vodka the barman was pouring into a solid glass tumbler.

'It's like Spain,' Jo said. 'They don't seem to have measures there, they just keep pouring until you say stop. If you don't know the rules and don't say stop,' she continued, 'every drink is a hangover waiting to happen. I remember the first time I went to Spain, it was a press trip when I worked with the *Sunday News*,' she explained, 'and the entire party spent four days fumbling for aspirin in the morning after the previous night's party.'

'There's a real drinking culture to journalism, isn't there?' asked Mark in a slightly tense tone. 'Is getting drunk all the time part of the scene?'

Jo took a sip of her orange juice and stared at him. He looked stiff, anxious, worried somehow.

'Well, it used to be, years ago. We spent a lot of time in the pub when I started in journalism. *Everyone* drank a lot more than they do now.' Why was she justifying it? She'd had every right to be drunk and silly if she wanted to. She was only twenty-one at the time, for God's sake!

'Why do you want to know?'

'No reason,' Mark said quickly, staring at her bottle of orange juice as if he was memorising the ingredients. He picked up his drink and drained it. 'I think you're right. I'll stick to orange juice too. Do you want another one?' he asked.

The penny dropped. Mark thought she was off the booze because she'd been an alcoholic. What a howl! She'd certainly been to enough press receptions where people got pie-eyed, but she'd never been stupid about drinking. It had been years since she'd been plastered. In fact, she could remember precisely the last time it had happened.

'Mark,' she said hesitantly. 'I'm not an alcoholic, I'm not on the wagon, you know. When I started off in journalism, the only people I hung around with were journalists and they all drank like fishes. But not any more. I think we all got sense,' she said, thinking of how the office booze-ups had changed nine years previously. Cirrhosis of the liver had finished off one of the paper's most talented reporters, a man famous both for his addiction to Scotch and his brilliant investigative journalism.

His death had shocked them all and they drank his health in one five-hour binge at the funeral. Jo said goodbye to the days of non-stop partying at that moment.

'I like wine and an Irish coffee now and again, and that's it,' she said firmly. 'Well, good champagne is nice, but only if it's good stuff, not the champagne cider they try and palm you off with at some press receptions.'

Mark stared at her intently. Jo considered the options for a moment – should she tell him the reason why she wasn't drinking? Or should she keep it to herself and have him constantly wondering why she wasn't joining him for a glass of wine?

No, she decided. She'd keep her pregnancy to herself. Even though Rhona was an excellent editor who'd juggled pregnancies, Caesareans, teething and first days at school along with an incredibly demanding job, Mark mightn't have the same faith in *her* doing it like that.

'I have this stomach problem, too much acid,' she improvised quickly. 'I can't drink when it flares up because alcohol makes everything worse. But I'll be fine in a few weeks.'

'I'm sorry to hear that you're sick,' Mark said, sounding concerned and relieved at the same time. 'You should have told me you weren't well, I would have got someone else to come to New York.'

'And there was me thinking that *I* was the only one who could help make the deal,' Jo said in mock misery. 'I think I'll go home now that I find I'm expendable . . .'

'No you won't,' said Mark quickly. 'I'm sorry. You *are* vital to the deal. I just didn't want to think that you came because you had to, because I'd ordered it,' he finished slowly. He turned away from her and raised his glass at the barman. 'Another screwdriver and an orange juice,' he commanded. He didn't turn back, he kept facing the bar as though he was fascinated by the bottles lined up against the back of the bar. The change in the atmosphere was palpable. It was as if he'd decided to close himself off, to put up the cool and aloof Denton façade again.

He thought she'd come because he was her boss and his word was law. Maybe it had been like that at first, she reflected. Of course it had. But now, everything was different. She liked him, liked the warm and funny man who'd been kind enough to keep her mind off her fear of flying, the man who'd noticed her pale face when they were pushing through the airport and had taken care of her luggage. None of these things were the actions of a boss. They were the actions of a friend. She'd worked for him for three years and it was only in the last week that she'd got a glimpse of the sort of person he really was. It was suddenly vitally important that he understood that.

'Mark.' Jo reached out and touched his shoulder, feeling the soft fabric of his jacket under her fingers. Cashmere, she realised, her fashion editor's instincts coming to the fore.

He turned and his grey eyes stared into her dark ones. 'Nobody made me come,' she said softly. 'I wanted to, and I'm glad I did because I'm really enjoying myself.'

He smiled, the tiny lines around his eyes crinkling up again in a way that Jo was finding unsettlingly sexy.

'Good.' Was it her imagination or was his voice deeper than usual?

The moment was charged with emotions. Jo didn't know what to say. He held her gaze, then his focus shifted and he stared intently at her face, eyes moving over her flushed cheeks, full lips painted in a burnished bronze colour, eyes fringed with chocolate-coloured lashes.

'Your table is ready, sir.' The slight, Italian waiter broke the spell and they both came to their senses again. 'This way.'

Mark gestured for Jo to go first and she followed the waiter, weaving through a maze of small tables, turning sideways to pass between the gaps where diners had pushed their chairs out from the tables.

She was thinking so hard about the tall man walking behind her, and hoping she looked all right from the back, that she nearly cannoned into another waiter with a tray of shellfish held high above the crowded tables.

'Sorry,' she apologised, stepping aside clumsily. In an instant, Mark's hand was on her waist, steadying her. It was like being touched by a burning poker, her flesh felt scorched by his touch.

'Madam,' said the waiter as he reached a table for two at the back of the restaurant. He held out Jo's seat and she sank into the chair. Across the table Mark smiled at her, but said nothing as the waiter handed them menus and a wine list.

The waiter reeled off a list of specials, but Jo heard none of it. Although her eyes were fixed on the waiter's face, her mind was racing back over the last few minutes, wondering exactly what had happened, what unspoken tension existed between them. She gazed down at the menu blankly.

'What do you think looks good?' asked Mark.

Choose something quickly, she thought. Scallops, yes, she'd have scallops. And melon and Parma ham for a starter.

'The melon and scallops,' she said quickly.

'The scallops are off the menu, or so the waiter said,' Mark pointed out gently. Jo felt herself blush, a warm flush of colour rising up her cheeks. It was like being fifteen again.

'Did he? I mustn't have been paying attention,' she answered. 'Maybe I'll have the grilled sole.'

'That sounds great,' Mark said. He flicked his wrist and the waiter appeared. Jo marvelled at his ability to summon people instantly. It was his presence, she decided, that made people jump to attention.

When the waiter had been dispatched with their orders, Mark leaned forward with his elbows on the table.

'We haven't talked business all day,' he remarked. 'I know we should just enjoy ourselves, but we better discuss our strategy for talking to these people on Tuesday.'

Jo felt herself shrink in her chair. So that was it. The moment was over. Obviously the spark of electricity she'd felt between them had been one-sided. Or else he wasn't interested and had decided to talk business to make sure she didn't get the wrong idea. The boss didn't mingle with the staff. She could take a hint.

'What sort of strategy did you have in mind?' she said coolly, determined to prove that she could be just as business-like as he. If Mark Denton wanted to give her a message, she'd show him what a fast learner she was.

After dinner, they walked back to the hotel in silence. Unaccountably tired, Jo could think of nothing more to say. They'd discussed business tactics for over two hours and she was tired of talking about the importance of readership surveys and ABC market share.

She just wanted to close the door of her suite and slap herself for being stupid enough to think there could be *anything* between her and Mark.

This time he didn't take her arm. They walked several feet apart. When they reached the hotel, he stopped on the footpath.

'I think I'll go for a walk,' he said abruptly. 'I don't think I can sleep yet.'

'Fine,' she answered, not even looking at him, but gazing at the leather shop across the road as though something amazing in the window had suddenly caught her eye.

'Do you want me to call you for breakfast?' he asked.

'No,' she said sharply. 'I think I'll have a lie-in and then wander down to the Village and Chinatown to the markets. I'm sure you've lots of things to do, you don't want me tagging along with you.' Her voice was harder than she'd intended it to be. But she couldn't help herself. She felt hurt, bruised by his sudden indifference and the way he'd turned the evening around. He'd changed it from a magical, electric moment into a cold business meeting.

If he thought she was going to follow him like a puppy, desperate for attention, he'd another think coming.

'Fine,' he said crisply.

Jo marched into the hotel without looking back. In her suite, she threw her handbag onto the desk and picked up the TV remove control She flopped onto the huge settee, kicked off her shoes and put her feet up with relief. Damn Mark Denton. Damn him to hell. Who did he think he was giving her all sorts of enigmatic looks and then treating her as if she were his bloody secretary, someone who'd come along to do his bidding? He was a pig, just like all men. Just like Richard.

She flicked through the shopping channels, CNN, a late-night chat show, the bizarre Manhattan Cable TV and some rubbish with a Barbie doll-style nurse taking the pulse of a patient transfixed by her bosom. Jo watched the show for a moment, waiting for the requisite handsome doctor to come in and tell the nurse he loved her, despite the fact that he'd married her half-sister, slept with her mother, whatever. She hated American soaps with a passion. Nobody in them ever looked like normal people, all the women had plastic smiles, plastic boobs and twenty-inch waists.

She felt her own waist, remembering when she had been just as slender as the women on the TV. At nearly three months pregnant, her body had changed only a little but the extra inches on her waist felt so noticeable to Jo. With careful dressing, she didn't look pregnant at all. Only someone with hawk eyes – like her mother or Rhona – would guess her secret. But she was hungry so often that she knew she'd start putting on too much weight if she wasn't careful.

She still swam twice a week and had been doing step aerobics at the gym. But all those chocolate biscuits, Twixes and ice cream had to go somewhere.

She changed channels again. Goldie Hawn was standing on a yacht screaming at Kurt Russell. *Overboard*, Jo realised happily. She loved that film. There was just one thing missing. She picked up the phone.

'Could you send up a pot of tea and, er . . . do you have any chocolate biscuits?' she asked. 'Chocolate chip would be lovely, thank you. You have shortbread ones made in the hotel? They sound great too.'

Jo awoke in a cold sweat at half eight. Even the soft cotton sheets felt damp and she sat up in the bed, dazed by her dream. What had she been dreaming about? Mark, that was it. She'd been in a hotel bedroom with Mark Denton, a room decorated with crimson wall hangings and with a four-poster bed in the middle, scarlet and gold muslin curtains hiding the bed from prying eyes. She could just about make out lots of people trying to look behind the curtains, men in striped shirts with braces and bow ties.

And she and Mark lay on the bed, half wrapped up in silk sheets, his naked body curled around hers. He'd been kissing her, stroking her belly and telling her he couldn't wait for the baby to be born. She was naked too, she had been able to feel his skin burning into hers, his hands roaming all over her body . . . Oh my God, what a dream!

She pushed back the covers and went into the bathroom, her puffy-eyed and tired face showing the after-effects of a troubled night's sleep.

She wet a white face cloth under the tap and gently wiped her hot face. You look awful, she told her reflection. Her lustrous dark hair was greasy at the roots, her skin was flushed and wrinkled from the way she'd been sleeping on creased sheets and her eyes were puffy from a mixture of jet-lag and dehydration.

Tea, that's what she wanted. It mightn't improve her face, but it would make her insides feel better. She wrapped the hotel's fluffy white bathrobe around herself and phoned room service. She could get used to this type of thing.

Fifteen minutes later, she had showered and washed her hair. A gentle knock at the door signalled that breakfast was ready. A freckle-faced young man with a broad smile and a broader Belfast accent carried a heavily laden tray into the room and left it on the coffee table. Jo, who was never quite sure how much to tip, gave him three dollars. She hoped that was enough. 'Thanks. Enjoy your breakfast,' he said with another smile.

Sitting comfortably on the settee, Jo turned on the TV and listened to the news as she lifted the silver lid from a huge Irish fried breakfast. It smelled beautiful and she hadn't had to cook it herself. Perfect. She poured herself a cup of decaff, buttered some hot brown toast and tucked in. Why were you always ravenous the morning after a big meal? she wondered, munching toast. Well, she hadn't been eating breakfast much lately. Jo stopped mid-munch. She wasn't sick, didn't feel even vaguely nauseous, for the first time in nearly three months. She was thrilled. Of course she'd read that morning sickness could disappear as quickly as it had arrived, but she had begun to think that she'd *always* feel sick. Yahoo!

After breakfast she dressed quickly in jeans, a white T-shirt and a periwinkle-blue cotton sweater, put some money into a small leather bum bag and hung her sunglasses on the neck of her sweater. New York on a clear, sunny Sunday morning was quiet and relaxed. Only a few bright yellow cabs drove down Lexington Avenue, mingling with the light traffic speeding up to Central Park or down to the bookshops and coffee houses in the Village.

Jo walked for a few blocks, savouring the sun on her face and the feeling of warmth on her skin. Two well-dressed New Yorkers strode past her, arms full of newspapers and brown delicatessen bags. Everyone rushed on the east coast, thought

Jo, watching a young man glide past silently on rollerblades, overtaking a cruising taxi.

'Taxi,' yelled Jo, waving her hand in the air. The car stopped and she sidestepped a fat pigeon who'd been scurrying around on the pavement ahead of her.

'The Metropolitan Museum of Art,' she said to the driver, a pale-skinned man with dark hair and a skinny moustache. 'Fifth Avenue and 82nd.'

He looked at her uncomprehendingly. She tried it again, slower and more clearly.

'Sure. I know!' said the driver in a heavy foreign accent. 'Fifth Avenue. I get you there!'

The cab lurched off and immediately picked up speed, dodging traffic recklessly. Now that he knew where he was going, he was going to get her there in double-quick time. Hopefully, alive. Just my luck to get one of New York's novice taxi-drivers, thought Jo, sitting well back in the tattered seat and wondering if a quick novena would save her from death by automobile accident.

Somebody was watching over her, definitely. She emerged from the cab outside the Met feeling decidedly shaky. The driver grinned manically when she handed him a ten-dollar bill and drove off rapidly.

Once inside the gallery, Jo headed for the European galleries where the early Flemish paintings she loved hung. She'd never been in the gallery before, even though she and Richard had planned to spend two days there the last time they'd been in Manhattan. Somehow they'd ended up spending all their time with Richard's friends listening to jazz in smoky clubs in the Village and had never got around to doing any of the things she'd wanted to do. But she knew exactly where to go now thanks to her guidebook. So did lots of other tourists. Even early on a Sunday morning, a large group of Japanese tourists walked along staring blankly at the museum signs before consulting their guidebooks. The Met was so big there was no way to see everything in a few hours. People did what Jo was doing and just picked one or two things they had to see, hoping to absorb as much as they could before everything began to blur.

After two hours staring at Van Eycks and Brueghels, Jo was weary and her stomach was rumbling.

She bought some postcards of her favourite paintings on the way out and dithered about buying two pretty Manet prints she wanted to frame. It would be too difficult to lug them around all day, she decided finally. They'd either get bent or she'd leave them behind somewhere. She could always come back and get them during the week.

The cab ride to Greenwich Village was uneventful, mainly because the driver knew where he was going and wasn't trying to break some sort of land-speed record.

It was nearly lunchtime and the small pavement cafés on Bleecker Street were full of people enjoying Sunday brunch and reading newspapers. Jo bought a *New York Sunday Times* and wondered how she'd ever read it all in one day. It weighed nearly as much as her handbag and that was saying something. As a couple left a table outside a chic coffee shop, boasting every sort of coffee under the sun, Jo quickly dumped her paper on the white metal table and sank into a seat.

Within fifteen minutes she was tucking into a soft bagel spread with velvety cream cheese laced with morsels of smoked salmon. It was wonderful to sit in the sun, sipping her fragrant coffee and watching the world walk by. But Jo couldn't help but feel a little sad, sitting on her own while everyone and their granny seemed to be in pairs. There were couples everywhere, couples laughing and talking with their arms draped around each other or couples simply holding hands.

She found a tissue in her bum bag and blew her nose, remembering the last time she'd been in New York. It had been Richard's birthday, the day before they flew home, and they'd had a marvellous lunch in the Oyster Bar in Grand Central Station. Then they wandered around the shops, stopping off to spend an hour in Bloomingdale's where Richard dragged her, giggling, into the lingerie department. He'd whispered all the erotic things he was going to do to her as she picked out a selection of sexy, lacy bras and knickers.

Typically, he'd got bored quickly. By the time she'd actually decided what to buy, Richard had vanished into the camera department and she ended up paying for the underwear herself. When he took off the coffee-coloured silky bra set later, she'd forgotten that he hadn't actually bought it himself. They'd done every crazy, romantic thing you could do in New York and even visited the Empire State Building. They stared down at the city from the windy eighty-sixth floor and held hands. Richard laughed that they were recreating *Sleepless in Seattle*. 'No, it's *An Affair to Remember*,' she'd argued.

That had been over a year ago. Everything had changed so much since then. Jo gently laid a hand on her belly, as though she could feel the baby's heartbeat with her fingers. She wouldn't have turned back the clock for anything. Maybe she had Richard then, but now she had something much more precious. Her baby.

She was sitting cross-legged on the bed writing her post-cards in the late afternoon sun when the phone rang. It was Mark.

'Hello,' she said coolly.

'Did you have a good day?' he asked.

'Marvellous,' she replied. 'I went to the Metropolitan Museum of Art for a few hours this morning. I wanted to try out Robert De Niro's restaurant in TriBeCa so I could write a funny piece about it,' she said airily, 'but I didn't get that far. I might go down later. Then I read the *New York Sunday Times*, well, read a bit of it, in a coffee house in the Village.' Stick that in your pipe and smoke it, she thought defiantly. Your employee wasn't moping in her room, dying for you to bring her out. She was enjoying New York and its rich cultural life. So there.

'That sounds great.' He sounded unmoved by the bite in her voice. 'I'm going to dinner with some friends of mine on the Upper East Side this evening. I wonder if you'd like to come? It's OK if you've something else organised. I just didn't want to leave you going to dinner on your own.'

Jo didn't know what to say. She'd been thinking he didn't want anything more to do with her and now he was asking her out to dinner with some friends. She would never understand this man. For a moment, she considered saying no. Then she thought of the alternative.

Dinner on her own in a strange city was something she'd never enjoyed, although she'd tried it often enough when she was a news reporter for the *Sunday News*. She'd found that a single woman invariably got the worst table in any restaurant. Returning to the hotel to have a drink in the bar afterwards was out of the question unless you *liked* strange men chatting you up.

She'd spent enough of the day on her own, Jo decided firmly. She needed to get out. Who knows, she told herself, an evening out with Mark could even be mildly enjoyable.

When the taxi drew up outside a tall, elegant apartment building off Madison Avenue, Jo was very glad she'd decided to dress up and wear the hand-painted chocolate brown Mary Gregory dress. The whole place reeked of wealth and opulence. She stared at a vast marble entrance hall, not one but *two* doormen in green uniforms with gold frogging and what looked like an antique table between the two lifts in the hall.

Even the lift smelled of old money, Jo thought, as she stood beside Mark, checking her reflection in the darkened mirrors on either side of the lift.

'You'll like Rex and Suzanne,' said Mark. 'They're very warm friendly people.'

And very bloody rich, thought Jo, when the lift stopped at the top floor and opened onto a small hall with just one door off it. They even had their own *landing*! Mark pushed the bell and the door was opened by a plump dark-skinned woman in the maid's outfit of black dress and frilly white apron that Jo thought only existed in black and white Forties movies.

'Manuela,' said Mark warmly to the woman, who managed

to blush and grin at him at the same time.

'Signor Denton,' she grinned. 'You have not been here for a long time. We have missed you. Madam is in the drawing room.'

Jo looked around the huge entrance hall, a white oval room with three pieces of modern sculpture and an utterly stunning art deco chandelier hanging over what must be a Persian carpet. If this was the *hall*, Lord only knew what the rest of the place was like.

Mark took her arm and they followed Manuela, heels tip-tapping on the marble floor, into a huge, airy room filled with paintings, enormous glass vases of exotic lilies and the sound of Mozart.

'Mark, darling.' A stunning blonde woman got to her feet and hurried over to hug him warmly.

'Suzanne, it's lovely to see you,' he said affectionately.

'And this must be Jo.' Suzanne turned towards Jo and took both Jo's hands in hers. 'We're delighted to meet you,' she said earnestly.

Nonplussed by her friendly welcome, Jo smiled back brightly, immediately liking the tall, graceful woman whose hair fell in soft curls to her shoulders. She was wearing a chic caramel-coloured wrap dress and what looked like a real pearl choker around her neck. Suzanne could have walked off the couture fashion pages in *Elle*.

Only a faint crêping around her throat and small lines around the beautiful blue eyes indicated that she would never see forty again. She looked the way Jo hoped *she'd* look when she was older.

'Now come and say hello to everyone. We're all dying to meet you,' Suzanne said in a soft Southern accent, still holding one of Jo's hands.

'This is Rex.' The tall, grey-haired man, who'd risen when Jo and Mark entered the room, took her hand firmly in his.

'So nice to meet you, Jo. We're delighted you could join our little dinner party tonight. I hope you like New York.'

'How could you not like New York,' interrupted a man with the faint accent and olive skin of an Italian.

'I'm Carlo and I'm pleased to meet you.' He kissed her on both cheeks and then smiled at her, lustrous dark eyes openly admiring. 'I can see why you've been keeping this lady a secret, Mark,' Carlo said.

'I haven't kept anything a secret, Carlo,' Mark said sharply, bending down to shake hands with a woman who was dressed in a navy linen dress and was sitting back on one of the settees. 'Hello, Margaret, how are you? I was so sorry to hear about your accident.'

'I'm fine,' said Margaret. 'I've just got to take care of my ankle.' She gestured at the cast on her right ankle. 'It's just so irritating, not being able to ride, you know.'

Suzanne introduced Jo to the other members of the party, each one more charming and elegant than the last. Gold cuff links and diamond earrings glittered in the light from the Thirties uplighters on the walls. Jo knew that the clothes the women were wearing were genuine Gucci, Jil Sander and Dior.

Even their handbags had labels, Jo realised, as she caught sight of a brown leather bag peeking out from the side of Margaret's chair. Definitely a Kelly bag from Hermès, she realised with a jolt. About four grand's worth of handbag. It was like stepping onto the set of *Dynasty*. These people had serious money.

They had serious jobs too. Carlo was a publisher, Margaret and her husband were in banking – not behind the bureau de change counter, either – Rex was in property, the red-headed woman in black velvet worked in Sotheby's, the short grey-haired man did something to do with computers and the plump woman who chain-smoked was an artist.

'I used to be involved with an interior design firm,' Suzanne explained. 'I'm so busy with my charity work these days, I've rather let my design skills go. The last thing I did was this room.' She waved one graceful, manicured hand at the pale mint walls with their museum-load of paintings.

'It's truly beautiful,' Jo replied. 'The paintings are fabulous, and I love the sculptures in the hall.'

'That's my husband's hobby,' explained Suzanne, 'he loves collecting things. Every time we go to Europe, he drags something back, usually something huge that takes a month to ship.'

'Champagne, madam?' inquired Manuela, who had appeared at Jo's side with a champagne flute and a bottle of Cristal.

'Just a little,' Jo said. Three-quarters of a glass wouldn't kill her. She needed it to stop her staring around open-mouthed. Her entire *apartment* would fit into this room.

The guests talked about stocks, shares and the shocking price of duplexes on Fifth Avenue, while Jo simply sat and listened.

'Tell us about your work,' Suzanne said, turning to include Jo in the conversation. 'I've always imagined that being a fashion editor must be very glamorous. Is it?'

Since it was difficult to imagine anything more glamorous than these sophisticated New Yorkers, Jo laughed out loud. 'Not really,' she said. 'There's a certain amount of glamour about fashion shows. But the real work often involves crawling around on your knees in a photographic studio, trying to pin up the legs of a pair of trousers on a model who's five foot eight instead of the six-foot girl you booked!'

She kept Suzanne entertained talking all about *Style* with Carlo listening intently from his position across the fireplace. Jo didn't think he was even vaguely interested in what she was saying but, from the way his eyes were glued to her chest, he obviously fancied women with curves, even if the curves in question were pregnancy ones. She'd have loved to be able to tell him that she used to be a 34B pre-pregnancy.

At exactly half eight, Rex got up and helped Margaret to her feet.

'Dinner should be ready now, people,' he announced. 'I believe it's lobster tonight.'

Everybody made appreciative noises.

'I hope you eat lobster,' Suzanne asked Jo suddenly.

247

'Of course,' Jo said with a straight face. I eat it all the time, especially with baked beans and chips.

She stood up as Carlo approached, one tanned hand held out to take her in to her dinner but, before he reached her, Jo felt Mark's strong arm link hers.

'Won't you let me escort you into dinner, Madame Jo?' he asked with a grin.

'Only if we're eating lobster,' she whispered back, glad that he'd got there before Carlo.

She was put sitting opposite Mark at the highly polished round dining table, with a delighted Carlo on one side and Rex on the other.

'We're not standing on ceremony tonight,' Rex said, handing around a latticed silver basket filled with warm bread rolls. 'Carlo, pour the wine.'

'Will you have some?' Carlo murmured, holding a bottle of red over her glass and smiling at her with hot, Latin eyes.

'No thanks,' said Jo, hoping he'd take the hint. No to wine and no to you, Carlo. The just-baked scent of the rolls filled Jo's nostrils and made her all too aware of her empty stomach. She ate hungrily, enjoying the Caesar salad, lobster and summer pudding, swollen with ripe berries.

It was going to be a culture shock to her stomach when she returned to Dublin and had to put up with frozen pizzas, eggs scrambled rock-solid in the microwave and lasagne from a packet.

Carlo tried to monopolise Jo during dinner, asking her to tell him about Ireland before launching into his life history, ending with the story of a particularly bitter divorce.

At that point, his eyes stopped being lascivious and looked merely sad, but Jo had enough trouble dealing with her own problems without counselling anyone else. Feeling a little heartless, she patted his arm in a sisterly manner and turned towards Rex.

The discussion ranged from the price Amanda hoped a Degas statue of a dancer would fetch, to the difficulties faced by parents of bored English literature students.

'She says she's bored,' shrugged Ned, 'wants to give up college and go abroad for a year. I just don't know what to do.'

'We've tried everything,' added Margaret. 'I even promised to buy her a new BMW if she stuck it out for another year, but she says no.'

'Do you have children, Jo?' inquired Rex.

'No.' She grinned to herself. 'Not yet, anyway.' And when I do, they won't be getting BMWs in return for going to college, either.

'Don't rush into it,' shuddered the grey-haired man. 'My boys have cost me thousands of dollars, always changing what they want to major in. I tell them I never had any choice when I was their age. My family didn't have two dimes to rub together and I had to work *my* way through college. I think that's their problem, they've had everything handed to them on a plate.'

Jo couldn't resist glancing at Mark. He was looking at her intently, fingers locked over his empty plate, the grey eyes locked onto hers with a frightening concentration. He was definitely thinking of Emma. Good. It would do the little cow good not to have everything handed to her on a plate for once. If Mark got the message, that was.

'Maybe that's the secret,' Mark commented, 'having to work for everything. I had to, so had you, Rex. It made us fighters, it made us determined to succeed. And when we have youngsters to spoil,' he paused and grinned at Jo, 'we spoil them. We give them all the chances we never had and more. And then we wonder why they haven't our fire, our drive to succeed.'

Suzanne clapped. 'You said it!' she said. 'Bryony never did anything we wanted her to until the day I stopped her allowance. "Go mad in Donna Karan, travel to Morocco and hang out on the beach," I said. "Just do it on your own money".' She smiled triumphantly.

'Bryony soon found out she couldn't afford to pay for her own dry-cleaning. By Fall, she'd got over wanting to travel to Morocco like a hippie. Hippies can't buy nice clothes, eat in good restaurants and put gas in the Jeep. In fact, they can't even insure their Jeeps!'

Everyone laughed, even Jo, who remembered what it was like to put three pounds' worth of petrol in the car when she was broke.

'So what does Bryony do now?' asked Jo.

'She's working in Sotheby's with Amanda, as an assistant.' Amanda must be the redhead, Jo thought. 'The pay is dreadful, but she's being trained in the china department. One day,' Suzanne paused and winked at Rex, 'she may even earn half as much as Amanda.'

Amanda, a tall and stately woman in what was either a knock-off peach bouclé Chanel suit or the real thing, peered over her glasses at Suzanne and shook one bejewelled finger slowly. An emerald the size of a Malteser winked in the light. 'My dears, I earn peanuts. Or at least, that's what I tell the IRS.'

They chattered over the cheese and then strolled back into the living room where Manuela had a huge tray of coffee and tiny forest-green china cups ready.

'Are you happy you came?' Mark asked Jo slyly.

She looked him in the eye. 'I'm having a lovely time and I'm sorry for being so childish earlier. You do bring out the worst in me.'

'I'm sorry,' he murmured, leaning close to her so she could feel his breath soft against her neck. 'I'd hoped to bring out the best in you.'

There was no chance to say anything in return. They had caught up with the others and everyone was sinking back into the comfortable brocade sofas.

Jo and Mark sat beside each other on a sofa made for two. When he leaned forward to take a cup of coffee from Suzanne, his thigh touched Jo's. It was like the other night, she thought. His very nearness unnerved her, made her heart beat faster. The hand holding her coffee cup shook slightly.

When she'd finished her coffee, Suzanne asked Jo if she'd like to see the view from the balcony and the study.

'The study is my favourite room,' the other woman confided, walking like a model down the hall. 'I decorated it like my grandfather's study in Mississippi. He was a judge and he had hundreds of leather-bound law books. They lined the walls and gave the place such character, I always thought.'

'I'd love to have a room like this,' said Jo. Huge dark bookcases stood from floor to ceiling, while an old mahogany desk and a worn leather chair sat in one corner. 'I have a small apartment and there's no room for any sort of office or study,' explained Jo, moving around the room, touching the gold-leafed spines of the books, 'but I have a dream of buying a little stone cottage in Wicklow and having lots of bookcases. And lots of books, of course!'

'I'm sure Mark would love that,' Suzanne said earnestly. 'He certainly loves books, never stopped reading that one time he stayed with us in Colorado.'

Jo didn't know quite how to respond, so she picked a leather-bound volume off a shelf and examined it carefully. *Washington Square* by Henry James. She'd been in the real Washington Square that afternoon.

Did Suzanne think that she and Mark were an item? Whatever had given her *that* idea? Jo couldn't very well blurt out that she and Mark had shared nothing more than one dinner, one lunch and a very long, boring transatlantic flight.

She turned the pages slowly, wondering if Suzanne and Rex were the sort of people who bought books they'd never read just because they looked good.

'Maybe I shouldn't say this,' said Suzanne suddenly. 'But when he asked could he bring you this evening, Rex and I were so thrilled. He hasn't even so much as mentioned another woman since, well, you know . . .'

Jo didn't know and she really wished she did. But she didn't want to let the side down by asking. So she nodded sagely.

'Rex and I were very worried about him. He's never missed visiting us for Thanksgiving since we met him in Boston all those years ago. And last year he just called the day before and said he couldn't come. We really missed his company. He's such a fascinating man, but then, what am I telling *you* that for, Jo. You already know! Anyway,' Suzanne patted Jo's hand, 'we're so glad he's got over it all, and so glad that he's got someone as wonderful as you. And I can tell he loves you, just from the way he looks at you.'

'You can?' asked Jo faintly.

'You bet. Just remember to ask us to the wedding!'

It was nearly half four on Wednesday afternoon when Mark and Jo finally left Mademoiselle Inc. The heavy white door, with MI emblazoned on it in gold, slammed behind them as they walked onto 39th Street after two hours of negotiating.

The director of the Mademoiselle chain of shops was eager to work with *Style* and their in-house designer was even keener, thanks to Jo's praise for his beautiful designs.

The New York traffic was building up into rush-hour proportions and Jo sighed with exhaustion as she realised they hadn't a hope in hell of getting a taxi. But she hadn't reckoned on Mark's ability to whistle up a cab as well as any New York doorman.

'I think that went pretty well,' commented Mark, slamming the taxi door and dropping his briefcase onto the seat beside him. 'You were brilliant, Jo. You really impressed them and telling Marco that his designs were, what was it, ". . . a breath of fresh air into the jaded world of fashion", clinched the deal!'

'I'd have told him he was the new Karl Lagerfeld to get everything signed and get out of there. Thank God it's all over,' Jo said fervently. 'All this wheeling and dealing is exhausting. And I don't think I could have managed another cup of herb tea, no matter how many fashion supplements they were going to advertise in.'

'I thought you *liked* that stuff,' Mark said, astonished. 'You certainly drank enough of it.'

Jo looked at him incredulously. 'I was trying to be polite. Have you ever seen me drink anything that smelled like boiled socks before?'

Mark burst out laughing. 'You never cease to amaze me, Ms Ryan.' His eyes gleamed with amusement. 'I'm beginning to wonder what else you'd do to clinch a deal . . .? Marco certainly liked you and I'm sure Tony wouldn't have turned down an intimate dinner date if you'd asked him nicely.'

It was Jo's turn to laugh. 'I might stand a chance with Marco, but I think you'd be more Tony's type.'

'Damn,' said Mark quickly. 'You mean I missed the chance of a date? You could have told me. He was just my type.' He flicked his head in a camp manner and did his best to pout. He never stopped surprising her.

'I'll tell you what,' she said, 'make a detour to Bloomingdale's to drop me off and I'll ring Tony and tell him you're *wild* to meet him but only if he brings you to a gay biker club, all right?'

'Maybe not,' grinned Mark, patting her knee. 'I've gone off gay biker clubs since PVC became fashionable. *Everyone*'s doing it and I prefer leather. Anyway,' he said, leaning forward towards the driver, and adopting his normal voice, 'I want to do some shopping myself. Bloomingdale's,' he told the cab driver. 'I want to buy a present for my sister. It's her birthday next month and I'd love to get her something really nice. Will you help? I hate shopping,' he admitted.

'Of course. What were you thinking of getting?'

'If I knew *that* I wouldn't be asking you,' he pointed out.

Silk scarves were out because Denise already had loads of scarves. 'That's what I usually buy her,' admitted Mark sheepishly. 'I never know what she'd like.'

He might not know what Denise would like, but he certainly had very fixed ideas about what she *wouldn't* like, thought Jo after half an hour trailing around Bloomie's, where he vetoed every suggestion she made.

Perfume, jewellery, handbags and a glorious chenille jumper in a mulberry shade had all been rejected and even Jo, steadfast shopper that she was, was getting tired.

'I'll tell you what, Mark, I want to have a look around myself, so why don't you potter around and think about what you want to buy Denise and meet me back here in three-quarters of an hour, right?' Before I kill you, she added silently.

Jo spent a blissful half an hour riffling through racks of Donna Karan, Prada and Emporio Armani. She hadn't enough time to try anything on and, since she didn't know how strapped she was going to be for money with the baby, she decided to keep her credit card firmly in her handbag. It wasn't easy. Being a cashless fashion editor in Bloomingdale's was like being a chocoholic with wired-up jaws in Cadbury's.

Next time, she promised herself, taking one last look at a beautiful jersey dress that would look perfect on her. She was passing the children's department when she stopped abruptly. They probably had the most divine baby clothes in the world: just a quick look wouldn't delay her too much.

Everything was so pretty, she thought, stroking the soft fabric of a tiny denim pinafore. There were even socks to match, tiny soft blue ones with miniature denim bows on one side. They'd look so beautiful on the baby, if it was a girl . . .

'I thought it was you.' Mark was beside her, leaning over to see what she'd picked up. 'I came looking for you because I assumed I'd have to drag you out of the premises once you'd got into a clothes-buying frenzy. You buying presents as well?'

The little socks felt so soft, so lovely. For some bizarre reason, Jo suddenly felt sad, felt like sitting down on the floor of the baby department and sobbing for herself and her baby, a baby with no daddy.

'No,' she mumbled, shoving the socks blindly at the rack they'd been on. 'Not presents.'

He caught up with her by the perfume counters. One large hand on her arm stopped her from rushing out the door.

'What's wrong, Jo? Did I say something wrong?'

'It's not you,' she sobbed. 'It's me.'

'Do you want to try some Poême?' interrupted a heavily made-up saleslady armed with a huge yellow bottle of perfume and a fixed smile.

'No thanks,' said Mark, putting an arm around Jo.

'Not you, sir. The lady.'

'No,' he snarled. 'Come on Jo, let's go.'

'I'm sorry,' Jo sniffled. 'I'm so sorry. It's just the baby, the baby's making me all mixed up and sad.'

'Baby. The baby?' repeated Mark in amazement.

'I'm having a baby and Richard has left me,' she mumbled. Then she leaned against his jacket and cried as if her heart would break.

CHAPTER THIRTEEN

Aisling zipped up her skirt and turned to look at herself in the mirror. Three months ago, she wouldn't have been able to get the grey herringbone skirt over her hips. Now she could slide into it with ease. Two months of Callanetics, lots of brisk walks and no chocolate digestives had worn her once-plump thighs and hips down a dress size.

She couldn't help feeling smug. When Michael came to pick up the boys tomorrow, she'd go outside and talk to him – something she'd avoided doing for ages – just to show him how well she looked. Nowadays when he picked up the boys at lunchtime on Saturdays, they ran out the front door with their overnight bags and Aisling never ventured out to say hello. When he brought them home on Sunday evenings before seven, she sat in the sitting room keeping an eye out for his car in order to have the front door open for the twins. She hadn't actually seen Michael for at least six weeks.

They'd talked on the phone of course, cool conversations with lots of silences and plenty of 'anyways'.

Two weeks ago he'd rung on a Thursday night to say he'd have to change his day to see the boys, thus ruining Aisling's plans to help Jo house-hunt.

'I can't pick up Phillip and Paul on Saturday because I'm going to London,' he announced. 'I'll pick them up on Sunday morning instead and bring them out to lunch.'

Aisling was furious, both at the cool way he'd told her the news and the fact that he'd given her only one day's notice of his change of plan. How dare he assume she wouldn't have any plans of her own!

'Thank you *so* much,' she hissed, 'for giving me plenty of notice. Do you have any idea of how this is going to affect the twins, do you, Michael? No, I suppose you don't. It's bad enough that you've left us,' she said, determined to put the boot in, 'but letting them down like this is appalling. How do you expect two ten-year-olds to understand that you can't see them as usual? They'll think you've dumped them too.'

Aisling knew she was being vicious, full of the bitterness she thought she'd managed to conceal for so long. But she couldn't help herself. She wanted to hurt Michael and she'd used the twins to do it. In reality, they appeared to be coping with the break-up quite well, something which amazed her. They seemed confident of Michael's love and loved visiting him at the weekends, excited at the idea of calling another place home. And since she'd started to get on with her life and no longer broke down crying at the drop of a hat, the happier atmosphere had cheered them all up.

'I'm sorry, Aisling,' Michael said, his voice suddenly hollow and exhausted. 'I've only just found out I have to go away. Letting the boys down is the last thing I want to do.'

Hearing the desolation in his voice, she immediately regretted the way she'd tried to hurt him. It wasn't as if she couldn't bring Phillip and Paul out with her and Jo. They'd love the chance to spend time with their auntie Jo, who always brought sweets, told them jokes and let them fiddle around with the windscreen wipers in the front seat of the car the way their mother wouldn't.

Anyway, Aisling missed them so much when they were gone at the weekend that she knew it would be lovely to have them with her on Saturday for a change. Guilt at her bitchiness overwhelmed her. She'd been a nasty, manipulative bitch on the phone, everything she hated in other people and Michael hadn't deserved it.

He hadn't phoned her since then. At least he'd had two weeks to forget what she'd said, she reflected. She wasn't proud of shrieking that he'd left her feeling less than useless. Damn him, she'd never meant to let herself down so much.

Now she had the chance to show him how much she'd changed, what she'd achieved. He'd get a bit of a shock to see that his wife wasn't the same old drudge.

257

The sight of Aisling Moran, career woman, would certainly take him by surprise. Not that she was exactly that – a career woman, she thought wryly.

Keeping her nose to the grindstone in the employ of Richardson, Reid and Finucane did not exactly qualify her for any Businesswoman of the Year awards. Nor did ignoring barbed and often salacious comments from Leo Murphy, in between doing his typing and answering the phone. But she wasn't about to tell Michael that. No way.

Let him admire her new figure, her increased self-confidence and her air of calm. Aisling sighed at herself in the mirror. Who was she kidding? She certainly felt more confident about lots of things, but unfortunately, her confidence wavered when she needed it most. With Leo. Losing nearly three-quarters of a stone had given her more energy and a smidgen of her old self-assurance.

Dealing with all manner of problems with clients and other lawyers' secretaries had given her a sense of job satisfaction that cleaning the oven never had.

But everything fell to pieces when it came to Leo. Aisling loved the days he was out of the office. She typed up letters, filed documents, made appointments and dealt with clients effortlessly.

She was good at the job, she realised happily, great at organising things and coolly competent when it came to the finer details of office work.

Then she'd hear him bounding up the stairs to her tiny office and she'd feel a queasiness in the pit of her stomach.

'How's my lovely Mrs Moran today?' he said sometimes, when he was in a good mood.

'Gimme my appointment book,' he'd snarl when he wasn't. If a woman had behaved the way Leo Murphy did, with mood swings verging on the psychiatric, she'd have been called a premenstrual nuisance or a menopausal old cow.

Leo was just moody, Caroline said the day Aisling had ventured to ask if he'd always been so 'difficult'.

Moody! He should have been locked up, she decided. In

fact, he was so nasty when he was in his bad moods, that she had almost preferred him when he was playful, patting her on the shoulder in an overfamiliar way or calling her 'Honey' or 'Sweetheart.' Almost.

Wednesday had been the last straw. He'd come back from what was obviously a boozy lunch – not for the first time – in rare good humour.

'How are you, Aisling?' he said sauntering into her office. He placed both hands on her desk and leaned over, as though trying to see what was on her computer screen. He was too close for comfort. The smell of brandy on his breath was enough to make Aisling recoil.

'Mr R . . . R . . . Reid was looking for you,' she stuttered, the hairs standing up on her arms.

'He can wait,' Leo said in the precise tones of someone who was drunk but determined not to show it.

'So,' he clumsily pushed her wire in-tray to one side and sat down on the edge of her desk, less than two feet away from her. Aisling slid her chair back furtively, but she was jammed up against the window.

'So,' he repeated, 'how's your husband, Aisling? Still gone?'

Had anyone else said something so blatantly rude to her, Aisling would have been furious, maybe even walked out of the room and slammed the door. But Leo Murphy wasn't anyone. He was her boss.

The phone on her desk leaped to life, its shrill ring breaking Leo's spell. Aisling grabbed it.

'Leo Murphy's office,' she said quickly, wondering how she could still speak with her mouth so dry. 'Of course, Caroline. He's here now. I'll tell him Mr Reid's waiting for him.'

She didn't have to say another word. Leo left as quickly as he'd come, leaving her wondering whether she'd just imagined the whole scary scene.

He'd been so normal and businesslike the next day that she'd been able to relax a little, able to think she'd over-reacted.

'What would I do without you, Aisling?' He smiled when

she brought him a sandwich at lunchtime. She smiled briefly, glad that everything was back to normal.

But the incident still simmered in her mind, looming large in her head when the lights were out and she lay on her own in the big double bed. Should she say something to someone? To Vivienne? Two months ago, she wouldn't have dreamed of asking the other woman what time it was, never mind what she should do about Leo.

Yet she'd come to really like Vivienne, to admire her courage and determination. Once Vivienne had realised that Aisling wasn't some bored housewife toying with the idea of a job and using her contacts to get it, she'd dropped her frosty demeanour. In fact, she'd become a good friend. A single mother to eight-year-old Christine, Vivienne was a veteran of the childminder search and had given Aisling lots of advice on finding the right person to look after the twins.

Maybe she should tell Vivienne about Leo, Aisling mused. She really wanted to. But she hated to admit to anyone that she didn't know what to do, that he'd beaten her.

Aisling unzipped her small make-up bag, found her mascara and applied some to her upper eyelashes. She quickly ran her new lipstick over her lips and she was ready. She couldn't resist turning sideways again to see her reflection in the mirror. Yes, she could feel her hipbones, she thought happily, smoothing her hands over the soft wool of the skirt.

Vivienne caught up with Aisling as she hurried along Fitzwilliam Square. It was ten past nine and they were both late.

'Bloody Leeson Street Bridge,' fumed Vivienne, walking as rapidly as a long, sleek red skirt and spindly high heels would allow.

'Some moron stalled his car and I was stuck for three changes of the lights. That made me so late, I'm parked practically at Baggot Street and today's the day of the director's lunch, so I really needed to be in early.'

'I got stuck on the bridge too,' said Aisling. 'I hope Leo isn't in yet, he'll go mad if I'm late. But I know he's going out about eleven, so if you need any help with the lunch today, call me.'

'You're a star,' Vivienne said gratefully. 'I could do with some help because Caroline is on holiday this week and she usually gives me a hand. *And* we're using new caterers today, so I need to double check to make sure everything is perfect.'

'Just ring me, I'd love to help.'

Aisling felt slightly comforted by the fact that Vivienne was late. It could happen to anyone. If Leo was already in the office, she'd tell him Vivienne had been stuck in the same traffic jam. Then he'd know she hadn't simply overslept and was lying about what had delayed her. That was it, she'd tell him about Vivienne and the traffic on Leeson Street Bridge.

Leo was already there when she arrived at twelve minutes past nine, hair flying as she bounded up the stairs. He always locked his office at night and it was now open, proof that he was at his desk and listening for her.

'Aisling,' he called out, as she put a foot on the staircase to her tiny office. 'Come here.'

Breathing heavily from her sprint from the car to the office and aware that she looked hot and flushed, she went into his office.

'I'm sorry, Leo,' she apologised, 'the traffic was dreadful and I got stuck on Leeson Street Bridge for five minutes behind . . .'

'I don't want excuses,' he snapped, obviously irritated. 'I want you here before me in the morning. I want coffee on my desk when I arrive and,' he stared at her with distaste, 'I want a secretary who looks respectable and not like she's just run the mini marathon!'

Shocked, Aisling blinked rapidly, feeling her eyes prickle with tears. If he said one more thing, she'd cry. As if she hadn't cried enough recently.

But Leo had obviously said all he wanted to say and had started reading his newspaper.

Aisling turned on her heel and fled. Once inside her own sanctum, she shut the door and dropped her handbag.

He's a pig, a pig and I hate him, she howled. I hate him. How dare he speak to me like I'm some sort of slave. How dare he think he can ask me personal questions, leer at me and then treat me like this! I hate him!

After ten minutes, she felt calm enough to get him a cup of coffee. He was still reading the paper and didn't even look up when she entered the office. She placed the cup on his desk and left as silently as she'd come in.

Then she took the mug of strong, sweet coffee she'd poured for herself and went to the women's toilet. She fixed her hair back into a neat pony tail, washed her face and reapplied her make-up. She added a squirt of perfume from the tiny Allure sample she'd got in the chemist's.

Finished, she took a draught of coffee and looked at herself in the mirror. She stared at her reflection as if she was a stranger seeing her own face for the first time. Dispassionately, impartially.

An attractive woman stared back at her, a woman with recently discovered cheekbones, an oval-shaped face, a strong chin and large, expressive eyes the colour of just-washed denim. It was a strong face, a womanly face. The face of a woman who was a working mother, a survivor, someone who refused to let life knock her down.

She'd done a lot in the past three months, coped with her marriage breaking up, coped with going back to work, even coped with looking after two boisterous boys. She wasn't going to let some jumped-up bully ruin everything she'd achieved so far, was she? No way, Aisling said aloud. No way. Watch out Leo Murphy. Don't try your bullying tactics any more.

She remained in her office all morning, talking several times to Leo on the intercom as she transferred phone calls. He didn't ask to see her. She was grateful to be left alone.

'I'm going out now. I'll be back for the lunch at one,' he said in clipped tones on the intercom at five to eleven. Hope you crash, pig, Aisling said to herself.

He had just left when Vivienne rang.

'Can you come down and help, Aisling? I saw Leo go out, so I hoped you'd be free.'

'Sure. I'll be down in five minutes.'

Vivienne was wrestling with a sash window when Aisling walked into the boardroom.

'Damn thing's stuck,' wheezed Vivienne, pink-faced with exertion. 'That painter we had last month glued everything together with paint. I'll kill him. I just can't open this window and it's like an oven in here if you don't.'

It took both of them to free the window from the painted frame, but once they did the window slid up easily. A welcome cool breeze drifted in along with the noise of cars and motorbike couriers racing over to Leeson Street.

'It's a lovely room,' said Aisling, admiring the gilt-framed hunting prints and an imposing mahogany table in the centre of the room, surrounded by twenty high-backed chairs.

Aisling had peered in the door a few times but she'd never been at one of the monthly directors' meetings where Vivienne took minutes in her perfect Pitman shorthand.

She knew that Caroline usually brought in coffee, tea and biscuits midway through the meetings, and that sometimes the senior partner, Edward Richardson, opened a bottle of vintage port if the company had enjoyed an especially profitable month.

Not that anybody ever got drunk, Vivienne explained. 'Except that time when Tom Reid was taking this flu remedy and he had two glasses of port at the meeting and practically fell asleep!'

Today was going to be different. Richardson, Reid and Finucane were welcoming two new partners to the firm and celebrating the most successful year of business in their thirty-two-year history. So Edward decided to celebrate in style.

They could have taken a room in Le Coq Hardi or any one of Dublin's posh restaurants, but he preferred to host a private luncheon in the boardroom, a tradition dating back to the early days of the business.

'There are eight clients coming,' Vivienne said, looking at a notepad where she'd drawn up a list of things to do. 'That makes sixteen place settings and I hope they all fit. We've never had so many people at a lunch before. I just hope the caterers are up to scratch,' she added fervently.

She'd been responsible for organising these annual lunches for seven years and had used the same caterers every year. Until this year.

'I can't believe they've gone out of business,' she told Aisling two weeks previously. 'They were so reliable and the food was always beautiful. I just left it completely up to them. Lord knows where I'll get anyone as good.'

Exclusive Dining, picked out of the phone book, sounded perfect. Vivienne had been crossing her fingers for ten days now, praying that everything would go according to plan.

'Is this the right room?' asked a masculine voice. A sulky-looking young man in jeans and a fluorescent yellow T-shirt stood at the door with a big cardboard box in his arms.

'Yes,' said Vivienne. 'Put it over there, thank you,' she added, gesturing at a long table which stood at the far end of the room covered with a white tablecloth. He put the box down with an ominous clatter. I hope that's not the china, thought Aisling with a twinge of unease, or they'll be eating off cracked plates. Miraculously, nothing appeared to be broken. He took white plates out of the box one by one, banging each one noisily as he stacked them on the table.

'Sabrina is supposed to be coming at half eleven with the food, isn't she?' Vivienne asked him.

'Sabrina's sick. Debbie's doing the food,' he muttered, shoving the empty packing case out of the way under the table. 'I'll get the rest of the stuff out of the van. There are two more boxes, if you come with me to help.'

'What do you mean, "Sabrina's sick"?' asked Vivienne anxiously. 'She was fine yesterday. And who's Debbie, is she a partner or what? I've never met her.'

'She works for Sabrina sometimes,' he answered disinterestedly. Vivienne caught Aisling's eye and grimaced.

'I'll get the rest of the stuff and you ring Sabrina,' advised Aisling. 'I'm Aisling,' she said to the packer. 'What's your name?'

'Bob.'

'Right Bob,' she said resolutely. 'Show me the way to the van.'

She and Bob had unpacked all the china, cutlery, wine glasses and napkins when Vivienne returned, her face as white as her blouse.

'Sabrina has a twenty-four-hour bug and she can't work. But she says Debbie will be here on the dot of half eleven and she's very reliable although she hasn't done many lunches on her own . . . I have a bad feeling about this,' she whispered to Aisling. You and me both, thought Aisling.

It was nearly a quarter to twelve before Debbie arrived with lunch. Vivienne had carefully arranged place settings and adjusted the four baskets of flowers with uncharacteristic nervousness.

'I hate doing this,' revealed Vivienne. 'Leave me a mountain of documents to organise or get me to type hundred-page contracts, and I'm fine. But organising catering is a complete nightmare. I've never been much of a cook. *Christine* makes better toast than I do and I certainly can't come up with menus at the drop of a hat. Oh, here she is! Thank God.'

Debbie was energetic, fresh-faced and about nineteen.

'Hello all,' she said brightly, as she walked into the room carrying a large aluminium cold-food container. 'I'm Debbie, Sabrina's stand-in. Oh, everything look so pretty. The carnations are nice, I love carnations. Grab this for me, Bob?' she asked.

She and Bob blithely carried in the cold and hot food containers, while she chatted away volubly, discussing the traffic, the weather and how she was dying for a coffee.

'Can I smoke in here?' she asked, producing a pack of cigarettes when Vivienne handed her a mug of coffee.

'I'm afraid not,' replied Vivienne.

Debbie shrugged good-humouredly and sat down to drink her coffee. The fact that she was late wasn't even mentioned.

Aisling wondered whether Debbie had ever catered professionally before.

For all she knew, Debbie could have been a junior Masterchef winner who simply wasn't into the formalities of catering as a business. Maybe cooking was her forte and she wasn't interested in making the clients feel relaxed and confident about the meal.

But when she got a look at the dressed salmon, Aisling knew they were in trouble. The fish was the see-through rose colour of undercooked salmon. Food poisoning time, she thought.

It was perfectly arranged, dressed with beautifully cut pieces of lemon and cucumber, and almost definitely half-raw. She ran an experienced eye over the dressed crab with Dublin Bay prawns. The crab looked cooked but, if the salmon was undercooked, God only knew what condition the prawns were in. Shellfish food poisoning registered about eight on the food poisoning Richter scale, bested only by botulism. They really were in trouble.

Aisling might be nervous about her typing and scared of dealing with her difficult boss, but if there was one thing she was perfectly sure about, it was food.

'Vivienne,' she said. 'We've got a problem.'

'What is it?' asked Vivienne, busy positioning the white and red wine goblets in exactly the right places.

There was no point in beating around the bush. 'The salmon is practically raw, Vivienne,' Aisling said as gently as she could. 'Debbie hasn't cooked the fish properly. It's definitely still raw. And I don't like the look of the prawns either. We'll give everyone food poisoning.'

'Oh my God,' said the other woman in horror. 'You're not serious. What can we do, it's twelve now, they'll be here in forty-five minutes. Debbie!' she shrieked.

'Yes?'

'The food is raw!'

'Don't be silly, it couldn't be. I mean, I did my best,' began Debbie defensively.

Aisling bent down and tasted the coleslaw. It was faintly bitter, definitely off.

'We're in big trouble, girls. This is off too. When did you do all this, Debbie? Coleslaw wouldn't go off that quickly.'

Debbie's face was shocked, but Vivienne's was worse. They both looked as if they were going to cry.

'I swear I did the salmon the way the book said,' wailed Debbie. 'I let the water boil and turned it off . . . honestly.'

'Did you leave the fish in the fish kettle until it cooled?' asked Aisling.

'No. Was I supposed to?'

'That's part of the cooking, Debbie. What happened to the coleslaw?'

'I don't know. I'm a pastry chef really. I've never taken on this big a job myself. I'm so sorry.' She looked horrified. But then so did Vivienne. For once, the cool and calm senior secretary was totally at a loss.

'Look,' Aisling took a quick glance at Vivienne's face and decided to take charge, 'what cooking equipment have you got here?'

'We've got a microwave in the van . . . I'm so sorry,' Debbie repeated miserably. 'I did my best . . .'

Aisling calmed her down. 'Look, Debbie, we don't have time to start blaming anyone. We've got to come up with something else fairly rapidly. Bring the microwave into the canteen. That way, we've got two microwaves which we can use to heat the salmon up. It's the only way we can use it. We don't have enough time to recook it and cool it and we better have a proper first course if we don't have the buffet any more. OK, let me think.' Aisling stood back and looked at the food Debbie and Bob had brought up. There were plenty of salads, along with a cooked ham, a huge bowl of mixed lettuce and a cheese board.

Vivienne sat down on a chair and rubbed her temples shakily.

'I can't believe this is happening,' she said. 'I just can't believe it. Today is so important to Edward and I can't let him down.'

The difference between the two secretaries' relationships with their bosses was amazing, thought Aisling briefly. Vivienne didn't want things to go wrong because she'd be letting Edward down. If Aisling had arranged a lunch for Leo and it had gone wrong, she'd have been terrified that he'd kill her, never mind not wanting to upset him.

'Don't worry, Vivienne,' she said calmly. 'I've an idea. Bob, get the microwave and any pots you have from the van. Vivienne, you go with Bob to Quinnsworth in Baggot Street – he can double-park while you shop. I want you to get a pound of beef tomatoes,' she instructed. 'Debbie, do you have any herbs with you?'

'Er, yes,' answered Debbie.

'I need oregano, basil, thyme, parsley and olive oil. Oh yes, we need to make a vinaigrette. Have you got the ingredients for that?'

'Yes. I'll get everything I have.'

'Put it in the canteen, it's downstairs, Vivienne will show you. Right Vivienne, get the tomatoes, three or four French sticks, potatoes and, let's see, courgettes. Debbie and I will divide the cooked ham into starters with salad and when you get back we'll cook the potatoes and salmon. We better forget about the prawns.' She reached out and patted Vivienne's arm. 'It'll be fine, don't worry.'

Vivienne ran to her office to get money from petty cash.

Aisling carefully transferred the food to the basement canteen. A tiny white-tiled room with a table and four plastic chairs, a microwave, a kettle, a fridge and a grill that looked about twenty years old, it was totally unsuitable for cooking and serving a meal for sixteen people. It would have to do.

She slipped one of Debbie's white aprons over her clothes and washed her hands carefully, her mind on the best way to turn a disastrous buffet into a top-class lunch. It was seven minutes past twelve and lunch was supposed to be ready at one. But she felt remarkably calm and focused.

She cut the salmon into large chunks which she put into one of the large serving dishes Bob had just carried in.

Debbie arrived panting, with a box of herbs, oil, butter and cooking equipment.

'We'll use the ham, the potato and the pasta salads and make individual starters,' Aisling explained, breaking open a garlic bulb and expertly peeling and crushing several cloves with an old bread knife she'd found in a drawer.

Debbie handed her a sharp Sabatier knife from her box.

'Thanks,' said Aisling, never taking her eyes off what she was doing. 'Keep it very simple, all right,' she added, assembling a speedy vinaigrette as she talked. 'Just drizzle a little vinaigrette on each plate, place the radicchio in the centre, a little of the cooked salads on the left and the ham on the right.'

'Yes.'

Delighted that someone else had taken charge, Debbie started arranging the plates immediately. They were nearly finished ten minutes later when Vivienne and Bob arrived back with the shopping.

'You were quick,' said Aisling astonished.

'Necessity is the mother of invention,' answered Vivienne. 'I skipped the queue by begging everyone in front of me on the express checkout to let me go first. I said I was going to be fired if I didn't get back to the office on time and it worked!'

Debbie blanched at the mention of the word 'fired'.

'OK, Bob and Vivienne, you peel the potatoes,' ordered Aisling. 'Then wash them and cube them into very small cubes. We need them to cook very rapidly. Debbie, you prepare the courgettes. We'll just cook them in the microwave and serve them with a little butter and black pepper.'

'What are we making?' asked Vivienne as she carefully rolled up the sleeves of her blouse.

'Salmon with tomato and fresh herb salsa and courgettes and mashed potatoes. Because men love mashed potatoes and it's the quickest way to cook them with two microwaves.'

By one o'clock, all the guests had arrived and the board-room was full. The salmon and mashed potatoes were being kept hot in Debbie's portable ovens.

269

Vivienne dispensed drinks while Debbie carried the starters up from the canteen and left them on the long white-covered table.

'Make up a couple of starters with just salad, Debbie,' instructed Aisling when the other girl returned to the canteen. 'Just in case there's someone who doesn't want to eat the cold ham.'

'What will we do if there is someone who doesn't eat fish?' asked Debbie. 'They won't be able to eat the main course.'

'Oh no, I never thought,' Aisling paled. 'I'll do the salad. Get Vivienne to check if everyone will eat the fish. We'll have to give them a cold plate or maybe I can make them an omelette. You do have eggs, don't you?'

'They're all eating the ham,' said Vivienne with a relieved sigh when she walked into the canteen ten minutes later, 'and everyone wants the salmon. I managed to tell Edward what had happened and he says well done to you. And sent down this.' She produced a bottle of red wine and two glasses.

'I need this,' she added, filling one glass for Aisling and another for herself. 'I don't believe in drinking at lunchtime but today is definitely an exception.'

When the last of the main courses had gone upstairs, Aisling relaxed.

'They love it,' Vivienne said, when she came back down from the boardroom. 'What a relief. I never want to go through that ever again. I'm wrecked.' She slipped off her impossibly high shoes and sank down into a chair.

'You were amazing, Aisling. You really saved the day. And you were so unflappable.'

'Cooking calms me,' Aisling replied, putting Debbie's olive oil back in the box along with the herbs and butter. 'It's one of my favourite occupations and one of the things I'm best at. Unfortunately,' she added drily, 'I spent more time over the last five years worrying about making a perfect soufflé than worrying about the state of my marriage. And I spent much too much time *eating* the products of my cookery classes. My answer to everything was to bury myself at home and learn

270

how to make flaky pastry and cream horns – and then eat them!' She laughed.

'Well, you're certainly not eating them now,' commented Vivienne. 'You look great. You've lost so much weight.'

Aisling flushed with pleasure at the compliment. Both Jo and Fiona had said the same thing yet she still didn't know how to take flattery. In her mind she was still an overweight, dull housewife waiting for twelve o'clock to chime and her carriage to turn into a pumpkin.

'Have you been dieting?' asked Vivienne.

'Not really. I don't have the time to cook stuff like I used to any more but I have been making a big effort to eat properly. Working certainly helps,' she added. 'It's easier to keep off the biscuits when you're not staring at the fridge all day long. Breaking up with Michael has done wonders for my figure. Maybe if I'd copped on earlier that he was bored with me and changed somehow, he wouldn't have left.'

Vivienne leaned over and poured Aisling another glass of wine.

'Well, I don't think it's ever that simple,' she said gently. 'I've never been married, but my relationship with Christine's father was a long-term thing, so I know all about letting relationships go stale. You can't say it was your fault things didn't work out any more than you can say it's the man's fault. It doesn't work like that. People change so much, that's what happens. Nobody ever tells you that in romantic novels, do they?'

'Christine's father didn't want the same things I wanted,' she revealed. 'He wanted to remain single and fancy-free, which was OK by me before I got pregnant. But afterwards, I wanted to settle down, I wanted security. He didn't.'

She shrugged. 'We drifted apart and it wasn't really my fault or his fault. Was that what happened with you?'

'I suppose so,' admitted Aisling. 'We both changed. I couldn't see that in the beginning. I blamed Michael for everything from global warming to cellulite, but I can see what happened now, thank God. I went one way and Michael went another. I'd stopped thinking of him in the same way, I suppose,' she said. 'He wasn't so much my husband as the father of the twins, and breadwinner. I cut myself off from his world and he did the same to me. I notice it now because his being there isn't much different to his not being there.

'Apart from late-night conversations about what the boys did and what type of dinner was overheated to a crisp in the oven because he was late home, we didn't talk at all. Wow,' said Aisling, 'this is a very intense conversation. Are you sure you didn't put something in this wine, a bit of truth serum?'

Vivienne laughed. 'Trauma makes you want to unburden yourself – or at least that's what it says in Caroline's latest psychology book.'

'*Caroline* likes psychology books?' said Aisling. 'I can't imagine it.'

'She loves them. She's been doing a night-time accountancy course for the last two years and she says she'd never have dreamed of doing it without her books. She says they've given her the encouragement her upbringing never gave her.'

They finished off the bottle of wine, leaving a flustered Debbie to serve dessert, a raspberry roulade with cream.

'If there's any left over, bring it back,' ordered Vivienne, buttering a piece of French bread. 'It looks yummy and we're ravenous.'

Aisling was beginning to feel distinctly tipsy. She hadn't actually eaten any lunch and the wine, a particularly potent Rioja, had gone straight to her head.

'Eat,' advised Vivienne, making an enormous French bread sandwich with some ham and potato salad, 'or we'll be plastered.'

She cut the sandwich in half without too much of the filling squelching out and handed one piece to Aisling.

'Was it very difficult bringing up Christine on your own?' ventured Aisling. 'It's just that I've a friend who is pregnant and her boyfriend has left her. I wonder how hard it will be for her.'

'God help her! It's very hard,' said Vivienne through a

mouthful of crumbs, 'if it's anything like my experience. I mean, I adore Christine, she's everything in the world to me, but there have been some difficult times. It's hard being alone, but you know that. You're responsible for *everything*, nobody else. And it can be lonely, too.'

'I know. You miss adult conversations,' said Aisling reflectively.

'It's not even that,' Vivienne added. 'Your social life just disintegrates when you're a single parent, that's what I've found, anyway. Nobody invites a single woman to parties because the women are all terrified you're going to run off with their husbands.' She chuckled as though remembering something. 'And the husbands all think you're dying for it and chat you up madly!'

Aisling said nothing. Did Leo think she was dying for it? Probably.

'You lose all the friends who are couples,' Vivienne continued, 'and end up hanging out with your single friends. Most of whom don't have kids and can't understand why you can't stay out all night or have to stay sober to drive the baby-sitter home. Am I making this single parenthood thing sound too attractive for you?' she inquired with a large grin.

'Fantastic. How do you ever get time to work with such a hectic social life?' Aisling asked.

'Oh, you know, I fit a few hours in every week between visiting Leeson Street, picking up bored married men and trawling through singles pubs looking for Mr Might-Possibly-be-Mr-Right.' Vivienne took a big slug of wine. 'That probably sounds very bitter,' she said quietly.

'Has it been that tough?' Aisling asked gently.

'Yes and no. I'd love to have someone in my life but it's so hard to meet someone who wants a single mother. It's so hard to meet someone full stop. I'm thirty-four and the men my age are all married. Or have no intention of settling down,' she added.

'Sorry, this isn't what you need to hear, Aisling. I've been having a miserable week because Christine has the flu. I've got the most dreadful PMT and the video conked out on Wednesday evening when we were watching *101 Dalmatians*. Lord knows how much it will cost to fix, or if it's even worth fixing.'

'Ladies, you've been asked to join the party upstairs seeing as how you saved the day,' said a loud voice.

Pat Finucane stood at the door of the canteen.

'I've been telling everyone about your amazing culinary skills, Aisling, and how you managed to transform a disaster into a wonderful meal. They nearly licked their plates, you know. Those mashed potatoes were delicious.'

Aisling and Vivienne laughed at the same time.

'What did I say?' asked Pat.

'Aisling maintains that men love mashed potatoes and she's obviously right,' explained Vivienne. She slid her shoes back on and winked at Aisling.

'You must come over to my house for dinner some night next week and we'll continue our moan, right?'

'I'd love to,' said Aisling warmly. Maybe that would be just the right occasion to talk to Vivienne about Leo.

'It'll be spaghetti or something equally simple,' added Vivienne quickly. 'Or I could always ask Debbie to rustle up some fish . . .!'

'Well done.' Edward Richardson stood up and clapped when Aisling arrived at the boardroom door. The guests looked totally relaxed, with pink faces and loosened ties evidence that the wine was going down a treat. 'Gentlemen, I give you the estimable Aisling Moran.' He smiled, his pale blue tie still knotted in a perfect Windsor knot.

'When you open your own restaurant, my dear, I want to eat there every night. And you could teach my darling daughter to cook while you're at it!'

'Do you do dinner parties?' asked one man, as Pat offered Aisling a glass of wine.

'Well,' Aisling said slowly, 'I've never cooked for anyone but myself and my family . . .'

'It's just that my wife hates cooking and she'd jump at the

chance to have someone like you come in and rustle up a dinner party,' the man insisted.

'It's a great idea, Jim,' said Pat seriously. 'You'd be wonderful at it, Aisling.'

'Absolutely,' agreed Vivienne, accepting a glass of champagne. 'You never panicked once.'

'You could certainly cook for my parties,' added Tom Reid, Caroline's boss.

'It really would be a marvellous business venture,' said Edward encouragingly. 'Your talent and my tasting skills. You'd cook and I'd test everything!'

They all laughed.

'A toast,' said Edward, raising his glass, 'to Richardson, Reid and Finucane, to our new partners,' he smiled at the two new lawyers, 'to our continued business success and, to Aisling, who made our lunch wonderful! Cheers!'

'I'm serious about that,' said Jim. He grabbed Aisling's arm as she and Vivienne left. 'I'm Jim Coughlan and I'd love you to cook for us. My wife, Rachel, has just set up a small public relations business and she plans to do a lot of entertaining in the future. Can I tell her she can call you?'

Startled and flattered, Aisling thought for a moment. 'Sure,' she said finally. 'But I could only cook after office hours. I couldn't compromise working here.'

'No problem. Here's my number.' He handed her a cream and black embossed business card. 'I'll get Rachel to ring you here and you can call back when it's convenient.'

The men were still chatting around the boardroom table at half four, all notions of work abandoned.

'I just want to go home and lie down,' sighed Vivienne, pouring a mug of coffee for herself and Aisling in her office.

'Me too. But I've got to send out two letters by courier this evening. All they need is Leo's signature, but I doubt if I'll be able to get him out of the boardroom.'

'I've got to ask Edward something,' Vivienne said, 'so I'll mention the letters to Leo.'

Aisling brought her coffee upstairs, wishing it was half five and she could go home. She was tired and the idea of a hot bath was very appealing. Yet she felt elated by the way she'd coped today, flattered by what everyone had said.

She printed out the letters Leo was to sign. She'd love to cater for dinner parties. But it would be a big thing to take on. Where would she start? And how could she do it all on her own?

'Very tasty, Mrs Moran,' said Leo's deep voice behind her.

Aisling whirled around in surprise. He was standing in the doorway grinning at her. Leering, actually.

'The food was tasty as well,' he chuckled, delighted with his little joke. Aisling could feel the anger she'd been hiding simmer up inside her. Steady, don't do anything, she cautioned herself. He's just drunk, he's harmless. Don't say anything you'd regret, Aisling, just because you've had a few glasses of wine. You need this job, remember.

'I wanted you to sign these,' she said as calmly as she could, holding out the letters. He didn't move. She walked towards him and handed him the two sheets of paper.

'Thanks, Aisling.' He took the letters, keeping his eyes on her. She leaned over her desk and picked up a pen from the other side. As she did so, he slid one arm around her waist and let it move quickly down to brush her behind.

Enraged, she swung around and screamed at him.

'How dare you touch me, you pig! How dare you!'

'Don't give me that rubbish,' he snarled. 'You know you want it. Don't be all coy.'

He stepped towards her again, a half-grin on his face. He was going to grab her, to touch her, she just knew it. And she knew that she'd had enough.

When her right hand connected with his jaw it made a satisfying noise.

'Listen, you pervert, you can stick your job,' Aisling yelled. 'I've had enough of your comments, your salacious remarks and your appalling behaviour. You're an asshole, Leo Murphy, and I'm leaving!'

With that, she grabbed her handbag from behind her desk and ran out the door.

★ ★ ★

'I can't believe I did that!' Aisling said at half eight that night when Jo called round. 'I was totally furious at the time, a mixture of red wine and release at having stopped that chauvinistic pig. But now . . .' She broke off, rubbing the bridge of her nose to relieve the throbbing headache which was threatening to explode in her head.

'Aisling!' said Jo angrily. 'Don't you dare feel sorry for what you did. I can't believe that bastard. I only wish you'd said something to me and I would have told you exactly what to do a lot sooner. Who the hell does he think he is? That's sexual harassment and it's illegal. He can't get away with this, he can't! The Employment Equality Agency will tell us exactly what to do and believe you me, he'll rue the day he ever abused his position!'

'That's all very well, Jo,' sighed Aisling, 'but I still need a job right now. Anyway, who the hell is going to believe my side of the story?' she demanded. 'Leo is a lawyer, after all. He spends his life dealing with the law. By the time he's finished with me, my name will be mud. I'll have been "asking for it" or something.'

'Don't be ridiculous,' snapped Jo. 'Sorry. I didn't mean it that way. I'm just so angry that you never told me about it. I could have told you what he was doing was wrong, that you don't have to suffer that sort of crap.'

'I know,' Aisling said miserably, 'I know I should have done something sooner. It was all so strange and difficult. Getting a job in the first place seemed such a huge thing, I just didn't know how to handle myself, or him,' she added despondently. 'I was so pleased with myself when I hit him, but that wore off. All I've been thinking about since is why I *did* do it.'

'You should have done it weeks ago,' Jo pointed out. 'Look, Ash, ring Pat Finucane and tell him what happened. Ask him what he thinks. I could be wrong, but I doubt if he'll let this end here.'

'I can't drag Pat into this,' exclaimed Aisling.

'He's in it. He is a senior partner in a firm where one of his colleagues is accused of sexually harassing someone else. He's hardly likely to brush the whole incident under the carpet.'

'Who's going to believe me though, Jo? I didn't tell anyone and it's his word against mine,' Aisling said dully. 'What have I done?'

CHAPTER FOURTEEN

Swathed in an ancient towelling dressing-gown with her hair in a wet pony tail, Jo lay on the settee and shuffled through a sheaf of estate agents' prospectuses. A can of Coke and a half-eaten Danish pastry lay on the coffee table beside her, on top of two property supplements.

She found the prospectus for the town house in Killiney and gazed at a photo of an elegant red-brick house with an off-white clematis flowering palely around a sage-green door. Number four had two bedrooms, one with an en suite bathroom, a kitchen/dining room, small sitting room and a tiny conservatory looking onto a pocket-handkerchief lawn surrounded by a rockery stuffed with alpine plants. Lovely. So, you couldn't swing a cat in any of the rooms, but she didn't want a mansion. Just solid walls so that the neighbours didn't come hammering on the door in the morning after a sleepless night listening to baby.

Jo leaned over to grab the can of Coke, careful not to overstretch because her lower back had been giving her mild twinges of pain all day. She turned her attention back to the serious business of house-hunting. The Killiney place was a definite possibility. It *was* expensive, but she had to move *somewhere* before the baby was born. The walls in her apartment were so thin that she could hear Mrs Roche's clock-radio go off every morning at half seven precisely. And, when the two girls who'd just moved into the apartment above had a dinner party, sleep was out of the question.

Jo wanted a garden for her child, somewhere to sit and mess around with toys, sand pits and Wendy houses. She had seen a lovely one in the Argos catalogue and had nearly rushed off and bought it until she reminded herself that it would be quite some time before her baby would be into

Wendy houses. She looked at the next prospectus, a small, whitewashed cottage in Dalkey which looked beautiful in the estate agent's photo. But she hadn't actually *seen* it yet and the descriptions, written in eloquent estate agent language, did not always match up with the actual premises once you got there.

On Monday, she'd seen one 'bijou des res with one rec, three beds, one bthrm, ofch and lge grdn. Nds sm modernisation,' and found a poky little house with zero charm, damp walls, three mouldy bedrooms that could have been used for a drug den and a wasteland out the back that looked suitable for botanic experiments into rampant weed growth.

'It needs some work,' admitted the weary-looking estate agent when he noticed Jo pulling her skirt close around her legs so it wouldn't brush against anything particularly virulent in the kitchen.

'If I was married to the person who ran Rentokil, and owned a builders' providers, I might consider it,' she replied. Then, sorry she'd sounded so sharp, she added, 'I need something that doesn't need too much work because I'm having a baby.'

After a lengthy conversation about first babies – Colm, the estate agent, had two and the second was only nine months and had never slept longer than four hours in his life – Jo drove off to see a ten-year-old mews house which didn't mention anything about modernisation in the prospectus.

As beautiful as the last place had been awful, Jo fell utterly in love with it and was disappointed to find out that someone had put in a successful bid for it that morning. Too depressed to even complain to the estate agent who could have rung up and told her not to bother coming, Jo flounced out to her car and drove home crossly. Two Twix bars sort of comforted her at home that evening while she watched *The Bill*.

After Monday's disasters, she decided to give house-hunting a miss on Tuesday evening. Instead, she'd gone to a reception for the launch of a new variety of eyeshadow and had eaten far too many vol-au-vents while watching four stick-thin models covered in body paint sashay elegantly around the room, leaving the waiters slack-jawed with amazement.

'They must be anorexic,' muttered Rhona, lighting another cigarette so she wouldn't break her diet and succumb to the lure of the Chinese sesame prawn toasts displayed invitingly on a nearby table.

'You'd be amazed at how many models eat like horses,' remarked Yvonne, the equally stick-thin fashion editor of a rival magazine.

Rhona raised one eyebrow sceptically. 'Yvonne, I've been on two press trips with you and I know that you think having more than half a grapefruit and one slice of toast for breakfast is sheer gluttony. You can hardly talk.'

Jo took a sneaky look at Yvonne's pert little behind encased in body-skimming lycra and swiped another two vol-au-vents from a passing waiter.

'I do love vol-au-vents,' added Rhona, inhaling deeply, 'but they're so fattening.'

Jo swallowed quickly and took a deep draught of orange juice.

'Goodies, girls.' Nikki appeared in front of the three of them waving elegant gold carrier bags.

Driving home, Jo examined the eyeshadow quartet, lipstick and nail varnish that the make-up company had given everyone who'd attended the launch. The lipstick would make her look like Morticia out of *The Addams Family*. She should have gone house-hunting, she reminded herself, but she'd needed cheering up and an evening with Rhona was the perfect antidote for misery.

The next day she skipped lunch – well, eating a McDonald's in the car was practically skipping lunch – and went to see a Sixties bungalow in Dun Laoghaire. Jo had felt suddenly tearful when she was elbowed painfully in the back by a tall blonde on the way to the tiny avocado-green bathroom. She hated bloody avocado green anyway. It was so Seventies.

She'd been too busy at work on Thursday and Friday to do any house-hunting but today she planned to spend the afternoon viewing properties.

She'd got a list of three houses to visit and that would probably take most of the afternoon. And she needed to go grocery shopping because she was nearly out of tuna. Her current pregnancy fetish was for tuna and peanut butter sandwiches.

Shuffling through the property supplements, Jo came across one advert that fascinated her. It wasn't so much the description of the house in the Dublin mountains that did it.

In fact, Number two Redwood Lane definitely sounded the worst out of all the properties she'd considered, especially when you read between the lines and realised that solid fuel heating probably meant dragging in turf for the fire. More worrying was the fact that there was no mention of a bathroom at all.

The words 'in need of enthusiastic restoration' would have put off all but the most dimwitted DIY fanatic and, since Jo's entire tool collection consisted of an oddly shaped 99p screwdriver with three different ends for different types of screw, it didn't make any sense for her to even *look* at the house.

But she didn't feel very sensible just then. Jo didn't know why, but the house fascinated her, more for the description of the view than for anything else.

'Set in a scenic spot in the Dublin mountains, the property is bordered by sycamore and beech trees and overlooks farmland. With a superb view of Dublin Bay, it has to be seen.'

Don't be silly, she told herself as she pulled on the red brushed-cotton tracksuit bottoms she seemed to live in these days. What in the hell would you want with a dilapidated old house halfway up the mountains when you don't have a clue how to do any of the renovation work yourself, probably couldn't afford it anyway, and are expecting a baby in four months?

It was no use. She put on the matching red baggy sweatshirt and brushed her still damp hair, a picture of a lovely cottage bathed in golden evening sun in her mind.

A cosy kitchen, its window seat filled with plump gingham cushions, where you could sit to look out at Dublin spread below in a vast valley. A pretty cottage garden with lavender and rosemary growing fragrantly outside the kitchen door . . . And a brass bed in a bedroom decorated with a pretty Victorian wallpaper, a pine wardrobe – well, maybe *two* pine wardrobes – and a dressing table with a bowl of coral pink roses on top, roses from her own garden . . . She could see it all.

Jo parked the Golf neatly outside the office, wondering what Mark's Porsche was doing there on a Saturday morning at half twelve. She'd dropped by the *Style* offices to pick up some papers she'd forgotten to bring home the previous evening. On Monday morning at ten, she was interviewing a TV fashion stylist about how to pick clothes for people to wear in various programmes and series. The RTE press office had faxed in a list of programmes the stylist had worked on and, while Jo knew she'd be able to talk to the stylist without this background information, she still preferred to have a person's accomplishments fresh in her mind before interviewing them. She'd never forgotten one of her first interviews when she'd been so badly prepared that she'd innocently asked an actress what it was like working with a theatre director rumoured to be very bad-tempered.

'It's not so bad working with him since he's my *husband*!' snapped the actress before storming off.

Jo unlocked the front door of the Georgian building that the magazine shared with another business and went up the two flights of stairs to the *Style* office.

The cream panelled door was open and Jo went in, expecting to see Mark in the conference room on the phone.

He was, however, sitting at Brenda's desk, flicking through the dummy for the October edition of the magazine, one shoulder jamming Brenda's phone up against his ear.

'Hello, Jo, I didn't think I'd see anyone in here today,' he said warmly.

'I forgot some papers for an interview on Monday,' she replied, hurrying over to her desk and cursing herself for being found wearing a tracksuit and ancient runners. She hadn't a scrap of make-up on except a bit of pale lipstick and her face was probably shiny with moisturiser.

'Who are you interviewing?' he asked. Jo was about to tell him when he spoke into the phone.

'Hello, Tim. No, that's OK. I wasn't holding for long.'

While he talked, Jo rooted around among the various press releases, magazines and colour transparencies on her desk and found the shiny, coiled-up fax paper.

Sliding the pages into her handbag, she walked past Mark, waving silently as she made for the door.

'Hold on, Tim,' he said suddenly. 'Don't go yet, Jo, will you? I'll only be on the phone for a few minutes.'

There was nothing she could do but wait. Well, she may as well take the weight off her feet. She returned to her desk and decided to phone Aisling again. Nobody had answered when she rang earlier that morning and Jo was worried about her after her horrific experience at the hands of that bastard of a lawyer. Jo could think of a few things she'd like to do to Mr Murphy and none of them would be legal. What a pig. The phone kept ringing in the Morans'. Nobody answered. Of course, the boys have Saturday morning soccer and Aisling is probably picking them up, Jo remembered. She'd try again later.

Mark was still on the phone.

She didn't want to sit there waiting for him to come off the phone, so she tried to look engrossed in her diary and wondered what he wanted. It was nearly two months since they'd returned from New York and in the intervening time he'd been courteous, charming and kind to her.

He'd taken her outburst about being pregnant in his stride, hugging her in a brotherly fashion when she'd broken down in Bloomingdale's. He'd brought her to a nearby coffee shop, ordered steaming hot chocolate for her and held her hand until she stopped crying.

At no point had he pushed her for information. He listened calmly and intently while she mumbled about the baby and how Richard had left her.

'I'm glad you told me, Jo,' he said later that evening, when she met him in the hotel lobby feeling mortally embarrassed for her earlier behaviour. 'If you need any help, you can count on me. We're like a big family in *Style* and I want you to know that I'll do anything I can to help,' he emphasised.

They had dinner in the hotel that night and Jo wondered if she'd imagined the charged atmosphere between them during the previous days. Now, he treated her like a favourite sister who'd just been ill, asked her was she too hot, too cold, did she want more water or would she like some orange juice. For all his bachelorhood, Mark obviously knew a lot about pregnancy because he scanned the menu like an experienced dad, vetoing anything with soft cheeses, pâté or alcohol in it.

'You can't be too careful,' he said, ordering mineral water for them both because he said it would do him good to abstain from wine during dinner.

Jo found this brotherly concern comforting and unflattering at the same time. It was lovely to be pampered and she felt sure that, had Mark been the baby's dad, he'd have ordered her to lie down and put her feet up as soon as he heard she was pregnant.

But it was a little disconcerting to be transformed from sexy colleague into sexless mum-to-be.

Just because I'm having a baby doesn't mean I'm not a sexual human being, she wanted to say. I'm not a one-dimensional creature who's desirable until she gets pregnant and then becomes every man's mother – sexless. Of course, she didn't say any such thing. Mark might be disgusted to find that she was even *thinking* about fancying him when she was pregnant with Richard's child.

For the past two months, every time he rang the office, he asked to be put through to Jo and asked her how she was feeling, how the baby was doing, and to tell her that if she needed time off, to take it.

'You've got to look after yourself,' he said, almost paternally.

She didn't know if he did this because he thought nobody else in the office knew she was pregnant and boyfriend-less, and therefore wanted to be discreet. Or if he thought he should ask about her health because she was an employee and he was merely following some sort of management protocol. But she was getting used to those conversations and found him much easier to talk to on the phone than she did in real life.

He made her chuckle – and displayed a surprising knowledge of what *really* went on in the office – by asking whether Brenda was actually working or ringing her current *amour*, when Brenda was sitting opposite Jo at the time and obviously listening in on the conversation with interest.

In person, however, Jo found herself avoiding Mark. She felt embarrassed by the way she'd flirted with him in New York. At least she hadn't thrown herself at him, that was her one consolation.

She was still lost in contemplating their changed relationship when he put down the phone.

'How are you today, Jo?' he asked. 'Is the baby still trying to kick his way out?'

She laughed, because that was exactly what it had felt like over the past few weeks. At first, she'd felt tiny movements inside her, something that left her thrilled and utterly amazed. Now, the baby was getting quite energetic and was kicking around like an embryonic Cantona.

'*She* is very active,' she corrected him with a grin. Although she didn't want to know what sex the baby was, Jo felt it in her bones that she was carrying a little girl.

'A female soccer player, then,' he grinned, coming over to stand beside her with his hands in the pockets of the jeans he wore with a casual navy cotton shirt. 'Does she kick all the time?'

'No. But she moves around a lot except when she's sleeping.' Jo stroked her bump lovingly and was disconcerted to look up and find Mark looking at her intently, his grey eyes tender and affectionate.

'I'd love to feel her kick,' he said hesitantly. 'Would you mind . . .'

'No,' replied Jo, astonished.

He placed one large hand gently on her bump, strong fingers spread sensitively as he tried to feel the baby's movements. They stayed like that for a few minutes and Jo wondered what this curious tableau would look like if any other member of staff happened to arrive unexpectedly.

She could smell Mark's aftershave, a spicy lemon scent she always associated with him. She could recognise most perfumes and aftershaves if she'd smelled them before, but she wasn't sure what type of aftershave Mark used. Maybe it was because the scent mingled with his own particular smell, a mix of just-washed hair, shaving gel, fabric conditioner from his shirt and the warm smell of healthy male.

She felt a sudden dart in her belly as the baby moved to the left, sending gentle ripples around her womb.

'I felt it! Did you feel it?' Mark said in awe. 'Stupid of me, of course *you* felt it. Wasn't it wonderful?'

As if delighted with this new audience, the baby wriggled again. Mark's face was a picture, Jo thought. His eyes were alight with amazement at feeling the baby move inside her.

'It's wonderful, a miracle,' he said finally, slowly moving his hand away from her.

Jo smiled back at him, embarrassment and uncomfortable scenes forgotten.

'You really are blooming,' Mark said, eyes taking in her flushed cheeks, glossy hair and the sparkle in her dark eyes. 'Tell me, Mum-to-Be, do you fancy a spot of lunch or are you doing something this afternoon?'

'Actually, I'm going house-hunting today,' she said, 'but I can't call around anywhere until at least half two. I was going to go swimming in Stillorgan and then head out to Killiney to see the first place.'

'Why don't you go swimming and then let me bring you for a quick lunch. I'll drive you around for the afternoon,' he offered. 'Go on, it'll be fun. I love looking at houses.'

'OK. You're on.'

Tired after her swim, Jo decided it was a great idea to let Mark drive her around for the afternoon, especially since she'd decided to visit the house in the Dublin mountains and her knowledge of anything further out than Sandyford was decidedly sketchy.

After soup and a sandwich in a pub in Stillorgan, they set off in Mark's Porsche. Jo relaxed back into the low leather seat.

The first house was crammed with viewers. Cars were parked for three hundred yards each side of the house and a stream of people stood trying to get in the front door.

'They can't all be thinking of buying this place, surely?' demanded Mark, trying to make a space for Jo to squeeze into the sitting room.

'It's the latest hobby,' she explained, 'and it's more fun than wandering up and down Woodie's. People just turn up to see what other people's houses are like.'

It was hard to get any idea of what the house *was* like, it was so full. They left soon after arriving. Next stop was an elegant two-storey Victorian residence in Greystones which was slightly beyond Jo's budget, but she'd decided to view it anyway. Obviously fewer people were prepared to trek out to Greystones from the city to indulge in their Sunday hobby. There were only five cars parked outside the house.

'This looks more like it,' said Mark, unfolding long limbs from the driver's seat. They gazed at the grey façade, large sash windows and fantastic harbour view.

Inside, the house was beautifully decorated and perfectly kept, yet it was so austere and cold that Jo disliked it immediately. She hated the formal sitting room with the black fireplace and the ornate cornices and she liked the long, narrow kitchen even less.

'I don't know what it is,' she leaned against Mark to whisper, 'but I don't like this place. It's just so . . . cold.'

'It is, isn't it,' he agreed. 'Let's go.'

The sun was shining as they drove towards Stepaside, the

Porsche's engine growling like a big cat with a hoarse throat.

'I wish my car sounded like this,' Jo said, thinking of the strange wheezing noise the Golf had been making recently whenever it went beyond thirty miles an hour.

'How old is it?' Mark asked, as he made a right turn up a steep hill surrounded by high hedges.

'Too old,' she replied. 'I need to get a new car, but I need a new house more.'

'Actually, I did wonder why you were house-hunting,' he remarked. 'I thought you'd only bought your apartment a couple of years ago and it was new, if I recall correctly.'

'It was,' she admitted. 'It's just that the walls are so thin, I don't know how it's going to work out when I have the baby. My next-door neighbour is a little old lady who gets up at half seven and goes to bed after the news at nine, so I don't know if she's going to be too happy listening to a crying baby half the night. She's terribly sweet,' Jo added, 'but she won't be able for all-night crying, I just know it.' Jo sighed. 'Mind you, I'm not sure I'm ready for that either.'

Mark chuckled. 'Some place up the mountains is perfect then,' he said with a grin. 'You can throw rock-'n'-roll parties, let the baby cry all night and nobody can complain!'

'I'd been thinking more of having extra space for the baby and starting a herb garden,' sniffed Jo, mildly insulted.

'I'm teasing you,' Mark said gently. 'Now, where is this place? Give me the brochure.'

Fifteen minutes later, after driving down several winding roads which they were sure were dead-ends, they arrived at Redwood Lane. It was a small tree-lined country lane with very few gateways. There were no cars parked outside number two, which wasn't surprising Jo thought, when they finally saw the place. A low granite cottage with a jungle for a front garden, dirty grey paint flaking off the woodwork around the leaded windows and a roof with more slates off than on, it was not your average estate agent's dream. It wasn't anybody's dream, thought Jo, wondering why she liked it so much. Was she out of her head to even *consider* buying it?

She gingerly picked her way along a path overgrown with nettles and dandelions with Mark following.

'Did the brochure mention that this place needs a total rehaul?' he asked incredulously.

'Er, yes,' Jo replied. She knocked on the front door, ignoring the peeling grey paint.

'Come in, come in,' said a loud voice. 'I thought you'd be late because it's so hard to find.'

Jo pushed the door open and went inside.

A tiny hall opened out onto a large kitchen on the left side and a sitting room on the right. The kitchen stretched right to the back of the house. A large leaded window gave a somewhat grimy view of the countryside beyond.

'I'm Margaret Middleton,' announced the large auburn-haired lady, getting up off a slightly dusty chair to greet them.

'Jo Ryan. We talked on the phone,' Jo replied.

'Do you want me to show you the house or would you prefer to look around on your own?' inquired Mrs Middleton.

'We'll look on our own,' Jo said firmly.

'Off you go, then. But watch those stairs, they're very steep,' the estate agent warned.

The wooden staircase at the far left side of the room did look very steep and led up to what had to be some sort of loft conversion. A huge old cream range took up most of one wall. A motley selection of cupboards and a battered dresser made up the rest of the kitchen fittings.

Dark beams criss-crossed the ceiling, giving the place an old-fashioned air, and Jo could immediately picture hanging dried flowers, strings of garlic and copper pots from the beams.

Nothing in the room had seen a paintbrush for a very long time and the scent of old cooking oil permeated the air. But even drab wallpaper and dirt couldn't hide its charm.

'Isn't it gorgeous?' said Jo, delighted with the place.

'It's got character,' Mark said slowly.

She turned around to grin at him before leaving the kitchen for a look at the sitting room. It had the same dark beams and leaded windows as the kitchen.

The large granite fireplace surrounded by black slate would have dominated the room had it not been for the lurid brown and orange carpet which clashed with the pale blue walls.

'I *love* the decor,' Mark said, feigning delight. 'I think we should get the person who did this place to redo the office, don't you?'

'Could we afford them?' Jo countered. 'Getting this hasn't-been-touched-since-1972 look can be very expensive.'

She got a tissue out of her handbag and went over to the window at the back of the room. As big as the window in the kitchen, it looked out on the same view. There was a window seat so you could sit and gaze out at the same time.

Jo perched on the edge of the dusty seat and rubbed the window with the tissue until she'd made a clean patch big enough to see out. There were several sycamores and a beech tree on the edge of the back garden and a wild hedge bordering it, but there were gaps in the greenery and you could look down at the fields below.

A couple of Friesians swished their tails contentedly in the field, enjoying the last rays of the early September sun. They obviously belonged to the farm she could see about half a mile away.

'As long as it's not a pig farm, we're flying,' she said.

'Why do I get the impression that you've already made your mind up about this house, Jo?' asked Mark.

Jo looked up at him. She really liked the house and was already thinking of all the possibilities it had with the right renovations and redecoration. But she wanted him to like it too, God knows why, she thought to herself.

'Do you hate it?' she asked.

'Jo.' He put a hand on her shoulder and smiled at her, grey eyes shining with amusement. 'I think it's got great character, but it's not what I like that's important. It's going to be your house, so it's up to you. But it's going to take some work,' he warned, looking around the room. 'It'll definitely need rewiring, which isn't cheap, and there are bound to be lots of other jobs to be done as well. I doubt if it's been occupied for a long time, so who knows what's broken down or jammed since then.'

Jo looked crestfallen for a moment, then her face brightened. 'If it's such a dump, it's probably been on the market for years and I should be able to knock a few thousand off the asking price. That's it! That way I'll save enough money on actual cost to renovate it. Come on, let's see what's upstairs.'

She took Mark's hand and led him out of the room. She was on the second stair when she realised what she'd done. She was *holding his hand*! It had seemed such a natural thing to do at the time, as though they were looking at the house together, like a couple.

His hand felt warm and strong, fingers clasping hers firmly. She couldn't very well let go, now could she?

The upstairs was an attic conversion. The low sloping roof was covered in honey-coloured tongue-and-groove pine which gave both bedrooms an unusual, cosy look. A large fitted wardrobe, also made from pine, covered one wall in the big bedroom.

'Now that's what I need,' Jo said. She slid her hand awkwardly out of Mark's and opened the wardrobe.

Like everything else in the house, it was grimy inside. But it was spacious and well designed with enough shelves and hanging space to accommodate even Jo's vast wardrobe.

'The bathroom is very nice,' said Mark, who'd left Jo to investigate the rest of the upper storey. 'There's no shower, though.'

'It's lovely,' Jo said in surprise, appearing at the bathroom door. 'There was no mention of a bathroom in the advert and I'd begun to think there was an outside loo. It's a relief to find this.'

'Thankfully the artist who decorated downstairs wasn't allowed to have anything to do with the upstairs,' Mark added.

Plain white tiles, a plain white bathroom suite and cork floor tiles meant that the bathroom was by far the most subtly decorated room in the house.

'Apart from getting a shower put in, this doesn't need any work,' Jo said.

They were standing in the back garden discussing how the hell you'd clear the wilderness of weeds and thistles without a JCB, when the estate agent appeared.

'What do you think?'

Jo felt Mark jab her in the ribs. 'It has possibilities,' Jo said, trying to sound utterly unimpressed. 'But it would cost a bomb to make it habitable and the price is way too high.'

The estate agent's mouth opened. Obviously, Jo was the first person in a long time to do anything other than leave very rapidly after catching sight of the house. The fact that she was even *discussing* the house price made it a red-letter day.

'You're interested, then?' the estate agent asked hopefully.

'I don't know, darling,' Mark said, sliding an arm around Jo's shoulders. 'I know you like it but it's out of the question at that price. You'd want six grand knocked off the price before you could even consider it.'

Trying not to smile, Jo played along with him.

'I know, sweetheart.' She just hoped he wouldn't convulse with laughter at her calling him sweetheart. 'You're right. He's always right,' she deadpanned to the estate agent who now had a resigned look on her face.

'I'll tell you what, Mrs er . . .' Mark said.

'Mrs Middleton,' supplied the other woman.

'I'll phone you during the week to have a chat about the house. Come on, darling. Let's go.'

He kept his arm around Jo's shoulders and tightened his grip when he felt her shake with suppressed laughter. She finally let it out when he slammed the driver's door.

'That was priceless! I never knew you were so good at lying, Mark.'

'That wasn't lying, *darling*,' he joked, switching on the engine. 'That was business. It's playing your cards close to your chest. If we string her along for a while – assuming nobody else is interested in the place because she looked so thrilled that we were thinking about buying it – we could get a much lower price.'

'Just as well you were here, then,' Jo said, 'because I've never been able to play anything close to my chest in my life. I'd have said I loved the house and she'd have *added* a few quid to the price by the time we were finished.'

'Anyway,' she said, shifting in her seat so she was looking at Mark, 'what do you think about it?'

They were on a very narrow road and he was concentrating on the road ahead, giving Jo a chance to observe him as he drove. His profile was harsh, eyes narrowed as he stared at the winding road. He looked so serious and intense most of the time that it was such a surprise when he let his guard down to kid around with her.

He really was a very different man once you got to know him, she thought. Behind the cool business exterior lay a funny, affectionate person. It was odd to think she'd ever imagined him to be an arrogant boss who expected people to jump when he clicked his fingers.

He glanced over at her.

'Sorry, Jo. What did you say?'

'I wondered what you thought of the house. Do you think it's totally mad to even think about buying it?'

'Totally mad, I'd say. Oh, you mean the *house*.'

She swatted his arm with the rolled-up prospectus. 'Don't take advantage just because I called you sweetheart. I could call you lots of other names and they wouldn't all be as flattering, all right?' He shot her a grin.

'Yes Ma'am. Or is it Your Highness?'

'Your Highness will do fine,' she replied. 'Now, what do you think of the house?'

'First of all, you need a surveyor to go over it with a fine-tooth comb to see if there are any major problems, structural ones, subsidence or whatever. Then, we need to get a contractor to have a look and give us an estimate on what all the work will cost. Don't even think about how you'll redecorate the kitchen until you've got some idea about how much you'll have to pay to make it habitable,' he advised.

'Then, if we can knock enough money off the list price to complete the repairs, it might be worth it. But it's probably going to take a couple of months to do. Are you ready for that?'

Jo didn't even take a moment to think about it. 'Of course,' she said impulsively. 'I love the house, it has so much character, so much . . . I don't know, warmth.' She searched for the right word, for once not able to find it.

'It feels like a home, despite all the dreadful carpets and everything,' she said finally. 'I've looked at loads of places over the past three weeks and I've only seen one I liked as much. Well, only one I liked as much and could afford,' she amended.

'You've convinced me,' Mark said. 'I've got a friend who's a contractor and I'll get him to look at the house during the week, if that's OK with you?'

'Wonderful.'

'It was very nice of Mark to drive you up to see the house,' said Rhona, putting a Canderel sweetener in her coffee and stirring it thoughtfully. 'I've always told you he was a nice man and you just couldn't see it. I'm so glad you're getting to know him now, personally,' she added, emphasis on the last word.

Jo looked at her suspiciously but Rhona's face was innocent. You never knew when Rhona was teasing or not, she was such a good actress. Jo put her cup of tea down on Rhona's desk and picked up a set of colour transparencies from an underwear company.

It was Monday afternoon and she and Rhona were going over all the articles they still needed for the October edition. Friday was printing day which meant everything had to be ready by Thursday, making this the busiest week for the *Style* team.

As usual, most of the big features were in, subbed and laid out. It was the niggly little details that still had to be sorted out.

Jo still had to chase up the illustrator who was supposed to have already sent in his watercolour illustration of the restaurant reviewed in the issue. Nikki had developed bronchitis and was unlikely to be in all week, which meant that Jo had to find someone else to rewrite all the beauty product press releases for the *Top Ten Beauty Products We Love* page.

And Emma, who had begged to be allowed to interview three top Irish models for their beauty hints, had rung Annette that morning to say she couldn't make it and could someone else go because she didn't want to stand the girls up?

'I'll kill her,' raged Jo, when she heard this latest piece of news. 'How dare she do that! I don't care if her bloody leg is hanging off, she shouldn't drop her mess into our lap and expect us to deal with it. If she couldn't go, she should ring the models up herself and cancel.'

In the end, Rhona rang a freelance journalist who sometimes wrote features for the magazine and begged her to do the interviews. Crisis solved, the editor and deputy editor still had a lot of work to do, which was why they were poring over colour trannies of clothes, shoes, handbags and glamorous celebrities.

'I thought we could use this one on the *Fifty Ideas* pages,' Jo said, showing Rhona a picture of a silky cream body with a built-in push-up bra and lovely lace detail on the front. 'It's the most versatile piece of underwear, it's very flattering and it's pretty good value.'

Rhona took the transparencies and held them up to the window. 'I do like the basque and the hold-up stockings. I bet Mark would just love that . . .'

'Bitch,' said Jo, as Rhona dissolved into laughter. 'You've a one-track mind, Rho.'

'I know, "one track and it's a dirt track",' recited the editor. 'I couldn't resist it. Anyway, Jo, there's no point pretending there isn't something going on between you, even if the pair of you behave like complete strangers when you're in the office.'

'But there *isn't* anything going on,' protested Jo.

'Are you trying to tell me that all that bonding and having dinner in New York was totally platonic, because I won't believe you,' Rhona said.

'You know you fancy him, you're just too stubborn to admit it. You told me yourself how you thought something was going to happen between the two of you the first night until he got all businesslike.'

'Oh God, I don't know.' Jo took a sip of tea and looked at Rhona blankly. 'Yes, I like him, but I'm not exactly a bargain in the girlfriend department, am I?

'I'm pregnant with another man's baby, so what the hell would someone like Mark Denton want with me? He's only being kind,' said Jo in a resigned voice.

'Don't be silly, Jo,' snapped Rhona. 'You're one of my best friends and one of the nicest people I know, and Mark is interested in you, I know for a fact. He's always liked you.'

'What do you mean "always liked me"?' demanded Jo.

'Well, there never really was a right time to tell you . . .' the other woman said slowly, picking up her cigarettes and extracting one from the pack.

'Rhona, stop prevaricating and tell me!'

'Well, the first Christmas after you arrived at *Style*, Mark and I went out for lunch and he was very interested in you. He asked if you were going out with someone, that sort of thing.' Rhona lit her cigarette and took a deep drag. 'You were going out with Tim at the time, so I told him and that was it. Then, when you broke up with Tim, Mark was involved with a woman and well, the timing was just never right.' Rhona shrugged.

'Why didn't you ever tell me, Rhona?' asked Jo, completely stunned.

'I would have if Mark hadn't been the boss, but it would undoubtedly have made you feel very self-conscious to think that he fancied you. It would have been awkward.'

'That might have been better than being so openly hostile to him all the time,' Jo said ruefully, remembering all the times when she'd sparred with Mark at the weekly editorial bought from a stall in Turkey years ago.

But by next month she was going to have to buy some dressy maternity clothes or she'd be stuck with wearing jogging pants and big T-shirts until she had the baby.

Jo sat down at her desk and looked tiredly at the list of things she had to do. All her energy had vanished during the conversation with Rhona. Now Jo wondered how she was ever going to transcribe that morning's interview, *and* write it up.

For two hours she worked solidly, oblivious to the noise of phones, conversations about missing pictures and Annette's radio tuned to chart music. She had finally finished writing up her interview and was setting up a new file on the word processor to write up the *Top Ten Beauty Products We Love*, when Emma breezed into the office.

Enveloped in a cloud of CK One, wearing what looked like a very expensive cerise dress and holding a brand new briefcase, Emma dispensed smiles all round before dumping the briefcase on her desk.

'Hello all,' she said airily before turning to Annette. 'Did anyone ring for me?' she asked.

The cheek of her, thought Jo. She completely messed up an interview and she marches in like there's absolutely nothing wrong, with no apology or excuse for her behaviour. And there was she thinking that her attempts to turn Emma into a responsible member of staff over the past few months had actually worked.

She'd trusted Emma's declarations that she wanted to learn and had been so sure the younger woman had turned over a new leaf and really wanted to fit in. How wrong could you be?

'Emma,' Jo said coolly, interrupting the other woman's conversation with Annette about phone messages. 'What happened this morning?'

'Oh, that was a bit of a mix-up and I couldn't make it this morning. I thought Nikki could do it,' Emma said blithely.

'Nikki is sick, as a matter of fact,' Jo explained, determined not to lose her temper or raise her voice. 'And Rhona had to go to a lot of trouble to get someone else to do the interviews. If you were sick, or if there was some crisis and you just couldn't do something you'd arranged, I'd understand.

'But I'd expect some sort of explanation. Instead, you swan in here without either an explanation or an apology and that's just not good enough, Emma.'

'Well, it's all right now, isn't it?' Emma said dismissively. 'So don't fly into a fit. It was hardly the cover story, anyway.' She turned away from Jo and went back to her desk, leaving the deputy editor incandescent with fury.

Even Brenda, who'd heard everything, sank back in her chair nervously as though trying to avoid the inevitable storm. Annette was staring at Jo anxiously, while Tom had stopped tapping away at his keyboard and was listening expectantly. The whole office was waiting for Jo to say something, but she couldn't speak. How dare Emma behave like that?

Nobody else would be so unreliable and indifferent, but of course Emma thought she could do anything she wanted because she was the boss's niece. Finally, Jo found her voice.

'How dare you speak to me like that,' she said, her voice shaky with temper. 'I gave you a chance to make up for all the misunderstandings between us, I gave you a chance to work at being a journalist. And you have the nerve to screw up an interview – something you begged for – and now won't even apologise for it. Is that the thanks I get for trying to help you, Emma? What the hell are you doing in this office if you don't want to work? This isn't a haven for bored twenty-somethings, you know!'

'No, it's a haven for stupid pregnant women,' sneered Emma, her pretty face screwed up with spite. 'Don't think I don't know you're after my uncle. You just want to use him like you use all men. Are you trying to get a rich stepfather for your bastard?'

'Emma!' Rhona stood outside her office with her mouth open, outrage written all over her face. 'In my office now,' she barked.

For once, Emma looked worried. She was afraid of Rhona. 'Get back to work everyone,' snarled the editor. 'Are you OK, Jo?' she said, putting an arm around her friend. Jo didn't speak. If she did, she was afraid she would cry. She'd tried so hard with Emma for Mark's sake and she thought she was finally getting through to her. Then, to experience this blast of sheer, barefaced hatred was devastating.

Why did Emma hate her so much? Why did she say such a horrible thing about Jo using men? She didn't, did she? Is that what Emma would tell Mark, that Jo was after him for his money? It was all too horrible to think about.

'I think I'll go home,' she said blindly, afraid that the tears would fall.

'Stay here for five minutes,' Rhona said firmly. 'I'll deal with that little bitch and then you and I are getting out for a coffee. Don't pay any attention to what she said.'

Brenda made her coffee, Annette abandoned the switch to mutter comforting words to her and even Tom produced two miniature bottles of whiskey from his desk and poured one into her coffee.

'I can't drink that,' sniffled Jo.

'Jo,' said Annette firmly, 'I've three children and I know all there is to know about pregnancy. You have to be very careful about alcohol for the first three months but there's no harm in taking the odd glass of wine or a drink for medicinal purposes after that. And this is medicinal. So drink it, you're as white as a sheet, you poor thing.'

The spiked coffee hit Jo's system like a bullet, leaving her feeling utterly light-headed and totally exhausted. She drank it back and wondered how she'd ever get home. She felt like she wouldn't have the energy to put the car in first gear.

Rhona would probably be ages with Emma, listening to whatever cock-and-bull story the girl would come up with in her defence.

But true to her word, a mere five minutes had passed when Rhona marched out of her office followed by Emma, her face now blotched with tears. Everyone stared with hostility at the younger woman who immediately snatched up her handbag and fled to the bathroom.

'Little cow,' hissed Annette. 'Don't mind her, Jo. She can forget it if she thinks I'm ever taking messages from her boyfriend, her mother or her seven best friends ever again!'

'I doubt if she'll ask you for a while,' Rhona pointed out drily. 'Come on, Ms Ryan.'

They sat in the bar in the Berkeley Court Hotel and ate nuts from the deep bowl on the table in front of them.

'Very good for protein,' said Rhona with her mouth full.

'And very high in calories,' replied Jo mournfully, grabbing another handful.

'Well, you need an energy boost after today.' Rhona waved at a young waitress and ordered decaffeinated coffee for both of them and a brandy for herself. 'I can't believe that Tom had booze in his desk,' she added. 'When I think of all the times when I've dearly needed a drink in that bloody office and he never opened his mouth, the wretch! You do have an effect on men, my dear.'

'But not on women, it seems.'

'Emma isn't a woman. She's a nightmare in human form and don't forget it. You'll be glad to know that I savaged her for her appalling behaviour, both for being utterly unprofessional in not turning up for that interview, and for being equally unprofessional in her attack on you.'

'What did she say to that?' asked Jo.

'She whinged that you didn't like her and then I told her I didn't like her very much either, but that wasn't the point. That certainly shut her up. Anyway, pet,' Rhona patted Jo's knee, 'I finished up by telling her that I wouldn't sack her – I'd let Mark sack her after I'd talked to him about her behaviour. The pièce de résistance, I thought. You should have seen her spoiled little face when I said that. She went white and then she cried. Hhhmph.' The coffee arrived and Rhona poured a cup for Jo.

'I told her that crying might work with her uncle, but it cut no ice with me. I'm going to ring him tonight.'

Jo thought about Mark hearing two versions of the afternoon's events. No doubt Emma would be phoning him that instant, giving him chapter and verse on what a bitch Jo Ryan was, how manipulative she was and how she tried to make poor Emma's life a misery.

By the time he heard Rhona's version, he would have probably decided that Emma was right – that Jo was just a conniving, manipulative person. Why did that thought depress her so much?

She got home at half nine after having a Malaysian meal with Rhona in Kites in Ballsbridge. Satay lamb, chicken with cashew nuts and a large helping of ice cream made her sleepy but gave the baby a new lease of life.

I hope you're not going to kick all night, Jo said to her bump as she switched on the lights in the apartment. The answering machine's messages light was on and she pressed the 'play' button before closing the curtains.

Mark Denton's deep voice filled the room.

'Jo,' he said, sounding very tired. 'I'm in London and I've just got this dreadful message on the mobile-phone playback from Emma. She sounds very upset and says something awful happened in the office earlier. She says she's really sorry and she apologised to you, but you won't forgive her. And then she just cries and hangs up. Listen, Jo, I won't be home until the weekend, so can you talk to her and calm her down. I know she's difficult but she genuinely looks up to you and it's obviously killing her that you're angry with her.'

He paused. 'It's nine-fifteen and I'm going out to dinner with someone. I'll call you tomorrow . . .' It sounded as if he wanted to add something, then the machine clicked. He'd run out of tape time.

There was no other message so he hadn't rung back to finish whatever he wanted to say to her.

Damn. She thumped the machine. It wasn't its fault but she wanted to hurt something because she felt so hurt. He hadn't even given her the benefit of the doubt, he'd just believed Emma. So that was all he thought about her.

CHAPTER FIFTEEN

'I'm glad you decided to come in, Aisling,' Vivienne said, handing her a mug of very strong-looking coffee. 'You'd have regretted it if you didn't. Edward really wants to get this sorted out properly. Harassment is not something he takes lightly.'

Aisling sat down nervously and looked around Vivienne's office as if she'd never seen it before in her life. She remembered her first day at work when she'd sat in this same chair and quivered with terror. Would she be able to work the computer or how would she deal with working in an office after years away from one? It had never entered her mind that the actual job itself would be the least of her problems. That her boss would make her life hell.

How could she explain to someone as confident as Vivienne what it felt like to tremble when you heard your boss's footsteps on the stairs every morning?

Would the other woman be able to comprehend that someone would force a smile onto her face every time she entered her superior's office, as if that would stave off his psychotic flights of temper? Probably not. Aisling picked a bit of dust off her navy shirt and cursed Leo Murphy.

If he hadn't been such a pig this could have been any ordinary Monday morning at the office. Instead, she was waiting to see Edward Richardson who had heard about Friday's encounter from Vivienne. He wanted to talk to Aisling about it. All she really wanted to do was forget about the whole damn thing and wish she'd never lost her temper with Leo – or told Vivienne what had really happened, for that matter.

'It's been going on ever since I joined,' she admitted shakily to Vivienne on Friday evening when she rang to find out

304

exactly what had gone on in Aisling's office after the partners' lunch. 'I didn't know what to do, Vivienne, I've never experienced anything like that before. Nobody tells you how to deal with men like Leo and I just didn't know what to do,' she repeated miserably. 'I'm sorry.'

Vivienne was furious. 'That bastard,' she said. Aisling started to cry silently with the relief of finally telling someone from Richardson, Reid and Finucane what Leo had been like. But her relief quickly turned to terror when Vivienne pointed out that she'd have to tell Edward Richardson what had happened.

'You can't,' said Aisling frantically. 'You can't!'

'I have to tell him,' Vivienne insisted. 'It's his responsibility to make sure that none of his staff have to experience harassment. Anyway,' she added, 'this isn't the first time this has happened.'

On the other end of the phone Aisling gasped. She was stunned. She *wasn't* the first woman Leo had harassed? The *bastard*!

'When Elizabeth was on holiday, earlier this year, we had a temp in because none of us could cover for Elizabeth at the time,' said Vivienne.

'The temp only lasted two days. When she left she claimed Leo had been scaring her by making all sorts of weird comments. I honestly thought she wasn't serious, but I can see now what must have happened. Aisling,' Vivienne continued earnestly, 'you should have said something to me about him. They're very serious accusations.'

The word 'accusations' hit Aisling like a slap in the face. Accusations! She hadn't needed to spend more than a week in a solicitors' practice to see that *accusations* were not statements to be tossed around lightly.

Aisling didn't want to make accusations, she didn't want Leo to tear her apart in public for daring to say that he'd tried to touch her and harass her. He was a *lawyer*, for God's sake! He'd make mincemeat out of her. She could imagine him telling everyone how she'd thrown herself at him, a lonely meetings. How awful to think that he'd actually liked her enough to ask Rhona about her romantic entanglements while she'd been oblivious to him. Jo cringed at the thought of it all.

'You see,' commented Rhona, observing Jo's horrified face. 'Imagine what it would have been like if I'd told you before now. You'd have been mortified. I'm only telling you now, Jo, because I'm very fond of Mark, I'd love to see the two of you together and the timing is perfect. You'd be perfect for each other and, Lord knows, you deserve a decent man after Richard.'

'I don't know,' Jo muttered. 'This is so weird. I did think there was something between us when we were in New York, but then he seemed to withdraw into being the ice man again. I don't understand him . . .'

A knock on the door interrupted her.

'Rhona,' Annette stuck her head around the door. 'I've got Claire on the phone for you. I know you didn't want to be disturbed but she says it's urgent.'

'I'll take it, Annette,' Rhona replied. 'Listen,' she said to Jo in a quieter voice, 'do you really think Mark would be so eager to spend the entire day driving you around crumbling cottages in the mountains if he was just trying to be kind to a pregnant employee? No. Think about it, Jo. You deserve him.'

The phone rang and she picked it up.

'Hi, Claire, what's the problem?'

Jo silently gathered up the transparencies from Rhona's desk and manoeuvred herself out of the chair. She felt quite big, even though the girls in the office kept telling her she was in great shape for six months pregnant. The only problem was clothes. For someone who loved clothes as much as Jo, it was sheer hell to have to bypass all her gorgeous outfits in the morning and pick something from her limited collection of elastic-waisted outfits.

Today she'd worn a soft navy knitted dress which was stretchy enough to fit her, bump and all, and a long, skinny-knit cardigan in silky French blue over it. It looked great, especially worn with the matte gold pendant she'd ex-wife with nobody to cling on to at night and a desire for vengeance on mankind in general. Oh God, she could see it all now.

When Vivienne rang back two hours later to say she'd spoken to Edward and he wanted her to come and talk to him on Monday morning, Aisling panicked. It didn't matter about the other woman Leo had harassed. She'd never told her story. The first person to accuse Leo Murphy of sexual harassment would be Aisling Moran. She wasn't even three months back at work and look what had happened. What a great way to kick-start her career.

Two Valiums meant she spent Saturday in a haze, staring blankly at the TV and not answering the phone. She knew Jo had promised to ring to see how she was, but Aisling really didn't want to talk to anyone.

After all her plans to say hello to Michael and show off her new-found figure, Friday had obliterated her self-confidence. There was no way she wanted to face him now. She stayed in her room when Michael picked up the boys and stared out the window at his car as he reversed onto the road.

She managed to burn the grilled cod and roasted vegetable dish she'd made from a low-calorie recipe in a magazine. And she blindly put her red silk blouse into the machine with the boys' soccer shorts and socks, turning the entire wash bright pink.

She downed most of a bottle of wine on Saturday night watching Pat Kenny, but she still hadn't been able to sleep. Instead she lay in bed, wide awake, turning Friday's awful scene over and over in her brain and wondering whether it really was her fault after all.

It was as if there were two voices in her head – one telling her she'd messed everything up, again. The other telling her that making a wax dummy out of Leo Murphy and sticking a few pins in him would be the perfect revenge. What am I going to do? She thought at half three as she sat up in bed with the light on and a barely read magazine propped up in front of her.

The only good thing was that the Finucanes were away for the weekend, so Pat – and therefore Fiona – obviously had no idea what had happened.

Oh God, she moaned over and over again, what sort of can of worms have I opened up? Why did I ever lose my temper with Leo? Why didn't I calmly and quietly tell Vivienne what was going on and let her deal with it? Why was I such a wimp? The whole bloody thing was a nightmare.

'I wouldn't have come in if you hadn't rung me, Vivienne,' she said, clutching her coffee cup tightly. It was the one with the poppies, her favourite. 'I never wanted to see this place ever again because of him.'

The other woman pulled up a chair beside Aisling's, sat down and clasped one of Aisling's hands in her own.

'I know it took a lot of guts to come in here today, especially after all the things you told me. You've no idea how guilty I feel about never saying anything to you about Leo before . . .' Vivienne looked at Aisling apologetically.

'If I'd known he would try the same trick with you, of course I'd have said something. But I honestly thought there was something going on with Leo and the temp, and *that* was why she'd left so abruptly.' Vivienne sighed deeply.

'She was very pretty, sexy and very sure of herself. That's why I didn't really believe her. I know that sounds awful – as if you bring harassment upon yourself if you're sexy or good-looking. But I never thought he'd try it again, on someone like you,' she added earnestly.

Aisling said nothing for a moment. There were so many bobbles on her skirt she realised absently. Maybe she could try shaving them off with a disposable razor. Vivienne was still looking at her intently.

'Poor girl,' Aisling said finally. 'At least she had the sense to get away from him. I've been thinking about it all weekend, you know. I was the perfect victim – I had zero confidence and was so scared I'd make a mistake in the job that I must have seemed like a heaven-sent opportunity to pick on,' she said quietly.

'Men like him gravitate towards twenty-one-year-old temps and terrified women returning to work. They know we haven't got either the experience or the nerve to tell them where to stick it.'

The grandfather clock in the hall outside struck nine. Aisling jumped, spilling coffee onto the pale carpet.

'Oh sorry,' she said. 'I'm very jumpy today.'

'Don't be sorry,' Vivienne urged, putting an arm around Aisling's shoulder. 'You've every reason to be nervy.'

Nervy was not the word. Terrified, apprehensive and anxious might just cover the feeling in the pit of her stomach. Vivienne's phone rang and she quickly picked it up.

'Yes, Edward. She's here. I'll send her in. I'll hold all calls.'

Aisling blanched. Hold all calls. How long was Edward planning to talk to her for? God, she wished she had another Valium with her. She'd gone through the stash Fiona had given her. She knew she'd have to see her own doctor for more. She walked along the thick grey carpet on the way to Edward's office and prayed silently.

She'd never been in his office before, only peered in the door on Caroline's whistle-stop tour of the premises.

'Go on in,' said Vivienne encouragingly, holding the door open.

'Hello, Aisling,' said Edward. He rose from behind his highly polished antique desk and held out his hand. Dressed in a dark pin-striped suit with his gold-rimmed glasses on, he looked very formal and more than a little forbidding.

During her months with the company, he always smiled and asked her how she was whenever they bumped into each other, his manner more like that of an old friend than an employer.

Today, however, the old friend-of-the-family persona was gone, to be replaced by a steely-eyed look. Edward meant business.

'Sit down, Aisling,' he said.

Aisling sat with her hands tightly clasped, her jaw locked with tension. She wished she were anywhere else in the whole world but here.

'I'm very sorry to hear that there's a problem between you and Leo,' Edward began. 'Naturally, I'd hate to think that any member of the staff felt they had been sexually harassed while working here and, if that is the case, this company will do their utmost to make sure that the full letter of the law is adhered to.'

Aisling listened intently. Edward seemed to be saying that he'd do anything to help her *if* Leo *had* harassed her. But there was a big question mark over the whole matter. She felt the faint stirrings of anger inside her.

'You understand that we have to listen to Mr Murphy's side of the story,' he said.

'Of course,' said Aisling automatically.

'Tell me everything.' Edward took an elegant fountain pen off the desk and opened up a legal pad.

Have you got all day? thought Aisling grimly.

When she'd finished, Edward rang Vivienne and asked her to bring in some coffee and biscuits.

'You need it, my dear,' he advised Aisling, looking at her pale face. She felt totally drained. Talking about Leo's advances was like experiencing it all over again. She'd told Edward that she didn't want any trouble and that she'd considered not coming back to the office.

'But I need the job,' she said candidly.

Vivienne was either psychic or listening at the door, because she arrived with a tray of coffee and a plateful of biscuits within sixty seconds. Grateful to have the spotlight off herself at last, Aisling took a cup and stirred in sugar and milk. She almost didn't hear Edward asking Vivienne to summon Leo Murphy to the boss's office.

'He's coming here now?' she asked in horror.

'Calm down, Aisling,' Edward said gently. 'Nothing's going to happen. I'm here. This is a very serious matter and I'll be honest with you, it won't go away until we can clear the air.'

He leaned across the desk and looked at her earnestly. 'I know that you don't want to create any problems, Aisling, but until this is resolved, it would be awkward for both you and

Leo. With my experience of these matters, a meeting between both parties, where the problem is discussed, is the best option. I want you to understand that you are fully entitled to take legal action if you so wish. This meeting doesn't preclude that.'

Even as Edward said he understood that she didn't want any sort of legal battle with Leo, a little voice in Aisling's head was repeating the same words over and over again. 'He's done it before, it wasn't your fault.' She couldn't make the voice go away, it kept nagging her. Did she want a quiet life or justice? Did she want to let him get away with it because she was too scared to fight him?

There was a sharp knock on the door. Aisling couldn't help turning to look at it.

'Come in,' Edward said loudly.

Vivienne walked in, followed by Leo, all smiles, in one of his black suits with the usual dusting of dandruff on his shoulders. His face fell when he saw Aisling. Instead of sitting on the chair beside her, he chose one to the far right of Edward's desk. She looked away. She didn't want to see his face.

'Leo, delighted you could come,' Edward said smoothly. 'We've a problem I want to discuss. Vivienne, could you stay and take notes.'

'What's this about?' began Leo, his voice a little loud.

Edward didn't beat around the bush. 'Mrs Moran has come to me with a complaint, Leo. She says that last Friday, a few hours after the partners' lunch, you sexually harassed her, both physically and verbally.'

Aisling noticed that Edward didn't suffer from Leo's long-windedness. He was precise and to the point.

'She also says that you have been making suggestive comments to her since she started working here. I wanted this meeting to decide whether this has to go any further, Leo, to hear your side of the story.'

The other man bridled. 'This is ridiculous!' he snapped. 'Utterly ridiculous! These accusations are totally unfounded.'

Aisling moved slightly further away from him on her chair. She kept her eyes firmly trained on Edward's face, but she could hear Leo's breath quickening, the way it did when he was about to embark on a fully-fledged tantrum. She hoped Edward noticed his junior partner's mood. This was not the way to win clients and influence people.

'Leo, I think I should point out to you that Mrs Moran did not want to come in to work after last week's incident,' Edward said. 'She has told me that she doesn't want to pursue this matter further. So far,' he added pointedly.

'She merely wants the matter cleared up. In fact, had it not been for Ms Hogan, who was looking for Mrs Moran at the time of the incident, I doubt that Mrs Moran would have ever sought this meeting. What I'm saying, Leo, is that I want this sorted out with as little trouble as possible.'

Thank you, Edward, said Aisling silently. He believes me. Vivienne must have told him about the temp. She allowed herself a quick sideways glance at Leo. He was now the colour of chalk. Behind him, Vivienne glanced quickly at Aisling and gave her the faintest flicker of a grin.

It was only then that Aisling realised what Edward was doing. He was cleverly giving Leo the impression that Vivienne had witnessed everything.

Leo didn't know whether she had or not, but he daren't risk denying everything, therefore forcing Aisling to take him to court, in case he was wrong. Leo had to own up, didn't he? She felt a flicker of triumph.

'I don't know what to say,' spluttered Leo. 'I mean, this is a ludicrous situation.'

'In that way?' inquired Edward silkily. Aisling could see how he'd built up such a successful practice. Charming and urbane, Edward Richardson was, nevertheless, every inch a tough lawyer when the occasion demanded it. She wondered if she could ask him to handle her inevitable divorce?

'Well, this whole situation is ludicrous,' protested Leo. He no longer sounded so cocky. 'Everything's been blown out of all proportion.'

Edward, Aisling and Vivienne all leaned a fraction forward in their chairs. Had Leo just thrown all professional caution to the winds or was he completely rattled?

'*What* exactly has been blown out of all proportion?' asked Edward. 'If nothing happened, how can anything have been blown out of all proportion?'

'I have to admit, I got carried away and kissed Mrs Moran . . .' stammered Leo, visibly shaken.

'*Kissed* her?' asked the other man sternly. 'Kissing implies that Mrs Moran was willing, Mr Murphy, and she says she wasn't.'

'It was a clumsy attempt, I'd had too much to drink,' Leo stuttered. 'I never meant to hurt or offend her.'

Aisling could feel the tension leave her body. She never thought he'd confess. She had won. Now she wanted him hung, drawn and quartered. No, that was too easy. She wanted him alone in a room with herself, Vivienne and Fiona wielding baseball bats. Maybe too bloodthirsty.

'But I deny ever having made advances towards Mrs Moran before,' Leo added sharply. 'This was a one-off occurrence for which I am profoundly sorry. In fact, I had planned to apologise to Mrs Moran today if I upset her with my clumsy advance.'

The way Leo was telling it, Friday's incident had become a love scene between a lovestruck admirer and his shy secretary, instead of an attempted grope. Aisling had had enough.

'Your behaviour was disgraceful!' she snapped at Leo. 'You are an absolute pig who made my life a misery. You deserve to be locked up and I shall see to it that you are!' she shrieked. 'How dare you try something like that on anyone. You completely abused your position and . . .'

'Mrs Moran,' interrupted Edward firmly. 'This is not the time for an argument which would only cause further distress. If you are willing to accept Mr Murphy's apology, we can leave it at that.'

'I will accept Mr Murphy's apology when he makes it to *me*!' said Aisling angrily. 'Apologising to you isn't the same.'

'Quite right,' said Edward. 'Mr Murphy?'

Leo's face was a picture. He was still pale under his tan but he had two red spots on his cheeks.

Leo turned to face Aisling. He could barely look at her and kept his eyes trained on some spot behind her head.

'I apologise if my attentions on Friday upset you, Mrs Moran. It won't happen again.'

'Good.' She smiled at him, a satisfied smile. 'Mr Richardson,' she said. If everyone was going to be formal, she might as well too. 'I'm afraid that I would find it difficult to work with Mr Murphy again and I would like some other position within the company.'

She hoped she wasn't pushing it too far. Her contract was still only temporary and, for all she knew, they could have booted her out of the company on the grounds that they only had one position to be filled and she was rejecting it. But she didn't think that was going to happen.

It was perfectly obvious to Aisling that Edward Richardson saw Leo as the guilty party. He would do his best for her, she was sure of it.

'I understand,' he said. 'If you'd excuse me, ladies, I want a word with Mr Murphy. I'll talk to you when I'm finished, Mrs Moran. Thank you.'

'No. Thank *you*,' replied Aisling, rising to her feet.

Outside the door, she hugged Vivienne with delight.

'We did it,' she whispered.

'I'm so glad,' Vivienne whispered back. 'That bastard deserved to be brought to court, so he got off lightly. Well,' she amended, 'maybe not. Wait till you see him when Edward is finished with him. Edward is furious about the whole thing. I told him about the temp who complained and he went ballistic. He's going to give Murphy a verbal warning.'

'Really?' Aisling asked.

'Yes. Sexual harassment is an extremely serious charge nowadays, Aisling, and the firm has taken on several harassment cases over the past few years. So think how damaging it would be to the firm if news of this got out? Come into my office and wait for Edward. But don't talk about what's happened. Caroline is there. She doesn't know anything about this. It would be better to keep it that way.'

Aisling arranged her spider plant so that the spindly leaves hung over the edge of the desk. She put a small framed photo of the twins beside it, and placed the little soapstone box, in which she kept paper clips, in front of the picture. The window was right behind her, so she adjusted the position of her VDU screen until it no longer reflected the bright sunlight streaming in the window. There. She was settled.

Vivienne had certainly been busy on Monday. She'd got a brand new desk for Aisling, a right-angled one which meant she had lots of space for both her computer keyboard and her wire baskets.

The senior secretary had despatched four of the filing cabinets in her office to the file room and had made enough space for Aisling's new desk. There were three desks in the office so there wasn't a lot of room, but Aisling couldn't have cared less. She was working with two women she liked and Edward had asked her to be secretary to Anthony Green, one of the firm's new partners. She'd met him at the fateful partners' lunch and immediately liked him.

What was more, Vivienne explained, he was just married and never stopped talking about 'my wife'.

'That's a relief,' said Aisling at eight forty-five on Tuesday morning as she finished arranging her belongings on her new desk.

'There's a price to be paid when you're irresistible to men,' Vivienne pointed out. She opened a black compact and peered at the mirror as she carefully applied some lipstick. 'I was afraid I'd have to ask you to wear a chador in to work.'

'Harassment is nothing to do with sex appeal,' Aisling shuddered. 'It's a power trip for the pig in question. Anyway, I haven't exactly been fighting admirers off with a stick since Michael left, you know.'

'I'm sorry,' Vivienne said. 'I didn't mean to be flip. I was trying to be complimentary. The only reason you aren't beating men off with a stick is because you don't get out enough.'

'Where am I supposed to go?' demanded Aisling. 'Most of the people I know are couples that Michael and I both knew and they don't invite me to be the odd one out at their dinner parties. My best single friend is Jo Ryan, and she's over five months pregnant.

'After a day at work, she just goes home and conks out on the settee – unless she's house-hunting. The only other option is to go to singles' nights out and I haven't the nerve.'

'Why don't you come out with me?' asked Vivienne. 'I've a couple of girlfriends I go out with once a week and we'd love to have you with us.'

'Would they mind me tagging along?' asked Aisling.

'I wouldn't have asked you otherwise,' said Vivienne sensibly. 'We're going out for a meal on Thursday. Probably just pizza and a glass of wine, nothing expensive. You'd enjoy it.'

'OK, I will come. I'd love to.' Aisling was delighted. She hadn't been out in ages – lunch in McDonald's with the twins didn't count – and the thought of a night out *and* adult conversation was bliss. She'd ask Fiona's baby-sitter to mind the boys.

It never rained but it poured, she thought that evening once she'd got off the phone with Fiona. After fifteen minutes listening to Fiona's shocked commiserations about the Leo Murphy affair – 'That bastard, Daddy should have fired him!' – the conversation turned to the party the Finucanes were giving on Saturday night to celebrate their tenth wedding anniversary.

'It's not going to be a big party,' Fiona assured Aisling. 'Only about fifty or sixty people.' Fiona and Aisling had wildly different views about how many people constituted a *big* party.

'I'm doing Marks and Spencer's dips and cocktails, which even *I* can organise so don't feel you have to volunteer to help. All I want from you is your presence at nine o'clock in a devastatingly glamorous outfit.'

'No problem,' Aisling replied cheerily. 'Should I wear the Dior off-the-shoulder number or would the Versace sequinned miniskirt be better?'

'Come in your bikini, darling. I'm inviting all the eligible single men I know, so I want you in something noticeable.'

'Me in a bikini would be noticeable, but not necessarily in the right way, Fiona,' Aisling said, thinking of her stretch marks.

'Don't knock yourself, Aisling, but do wear something sexy. I've told them all you're a red-hot career woman who wore out her last man, so don't let me down!'

Aisling hung up laughing.

There was absolutely nothing red-hot in her wardrobe and she couldn't see herself shopping for anything that would make her stand out from the crowd.

She wasn't *that* confident about her new figure. And she didn't have either the time or the energy to trawl the shops during lunchtime. But she could always get her hair done on Saturday morning when the boys were at soccer. Maybe she'd get a few inches cut off or have it styled differently.

Wednesday was manic. Caroline was sick so Vivienne and Aisling had to divide her work between them. Another new partner started work and he didn't like his new office, wanted help working his computer and required business cards *immediately*. And then the men putting in the new alarm system managed to turn off the electricity, losing all the computer files that people were working on and hadn't saved. The air in Aisling and Vivienne's office was blue with swearing.

Yet in the middle of all the power cuts, lost files and surprised yells coming from the people stuck in the windowless file room, Aisling felt happy, almost serene.

She didn't really mind if the power went off all day, as long as she wasn't sitting in Leo Murphy's office. She sang along to the radio going into work and tapped her fingers to the music blasting out of the canteen at lunchtime. Nothing could dim the relief she felt at the thought that her ten weeks working for that bastard were over. He'd stayed out on Tuesday, 'ringing his lawyer, no doubt', muttered Vivienne.

On Wednesday he kept his office door shut, an unusual occurrence unless he had a client in.

Buoyed up by her victory over him, she no longer quivered when she heard his step on the stairs. Aisling knew he wouldn't come near her ever again.

It was after six on Wednesday by the time Aisling left the office and hurried to the car in the pouring rain, a plastic bag held over her head to keep her hair dry. Her head was aching from working at double speed to make up for lost computer time, but she was still in good humour.

The twins waltzed out of the childminder's house each carrying a balloon, a small plastic bag and a party blower along with their schoolbags.

'Hiya, Mum,' they yelled in unison, obviously in the best of spirits.

'Where did you get the balloons and the sweets?' she asked as Paul thrust his small plastic bag at her and urged her to take one.

'Lorrie's party,' replied Phillip thickly as he chewed on a toffee. 'She's ten.'

'She's Phillip's girlfriend!' shouted Paul, dodging his brother's immediate kick.

'She isn't,' howled Phillip.

'Is! Is!' screeched Paul.

'Boys! Stop!' pleaded Aisling. 'I've got a headache. I hope Mrs O'Brien hasn't been giving you fizzy drinks,' she said once they were in the back seat of the car still squabbling energetically.

'Ribena,' said Paul, dodging Phillip's well-aimed thumps. 'I hate Ribena.'

'Well *I* love it,' Phillip answered.

They kept it up all the way home, scuffling and whispering threats at each other until finally Aisling told them she'd throw them both out of the car to walk home if they didn't shut up.

317

At home, they belted up the stairs together, leaving a trail of schoolbags, anoraks and sweets in the hall. Aisling just walked past the mess.

In the kitchen, she took a dish of lasagne out of the fridge and slid it into the oven. The was dinner organised. She quickly boiled the kettle, made herself a cup of tea and carried it into the sitting room where she slid off her shoes and sank into an armchair. She deserved a rest. She smiled to herself.

The lasagne would take around forty minutes and she wasn't budging until it was cooked. The terrible twosome could kill each other upstairs if they liked, but she wasn't going to investigate.

After dinner, the boys sat at the kitchen table and Aisling refereed while they did their homework.

'Phillip must work at his handwriting,' the teacher had written at the "teacher's comments" section of his homework notebook. Looking at the childish scrawl all over his English copybook where sentences rambled with little regard for the lines on the page, Aisling could see what Miss Devine meant.

'I'm trying,' he said sweetly, leaning up against his mother.

'Are you?' she asked.

'Yes.' Phillip nodded. 'I'm very good at maths. I got ten out of ten in my test yesterday. So did Paul. But Miss Devine took a mark off him because he broke Shane's pencil.'

'Why did you do that, Paul?' asked Aisling, astonished that the quieter of the two had been involved in any sort of argument. Phillip was the truculent one, the twin most likely to fight. Left to his own devices, Paul wouldn't have hurt a fly.

He was saying nothing. Eyes focused on his open copybook, he wrote slowly, his left hand bent awkwardly as he wrote.

'Paul. Talk to me!'

'Shane said you and Dad would get divorced and never live together again, so Paul took his pencil. It wasn't Paul's fault,' Phillip said defensively.

'Is this true?' asked Aisling quietly.

Paul nodded.

She put one hand on his dark head and ruffled his hair, trying her hardest to smile even though she wanted to cry. Poor Paul. He did his best to pretend everything was all right when, deep down, he was a miserable little boy caught in the crossfire of a marriage break-up. Phillip had coped so much better. Or at least, it seemed that way.

He was eager to see his dad every Saturday and loved being driven around in *her* sports car. The time spent with their father was always jam-packed with excitement, Aisling complained to Fiona, because he brought them to McDonald's, to the cinema or bowling. 'To make up for not being there all week. He gets the fun part,' she pointed out. 'Meanwhile, I get them up in the morning, dole out the Coco Pops, get them to school, pick them up at night, feed them, help them do their homework, wash their clothes and buy the groceries. I think we should swap now and again,' she added crossly, knowing in her heart that she would have hated it if the twins lived with Michael and not with her.

Both boys came back home happy and tired after the weekend, but the previous Sunday night Paul was very subdued. Would Dad ever be coming home to live with them again? He asked, staring at her with confused dark eyes. Aisling hadn't known what to say at first. She'd simply hugged him and said that Dad loved them and would see them all the time, but that he wanted to live somewhere else.

Now, Aisling put down Phillip's homework notebook and looked at them both earnestly.

'Boys, there's no point in getting upset when people talk about your dad and I splitting up,' she said. 'It happens to lots of families and the important thing to remember is that even though Dad and I aren't getting on well, we both still love you two, OK? You know,' she added conversationally, 'you're lucky because you have *two* homes now. That's special. I bet Shane won't get two lots of Christmas presents, either. Tell him that next time he bothers you, Paul.'

'I will,' said Paul, his jaw set as firmly as his father's. It was hard to put Michael out of her mind when the kids looked so like him. Somewhat cheered up, Paul returned to his home-work and Phillip carefully tugged his notebook out from under Aisling's elbow.

'Work on your handwriting, brat,' she said, ruffling his hair affectionately.

When the boys were finally in bed, Aisling finished the ironing before mashing the potato for the following evening's shepherd's pie. It wasn't their favourite dish but she wanted something quick and easy to give them before she went out. She'd hoovered earlier in the evening and now she dusted the sitting room, cleaned the downstairs loo and put another wash on. Even though the baby-sitter was a seventeen-year-old Leaving Cert student who had more on her mind than untidy houses, Aisling's pride meant she didn't want the place looking messy the following evening.

As usual, she was halfway through bleaching the worktops before she remembered her rubber gloves lying untouched in the cupboard underneath the sink. That's why Vivienne has elegant nails and I have dry hands and flaky nails, she muttered. There was no point bothering with them now. She'd rub cream on her hands later. If she remembered.

It was half ten by the time she'd finished cleaning and polishing. Roll on tomorrow, Aisling thought, sinking into the settee with a small gin and tonic. If ever a woman deserved a night out, she did.

Thomas Read's was buzzing when Aisling ventured in, clutching the folds of her raincoat around her legs self-consciously. She was wearing a new on-the-knee black skirt which showed off lots of leg in her seven-deniers. The short skirt was a mistake, she decided passing the bus stop and getting a flash of herself tottering in her black suede stilettos. She loved short skirts but was never sure whether she had the legs for them or not. Definitely not.

As she stood, she scanned the pub anxiously. She couldn't see Vivienne anywhere. The place was jam-packed even though it was only after eight o'clock. The tables were full of well-dressed people, all looking at home in the trendy city-centre pub. Aisling felt totally out of place, as if she had a sign over her head proclaiming that she was thirty-five, separated and wasn't used to going anywhere more exciting on Thursday evenings than Quinnsworth.

She spotted Vivienne standing up and waving at her. Relief flooded through her as she wound her way through the crowd. It was *horrible* arriving on her own, trying to fit in and find people at the same time when she felt so self-conscious and out of place.

'Awful, I know,' said the dark-haired woman sitting beside Vivienne when Aisling arrived at the table and sat down, raincoat still on. 'There's nothing worse than arriving somewhere on your own.' Wow, thought Aisling, I really *must* have a sign over my head.

'Glad you made it.' Vivienne looked marvellous in a crimson velvet fitted shirt with her hair in an elegant topknot.

'Aisling, this is Maria.' She gestured at the woman who had spoken when Aisling arrived, a large brunette wearing a grape-coloured satin jacket which revealed an impressive cleavage. Maria was wearing a lot of make-up which emphasised full lips and high cheekbones and a jet pendant necklace which drew the eye directly down. 'And Annie.'

'Nice to meet you,' said Annie, pulling up a chair for Aisling. She was petite, blonde and wearing a rich brown lycra dress Aisling had already spotted in Dunnes.

'I'm afraid we've already started,' Annie said, picking up her glass of red wine. 'Maria, catch that waiter's eye, will you?'

'Hello, Aisling, welcome to our little gathering,' said Maria warmly, leaning over the table towards Aisling. 'When you walked in, you reminded me of myself four years ago just after I split up with my husband,' she confessed. 'I was terrified of going anywhere on my own after years of being part of a couple. Every time I went out, I felt so strange and out of place, being on my own and not being used to it. And now look at me!'

Several people did and Maria smiled at them, shooting smouldering looks at a handsome young man at the table beside them who was chattering in Italian to two girls.

'Maria likes to stand out from the crowd,' explained Vivienne gravely.

'It makes a change from all those times when I wanted to sit in the corner and die because I was a size eighteen and I wanted to be a ten,' said Maria, turning away from Mr Latin with a wink. She waved at a bar girl. 'Now, what's your poison, Aisling?'

'A gin and tonic, please,' said Aisling, feeling more at home in her little black skirt and silky grey wrapover blouse now that it appeared that the other women were dressed to kill.

'Enough about us. Tell us all about you. Vivienne has been filling us in on the boss with the roaming hands and I want to hear every gory detail of how you thumped him! I wouldn't like to tell you what I'd do if he tried it on me!'

Aisling burst out laughing. She'd love to see what the voluptuous Maria would do if she got her hands on Leo.

They talked so much that they were half an hour late for their table in Sinners, the Lebanese restaurant a few doors away. In between hearing about Maria's gorgeous new dentist, Aisling discovered how the three other women had met. They'd been doing a computer course five years before, had struck up a friendship during the first lunch-break and had remained friends ever since. They were all totally different – the extrovert and risqué Maria, down-to-earth Vivienne and Annie, a quiet woman with a wry sense of humour – yet they got on like a house on fire.

'This place is lovely,' said Maria as she squeezed into the pew-style seat at their table and dumped a bulging suede handbag onto the seat beside her. 'And so's the waiter, she whispered.

'Are we going to order or not?' Annie demanded ten minutes later, while Maria flirted with the waiter. 'I'm ravenous.'

'Sorry,' Maria said repentantly. 'He's so cute. It's a pity he's so young. He's just my type.'

On Vivienne's advice, Aisling ordered the house speciality,

Mezes, a selection of different types of Lebanese food.

'It *sounds* like lots of teeny-weeny dishes and you think you'll still be hungry afterwards,' said Maria, 'but wait until you see the amount you get. You'll be stuffed.'

They ate char-grilled lamb, stuffed vine leaves and beautiful deep-fried goat's cheese, and talked non-stop about what had happened to each of them over the past week.

As they chattered about everything under the sun, Aisling found herself joining in as if she'd known them all her life. Funny, down-to-earth and warm, the three women were the sort of people you could tell anything to.

She found herself talking to them about her separation from Michael in a way she'd never been able to do with her sister, Sorcha. It was a relief to talk about how scared she'd been at the thought of going back to work after so long.

'I was terrified of *you* at first, Vivienne,' Aisling admitted, now knowing the other woman well enough to actually say it.

'You poor thing,' Vivienne said apologetically. 'That was a dreadful day for me because Christine had been awake all night with a stomach bug and I hated leaving her with my mother that morning. I was a complete zombie with exhaustion. It took me five minutes to hide the dark circles with concealer. And when I met you for the first time I thought you were just some bored well-heeled housewife amusing herself with a job . . . Oh, I'm sorry, Aisling, I really am.' She leaned over and patted Aisling's arm. 'I'd always prided myself on not judging people until I knew them and I did just that with you.'

'Oh, it doesn't matter now,' Aisling said sincerely. 'Look how good you've been to me since.'

'I should have told you about bloody Leo, that's what,' Vivienne replied. 'I was thinking of how legally risky it would be to spread a rumour like that especially when I didn't really have any proof, so I said nothing and you had to deal with the consequences.'

'That's in the past, Viv. So let's forget about it.' Aisling patted the other woman's hand gently.

'You're absolutely right, Aisling,' Maria said firmly. 'We're not here to dredge up bad experiences. We're here to have fun.' She lifted her glass for a toast and the others followed suit. 'To us and to fun!'

'Cheers,' the others said in unison.

Maria was separated and had two teenage children, a fact which amazed Aisling as the other woman only looked about thirty-two or -three.

'Thirty-three and a few months,' confirmed Maria, with a cheesy smile. 'Ninety-six months, actually. It's my lifestyle, you see. Some people diet, drink lots of water and buy horrifically expensive moisturisers to stay young,' she confided to Aisling.

'Personally, I use the dairy chocolate bar method of staying young,' she continued. 'Eat lots of chocolate – yes, you do put on weight, but you're happy – only use water for making tea, coffee or hot whiskies, go out with plenty of nice men and make sure you've got two mad young girls around the house. That keeps me young.'

'Sounds like a great recipe,' Aisling said. 'How old are the girls?'

'Shelley was fifteen last month – I can't *believe* how fast she's growing up,' exclaimed Maria. 'Lynsey is seventeen. She's doing her Leaving this year and Shelley's doing her Group. The house is an exam time bomb waiting to go off. I'm afraid to have the telly up loud at night because they're studying so hard.'

'You're lucky they both want to study,' said Aisling.

'Shelley really looks up to Lynsey, she hero-worships her,' explained Maria. 'Because Lynsey got the best Group Cert results in the school, Shelley wants to do the same, which is wonderful. I'm delighted.'

Annie was in her late thirties, was married to Greg, a carpenter, and had one little girl. She told Aisling that she'd been engaged for five years to her childhood sweetheart until she was twenty-nine when she fell in love with a man she worked with. She left her fiancé to move in with Greg and had never looked back.

'I know because of your experience, you probably think it's a dreadful thing to do,' Annie said slowly, stirring sugar into her coffee.

'I was living with Ray for six years and I thought we'd get married and have kids eventually, you know, the whole nine yards. Then I met Greg and fell in love.' She paused for a moment, obviously thinking about him. Vivienne said she'd never seen a couple so incredibly in love. 'They hold hands when they walk,' Vivienne explained. 'How many couples do you know who do that after nine years together?'

'You don't choose who you fall in love with,' continued Annie. 'It was so dreadful at the time of the break-up, but I'm so glad I did it. I'm so happy now,' she added.

'Annie is proof that true love exists,' remarked Vivienne, pouring the remains of the third bottle of wine into their glasses.

'Well, you're not doing too badly in the love department yourself,' Maria pointed out.

'I don't know,' Vivienne said gloomily. 'I think Pat's getting cold feet about the whole thing. We're supposed to be going away next weekend and yesterday he phoned to say he might have to work on Saturday after all.' She took a gulp of wine. 'God, I'd love a cigarette. I always want to start smoking again when I've had a few glasses of wine.'

Vivienne was going out with a detective she'd met at a wedding ten months previously. Good-looking, kind, solvent and with a great sense of humour, he was almost too good to be true, Vivienne said. She kept waiting to discover some fatal flaw in him. Privately, Aisling thought Vivienne was probably right. What man *didn't* have a fatal flaw?

'Pat's job is hardly routine, Viv,' Annie said sensibly. 'He never knows what's going to come up or when he has to work, so you can't blame him for that.'

'And Christine loves him,' put in Maria. 'She may only be eight but she's very clever, cleverer than her mother when it comes to men!' She wagged a finger at Vivienne.

As the staff in Sinners seemed in no hurry to close the place up, the four women sat and talked until nearly one.

'Oh God, is that the time?' gasped Aisling, looking at her watch in alarm. 'The baby-sitter will go berserk. I didn't mean to be home so late.'

'You need to get out, Aisling,' Vivienne said quietly. 'Otherwise you'll go mad. Think of this evening as therapy. It's more fun and much cheaper than Prozac!'

Aisling and Maria shared a taxi home. The other woman lived in Sandymount, which was on Aisling's way home.

'You will come out with us again, won't you?' asked Maria when the taxi pulled up outside a pretty terraced house in a quiet street.

'Of course, I'd love to,' answered Aisling warmly.

After her night out with Vivienne, Annie and Maria, all of whom obviously enjoyed her company, Aisling felt more confident about going to the Finucanes' party. On Friday evening while the boys were watching TV, she tore her wardrobe apart looking for something that would live up to Fiona's description of 'red-hot'.

She found nothing. The evening clothes she'd worn for the past few years were generally size sixteen, black, navy or grey and all-encompassing to hide the tummy she hated and her fat thighs. All she found were long, A-line tunics, several sloppy jumpers and a pink silk overshirt that had always made her look like she was pregnant. Now that she fitted into a size twelve with ease, everything looked frumpy and far too big on her. There was nothing terribly sexy in the evening-clothes department apart from a black body with a low-cut neck. Worn with her new black skirt, the outfit looked nice but rather boring. She poked around in the drawer where she kept her costume jewellery, looking for something that would enliven the outfit. Nothing. She was about to strip it off in despair when the doorbell rang.

When she got downstairs, Phillip had already answered the

door and Fiona was standing in the hall.

'Looks like I came at the right time,' Fiona said gaily, waving a big Next bag.

'This is what I'm thinking of wearing tomorrow night,' Aisling said, doing a twirl in her stockinged feet. 'I can't find anything else, basically. Is it OK?'

'It's OK, but you want to look better than OK, my dear. That's why I came over. Come on upstairs. I've brought over a few gorgeous things for you to try on for the party. I knew you wouldn't buy anything new.' Fiona marched upstairs with Aisling following her.

Even though she had probably been having a mini-breakdown at home organising the house for the party, Fiona would still make time to make sure her friend was wearing something drop-dead gorgeous. She was a great friend, Aisling thought as she followed Fiona's petite jeans-clad bum up the stairs.

'I know you don't want to spend all day tomorrow buying clothes, which is a good thing as I can't come with you.' Fiona talked as she opened the bag and laid various items of clothing on Aisling's bed. 'One day we must go shopping together because I still don't trust you not to buy boring dark things because you think they make you look thinner. But until then, here are a few bits and pieces for tomorrow night. What do you think of this?'

She held up a bronze-coloured body with a wrapover front which was made of spray-on lycra and would undoubtedly reveal plenty of cleavage.

'It's very Maria,' Aisling said, holding the body up to herself and looking at the mirror. 'But it's also very small. How the hell can any of *your* clothes fit *me*?'

'It's all down to the Goddess of Lycra,' Fiona said. 'This stuff is stretchy, so it'll fit you, no problem. Is Maria one of Vivienne's friends?'

'Yes, she's a howl,' Aisling said, unzipping her skirt. 'She's a real individual, mad as a bicycle. She had us all in stitches the whole night. You'll have to meet the three of them.

327

You'll really like Vivienne and Annie as well. What do you think?'

She stepped back from Fiona and looked in the mirror. The body fitted her as if it had been made for her. It moulded her curves like a second skin and the subtle colour suited her much better than the black body she'd been wearing minutes before.

'Gorgeous. It's lovely.' Fiona eyed the outfit with her head at an angle. 'Try it with trousers or with your long black skirt. I think it'll look great with a long skirt and this gold chain belt.'

She was right. Aisling stood in front of the mirror, delighted with the slim and toned body she saw. Thank you Callanetics, she said to herself.

'Try on this,' ordered Fiona, handing Aisling a black lace top.

'This is perfect, Fiona,' protested Aisling, gesturing at what she was wearing. 'I don't need anything else.'

'Go on, Aisling. You need more than one sexy evening outfit now that you're turning into a party animal. Anyway, that top suits you much better than it suits me, so you'd be doing me a favour if you keep it . . .'

'I can't keep it,' Aisling said.

'Don't be silly. I never wear the bronze thing because I just don't have the boobs for it.' Fiona looked down at her rather flat chest ruefully. 'And you should take the black thing too. It never really suited me. Go on, take them. They're just cluttering up my wardrobe. Or rather Pat's wardrobe, since I've taken over most of his as well. I think I'll soon have to buy one of those clothes rails you see in shops.'

Aisling quickly tried on the lace top. Beautifully cut with a high neck and long sleeves, if it had been made of anything other than lace, it would have looked very plain. But because it only had a built-in bra lining the fabric under the lace around her breasts, the effect was of a very revealing and incredibly sexy outfit.

'Fiona, I cannot go out in this. You could see my bra at the back,' Aisling pointed out. 'In fact, you couldn't wear a bra with this at all.'

'That's the whole point.' Fiona sat back on the bed and gave her friend a mischievous grin.

'What do you mean? Am I supposed to break into *Patricia the Stripper* and undress when there's a lull in the conversation?'

Fiona looked cagey. 'Well, I've got a couple of nice single men coming and I *did* promise them a live strip show in the dining room . . .' She chuckled at the idea. 'No, Aisling, I just want you to live up to your potential. You're gorgeous and it's about time you realised it. There's no point hiding behind loads of clothes any more. I won't let you.'

Aisling was unbelievably touched.

'You're very good to me, Fiona. What would I do without you?'

Fiona considered this. 'Well, you wouldn't have an appointment with my hairdresser at ten tomorrow morning. I'm going in for a blow-dry and I thought it would be great if we went together.'

She looked at Aisling expectantly. 'What do you think?'

'That's a great idea,' Aisling answered. 'I didn't book anywhere because it slipped my mind today. Actually, I was thinking of getting highlights put in, just a few, nothing much,' she added hurriedly. She shouldn't have said that. Now Fiona would pester her unmercifully to get the full Marilyn peroxide look.

'Brilliant!' Fiona clapped her hands delightedly. 'I know you'll look wonderful with highlights. Watch out boys,' she said with a wicked laugh. 'The newly single and available Aisling Moran is going to hit the scene!'

'They'll think I'm really available if I wear this,' Aisling pointed out.

'All the more reason to wear it. You don't want to become a nun!'

Aisling couldn't think of a suitable answer to that.

The smell of ammonia filled Aisling's nostrils and she was glad when a cup of coffee was put before her. Taking a sip, she turned her attention to *Vogue* magazine and relaxed. It was lucky that Fiona had made an appointment for her as the salon was already buzzing and it was only a quarter past eleven.

'We're doing a wedding party with *six* bridesmaids,' explained the colourist as he painstakingly divided Aisling's hair into tiny sections, slipped tiny pieces of easi-meche paper under each section and painted different types of bleach on. 'They *all* want ringlets,' he whispered. 'It's like a Helena Bonham-Carter lookalike competition in here.'

An earnest young man wearing all black, the colourist chattered away as he worked on Aisling's hair. She was fascinated by the whole procedure. By using the meche method, he explained, he could apply different colours to her hair and this would make it look more natural than just being bleached with one colour.

She had a lot of hair and it took a solid hour to do her whole head. When he had finished, he gave her a pile of glossy magazines, asked her did she want coffee and put her under a rather strange hairdryer which looked like a three-bar fire more than anything else.

It felt wonderful to be pampered, to sit back, read magazines, drink coffee and let someone else run around like a headless chicken. She'd been up at eight, organising the boys' soccer kit which she hadn't done the night before, getting their breakfast and bringing them to soccer. She'd ended up putting her make-up on at traffic lights because she didn't want to go to the hairdresser's barefaced. Nothing accentuated lines more than the unforgiving light in a hairdressing salon.

But today wasn't like any of the other times she'd gone to the hairdresser over the last few years. Since she'd put on weight, sitting for ages in front of a mirror with nothing to do but stare at herself was painful. Not any more.

Today, the woman in the mirror was a slim, independent working woman.

She turned a page. She never bought *Vogue* so it was nice to read it for free at the hairdresser's. And it certainly gave you a glance into how the other half lived, she thought, marvelling at how a simple dress could cost over a thousand pounds, even if it was made by Gucci. For that money, it would want to be able to do the dishes, hoover the sitting room and cook the dinner.

She looked up to see how Fiona was getting on. Her neighbour was seated at the other end of the salon having her hair blow-dried into a sleek bob.

Aisling didn't know who was more pleased when she said she wanted her whole head highlighted – the hairdresser or Fiona.

'Well, how are you doing?' asked Fiona, appearing at Aisling's side suddenly.

'I'm doing marvellously,' said Aisling with a smile, holding up her coffee cup with her little finger crooked in a parody of the way her granny told her was ladylike. 'I think I should spend all Saturday mornings in the hairdresser.'

'Good, said Fiona, who *did* spend all her Saturday mornings in the hairdresser. 'You'd be great company for me. What time will you be ready?'

'About another hour, I reckon,' Aisling replied.

'I'll nip off to do some shopping then. I saw this divine little dress in Jackie Lavin's window yesterday and I'm going to try it on. Yes, I *know* I said I wasn't buying any clothes for ages, and I know Pat will murder me if he sees another shopping bag in the house. He says I'm a shopaholic,' Fiona added in a surprised tone. 'But this dress is lovely. It's silver-beaded and has a halter-neck . . . Divine. I'll be back in an hour, OK?'

You just had to laugh at Fiona, Aisling thought. If she knew anyone else who spent half her life shopping and the other half thinking about shopping, she'd think they were one of society's rich bitches. But Fiona was so kind and funny, you didn't mind the fact that she spent more on clothes in one week than many people earned in two. It must be nice to have an inheritance.

By the time Fiona returned with two large bags of shopping, Aisling was ready. The colourist was showing her the back of her head with a hand mirror and she was bursting with delight. The long lank mousy hair had gone, to be replaced by soft waves of shoulder-length glossy blonde hair which framed her face beautifully. The face was the same, Aisling thought, taking in the perfectly styled hair, but it looked totally different now.

Her skin glowed beside the soft gold and ash blonde strands of hair. Her eyes looked large and luminous now that her hair was swept back from her face.

'Aisling! Wow!' Fiona's voice was high-pitched with surprise.

'Well, what do you think?' Aisling swivelled around in her chair and grinned at her friend.

'You look amazing, absolutely amazing. You should have had this done years ago,' said Fiona. 'I'd probably walk past you on the street if I hadn't seen you here. You look so *different*.'

'I know. Isn't it wonderful?' Aisling couldn't keep the delight out of her voice. She felt transformed. She wanted to run outside and march into all the expensive shops in the Blackrock Centre. Now she looked as if she belonged in them, looked as if she was a stylish and attractive woman instead of the drudge she'd been for so long.

She shook her head slightly for the third time, enjoying the feeling of her hair rippling around her head. Aisling felt as if she'd never get tired of doing this, delighted with how light her hair felt and fascinated at the way it fell perfectly into place each time.

'Come on, we better get out of here,' she said. 'I have to pick up the twins and you have to organise the party of the year.'

Fiona grimaced. 'I love the idea of having a party until the actual day I'm having it. Then, I want to sit curled up on the couch with a dry Martini and a good book.'

'It'll be fun, Fiona, you know you'll start enjoying yourself after the first half-hour. You always do.'

The twins loved Aisling's new hairstyle.

'You look great, Mum,' Paul said.

'Yeah, it's lovely,' added Phillip.

But they weren't the ones she wanted to impress with her new look. Once they got home, she raced upstairs to look at herself in her bedroom mirror. Maybe she only looked good in the hair salon, she thought anxiously. Maybe she'd revert back to her normal, boring self as soon as she looked in the mirror at home. The woman who stood in the centre of the bedroom was totally different from the woman who'd left that morning. A deep, slow smile spread across Aisling's face. She took her lipstick out of her handbag and quickly applied some. But the colour which had looked fine with her mousey long hair looked pale and uninteresting on the blonde Aisling.

She rummaged around in the dressing-table drawer until she found what she was looking for – a rich pink lipstick she'd bought ages ago and never worn. It went perfectly with the pink short-sleeved cardigan she wore with her jeans, jeans she needed to belt at the waist.

It was after two when Phillip roared down from his bedroom, 'Dad's here, Dad's here!'

Aisling put down the knife she'd been using to peel the potatoes and quickly washed her hands. OK, Michael, get ready to meet the new, improved Aisling Moran.

She fixed a smile on her lips and opened the door slowly, her heart thumping madly. He was standing a few feet away from the front door, obviously expecting the boys to run out to the car the way they usually did. Dressed in dark grey cords and his ancient marl grey Nike T-shirt, Michael looked tired and drawn. She'd have sworn that there were more grey hairs around his temples than there had been the last time she'd seen him.

'Hello, Michael,' she said coolly. 'The boys will be down in a minute. We had a late lunch and they haven't got their stuff ready.'

Ignoring the look of astonishment in his eyes, she turned

and yelled up the stairs. 'Come on boys, get a move on.'

When she turned back to Michael, he was studying her as if they'd only just met. His gaze came back to rest on her face and the look in his eyes was one of admiration.

'You look fantastic, Aisling,' he said slowly. 'Your hair is different, it's great.'

'Thanks,' she murmured casually, as though she didn't give a damn what he thought of her. She flicked back a tendril of ash blonde hair off her face, enjoying his discomfiture. Just because you left me, doesn't mean I turned into a one-woman disaster area, she thought.

'How are things? You're coping all right with the money I'm paying into your account?' he asked awkwardly.

Despite their earlier fight about money, he'd been generous with his maintenance payments. She was doing fine financially, what with his money and her wages, but Aisling was still nervous of splashing out on anything. The thought of the first few days when she'd found damn-all money in their joint account was still too fresh in her mind.

'Fine, we're doing great.'

'Good. How's the job?'

'Fine.'

They stood in silence for a moment. Michael seemed to be searching for something to say. Under normal circumstances, Aisling, who couldn't bear awkward silences, would have said something inane just to keep the conversation going. Today she was master of the situation. She said nothing.

'What are you up to tonight?' he asked finally. 'Any plans?'

Wow, she thought triumphantly, I *must* look good. A few months ago, Aisling wouldn't have had any plans for a Saturday night and he knew it. Now, she obviously looked good enough to merit an inquiry about her social life.

'Going to a party,' she said.

'Really. Who's having the party? Anyone I know?'

'No.' She was cool and calm on the outside, but on the inside she was laughing to her heart's content. He wanted to know where she was going, who she was going with and how the hell she was looking this good. But he wouldn't say a word. He didn't want to let on that he was consumed with curiosity about the newly blonde Aisling Moran.

After a full two minutes' silence, she mentally chalked up a point to herself. I bet you're burning up with curiosity, Michael. Hah!

'You look tired,' she commented. 'Lots of late nights?' Score two to Aisling.

'You know what it's like in the *News*,' he said wearily. 'To make up for the Saturdays I take off to see the boys, I'm working on Mondays now and end up working very late on Friday.'

'Dad!' roared Phillip, appearing beside his mother with a bulging hold-all. God only knew what he'd packed. Both twins were magpies who loved collecting junk and loved having it with them at all times, something they'd inherited from Aisling. Her handbags routinely had to be repaired when the handles broke or the stitching came undone from all the bits and pieces she carried around with her.

She gave Paul a hug before doing the same to his brother.

'Be good and take care, darlings.' She stood back in the doorway, making it crystal-clear that the conversation with Michael was over. Her smile was frosty.

'Bye. See you tomorrow,' she said.

'Yeah, bye.' Michael looked at her blankly for a moment, as if he wanted to say something but decided not to. Then he turned and walked to the car. She watched for a moment, waved goodbye to the boys and shut the front door. Her euphoria vanished instantly. It had been wonderful to give Michael a shock, wonderful to see him re-evaluating her. It had been a short-lived feeling. Without the boys the house felt empty. And so did she.

There was no point staying home and moping, she told herself firmly as she grabbed her handbag, her shopping list and her car keys. Get out of the house or you'll go mad. Show off your new look.

She dawdled around the Stillorgan shopping centre for over

CATHY KELLY

an hour, browsing in the bookshop and running her hands
along rails of clothes in A-Wear.

She picked up a couple of things and tried them on, but
even the thrill of fitting comfortably into a size twelve didn't
cheer her up. She'd felt great earlier. Why had meeting
Michael for the first time in weeks plunged her into such
despair? Was it because seeing him brought all the pain back,
pain that she'd pushed to the back of her mind when she was
working or with the twins? Or was it that she missed him?
Damn Michael anyway.

In Quinnsworth, she shopped slowly, meandering between
the aisles and picking up the ingredients for the pesto
tagliatelle that Jo loved. She was coming to dinner on Sunday
and Aisling wanted it to be a special night.

On the phone a few days earlier, Jo had sounded very
miserable but couldn't talk properly because she was working
late in the office and wasn't alone. The poor thing. She was
obviously finding it hard coping with pregnancy on her own.

Aisling threw several packets of pasta into her trolley. The
boys loved spaghetti and never tired of sucking individual
strands of pasta into their mouths and seeing who could suck
fastest.

Michael loved ravioli because his Italian grandmother had
made 'the most delicious ravioli in the world'. Despite all her
culinary skills, Aisling had never been able to match his
granny's recipe. There'd been no pleasing him, had there?
Why had she even tried? Why was she thinking about him, in
fact? He was gone. There was no point crying over Michael.
He had his own life and she had to get on with hers. Tonight
was a good time to start. She'd get dressed early and go over
to help Fiona with the party preparations. Then she'd chat up
all the eligible men Fiona had promised to invite. Ciao,
Michael. Hello new life.

'So, you work with Pat. Are you a lawyer?' Gary eased himself
into the armchair beside Aisling and gave her the benefit of a
gleaming white smile. He was tall, fair and quite overweight,

336

dwarfing the armchair with his bulk.

For someone who'd only been introduced to her a minute ago, Gary was staring at her in a very familiar manner. His eyes were travelling over her body slowly and carefully as if he were a surveyor looking for dry rot.

'No,' she said loudly, to get his attention away from her chest. She loved wearing the slinky black lace top but it was very revealing and Gary was the second man to be transfixed by her boobs. What was more, he was wearing a wedding ring, although his wife had been nowhere in sight when Pat introduced him. This was her first party as a separated woman and she was very nervous about the whole thing. After twelve years married to one man, her socialising-with-men skills were, as she'd said to Fiona, nil.

'I'm a secretary at the firm,' Aisling said. 'I work for Anthony Green.'

'Really,' muttered Gary, his mind elsewhere.

'What branch of law do you specialise in?' she asked pointedly. 'Divorce?'

He sat up like a shot. 'Er, no. Conveyancing.'

God, she couldn't believe she had the misfortune to meet *another* leering conveyancing lawyer. She'd thought Leo was the only one, a freak of the legal system. She tried out a frosty stare on Gary. It had worked on Michael earlier.

Gary got the message. 'Excuse me,' he said. 'I must talk to my wife for a moment. I'll talk to you later.'

Not if I have anything to do with it, Aisling decided, abandoning her chair quickly and heading for the dining room.

It was nearly nine-thirty and most of the guests had arrived, mainly couples with a bottle of wine in hand. She'd spotted only two men arriving without female partners, one a very handsome Scandinavian type in his late thirties and the other slightly older, dark-haired and equally good-looking.

Arriving together, they'd brought champagne and a huge, feathery fern for Fiona who would, as Aisling knew, immediately kill it. The men hugged Fiona, shook hands with Pat and

CATHY KELLY

went into the dining room to get a drink. As Maria would have said, you wouldn't kick either of them out of bed for eating crisps. But the more Aisling watched them surreptitiously, the more she became convinced that they were a couple. She drained her glass of red wine and found Fiona holding court beside the bar, with four men around her.

'Typical, Finucane,' she whispered in Fiona's ears. 'The only blokes I'm interested in are gay and the only ones who are interested in me are lecherous or married!'

'The dilemma of the modern single woman,' Fiona whispered back. 'I did notice Gary move in on you. I decided not to rescue you because I knew he was *just* your type. Actually, his wife has known Pat since college which is why he's here, otherwise I wouldn't have him in the house. He's a pig.'

'You can say that again,' Aisling remarked. 'I don't think he actually looked at my *face* once during our entire conversation.'

'That's what happens when you flaunt yourself, you trollop,' Fiona said deadpan. 'Seriously, you'll love Anders and Peter. I'll introduce them to you. Anders is from Sweden, as if you couldn't tell, and they're both brilliant fun. But don't worry,' she added with a grin. 'I promise you, there are some lovely men coming later who aren't gay, married or devoted to their mothers. Now, have another drink.'

For the next hour, Aisling had a whale of a time. Fiona's clique of men friends were delighted to talk to the attractive blonde in the sexy outfit, while Aisling enjoyed a little flirtation, knowing that Fiona was there to bail her out if anything got too serious.

'If I wasn't married, I'd definitely chance my arm there,' one man said to Fiona.

'Giles, if you weren't married, you wouldn't be interested in her,' Fiona pointed out reasonably. 'You'd be running after some mysterious married woman. It's all the thrill of the forbidden, you know.'

Fiona dips, crudités and small bowls of black and green stuffed olives were going down a treat. Aisling had eaten far too much and was sitting on the corner of the settee talking to Fiona's sister-in-law, Sandra, when Fiona tapped her on the arm.

'Sorry to interrupt, Sandra, but I've got this divine man I want Aisling to meet.'

'Goody,' said Aisling getting to her feet. She felt very confident and quite tipsy thanks to five glasses of Australian red. She followed Fiona into the kitchen where a man in an open-necked denim shirt and chinos was sprawled on a kitchen chair laughing and joking with Pat. He looked up as she walked in and her first impression was that he had the same olive skin as Michael, but there the resemblance ended.

He had the most incredible bright blue eyes, a wide, mobile mouth which was curved into a grin and chestnut hair worn down to his shirt collar.

'Sam Delaney, meet Aisling Moran,' said Fiona.

Sam jumped to his feet and held out one hand.

'Delighted to meet you, Aisling. I've heard all about you and now I want to hear your side.'

Everyone laughed, especially Pat, who was well on his way to being plastered.

'Nice to meet you too,' said Aisling. She took his hand and looked down, seeing strong tanned wrists feathered with coppery hairs. Was she imagining it or had he held her hand for longer than was strictly necessary?

She looked into his face and smiled a five-glasses-of-red-wine smile.

'Are you gay, married or devoted to your mother?' she asked.

Fiona snorted into her gin sling.

'No,' breathed Sam, leaning forward so that his face was only a few inches away from hers. 'I'm available.'

'Me too,' said Aisling with a large grin.

'Sit down,' said Sam, pulling up a chair for her and positioning it close to his. Aisling sank onto the chair, put her empty glass on the table and turned to look at Sam. He was watching her, the blue eyes taking in every movement. Unlike the lecherous Gary, Sam's eyes didn't linger too long on the curves revealed by her lacy outfit. But he looked long enough to tell Aisling he was interested. Very interested.

Stone-cold sober, she knew she'd have been nervous at the thought of chatting up such a handsome man. But the combination of wine, her new image and the compliments from Fiona's male friends made her feel ready for anything. As Sam filled her glass from a full bottle of red wine, her normal inhibitions drained away. She felt attractive, flirtatious and reckless.

'How come I've never met you before, Sam?' she said, savouring the sound of his name on her tongue. Sam. What a sexy name.

'I could say the same about you,' he answered.

'Sam's been abroad for five years,' interrupted Pat from the other side of the table. 'Working in Texas.'

'Texas. Wow. That must have been interesting,' Aisling said. She put her elbow on the table and propped her head up with one hand, letting silky strands of blonde hair hang between her fingers. She'd seen Jo do it and it had looked very provocative. 'What do you do?'

'I'm in computer software. I was in Texas for four years working for one company and in Louisiana for another two years,' Sam explained.

'That's six years,' said Pat, sounding surprised. 'I thought it was five.'

'I think we better mingle with our guests,' said Fiona firmly. She dragged Pat off with her, leaving Aisling and Sam alone in the kitchen. Their eyes met and they both broke out laughing at the same time.

'I get the idea that Fiona is doing her best to fix us up with each other,' Sam said.

Aisling flushed and took a deep slug of wine.

'I know. Sorry,' she said quickly. 'I'm sure it's a real pain in the ass having women thrown at you every time you come back to Ireland for a holiday.'

'I didn't mean it like that, Aisling,' Sam said softly. She liked the way he said her name. 'I'm delighted they left us alone. I'm enjoying myself. And,' he added, picking up his glass and holding it towards hers, 'I'm not on holiday. I'm home for good.'

They clinked glasses companionably.

'Tell me about Texas,' Aisling said. 'I've never even been to America and Texas sounds so exotic, so *Dallas*!'

'It's not really like *Dallas*,' said Sam with a chuckle. 'It used to be, or so they tell me. Houston, where I worked, is a very cosmopolitan city, all mirror-windowed skyscrapers and Cadillacs. But the oil boom was over in the early Eighties and the whole city suffered. So there aren't as many millionaires as there used to be. None like J. R., anyway.'

'Damn,' said Aisling. 'You mean there isn't a Cattle Baron's Ball after all?'

'There probably is. There are certainly enough people wearing Stetsons and cowboy boots, but you don't see many suede fringed jackets. It's too hot.'

'Really?' she asked.

'Oh, it's unbelievable. In the summer, you can't drive with your windows open. You just keep the air-conditioning on the whole time,' Sam said. 'Putting your arm out the window of the car when you're on the freeway is like being hit with a blast from a hot-air dryer.'

'Have some dips,' announced Fiona as she swept into the kitchen with a tray of empty glasses. She took a bowl of taramasalata and a large plate of cut vegetables out of the fridge and left them in front of Sam. 'Are you having fun?' she whispered into Aisling's ear.

Sam's mouth curved into a knowing grin as he looked Aisling in the eye.

'Loads of fun,' she replied, never taking her eyes off his face.

'Maybe we should just have sex on the table and then they'd all be happy,' suggested Sam with a glint in his eye when Fiona left with a tray of dips for the rest of the guests.

'I don't know,' replied Aisling, as though she were thinking

341

seriously about the idea. 'Maybe we should know a little about each other before that, what do you think? Sex on the first date is one thing, but I always find that sex within the first ten minutes is pushing it!' He laughed uproariously. Aisling couldn't believe she'd just said that.

What the hell, she didn't have to play Michael Moran's quiet little wifey any more.

They scraped the bowl clean as they sat at Fiona's spotless kitchen table and talked. Aisling found out that Sam was originally from Cork where his parents still had a small dairy farm near Clonakilty. He'd lived in Dublin for seven years before moving to Texas.

'The money was incredible,' he explained, 'even if the change of climate nearly killed me. I thought I'd feel at home somewhere like Texas because I had this idea that it was a rural sort of place, like home. Unfortunately, in Houston, the nearest you got to cows was in a steak house. For the first six months, I didn't see much apart from the office.'

'But you must have seen lots after that,' Aisling said.

'Yeah, I did. I loved Galveston, that was my favourite place. It's this old Victorian town on the Gulf Coast, all pretty wooden houses and ornate Victorian mansions. And miles and miles of sand covered with this sea grass you can't pick because it's the only thing holding the sand together and keeping the ocean out!'

'It must be wonderful to have travelled so much.' Aisling picked up the last bit of carrot off the plate.

'It was.' Sam sat back in his chair, his mind suddenly elsewhere. On whoever he left behind, Aisling thought to herself. Why else would a successful man leave the States to come home? He must have been married. He had to be forty or near it and he was charming, funny and good-looking. No way a man like Sam would have remained single for long.

God, how did I ever think I was the only person in the world to have their marriage break up? she wondered. That was just my self-obsession and self-pity.

It's happening all the time. Is there anyone out there who

doesn't carry the remains of their past around with them, memories of happier times, different times?

'You look like you're lost in time,' she said softly.

He smiled apologetically. 'Sorry. You're right. I was a bit.'

'You know, if I'd met you six years ago, we wouldn't be having this conversation in the kitchen,' she said. 'I'd have been in there with my husband and I'd never have flirted with you.'

'I know. Fiona told me you were separated. He must be mad.'

'So must she.'

He grimaced and drained his wine glass. 'That obvious, huh?'

Aisling pretended to consider it. 'Maybe not to most people, but let's just say, I'm sensitive to that sort of thing now. I find myself looking at people in the supermarket, staring at their ring fingers and working out if they're married, separated, whatever. It's my little game.'

'You still wear your wedding ring,' Sam said, almost accusingly.

She looked down at her left hand, at the sapphire surrounded by tiny diamonds and the slim wedding band she still wore. She was so used to wearing them that she couldn't imagine taking them off. But why, she thought? Michael was gone. He was living with somebody else and he wasn't coming back. So why was she still wearing his rings?

For a moment, she was back in McDowell's on the day he'd bought her engagement ring. Thirteen years ago.

'The sapphire ring suits you best,' Michael said, leaning on the glass-fronted case with her fingers held tenderly in his hand.

'I like the diamond solitaire,' she answered. 'I've always dreamed of having a diamond ring.'

'The sapphire one has little diamonds around it,' Michael pointed out, sensible as ever. In the end, he'd won. He bought her the sapphire ring and promised her a ring with a solitaire – sometime. He'd never bought it.

Aisling looked at Sam and shrugged. 'You're right,' she said, looking into his eyes, wondering how anyone could have eyes so blue. 'I don't know why I still wear them.'

She straightened out her fingers and slid the rings off. With all the weight she'd lost, they came off easily. She left them on the table beside her wine glass. Twelve years of marriage down the Swannee.

'We'll have to celebrate,' Sam said gently, moving his chair right beside hers. He put one hand around her neck and pulled her face closer to his, so close that she could feel his breath on her skin. Then his lips met hers, softly touching hers.

For a moment, Aisling panicked. This was happening so fast. Then she felt Sam's arms reach around her waist, gently holding her to him. She relaxed and let herself go, feeling her mouth open under his. He tasted sweet and faintly bitter, the wine on his breath mingling with something else. Her skin felt warm where he was holding her.

Nobody had held her like this for so long. She'd spent so many nights alone in the big bed, only Flossie or her books for company. Now, she was in a man's arms, a man who wanted her.

Suddenly, she wanted to go to bed with him. Now. This instant. Shocked, she wondered if she'd lost her mind, but no. She hadn't. She simply wanted him, hungered for him, as she used to hunger for jam doughnuts or ice cream. She didn't care if she never saw another doughnut ever again, all she wanted was Sam.

'Aisling,' he murmured into her hair, his lips brushing against her neck and her ear. 'I shouldn't have done that, but I couldn't help myself.'

She arched her neck back, leaving her skin exposed for him. He was a quick learner. 'I'm glad you did,' she said softly, as he moved along her neck to the soft hollow at the base of her throat.

'Oh!'

Aisling would have recognised Fiona's voice anywhere. She

344

made a sort of strangulated squeak and turned on her heel.

Aisling and Sam started laughing at exactly the same moment. She clutched Sam's head against her neck and roared.

'We've been caught,' she said between laughs.

'I feel like I'm fifteen again and my mother has just caught me groping my girlfriend in the dairy.' Sam could barely talk he was laughing so much. 'I don't think I enjoyed that so much.'

He moved up until they were face to face. He held her face cradled in his hands and kissed her again, gently on the lips.

'I never thought I'd be found snogging in the kitchen at a party at my age, but that was wonderful,' he said. 'I hope you don't regret this tomorrow, Aisling. I'd like to see you again.'

'I'd love that.' It was true. But Fiona's interruption had brought her to her senses.

A flirtation and a kiss in the kitchen was one thing. Going off with a man she'd just met for wild passionate sex was another.

It would be wild and passionate sex, she knew that for sure. The way he kissed sent ripples of excitement down her spine.

Aisling gently stroked Sam's cheek and smiled at him.

'I better go. It's late.'

It was nearly twelve and the baby-sitter said she didn't want to stay the night. Aisling got up from her chair. Sam jumped up instantly.

'Will you let me walk you home?'

'Of course. But I don't want the neighbours to think I'm a scarlet woman, so we better be discreet,' Aisling said quickly. She had a sudden vision of all the guests from the party craning their heads out of Fiona's upstairs windows for a better view of Sam kissing her passionately at her hall door. Or worse, the boys seeing her kissing Sam passionately.

'Damn, you've ruined my whole plan.' Sam put his arms around her waist and grinned. He wasn't as tall as Michael, she thought suddenly. Stop it, Aisling, she said silently. She didn't want to think of Michael. She kissed Sam again. He tasted just as good this time round.

'I'll just get my handbag,' she said. She hurried up to Fiona's spare room where she'd left her things.

Fiona caught her rushing down the stairs.

'Are you going?' Fiona was doing her best to conceal a smirk but she couldn't quite manage it. 'Both of you?' she asked meaningfully.

'Sam is walking me home,' Aisling said. 'Walking. That's all. So don't focus the telescope on my house!'

'I'm so pleased you like him, he's a dear man.' Fiona gave her a big hug. 'Phone me tomorrow and tell me *everything*, right?'

'I promise.'

CHAPTER SIXTEEN

Jo sat on a stool in the small dressing room and watched Frederick paint one last coat of ruby-red lipstick on the model's perfect mouth. The girl sat perfectly still in the chair. Dark arched brows framed pale blue eyes edged by expertly applied eyeliner, giving her an exotic, faintly Egyptian look.

'We want vampish make-up, dark, smoky eyes and dark lips,' Jo had explained to Frederick on the phone the previous week. 'I'm calling it the Christmas Glamour Look and I've got three long dark evening dresses, one black velvet tuxedo and a sequinned minidress for the shoot. The make-up has to be dramatic.'

Frederick was doing his best to be very dramatic, although the heavy make-up required for the camera looked out of place in a draughty photographic studio on a cool Monday morning in September.

Exhausted after a restless night, Jo didn't feel up to organising the shoot for the December issue. It was two months to the Christmas production day, but that edition traditionally carried lots of fashion pages and Jo knew that Ralph, the photographer *Style* used, had a catalogue shoot lined up for half of October and was going on holiday to Jamaica in November. That left September for everything – the skiing clothes shoot, the knitwear shoot, the working woman's suit shoot and the lingerie-to-get-your-man-to-buy-you-for-Christmas shoot.

She had to organise all those over the next two weeks, which would mean lots of dashing around the shops searching for the right accessories and perfect shoes. At least she'd got absolutely everything she needed today.

Several elegant dresses hung from the rail in the small

dressing room, ready for the two models to transform themselves into glamour queens. Boxes containing high-heeled suede and satin sandals were lined up on the floor, while packets of tights lay on the cupboard top alongside the simple silver earrings Jo had picked for the shoot.

Frederick's huge bag of tricks were spread out on the counter top, palettes of every colour under the sun, eye pencils, brushes, jars of foundation and cotton buds jostling for space beside the hairdresser's heated rollers, cans of hairspray, pins and brushes.

Outside the door, Ralph yelled instructions around the large, high-ceilinged studio. It was nearly eleven on Monday morning and they had to be finished by half two because Ralph was photographing a group for a business magazine at three. It didn't leave them much time for the *Style* shoot and as the other model was late, they were definitely in trouble.

The photographer's favourite Eric Clapton CD was belting out of the sound system and Jo could feel the stirrings of a thumping headache. This was shaping up to be a disastrous day. It had been a pretty bad weekend, as she'd waited for Mark to ring so she could explain exactly what had happened at the office.

She'd gone over it in her head many times, telling him how she'd really tried to get on well with Emma. How she'd worked with the younger woman to make her part of the *Style* team. How Emma had thrown it all back in her face in a fit of spite. But Mark hadn't phoned.

By Sunday night, Jo had convinced herself that he'd heard Emma's side of the story and had made up his mind not to ring her at all. She felt utterly miserable. The only bright spark on the horizon was the thought of her cottage, which Mark's contractor friend had told her was structurally sound even though it needed some work.

'Finished,' announced Frederick. He stood back and admired his handiwork. The model, Carol, unfurled her long, impossibly slender body, stood up and reached into her denim shirt pocket for her cigarettes.

'Don't worry, I'll smoke outside,' she said, patting Jo on the shoulder. The model pulled on a tatty leather bomber jacket over her jeans, careful not to dislodge the heated rollers in her dark hair and left the room, lighting up as she went.

'We're nearly ready,' shouted Ralph from the studio. 'Where the hell is Stephanie?'

'Here,' came another voice, as a tall blonde girl dressed in grey sweatpants and parka hurried into the dressing room, hair flying. 'Sorry I'm late,' she said to Jo. 'I got stuck in traffic.'

'Steph, your hair!' shrieked Alan, the hairdresser, pushing into the dressing room with a tray and four mugs of tea. Stephanie's high-cheekboned face was stunning even devoid of make-up, but her hair was definitely greasy at the roots. 'I won't have time to wash it now. It'll have to be sleeked-back hair,' Alan muttered to Jo.

'Fine.' Jo was tired, cross and ready to belt Steph's beautiful head. She didn't care what Alan did to the model's bloody hair. Damn Mark. Damn, damn, damn.

Thirty-five minutes later, Steph and Carol reclined gracefully on a leopardskin chaise-longue, looking as if they had been born in floor-length satin. With their hair beautifully styled, flawless make-up on their faces and perfect size-ten bodies encased in sleek designer clothes, they appeared a million miles away from the two casually dressed young women who'd rushed into the studio earlier.

Jo had been involved in the fashion business for years, yet she never ceased to be amazed at how a team of experts, with the right tools and lighting, could turn a pretty woman into a spectacular one.

Nobody looking at the finished photos would ever be able to tell that Carol had a spot on her chin and dark circles under her eyes or that Stephanie's hair had been slicked back into a knot because the hairdresser hadn't the time to wash it.

'Turn your head a little to the left, Carol,' ordered Ralph, squinting at the models through his viewfinder. 'A little more, that's good. Alan, fix her hair, there's a bit sticking out.'

Jo tried to relax while Ralph was shooting. She sat down in the leather armchair he often used as a prop, put her feet up on the arms and poked around in a pot of strawberry yogurt with a little plastic spoon. Frederick was up and down from his seat like a jack-in-the-box, powdering away the shiny faces brought on by strong lights.

'We'll never be out in time,' Frederick grumbled, sinking back into his chair after the tenth powdering break. 'I'll kill Stephanie if we aren't. I'm due somewhere at half three.'

'And I'm due in four months if I don't have a nervous breakdown first,' Jo answered glumly.

'It's not that bad, pet, is it?' asked Frederick in concern. 'You look wonderful and I thought everything was going so well. It's not Richard, is it? That pig, I don't know why you stuck with him for so long, he wasn't worth it.'

Ralph bellowed and Frederick leaped up with his powder puff at the ready.

Richard? thought Jo. She couldn't give a damn about Richard. He'd dumped another pregnant girlfriend before her and she'd lost every ounce of respect or love for him. He'd only phoned once in the past few months – a faltering message left on her answering machine.

'It's me, er . . . Richard. You're not here and I'll,' he paused, 'ring you some other time. Hope you're all right,' he added awkwardly.

Hope you're all right? Snarled Jo when she got home. What sort of a greeting was that to the mother of your child? she wanted to know. His lack of interest only hardened her heart even more against him.

When she went to the hospital on her own for her check-ups and sat, tears flowing down her face as she looked at the ultrasound picture of the baby, Jo felt immeasurably sad that she had no one to share the experience with. But she never regretted the fact that Richard wasn't with her. She couldn't imagine anyone worse as a father or would-be father. She and the baby were better without him. Now, when she thought about him at all, it was with a mixture of irritation and disgust. Irritation at his childishness and immaturity, and disgust that she'd been so stupid not to see through his lies and recognise him for the coward he truly was.

'Do you want another cup of tea?' Frederick asked kindly, perching on the edge of the armchair. Seeing Jo's look of misery, he took her hand. 'He's not worth it, pet,' he said, misinterpreting her sad face.

'Forget Richard, for your own sake. I didn't mean to tell you this,' he hesitated, 'but you better know.'

Jo sat up straighter. What news of Richard did Frederick have?

'I've seen him out with that Freeman girl, the tarty one with the little red Mazda and the vacuum in her skull,' Frederick continued.

Jo knew exactly who he was talking about. Rachel Freeman, a twentysomething model who'd materialised beside Richard at several parties, smiling at him coyly and completely ignoring the fact that Jo was holding his hand.

'She's just a kid,' he'd said to Jo, adding that he preferred mature, beautiful women to silly youngsters. His words had rung true at the time and she had believed him, foolishly, as it now turned out.

Had Richard been having a fling with the gormless Rachel all along? Had the last laugh been at *her* expense? Probably. She felt inexplicably tired all of a sudden.

'She was practically glued to him at the hip, all kissy-kissy and holding hands,' Frederick divulged, outrage popping out of him. 'You'd think they were Siamese twins. So just forget him, Jo. He doesn't deserve you.'

'Anyway,' he continued, with a smirk, 'I happen to know that one captain of industry is very smitten with you, so you won't be on your own for very long!'

Jo tried to smile but she couldn't manage it. If only you knew, Frederick, she thought. With my record for choosing men, I should start writing to a death row prisoner in America so I can fall in love with him.

'Phone,' yelled Ralph's assistant from the studio's darkroom. 'Call for Jo Ryan.'

'The Louisiana Penitentiary, no doubt, with a list of fanci-able prisoners,' she muttered, hoisting herself out of the seat.

'Jo,' said Rhona, sounding relieved. 'I thought nobody would ever answer the bloody phone.'

'That's because Ralph is attempting to blow all our ear-drums as well as his own with ten billion classic rock tracks. It's a miracle anybody answered at all. What's up?' she added, leaning against a counter top covered with contact sheets of tiny photos.

'Mark was looking for you,' replied Rhona in a softer voice. 'I can't really talk too loudly because my office door isn't shut, but he arrived this morning looking like a thunder-cloud.'

'So?'

'So, he'd got back late on Sunday and must have got an earful from dear sister Denise about her poor little Emmy Wemmy having a spot of bother at work.'

'Surprise, surprise,' said Jo sarcastically. 'Has he advertised my job yet?'

'No,' hissed Rhona, 'listen. He demanded a meeting with me and wanted to know everything that had gone on last week. I told him everything up straight and I said that it was virtually impossible to see how Emma had a future with the magazine since she's so incredibly hostile and unprofessional to my staff, *especially* my deputy editor.'

'Thank you, Rhona,' said Jo, suddenly tearful. The way she felt right now, she'd blub at the slightest hint of sympathy.

'Well, it's true,' stated Rhona. 'You're a fantastic deputy, a great fashion editor and a real pro. Not to mention a great friend. But our friendship isn't the point. The point is my editorial control – or the lack of it – when it comes to staff,' she added. 'I wanted Mark to know that we wouldn't take that kind of crap from any other junior and Emma has been trading on that fact. And I said that her personal attack on you was vitriolic in the extreme.'

'What did he say to that?' asked Jo quietly.

'He didn't say anything, actually, but the look on his face

was enough. I'd bet next month's salary on darling Emma getting an earful.'

'Well, what was the outcome? What did he say at the end?' Jo desperately wanted to know what Mark thought of her, whether he believed Emma's side of the story or Rhona's.

'He said he wanted a meeting with me at four and that he wanted to talk to you first.'

'Huh. To tell me poor Emma is his flesh and blood and that I can take a hike.' Jo knew she sounded bitter. 'I better go. We've still got three more outfits to go. We'll be lucky to be finished by half two.'

'Are you coming back to the office?' Rhona asked.

'I don't know,' Jo said sharply. 'I've got to get groceries and I have to buy some trousers because nothing fits me very well right now, so I probably won't come in today.' Or tomorrow. She didn't want to come in all week if it meant she could avoid Mark.

'Mark wanted to phone you after we talked, but I knew you were upset and I said I'd try and track you down,' Rhona explained. 'I didn't want you to fly off the handle with him. You should come in to the office after the shoot. He'll be here.'

'I might. Thanks for standing up for me, Rho,' Jo said. 'Bye.'

'Jo, don't go yet. You sound upset.'

Damnit, where had she hidden those bloody tissues? Jo looked wildly around the office, searching for a tissue in the midst of bits of paper, contact sheets, negatives and newspapers.

'I'm sorry, Rhona,' she muttered, wiping her eyes on the sleeve of her sweater. 'I have to go. Really.'

It was three by the time Jo finally left the studio, with Frederick walking beside her, arms full of plastic-wrapped dresses. He was bringing them back to the safety of the office because Jo had decided to go shopping and didn't want to leave hundreds of pounds' worth of borrowed clothes in the car at the supermarket.

'Brenda knows what has to go where,' she said, as she put two shoe boxes into Frederick's car. He stowed the dresses carefully on the back seat. 'I'm sorry to leave you with all this, I know you're in a rush.'

'Don't worry. I don't mind being a little bit late and you look as if you need a bit of time to yourself. Take care.' He reached out and threw his arms around Jo, giving her a warm hug. 'Listen to Uncle Frederick, go home and go to bed. Or read a trashy novel and eats lots of ice cream.'

Jo sniffed. 'I will. Thanks for being so good, Frederick.'

Mothercare was jammed. It took several trying-on sessions to find a pair of trousers she liked. She'd been hoping she wouldn't have to buy too many maternity clothes but it seemed that trousers were one thing you couldn't economise on.

She bought one black and one grey pair of trousers and three pairs of maternity tights. Worn with overshirts or jumpers, they ought to see her through the next few months.

Her answering machine's message light was winking at her when she got home. Had Mark phoned her? Rhona had left two messages asking her to ring the office. 'Mark wants to talk to you,' Rhona said the first time. Then, 'Please ring. He's driving me mad.'

'Let him phone, then,' said Jo crossly. Had his dialling finger seized up suddenly? Or wasn't he able to make a simple phone call unless his secretary did it for him? She unpacked the shopping and sank down onto the settee with the TV remote control.

When the phone finally rang at half seven, she was in the bath, relaxing in a cocoon of aromatherapy bubbles with a face mask on. Even if she'd wanted to answer it, she wouldn't have got out of the bath in time.

She sank back into the bubbles feeling cross.

She sat in the bath for another two minutes, then, consumed with curiosity to see who'd phoned, she got out and headed for the answering machine, wrapped up in a towel, rivulets of water dripping onto the carpet.

354

Mark's voice was formal. 'I'm going to a charity dinner in the Shelbourne at eight so call me back on the mobile before then.'

The barefaced cheek of him! Hell would freeze over before she'd bother phoning him. She pressed the delete button with venom and stormed back into the bathroom to remove the face mask.

After another restless night, Jo rang the office first thing.

'Annette, tell Rhona I'm not feeling well and I won't be in today,' she told the receptionist.

'Oh you poor dear, what's wrong?' asked Annette anxiously.

Hating herself for lying, Jo muttered that she was feeling very tired. 'I think I'll spend the day in bed,' she added. 'Tell Rhona not to bother ringing me unless it's urgent and then I'll have the answering machine on. I need some sleep.'

'Don't worry, Jo. I won't let anyone disturb you on pain of death.'

Does that apply to the boss? Jo wondered. Could she add 'pain and torture' to the prescription?

She spent a boring morning sorting out her wardrobe, Gareth O'Callaghan's mellifluous tones in the background. She tried on lots of things to see if they could accommodate her swelling belly, and was dismayed to see how few things actually did. I'll probably never get into any of this stuff again, she realised miserably, as she looked at all the beautiful slim-fitting outfits she couldn't even button up.

She loved that grey wool pinstripe. It would be awful not to be able to wear that ever again. And the black leather miniskirt. She'd bought it with one of her first freelance cheques and worn it almost to death for a year. It was in pretty good condition considering. She'd hate not to fit into it again.

Nibbling a Ryvita to keep the Hobnob pangs at bay, she stashed everything she couldn't wear in the left side of her wardrobe and arranged the rest on the right. The few items hanging in the wearable side of the wardrobe made her even more depressed.

The phone rang twice but the caller hung up abruptly when the answering machine answered. It must be her mother, Jo thought, she hated answering machines. When the doorbell rang loudly half an hour after the last hang-up, Jo peered out of her peephole. It was Mark.

Blast. She leaned up against the door, wondering whether he'd heard her stomping into the hall. He rang the bell again. Obviously he had.

She stood silently, hoping he'd go away. No such luck.

'Jo, it's Mark.'

Double blast.

'I was worried when you rang in sick today. Can I come in?'

She toyed with a whole range of answers. 'No.' 'No, you pig.' 'Not until Hell freezes over.'

'Jo. Please let me in. I know you're there.'

She wrenched the door open. 'Yes?' she said icily.

'Can I come in?' he asked, grey eyes serious as they stared down at her brown ones.

'Why do you want to come in? Can't you sack me in the office like normal despots? Or do you like the personal touch?'

'For God's sake, Jo,' he muttered, running a hand through his hair. 'Let me in, won't you?'

'Five minutes,' she announced. She stood back to let him enter. He walked in, looking strangely out of place in his navy pinstripe suit, blue shirt and yellow tie. His hair was rumpled and so was his face.

'You've got five minutes,' repeated Jo. 'I'm updating my CV, you understand, and I don't have any time to waste.'

Refusing to rise to the bait, Mark walked into the small sitting room and stared around for a moment before sitting down on the settee. He stretched long legs ahead of him and looked up at her. 'Sit down, Jo.'

'This is my house, smart ass,' she hissed. '*Don't* tell me when to sit down.'

'Sorry, sorry.'

She sat. The sheer *nerve* of him. Marching into her house and taking over.

'So?' Jo arranged her cotton jumper over her blue jogging pants to hide the ink stain on the front. She was angry and she hated being caught out wearing a dreadful outfit. And this – ancient white hand-knitted jumper with threads hanging out and threadbare jogging pants with no socks – was pretty dreadful. The carpet could have done with a good vacuum into the bargain and the weeping fig had wept a new batch of dead leaves onto the fireplace . . .

'I've come to apologise.'

Jo blinked.

'I should have rung you but I was in the car, I'd left your number in the office and,' Mark paused and tried to look her in the eye, but she avoided his gaze, 'I didn't think it was that important. At the time.'

'It wasn't important at all,' she replied coldly. 'Just your average day in the office when nepotism runs amok. There's nothing to apologise for.' Jo knew she was pushing it but she didn't care. For once she felt gloriously like flinging caution to the wind.

'I just can't work under those circumstances, that's all. I've worked in journalism for thirteen years and I've never been treated with the sort of disrespect Emma showed me. What's more,' she was beginning to enjoy this, 'I've certainly never treated anyone else that badly, either. It just isn't in my nature and it certainly isn't the way to win friends and influence people, or get the best out of them. But your niece is a law unto herself and quite frankly, I won't work with her any more.' She snorted. 'Anyway, you've made it quite plain what way your allegiance lies.'

'What way is that?' he asked calmly.

'*What way is that?*' she mimicked.

'Do you honestly want me to answer that?' Mark looked tired.

'No.' Jo was really angry now. 'I don't. You've already answered it by your silence. When I thought you'd want to talk to me to find out what had happened, you simply didn't bother ringing. When I thought you and I had a friendship, a . . .'

'A what?' he prompted.

She'd been on the verge of saying 'a relationship', and he knew it. Damn him, but he wasn't getting her to play his bloody games. She didn't want to be his amusement for the evening.

'A *nothing*,' she said angrily. 'We have nothing, I can see that now. And I can see I can't work for you any more.'

'Don't be rash,' snapped Mark.

'Don't tell me what not to be!' she shrieked. 'You're just like all bloody men, telling me what not to be. Just get out! Get out of here and stick your bloody job where the sun doesn't fucking shine!'

He stood up slowly and sighed. 'Jo, I'm sorry. I came here to apologise, I wanted to explain what had happened.'

'I don't want your apologies,' she said, feeling her eyes smart. God, she didn't want to cry in front of him. What sort of whinging idiot had she turned into, always crying at the drop of a hat? 'Just go.'

'Please, Jo. Listen to me.'

'Just go.'

He said nothing, but he didn't move either.

Jo poked around in her sleeve looking for a tissue. Why wasn't he going? Was she going to have to throw him out?

'Jo, just let me say one thing, all right?' His eyes were alight with something she couldn't identify. It was probably amusement, she thought, since it felt as if the rest of the world's male population were laughing at her for her naïvety and sheer stupidity. Jo Ryan falls for another man's lies, *again*. Ha bloody ha.

'I'm sorry I didn't ring you over the weekend, but believe me, I didn't take Emma's explanation at face value,' Mark said in a low voice. 'And I'm sorry if I sounded angry with you when I rang you from London about it, but it had been a very bad day. Emma's latest crisis was all I needed and I thought you'd be able to handle her until I got back.' He leaned against the back of an armchair tiredly and folded his arms. 'I trust your judgement, Jo, that's why I wanted you to sort things out. Please believe me.'

Jo stared at him fiercely, determined not to be swayed by any trumped-up explanation.

'The problem was that I had no idea what Emma had actually said and done until Rhona told me and since I've heard, I've been trying to get hold of you to apologise for her behaviour. Please understand,' he said, looking at her intently. 'I wouldn't hurt you for the world.'

He stood up and fished his car keys out of his trouser pocket. 'I'm going to go now because I've upset you. And let's just forget about where I can stick the deputy editorship.'

Jo flushed.

'Take as much time off as you need, Jo. Bye.'

He went, leaving behind him a scent of cologne, the same one she'd smelled when they sat together on the plane, when they'd gone out to dinner, when he'd brought her looking at the house in Redwood Lane.

She stared at the door for a moment, feeling the anger subside as rapidly as it had erupted. In the kitchen, she got a glass of water and drank it quickly, her hand shaking.

Hell, what had she said, what had she done? Jo felt her face flame when she thought about it. She told *the boss* that he could 'stick his job'. Oh God. At least he hadn't accepted her resignation.

How would she ever face him again? How could she sit in at the editorial meetings and have him look at her with those grave, sad eyes as if she'd hurt him deeply? And she must have. He'd been trying to say the right thing and she'd flown off the handle and ruined it all. As usual. It wasn't Mark's fault that she was utterly at sea emotionally. That was Richard's fault. Richard and the pregnancy which was responsible for mood swings like tidal waves.

And Mark wasn't just the boss, anyway. He was more than that, much more, if she admitted it to herself.

She had a sudden impulse to phone him on his mobile. She had the number, although she'd never used it before. If she rang and apologised now, maybe he'd come back and she could say she was sorry properly.

Tell him that she simply felt alone and miserable at the thought of having the baby on her own and that he'd arrived when she was at her lowest. Then she thought again.

Face facts, she told herself. Mark is your boss, not your lover. Phoning him would look stupid, desperate even. You've messed everything up. Think about what you're going to do now.

When she'd made a cup of sweet tea and taken the last couple of chocolate digestives from the packet, she phoned Rhona. Rhona would know what to do. Or, at the very worst, she'd know what sort of hat Jo could wear into the office for the rest of her life so she wouldn't have to either look at Mark Denton or let him see her face puce with embarrassment.

'Rho, you won't believe what I've done.'

'I can't imagine, Jo,' Rhona replied. Jo could hear her take a deep drag of a cigarette. 'But you don't sound the best. Are you feeling OK?'

'Apart from a hollow feeling in the pit of my stomach, I'm fine,' Jo explained. 'Mark's just been to see me,' she added, more slowly.

'Why do I get the feeling that all did not go well on this visit?' Rhona inquired.

'Because you're psychic?'

'Nope. It's probably because I can always tell when you're gearing for a complete blow-out,' Rhona said. 'You do get to know people when you've worked with them for three years. So what happened? Is he still breathing?'

'Oh Rho.' Jo sat on the edge of the settee with the phone balanced on her knees. 'I've known myself for thirty-four years and even *I* wouldn't have predicted this one. I've been such a fool. Within the space of about five minutes I managed to insult Mark, tell him where to stick his job, *and*,' she grimaced at the thought of it, 'I nearly said that I thought we had a "relationship" before he messed it all up. I didn't say it but he knew I was going to. You've no idea how I feel,' wailed Jo. 'What is it about me that I can't be normal where men are concerned?'

'It's impossible to be normal when men are involved because they're impossible,' Rhona replied. 'They give the phrase "mission impossible" a whole new dimension. Now look, Jo, this is hardly the end of the world. You're just overwrought. I'm sure Mark knows that.'

'Oh, so he thinks I'm hysterical and that's supposed to be good?'

'It's better than him thinking you meant it about sticking his job. He didn't accept, did he?' Rhona said knowingly. 'Course he didn't. You know he likes you. What am I saying *likes* you, he fancies you like *mad*. He's just unfortunate to have been caught in the crossfire of pregnancy hormones.'

'Do you think he'll understand?' Jo finished the second biscuit and licked the crumbs off her fingers.

'Honestly, Jo, for a woman who *looks* as if she should have the entire male population slavering at her feet, you really haven't a clue about men, have you?'

Not waiting for an answer, Rhona ploughed on. 'It's obvious to me that Mark is crazy about you. But because he's trying to tread carefully, and because you're hopeless at reading the situation, you're making a complete mess of the whole thing.'

'Do you think so?' Jo said doubtfully. It all sounded so much more reasonable when Rhona said it.

'Yes. Now listen to your auntie Rhona – or Madame Rhona the psychic as I want to be known in future – and go off and have a nice swim, or something energetic like that. Then go home, relax and come in here tomorrow morning as if nothing ever happened. OK?'

'OK. What about Emma? I simply couldn't face her tomorrow.'

'You won't have to. I've suspended her. Actually, I've never suspended anyone before,' the other woman said thoughtfully, 'so I had to make it up as I went along. It went pretty well, though.'

'What did you say?' demanded Jo, dying to know every gory detail.

'Well, remember that time we were at the Prêt A Porter

première party in the Chocolate Bar and that drunk pulled me onto his lap and tried to stick his hand down my Ben De Lisi shirt?' Even in times of crisis, Rhona was exact about clothes.

'Oh my God yes, I'll never forget it! I didn't think you knew how to be so vicious.'

'I was worse than that with Emma,' Rhona said. 'That girl will think twice – actually, she'll think three or four times – before ever speaking to anyone in *Style* like that ever again. I pointed out that word quickly gets around about someone who's trouble to work with. It's one thing to be pig-ignorant and rude if you've made it, if you're a damn good journalist or whatever.'

She took another drag of her cigarette. 'But if you're trouble and you're only a junior with no evidence of any talent whatsoever, forget about a career in journalism, I said. There are thousands of freelances out there just waiting to step into your shoes, Emma, so wake up and smell the coffee.'

'I'm impressed.'

'So was I,' Rhona said smugly. 'I gave Ted a brief version of it at home afterwards and he was shocked, I can tell you. He says he's going to disown me when the kids get into trouble at school and I have to go down to give the headmistress a piece of my mind. He couldn't face the carnage, he said.'

Jo suddenly realised she was laughing and that the knot of tension in her belly was loosening.

'Thanks, Rhona, you're great at getting people to forget their problems. Can I stay in your house until I have the baby so you can stop me going berserk every second day?'

'With three under-tens running around constantly, you'd really go mad, I can tell you,' Rhona replied.

'You're right.' Jo managed a weak laugh. 'If I take lots of deep breaths tomorrow morning, I think I'll be able to face the office. Mark's not due in, is he?'

'Nope. Anyway, he's not going to bite you.'

'No, but I may pass out with embarrassment when I see him,' Jo pointed out.

'No you won't.' Rhona's voice was firm. 'Go and do something energetic so you don't have a second to think about it. I'll be in the office at half nine tomorrow morning with the kettle boiled.'

Nerves got Jo out of bed early, so she was the first person in the office and had already made a cup of tea when Rhona arrived.

'How come I always have so much junk with me?' demanded Rhona, staggering into the office weighed down as usual by a capacious handbag, a bulging briefcase and the fat black velvet make-up bag she could never fit in her handbag.

'Get pregnant, split up with Ted and you'll be able to spend many happy hours at home feeling exhausted and bored, and you'll end up tidying your handbag/wardrobe/kitchen cupboards/whatever,' said Jo, pouring water on a tea bag for Rhona.

'Did you do all that?'

'Yes. I feel very virtuous, I can tell you. I even threw out all the saggy knickers I never wear, found and binned the tights with holes in them and rounded up all the black socks and found them partners, or the closest thing to a partner.'

'I'm impressed. Will you do mine?'

'Do what?' inquired Nikki, the beauty editor, who'd just arrived in a cloud of Opium.

'Jo has turned into a living, breathing "de-junk your life" feature,' Rhona explained, taking her tea into her office so she could smoke.

'Oh please de-junk my life.' Nikki shrugged off her black suede coat. 'I spent half of yesterday afternoon writing an article about the beauty essentials and how you only needed blusher, lip gloss, concealer and mascara in your emergency make-up bag. While I, naturally, carry half of Boots around with me every day and it necessitated a ten-minute search this morning to locate my new eyebrow make-up. By the way,' she said to Jo as she switched on her computer, 'you haven't forgotten the make-over session this morning?'

'Shit,' said Jo, who had. 'It just slipped my mind. What time are they coming in at?'

'Ten-thirty. We're going to the hairdresser's at eleven and Michelle – she's the new make-up artist I was telling you about, Rhona – she's doing their make-up in the salon. Then we've lunch in Spinelli's at one and the photographer will take the pics there.'

'Oh no, I forgot to remind Annette to get the clothes picked up yesterday,' shouted Jo in horror.

'Don't panic, I did it,' said Nikki. 'I knew you were sick,' she added. 'How are you today?'

'Fine,' Jo replied. 'I just needed a few days in bed.'

'Ah yes, but with whom?' called Rhona from her office, winking lewdly at Jo.

'Watch it McNamara,' she replied. 'Just because you can take on headmistresses, don't try anything with me.'

'What's this about headmistresses?' inquired Nikki.

Jo, Nikki and Michelle, the make-up artist, all tilted their heads sideways and looked at the second make-over candidate through narrowed eyes. It was hard to see where to begin. They were in Peter Mark's Hair and Beauty salon in the Stephen's Green shopping centre and the day was deteriorating rapidly.

The first woman to be made over was an already stunning redhead in her early forties who needed a make-over like Ivana Trump needed dresses. With a fabulous figure, perfect make-up, glossy hair and an outfit that must have cost a week's wages, there was absolutely nothing any of them could do to improve Helen.

'How the hell did we pick her?' whispered Nikki into Jo's ear when Helen was brought off to the washbasins.

'Her letter said she was a mother of four with kids ranging in age from twenty to four, that she worked part-time as a nurse and helped her husband run a garden centre outside Cork,' replied Jo. 'The picture was blurry and she said she'd love a change of image and I thought she deserved it . . .'

'*She* could probably give us lessons on changing our image,' groaned Nikki. 'I don't know what we can do to improve her.'

The second make-over candidate, however, was going to be a huge headache for the hairdresser. As a result of a perm gone wrong, twenty-nine-year-old Sharon – who had long mousey hair in the passport-sized photo she'd sent in – now sported layered hair that sat at an unflattering length between her ears and her jaw. The hairdresser was nearly tearing her own hair out at the thought of doing anything with Sharon's hair in its present state.

'You'll have to think of something,' Jo hissed at the hairdresser and make-up artist. 'The poor girl travelled miles to be here and she's going to have a wonderful day and look beautiful if we have to buy her a bloody wig!'

To make matters worse, Sharon wasn't the size fourteen that she'd claimed in her letter. Instead, she was an eighteen at least which meant that the elegant wool jacket and skirt Jo had carefully picked for her definitely wouldn't fit.

'I've seen some fabulous suits in the shops that would have looked really gorgeous on her,' groaned Jo, 'if only she'd said she was a size eighteen in the letter, I could have brought her off and we'd have picked something amazing. There just isn't the time now!'

'Well, what will we do?' demanded Nikki.

'I'm going to race down to Marks and Spark's to get her a different outfit because they have great clothes in right now and we simply don't have the time for a proper shopping trip. Damn,' she added, 'I'd have *loved* to have gone shopping with Sharon.'

Marks was blissfully empty and Jo spent an enjoyable fifteen minutes browsing, wishing she could buy something instead of saving her money for the new house. Now that she'd rung an estate agent about selling her apartment, the idea of moving had finally become reality and she knew she had to economise. She'd stuck her credit card at the back of her dressing-table drawer and vowed to keep it there no matter what sort of mid-season sales started.

She'd have to be very careful with money until she was settled in her new home. Luckily, the woman from the estate agent's said apartments in her block were always in demand and she'd have no trouble selling, despite the time of year.

'It's such a pretty complex and the apartments are quite spacious compared to the ones being built now, so I doubt if you'll have to wait long,' the estate agent said.

Jo was so busy working out how much money she'd need to borrow to buy the cottage and wondering whether she could afford a sloppy chenille jumper to hide her bump, that she totally lost track of time.

Oh no, she thought looking at her watch in horror. It was half eleven and she hadn't even started looking for clothes for Sharon.

But Jo wasn't a clothesaholic with an encyclopaedic knowledge of where to get what in her favourite shops for nothing.

It was just twelve as she rushed up Grafton Street with a large M & S bag in each hang. Jo really wished she hadn't worn the long caramel wool cardigan over the cream silk shirt and black trousers. As she hurried past the crowds ambling along the pedestrian street, she was soon roasting hot and felt ready for a make-over herself. Or at least a chance to redo her foundation which had undoubtedly disappeared with sweat.

She struggled up the escalator and into Peter Mark's to find Nikki relaxing on a couch, reading a magazine and leisurely sipping a cup of coffee, oblivious to the controlled chaos of the salon. Nikki's blonde hair was immaculate, her face wasn't shiny and red, and her off-white trouser suit looked as fresh as if it had just been returned from the dry-cleaner's. Hot, sticky and convinced that she smelled like a jockey's armpit, Jo felt like bag lady by comparison.

'You got the clothes all right, then?' Nikki got up and took the two large bags from Jo. 'You look wrecked. Sit down and I'll get you a cup of tea.'

'Thanks,' panted Jo, sinking gratefully onto the seat Nikki had just vacated. 'I *feel* wrecked. But I got this beautiful crimson Mandarin jacket and matching palazzos that will look great on Sharon. How's it going?' she asked anxiously.

'Brilliantly,' said Nikki enthusiastically. 'You wouldn't believe how Sharon's hair has turned out. That hairdresser has worked miracles. And Helen looks amazing. Mind you, she looked amazing in the beginning.'

'Well,' said Jo, relieved to find that the make-over had been a success after all, 'we'll just make her "before" picture very, very small. Or else say she didn't really get a make-over but just wanted to feel pampered for a day.'

Nikki had been right. Sharon's new look really suited her. The hairdresser has shaped her hair, added a rich chestnut rinse to make it glossy and given her a short, feather cut. 'The only thing I could think of,' she told Jo, 'and it worked!'

Sharon looked a million dollars thanks to the elegant crimson suit that Jo had picked for her, teamed with the right make-up and a new haircut which emphasised her beautiful dark brown eyes.

'It's fantastic.' She beamed at Jo. 'Thank you so much. I never thought I could look like this.' She threw her arms around the fashion editor.

'I'm so pleased for you,' said Jo with a big smile. 'This is my favourite part of make-overs,' she added as the photographer took a couple of quick pictures, 'when people are pleased with what we've done. Normally we just take the pictures and go. But today we've got a wonderful lunch lined up where you two ladies can show off your amazing ladies-who-lunch look!'

'Have you got any deodorant?' Jo whispered to Nikki in the restaurant loos. She'd managed to tone down her red face, but she still felt sticky after her run up Grafton Street.

Nikki handed Jo some deodorant and a bottle of Opium.

'Thanks,' said Jo gratefully, spraying herself liberally. 'I've left my perfume in the office by mistake and I'm sure all my Trésor has worn off.'

She glanced at Nikki as the other woman expertly applied a fresh coat of subtle beige lipstick and wished, for once, that she didn't work with such a paragon of style and beauty. Nikki was always perfectly turned out, never wore chipped nail varnish and never got lipstick on her teeth. And today was no exception.

Jo ran a brush through her tortoiseshell curls and wished she had something to tie it back with because it was greasy at the roots. Then she followed Nikki into the restaurant. Helen, Sharon and Nell, the photographer, were at the table getting stuck into pre-lunch gin and tonics, the other two laughing at some filthy joke Nell had just told them.

Jo was just manoeuvring herself around the table into her seat at the wall when she spotted them. The woman wore a figure-hugging black shift dress and an eye-catching red jacket which a very suave and elegant Mark Denton was helping her out of. He must have said something funny because she laughed suddenly, the sleek dark hair rippling as she leaned her head back. Even her laugh was warm, husky and sexy.

Bitch. Jo felt jealousy spear her as she watched Mark, very attractive in a steel grey suit to match his eyes, pull out the woman's chair before sinking into his. He took the menu and wine list from the waiter almost without looking at him, eyes on the woman all the time. Not surprising, Jo thought maliciously, when the bitch was wearing a dress with a deep vee in the front showing a Grand Canyon cleavage that had to be thanks to a Wonderbra. Who the hell was she? thought Jo venomously, taking in the glint of serious gold bangles.

'Madam?' inquired a voice. Jo came to her senses to find a waiter smiling down at her, pen and order pad in hand.

'Oh er . . . I'll have, what will I have . . .' she muttered, casting a quick glance at the menu she'd been dying to get her hands on ten minutes earlier.

'Today's specials are Dublin Bay prawns in Pernod and monkfish tails in a Provençale sauce,' said the waiter hopefully.

'Fine.' Jo shut the menu with a snap and handed it to him. She didn't care if she ordered rats' tails in Pernod at that precise moment.

Nikki was filling Helen, Sharon and Nell in on the finer

details of the party she'd been to at the weekend where one woman turned up with her husband and left with somebody else's.

'She's Dublin's Zsa Zsa Gabor.' Nikki giggled. 'Ask her how many husbands she's had and she'll say "Mine or other people's?" '

Jo craned her head to see what Mark and the mystery woman were up to in the far corner of the restaurant. Laughing a lot, she thought grimly, watching the dark head shake with mirth yet again. He doesn't waste any time, does he?

'You know her, don't you, Jo?' asked Nikki, breaking off mid-story to include Jo in the conversation.

'Know who?'

'The Zsa Zsa woman at my party, Lizzie Something-or-other. Lord, you're a million miles away, aren't you, Jo?' Then, noticing Jo's face, which had gone quite pale, Nikki said, 'Are you feeling all right? Are you ill?'

Jo grabbed the glass of water in front of her and took a huge gulp. 'Fine,' she lied, 'fine. I'm just hungry. Hand me a bread roll, will you?'

She sneaked a glance at Mark's table just in time to see the waiter arrive with a bottle of champagne and an ice bucket. What the hell were they celebrating? Jo half-listened to the conversation going on around her as she nibbled at her bread roll listlessly. Who was that woman? She thought murderously.

She was very quiet during the meal, barely touched her prawns and poked the monkfish around the plate in a desultory fashion.

The others drank three bottles of wine and were so merry that Nell had to use up three rolls of film before she got any pictures where the two newly made-over women weren't laughing hysterically.

The waiter was serving coffee when Nikki finally noticed Mark and his companion.

'Look who's having lunch with his ex,' she murmured to Jo

369

with a smirk. 'I thought that liaison was finished.'

Jo dropped her teaspoon with a clatter. 'What?' she asked.

'It's Eva Marot,' said Nikki. 'I thought they'd broken up a long time ago.'

Trying not to look as though it mattered to her, Jo asked who Eva was.

'You must know.' Nikki raised one perfectly shaped blonde eyebrow in amazement. 'He was involved with her for years, even after she got married. She married some filthy-rich French guy and lives in London most of the time. But she comes back to Ireland a lot – she's an artist and she often paints here. The light is wonderful, apparently.'

Nikki took a sip of brandy. 'They were quite an item for a long time. Up to a year or so ago, I think,' she added thoughtfully. 'I can't believe you never heard of her. She was Eva Ward before her marriage.'

'No, I didn't hear anything,' said Jo faintly.

'She's half-French on her mother's side and very chic. Always wears the most gorgeous clothes.' The other woman took another long look at Mark and his companion. 'That *has* to be Armani she's wearing, don't you think?'

'Mmm, you're probably right.' Jo toyed with the brown sugar crystals in the bowl in front of her. Stop looking at them, Nikki, she pleaded silently. Or else Mark'll come over and I couldn't bear to meet him like this, with me looking like hell and him with Ms Epitome of Chic with the sexy laugh. I bet she whispers sweet nothings in French in bed, she thought jealously.

The waiter arrived with more brandy for everyone except Jo. Nikki turned her attention to Helen's story about Brandy Alexanders and how the first one she'd ever had made her instantly drunk – and madly sexy.

'Have one,' squealed Nell. 'You're getting the train home and both you and your husband will have something to remember today by!'

Jo smiled but her mind was miles away. *She* was the woman Suzanne had told her about at the party in New York. The mystery woman who'd broken Mark's heart, the one Suzanne assumed Jo knew all about. Eva Marot. Jo said the name to herself several times, wondering why she'd never even heard the tiniest piece of gossip about her and Mark.

To cap it all, Rhona must have known all along. Jo would just kill her when she got her. Imagine not saying *anything* about Mark's past love? She was staring blankly into her half-drunk cup of coffee when she heard that deep, rich voice she'd recognise anywhere.

'Hello, ladies,' Mark said warmly. 'Did you have a nice lunch?'

Jo looked up sharply. He was standing at the other side of the table, smiling at the five of them. *She* stood just behind him, an elegant vision straight out of the pages of *Vogue*. Jo could have sworn that the string of pearls around her neck was real, they had that expensive real-pearl lustre.

'This is a lunch for our make-over ladies, Mark,' Nikki was saying. 'Helen and Sharon, meet Mark Denton, *Style*'s publisher. And you know Nell, don't you?'

'Yes, hello, Helen, Sharon and Nell. And how are you, Jo?' he asked, looking directly at Jo's startled face.

'Fine!' she said brightly. 'Marvellous! How was your lunch?' she inquired in the same high-pitched tone.

'Very nice,' Mark answered, looking at her curiously.

'The food is just wonderful here, isn't it?' Eva said in her faintly accented voice, as she slid one arm through Mark's. 'It's hard not to eat too much.' She patted a stomach flat as a pancake.

Cow, thought Jo. Just because she's skinny, she doesn't have to look down on the rest of us.

'Eva, this is Jo Ryan,' introduced Mark, '*Style*'s deputy and fashion editor, Nikki Ahearn, our beauty editor, Nell Deane, who's a photographer and Sharon and Helen who've just had a make-over and look gorgeous, if I may say so.' Sharon went pink with pleasure.

'How nice to meet you all.' Eva's smile looked remarkably genuine, Jo thought sourly. But then it would, wouldn't it? A husband *and* a lover – she was having her cake and eating it too.

'I'm glad to see that you're back at work, Jo,' Mark said gently, looking her straight in the eye. Jo glared at him. Was that some sort of dig?

'I have felt better,' she snapped.

'I can see that,' he replied. 'You look worn out.'

The bastard. Just because she wasn't done up like a dog's dinner, he didn't have to be so smart.

'When is your baby due?' inquired Eva politely, gazing at Jo's stomach.'

'Four months – well, four and a half, actually.'

'Is it your first?' Eva asked next.

What was this, Jo fumed, bloody *Mastermind*?

'Yes.'

'Oh.' The other woman appeared to notice her coolness. 'We should go now, Mark,' she murmured, her dark glossy head close to his. Eva was tall, Jo realised, around five ten if she could talk to Mark without craning her neck the way Jo had to.

'Of course, Eva. We don't want to be late,' he said. 'Bye, ladies, it's been nice meeting you.' Mark looked at Jo briefly. 'I'll see you next week at the editorial meeting.'

'Yeah, bye.'

'So nice to meet you all,' Eva said warmly.

Jo took a sip of her coffee even though it was practically lukewarm. She was determined not to watch them leave. But she couldn't resist. As she glanced up they were at the door, Mark's strong arm opening the door for Eva to walk through. Chivalrous as ever.

The waiter brought the bill along with a small plate of After Eights. Nobody touched them. No point wasting them. Jo reached in and took three. What was the point of watching her figure anyway? Nobody noticed.

'I can't believe you never told me about her!' Jo's voice was angry. She stood in Rhona's office and stared crossly down at her friend. Rhona, who'd been working on her monthly editorial when Jo stormed in after lunch in Spinelli's, leaned back in her chair and looked at Jo.

'Listen, Jo, Mark told me about Eva in confidence.' Rhona's voice was very firm and very serious. 'He told me one night a long time before you joined *Style* and he told me as a friend, asked me not to tell anyone about it. I'm not saying it was easy to keep it to myself, especially that day when I told you Mark had been interested in you for a long time. But honestly, Jo,' Rhona said earnestly, 'by then I thought you could do without hearing about his beloved ex-girlfriend, a woman he'd adored for years. That would hardly have made you feel very special, would it?'

'I suppose . . .' said Jo slowly. *A woman he'd adored for years?* What hope had she against that sort of competition?

A pregnant woman who flew off the handle at the drop of a hat could hardly compete with an exotic artist who'd loved him for years.

'Anyway, it's over. They split up a long time ago,' Rhona said.

'They looked very much together at lunch today,' Jo pointed out. 'They were all over each other.'

'Believe me.' Rhona's voice was serious. 'They're not together any more. Look Jo, I'm sorry I couldn't tell you about her, but that would have been breaking a confidence and I couldn't do that to Mark. I've known him a long time and he trusts me. He's also very perceptive. If I'd spilled the beans to you, he'd have worked out who told you in two minutes flat. And he'd have gone mad.'

Rhona lit up a cigarette, then stubbed it out hurriedly. 'Sorry, I keep forgetting not to smoke in front of you,' she said. 'Jo, I wanted to tell you loads of times, but when you really became interested in him, you wouldn't have appreciated it. And I knew Mark would want to tell you himself if he was serious about you. Can't you understand the dilemma I was in?'

Jo sighed and sat down in the chair opposite Rhona.

'Sorry, Rho,' she apologised. 'I've no right to barge in here and screech at you. I'm angry at myself really, for even thinking he could be interested in me. And if he was,' she added quickly, seeing that Rhona was going to interrupt, 'I've screwed it up myself. I should have business cards made up – "Jo Ryan Incorporated. Will Destroy Any Relationship in Ten Minutes Flat." '

'Don't be daft,' said Rhona impatiently. 'You've just had a bad couple of weeks. He's not still involved with Eva, I'm sure of it.'

'Even if he isn't, he's definitely not interested in me any more,' Jo said sadly. 'So, now that I'm no longer an interested party, is there anything else I should know about Mr Denton? Has he ten kids hidden away somewhere, or a mad wife locked in the attic, perhaps?'

She tried to sound flip but Rhona knew her too well for that.

'No,' Rhona said. 'He has remarkably few skeletons in the cupboard. A lot less than I have,' she added with a wry grin. 'But let him tell you about Eva.'

'He's not going to tell me anything.'

'You have it your way,' Rhona replied. She changed the subject. 'So tell me, is the November issue too early for the "I know we all want to go on a diet for Christmas, readers, but let's be grown-ups and accept the way we are" editorial?'

'No, November is fine,' Jo said. 'Let's leave the "diet your way to beauty" until the January issue and I'll be one of the guinea pigs when I have to lose the two stone I'll have put on by then.'

She had just switched on her computer and was looking at the Christmas Glamour Look photos that Ralph had delivered, when her phone rang.

'Jo. I wonder could I have a word with you?' Mark said.

'I'm busy,' she snapped.

'I'm sure you are,' he replied. 'But this is important.'

'Fine. Talk.'

'I want to *see* you, Jo, not have you talk in monosyllables on the phone.'

Oh no, she thought, she couldn't handle that, she couldn't handle actually *seeing* him. She didn't want to see him ever again because she knew she'd just break down and cry if she did. If she could keep away from him for a while, then she'd be fine, she knew it. She'd get over Mark Denton. She'd have to.

'I can't see you right now, Mark,' she said firmly. 'Can't you talk on the phone? Anyway, I thought you were tied up for the afternoon?' she added smartly.

'I'm not busy,' he said slowly. 'I think we've got some unfinished business and I want it sorted out right now.'

'Oh, you mean me calling you names and telling you where you could stick your job. I'm sorry,' Jo said in a low voice. 'I apologise, I had no right to say those things.'

'That's not really it,' Mark said, 'that's just part of the problem. I want to know what's behind it, what's going on. There seems to have been some sort of misunderstanding between us . . .'

Jo froze. She knew exactly what he meant. He was talking about her feelings for him, her 'infatuation'. *She'd* all but chatted him up in New York, flirted shamelessly with him and behaved like a spurned girlfriend when he hadn't rung her over Emma's little explosion. Now he was going to warn her off. Of course he was. He was back with the love of his life and he wanted all the loose ends tied up. He didn't want to subject poor Eva to any more of Jo's ferocious stares, did he?

What a mess. She couldn't let him think that she really fancied him, that would be too cringe-making. She had to say something.

'I'm sorry,' she gabbled at high speed. 'I know I've been acting strangely, but it's the baby. The baby,' she paused, before inspiration struck, 'and Richard. He's back and we're talking, and I'm going through a difficult time, sorting everything out. You know.'

'Oh.' Mark's voice sounded different, remote. 'I see,' he said coolly. 'Of course, I understand. Sorry to bother you, Jo, I'll let you get back to work.'

He hung up. Jo sat with the phone against her ear and wished Brenda wasn't sitting at the desk opposite, gabbling away to her boyfriend, so that she could cry.

CHAPTER SEVENTEEN

'Tell me all about Sam. Is he drop-dead gorgeous? Or,' Jo curled her stockinged feet up under her on the armchair in Aisling's sitting room and adjusted her huge grey woollen cardigan until she was comfortable, 'does he have any brothers?'

'Not that I know of,' replied Aisling, 'but then, there are lots of things I don't know about him.'

It was true. Since the party seven days ago, Aisling had spoken to him on the phone twice and both conversations had been funny, jokey and absent of any information. It had been so blissfully unlike all those stilted boy/girl conversations she'd had years ago when she started going out with boys. You talked about what school you'd gone to, or what courses you were doing in college and where your parents came from. So you could 'place' the person and figure out if it was safe to bring him home.

She'd been married so long that she could barely remember life before Michael, life when she had gone on dates with a variety of men – who were always unsuitable in her father's opinion. Dating as a grown-up was much more fun. No one had to approve of her choice, except herself.

'No,' she said thoughtfully, 'I'm pretty sure Sam has a couple of sisters but no brothers.'

'That's perfect.' Jo reached for another chocolate-chip cookie. 'If he has sisters, he'll understand women. Not like those MCPs who've grown up with an adoring mammie and no female company to educate them about the ways of the world. These biscuits are delicious,' she added, taking a big bite. 'Did you make them yourself?'

Aisling laughed. 'These days I'm lucky if I get to make the bed in the morning, never mind bake biscuits.'

'Well, they look home-made.'

'They *are* home-made but not from *my* home. I got them at the boys' school fête along with a ton of apple tarts and fairy cakes I've frozen so I can drag them out and impress people with my home cooking all year long. Pity I never copped on to that when I was a housewife,' Aisling remarked drily.

'You're not having any,' said Jo. While she'd been enjoying a mug of frothy hot chocolate and biscuits, Aisling had been sipping black coffee.

'I never eat biscuits any more, unless I can see the pack and know exactly how many calories there are in each one,' Aisling explained. 'It took me long enough to get the weight off, so I'm not putting it back on again.'

'You look great,' Jo said with sincerity. The slightly plump, out-of-shape Aisling was a thing of the past. She was svelte in a pair of slim black trousers and a soft angora jumper in a caramel colour which matched her newly dyed hair. It wasn't even how Aisling *looked* that made the difference, Jo realised. She had changed from the inside out.

The nervous, miserable woman of four months ago, constantly on the verge of tears, had gone to be replaced by an attractive woman who had learned to live life on her own terms.

Jo remembered when she'd felt that she was living life on her terms. That had been before she'd become pregnant, before Richard had showed his true colours, before she'd fallen, disastrously, for Mark. Now, she hurtled along a path she hadn't chosen, scared and exhilarated at the same time.

She felt Aisling's hand on her shoulder and looked up to see her friend sit on the arm of the chair with a concerned expression on her face.

'Are you all right?' Aisling asked gently.

'Yes.' She snuffled. 'I was thinking about this time over three months ago when I thought everything was fine. When I first got pregnant and I thought he'd want the baby as much as I did.' She stroked her belly lovingly. 'I want the baby so much, I can't understand how he didn't. I thought it was all going to be so perfect.'

378

'But it wasn't, he wasn't. Richard was lying and sooner or later he'd have shown his true colours,' Aisling said earnestly. 'You couldn't have lived with the sort of man who'd want you to have an abortion so you could both go abroad to work with no strings attached.'

'I know,' Jo said simply.

Aisling wasn't finished. 'The life you had was a house of cards, Jo. Mine was the same and it was bound to tumble down sooner or later. I know it was agony when it all fell apart, but let's be honest, there's no easy way to break up a relationship. And we've passed that horrible, depressing stage, both of us,' she insisted. 'We're on to the next stage. I know you're in bits about having the baby on your own and of course it would be better to have a father for him . . .'

'Her,' said Jo with a grin. 'I know it's a girl, I just feel it. Aren't you, my darling?' she cooed at her bump. 'I understand what you're saying, Ash, I really do. No father is better than a father like Richard,' she recited, as if she was repeating a mantra she'd said to herself many, many times before.

'At least if you're on your own, you've got the chance of meeting someone else and finding a good dad for her,' Aisling said.

'I thought I'd found him,' Jo explained.

'Mark Denton?' asked Aisling.

'Yes. Dear, dear Mark. And I screwed it up. Oh God, I hate to even think about it.' Jo leaned back in the chair and massaged the bridge of her nose with her right hand. She felt tired, exhausted even. It had been a horrible week. She hadn't even had to avoid Mark because *he* studiously avoided the office. He phoned Rhona when he needed to talk to her instead of dropping in as he usually did. To make matters worse, she couldn't go home until late every evening as the estate agent was showing the apartment to prospective buyers. So she'd ended up sitting in the office with a takeaway until eight on Wednesday, Thursday and Friday.

If she hadn't promised to visit Aisling this Saturday morning, she wouldn't have got out of bed at all. Even then she'd only managed to drag on her ancient woolly cardigan, a faded pink T-shirt and her grey jogging pants. She hadn't had the energy to wash her hair and knew it fell in lank waves around her shoulders.

Aisling contemplated her for a moment and then got up. 'Come on into the kitchen and I'll make you something decent for lunch,' she said firmly. 'You can tell me all about Mark while I'm cooking.'

The scent of the herb and mushroom omelette she'd made Jo still lingered in the air as Aisling hurried round the house that evening, collecting tights, socks, knickers and jumpers off the radiators. Sam was picking her up at half seven and she only had an hour to dry her hair, dress and put on her make-up. It was her own fault for spending too long planning the menu for her first catering dinner.

When Rachel Coughlan had rung on Monday morning, tentatively booking Aisling for a dinner party for twelve, she'd been so stunned she'd been speechless for the first minute.

'I thought I'd book early in case you're really busy,' Rachel said on the phone, not sounding anything like a high-powered businesswoman who'd just set up her own PR agency. 'Jim said everyone was thrilled and very impressed with your cooking and he's sure you're already madly busy. I do hope you can fit me in. It's for my brother's forty-fifth birthday. He's coming home from the States and his wife is so fussy, I'd love to outshine her.'

Thrilled to be asked, and even more thrilled that Jim Coughlan thought so highly of her that he assumed she'd be snowed under with work, Aisling said she'd dream up a very posh menu if that's what Rachel wanted.

'Yes,' the other woman said enthusiastically, delighted to have found an ally. 'You can't imagine what it's like to feel like a second-class citizen to this New York career woman who can whistle up a four-course meal at the drop of a hat and still look like something from a fashion magazine at dinner.'

'Oh yes I can,' said Aisling grimly. 'Don't worry, Rachel.

She'll be dumbstruck when she sees what we'll do.'

'Unfortunately, my sister-in-law has never been dumbstruck in her entire life, more's the pity,' muttered Rachel.

Aisling had been so engrossed in deciding whether rack of lamb would be suitably classy for the meal, or if she should try something more difficult like pheasant in Calvados, that she hadn't noticed the time. When she finally looked at her watch, she abandoned the menu and raced upstairs to the bathroom.

An hour later, wearing the crossover bronze body Fiona had given her, she sat in the kitchen picking cat fur off her long black skirt. Flossie, disgusted at the prospect of being left alone, wove herself in and out between Aisling's ankles, leaving enough fur on her owner's sheer black tights to knit another cat.

'I'm sorry, Flossie.' She stroked the cat's silken chin and wondered how Flossie always knew when she was going out. 'I won't be out late. Wait till you see the treat I've got you.'

She checked her make-up one last time, gave herself a blast of Magie Noire and got up to feed Flossie.

'Isn't that nice?' she asked as the cat tucked into a bowl of tinned salmon.

When the doorbell rang at a minute after half seven, her stomach was rumbling with nerves. She had no idea how she was going to be able to eat anything at all, but she didn't care.

Sam stood on the doorstep, holding a small bouquet of flowers in his hands. For a moment Aisling was stunned. She'd forgotten how heart-stoppingly attractive he was. He wore a pale blue cotton shirt that brought out the bright blue of his eyes and set off his tan. A well-cut dark jacket and jeans showed off a physique that spoke of many hours in the gym. He looked like a Calvin Klein aftershave advert come to life, from the tips of his brown suede boots to his all-American grin.

'You look lovely, Aisling.' His eyes glinted in admiration. 'Can I come in?' he added.

'Oh God, yes, I'm sorry.' Blushing bright pink, Aisling stood back and let him in. She'd been so busy staring at him that she'd quite forgotten to ask him in.

'These are for you,' he said, handing her the bouquet, 'for making me feel at home in Ireland again.'

To hide her red face, she buried her nose in the flowers, breathing in the heady scent of pale yellow roses and the fragrance of the forest green ferns. She couldn't remember the last time anyone had given her flowers, apart from Michael's guilt-ridden garage forecourt arrangements.

'They're beautiful,' she said fervently.

'So are you.' Sam looked deep into her eyes and gave her another slow, lazy grin.

Aisling felt the fluttering in her stomach move lower. God only knew what it would feel like if he actually touched her.

'The table is booked for eight,' he said. 'Do you want to go out or aren't you hungry?' he asked, one eyebrow raised in amusement.

'Oh, of course. I'll just put these in water,' she muttered. She wondered if he could tell what she was thinking. She hoped not.

He held the door for her to climb into the taxi. She'd been sure he'd have a car.

'Can't drink and drive,' he said. 'I thought we'd have champagne and you simply couldn't drive after drinking that.'

'No, of course not,' replied Aisling in a knowing tone, as if she had champagne all the time. She wasn't sure she believed that stuff about him not drinking and driving. Sam had the air of a man who never did anything by the rules. There was something about him, a sense of recklessness, that made him very, very attractive. And just a little bit dangerous.

He'd chosen a small French restaurant, with dim lighting and small tables set far enough apart from each other to allow couples to talk privately. Their table was in one corner, the golden glow of a candle cast flattering light on the snow-white damask tablecloth and gleaming silverware. Good, thought Aisling. Candlelight was much more flattering to crow's feet than harsh lighting.

The waitress handed them the menus and then disappeared, leaving them alone. The place was jammed with couples, obviously enticed in by the fact that the restaurant was dark and dim, making it perfect for illicit encounters. Probably the sort of place Michael had taken that cow to.

The staff kept firmly in the background while Ella Fitzgerald's rich voice crooned love songs in the background.

'Do you like this place?' asked Sam softly.

'I love it,' she answered.

'Good. We should come here every Saturday night,' he replied.

Aisling's pulse raced. It was only their first date and he was already talking about a future together! She couldn't wait to tell Fiona and Jo.

She shot him what she hoped was a sexy smile, and looked at her menu. Who needed food on an occasion like this?

They drank Moët from elegant crystal champagne flutes and Sam told her all about working in Texas and Louisiana.

'I'd love to bring you to New Orleans,' he said, sliding his hand past his empty soup bowl to grasp Aisling's hand. 'You'd love it. It's so atmospheric and European, it's the most European city I've ever been to in America. You can walk along the streets in the French Quarter and it's like being in Paris or Budapest.'

'You've travelled so much,' said Aisling enviously. 'I've been to Greece, Portugal, France and Britain, and that's it. You've been everywhere.'

He shrugged. 'I travelled for a couple of years after leaving college, that's how I've seen so much. You simply didn't have that chance, you were bringing up two kids.'

'I can't wait for you to meet them,' Aisling said eagerly. 'They'll love you.'

Oh no, she thought in horror. She couldn't believe she'd just said that. Single men were not fascinated by the notion of other men's children.

'I can't wait either,' Sam said. 'I love kids. My sisters' children are fantastic and the two older ones – Jerri's boys – came out to stay with me last year for a month. They went wild for New Orleans and had me down at the aquarium for two days solid.'

'It sounds fascinating,' said Aisling, mentally giving him ten out of ten for loving children. Handsome, kind, funny, romantic *and* dying to meet the boys. What more could a woman ask for?

'It *is* fascinating,' Sam was saying. 'It's got every sort of sea creature you can imagine, apart from whales, that is. You walk along these corridors with glass overhead and around you and you can see sharks, stingrays, giant squid swimming around these massive tanks.'

He stopped as the waitress placed their main courses in front of them and refilled their glasses with Moët.

'Anyway, that's enough about sharks. My favourite sort of wildlife doesn't reside behind glass.' Sam flashed her a killer smile.

'What do you mean?' Aisling asked demurely.

Sam slid one hand across the table and grasped hers, his fingers putting gentle pressure on the palm of her hand.

'That I enjoy life, in every sense of the word. I've always believed that you've got to live life to the full, take all the pleasures and passion from life while you can. That can mean being a little wild sometimes,' he said, gazing at Aisling intently, leaving her in no doubt as to what he meant.

She felt herself grow pink under his scrutiny.

'I don't get much of a chance to be wild,' she said, picking up her glass with the hand he wasn't holding. 'Work, kids, exhaustion – none of it leaves time for acting wild. Coming out to dinner instead of staying at home doing the ironing is my idea of wild these days!'

Aisling knew that this wasn't what he'd meant but she wanted to change the subject rapidly. The whole conversation had taken a distinct dive into territory she wasn't either comfortable or familiar with, and she wanted it back on track. Until she'd had another couple of drinks, anyway.

'Of course, there was another reason for the boys' fascination with the aquarium,' Sam said with a smile, returning to their original conversation. 'They came during their summer holidays in July and in the summer walking around New Orleans is like being baked in a hot oven with ninety per cent humidity thrown in to make it worse. After an hour meandering around the markets by the river, the aquarium is beautifully cool!'

As they ate he told her about his two years of travelling with a college friend. Aisling listened wide-eyed as he recounted tales about backpacking in India – 'an unbelievable experience' – driving across America in a rent-a-wreck – 'New Mexico has got to be one of the most beautiful places on earth' – and working on a kibbutz in Israel.

He made her laugh telling her stories about ending up in cockroach-infested motel rooms, and how he ended up in hospital in Ecuador thanks to a virulent stomach bug.

Aisling couldn't help but notice that he never talked about his feelings. There was no mention of the woman he'd been involved with in Texas, or of their split-up. Still, Aisling thought, there was plenty of time for those sort of confessional conversations later.

Accustomed to being a listener after years of marriage to Michael, she sat in rapt silence as Sam talked her through all the places he'd seen in his thirty-nine years. Everywhere he went, he tried some new sport or pastime to fulfil his love of danger.

His favourite had been rock-climbing in Colorado.

'That sounds terrifying,' she said with a shudder, as he explained how difficult it was to scale a two-hundred-metre cliff-face with a deadly overhang at the top which had claimed the lives of two climbers.

'The adrenaline buzz is something else,' Sam said, his eyes distant as if remembering. 'I can't explain it, it's primeval, the feeling that it's just you, one man, against nature. When you're up there, you can imagine what it must have felt like for primitive men battling the earth just to survive.'

For a moment he stared into space. Then, just as quickly, he came back to her.

'There's a climb in Arizona every year, in one of the canyons off the Grand Canyon,' Sam said. 'I've never done it but I'd like to. You see, I always dreamed of being a stuntman when I was a kid,' he explained. 'It was all those years of watching Steve McQueen movies or Clint Eastwood ones. But my mother told me not to be stupid and to go to college. Still, I think I would have made a pretty good stuntman, what do you think?'

Aisling didn't even need to consider it. The more Sam talked, the more apparent it became that he'd love risking life and limb every day with lots of people watching. For a moment, she wondered why Sam had come back to Ireland since he loved the States so much. But she didn't want to ask him difficult questions, any more than she wanted him to ask her awkward ones. Tonight, she merely wanted to feel good, sexy and wanted.

'It was the biggest goddamn shark I'd ever seen in my life,' Sam said, telling her about the weeks he'd spent shark-fishing the previous summer, when he'd caught a monster shark.

A little voice in Aisling's head reminded her that Sam in 'action-hero mode' was not a million miles away from Michael telling her about the brilliant political profile he'd just written. But then Michael wouldn't have been feeding her strawberries from his plate while he did it.

She loved the way Sam carefully coated each strawberry in cream before gently holding it to her lips, letting her take a huge bite before he finished the half-eaten fruit. There was something very sensuous about the whole thing. Aisling found herself responding to it. Her inhibitions drained away as she tasted strawberries and champagne, and enjoyed the heady atmosphere between them.

When Sam went to the bathroom, she sat back in her chair and took a quick glance around the restaurant. She was enjoying herself hugely. It had been a long time since she'd enjoyed a meal out like this, an intimate dinner where she didn't feel frumpy, boring and, eventually, plastered. When Michael brought her out to dinner, she felt so depressed at her size and miserable because she hated whatever dreadful outfit she was wearing that she ate everything put in front of her and drank like a fish.

It was a glorious change to feel confident and slim, to dine with an attractive man who looked deep into her eyes.

They worked their way through a second bottle of champagne and four Irish coffees, by which time Sam was gently playing with Aisling's fingers across the table and giving her veiled looks from heavy-lidded eyes. 'Do you miss your husband?' he asked suddenly.

Three months ago, Aisling would have burst into tears at that question. Now she watched Sam's fingers gently stroke the fleshy part at the base of her palm and answered, 'Yes and no. I miss him because we were together so long, I miss the person in the bed beside me at night, the man who put out the bins. Sometimes,' she added, 'sometimes, I don't even think about him, when I'm very busy and I don't have time.'

'That's not quite what I meant,' Sam whispered, increasing the pressure with his fingers.

She looked up at him. It was strange and exciting to watch his want for her. Curiously liberating. It made her feel free from the past, free to say what she wanted instead of saying the right thing.

'I haven't even thought about sex since he left,' she replied candidly. 'Until I met you.' She gasped. 'I can't believe I said that,' she said, laughing. 'That's the effect you have on me, Sam Delaney.'

'I'm glad to hear it. Didn't you ever feel the need to break out when you were married? The desire to do something different?' Sam asked idly.

'Or do *someone* different? Isn't that what you mean?' Aisling said. 'That's not me. Well,' she corrected herself, 'that wasn't me.' It is now, she thought silently.

She caught the waitress's eye. 'Could I have a brandy? Do you want one, Sam?' If she was going to do this, she needed some more liquid confidence. Her head was definitely going to ache in the morning.

'Is the new Aisling ready for something different?' Sam asked in a low voice when the waitress had placed two brandy balloons in front of them.

It was now or never, she told herself. Go for it. She finished her brandy in a couple of burning gulps before answering. 'Yes.'

Sam grinned and drained his glass. 'Shall we go and continue this conversation at home?'

'Sure.'

Amazed at her own audacity, she sat in the back of the taxi and held Sam's hand. Hand-holding wasn't what he had in mind. He didn't seem to care what the taxi-driver saw, he simply slid his arms around her and kissed her passionately. Once, Aisling would have died of shame thinking about the driver watching them in his rear-view mirror, two adults behaving like sex-mad adolescents. But, insulated by alcohol, she didn't care, even when Sam's hand slid up her skirt to stroke between her thighs.

When she fumbled with her keys before finding the right one to open her front door, Aisling briefly wondered if the neighbours were watching her arrive home with a strange man.

At least they wouldn't know how late he stayed, she reflected, since he hadn't brought his car. Nobody could squint out of their windows and tut-tut if a strange car was parked outside the Morans' in the morning.

Fiona was probably peering out, Aisling realised and stifled a laugh. She should have come up with a secret signal with her neighbour – two flashes of the torch from the master bedroom if Sam made mad passionate love to her, and one flash if he fell asleep on the settee after too much booze.

Sam ambled into the sitting room and lounged on the settee.

'Nice place. Sit down, darling,' he said patting the space beside him.

Suddenly, she felt stone-cold sober. Here she was bringing a strange man into her home, the home she'd shared with

Michael and the boys, and this man was sure that they'd make love. So sure, that he was making himself completely at home, taking over her settee possessively. What am I doing? She thought.

'I have to let the cat out,' she muttered nervously, backing out of the room and into the kitchen. 'Flossie, Flossie, where are you?' she called.

Typically, Flossie had vamoosed when she was required. She wasn't in her wicker basket beside the double radiator. She couldn't be used as an excuse or plonked on Aisling's lap so Sam couldn't drag her onto his.

'D'you have any brandy?' he asked, appearing behind her in the kitchen.

'Of course,' she answered. 'Funny, I always thought I was the only one who wanted another drink after a meal out.'

'Me too. Brandy makes me want more brandy,' he added, looking around the kitchen. 'No cat, huh?'

'She must have gone upstairs to the hotpress.' Aisling rummaged around in the cupboard for decent glasses. 'She loves snuggling up on the socks at the bottom. Here we are,' she said triumphantly. She took two whiskey tumblers made of heavy glass with a green tint. 'Damn, I've just remembered I've no brandy. There's whiskey in the cupboard beside the notice-board.'

She rinsed the glasses and turned to find him examining the photos and notes stuck to the cork notice-board. There was a picture of the boys in Portugal, sliding down a huge water slide, their hands in the air and their mouths open as they shrieked in delight. It was three years old, but Aisling loved it. There was a picture of the boys and their soccer team after winning a cup match, faces dirty and proud. And there was a photo taken at a barbeque in Fiona's garden the summer before, a shot of Fiona dancing with Nicole with Pat in the background wearing an apron and waving a large fork with a sausage on each prong. There weren't any pictures of Michael. There had been a really nice one of him and the boys in Portugal, lying on the beach pretending to pose like body-builders with white zinc striped down their noses to protect them from the sun.

She had taken it down and stuck it at the back of the drawer in the dining-room sideboard. She had briefly thought of cutting Michael out of the picture altogether, but decided that was a bit childish.

Sam stared at the photos and notes, looked at the postcard from Sorcha in Istanbul and the Mickey Mouse one from the Finucanes in Disneyland, and Aisling's shopping list reminders to get loo roll and fabric softener.

'There are none of you here,' he remarked, turning to her.

Aisling took a half-full bottle of Jameson out of the cupboard and sloshed some into each glass. 'I'm not photo-genic.'

'Don't say that,' he said firmly. 'I'm telling you, Aisling, you mightn't think so but you're one gorgeous lady.'

She was about to contradict him when she remembered an article she'd read in a magazine about compliments and how to take them graciously. *You'll never have confidence in yourself if you can't take a compliment. Your lack of confidence will eventually convince people that they're wrong – and you're right about yourself.*

'Thanks,' she said. That wasn't so hard, now was it? she thought.

'I guess nobody's told you you're beautiful often enough,' Sam said.

He leaned back against the worktop and took a long draught of whiskey. Aisling did the same. The fiery liquid hit her system with a jolt.

'Come here,' Sam said.

Still holding her glass, she stood in front of him. He stroked her cheek and let his hand lazily slide down her face to caress her neck. She could feel her skin burn where he'd touched her and she unconsciously leaned forward so he could touch her some more.

'You are beautiful,' he murmured, taking her glass away from her. He slid both arms around her waist and pulled her forward. Their lips met and it was as if Aisling had never been kissed before. His mouth was hungry on hers and she pressed her body close to his, throwing reservations to the wind. They clung together, bodies melting into each other. His body was solid, from all that rock-climbing, no doubt.

She held his head close to hers, her fingers running through his chestnut hair while she kissed him open-mouthed. He tasted good. Fantastic, in fact. She kissed him again, lots of small kisses melting into one long one.

It was the previous week all over again. Her nervousness had gone and she felt greedy for him, eager to feel his body pressed up against hers, inside hers.

'You're something else, Aisling,' he breathed, pulling his mouth away from hers for a moment. 'Should we continue this upstairs?'

'Yes.' Aisling couldn't believe what was going to happen. Here she was, a separated woman of thirty-five clinging to a man she barely knew – ready to have sex with him. On the first date, too. Did that make her the ultimate trollop, a complete slut? Probably. But who cared? She could do what she wanted. But it had to be safe. If she was going to do something this crazy, she'd better think about pregnancy or AIDs.

'Do you have condoms?' she asked bluntly, amazed at her own daring.

'Yes. Are you sure you want to do this?' he whispered, as he covered her in tiny, hot kisses.

'Yes. Come on.'

She'd made the decision, there was no going back. So what if she was about to have sex in her marital home with someone who wasn't her husband. Her bloody husband had shagged off with someone else. God, she needed a drink.

She moved out of Sam's embrace and picked up her glass, draining it. He smiled and drank his down too, proffering his glass for a refill. She poured two more huge whiskies, then took him by the hand and led him upstairs.

The bedroom was in darkness. Before she'd had a chance to

turn on the bedside lights, more flattering than the overhead one, he put his glass down and took hers away from her, then put his arms around her again.

They fell on the bed and rolled over until she was on top of him. He kissed her ardently while one hand burrowed under her skirt, sliding it up her thighs. Stockings and suspenders, Aisling thought, I should be wearing stockings and suspenders. Not tights.

Sam tried to reach the waistband of her black sheer tights but couldn't manage to hoist her skirt up high enough.

They'd be there all night if she didn't help.

'Hold on,' she whispered. Why am I whispering anyway? She wondered. There was nobody to hear them.

Aisling kissed him again and then wriggled off him, getting to her feet shakily. God, she'd had too much to drink. She was pretty pissed.

He gazed up at her expectantly as she unzipped her skirt slowly. Damn. There were few sights more unerotic than a pair of tights worn over knickers. Or a body. She didn't want him to see her like that.

'I'm waiting,' Sam sounded amused. 'Turn on the lights so I can see you.'

Aisling walked around the bed to turn on her bedside lamp. As she switched it on, Sam grabbed her, one hand unzipping her skirt. It slid down to her ankles and she quickly dragged off her tights before he pulled her into his arms. They kissed again, his tongue exploring her mouth while his hands gently explored her body. Thank God she'd shaved her legs earlier.

'Can I take this off?' Sam asked, fingers at the snap fasteners at the crotch of her bronze body.

'Only if you take everything off as well.'

Aisling unbuttoned his shirt, her fingers clumsy as they fiddled with the small buttons. She'd nearly finished and was sliding her hands under the fabric to touch his chest, when she felt him unpop her bronze body. She shuddered with pleasure as she felt his fingers on her bare flesh, stroking and probing her intimately.

'Oh Sam,' she murmured.

'Is it good?' he asked.

'Wonderful,' she replied, giving herself up to sheer pleasure. Sam pushed the body up until he'd exposed her breasts encased in a cream cotton bra.

'You're gorgeous,' he said, nuzzling the soft flesh of her breasts. 'Help me get this thing off.'

Aisling sat up and pulled the body off over her head. Sam reached behind her back and unclasped her bra swiftly.

'Now you,' she demanded, pulling his shirt tail out of his jeans. He stripped off quickly, then pulled down the duvet, and slid into the bed. Aisling got in beside him and snuggled up to him, loving the sensation of his warm silky skin on hers.

'You're beautiful, Aisling,' he repeated, tracing soft kisses down to her breasts, kissing her until Aisling was wild with pleasure.

'That's wonderful,' she said softly. 'Your turn.'

'No.' He propped himself up on one arm and gazed at her. 'Tonight I'm in charge and my job is to make you come over and over again,' he added. 'So lie back and think of the Empire!'

He kissed her breasts again as one hand gently stroked the sensitive skin on her inner thighs.

Aisling moaned with pleasure.

'If you insist, Mr Delaney,' she said.

'I do.'

Wow, thought Aisling for the second time as she lay propped up on the pillows with Sam sprawled out in the bed beside her. He was snoring, not loudly but still enough to keep her awake.

After two orgasms, she should have been out for the count, but she couldn't sleep. Even though it was four in the morning, she felt incredibly awake, utterly relaxed and totally sated. She hadn't realised quite how boring and mundane sex with Michael had become until now.

He'd been unstoppable, determined to send her into paroxysms of pleasure twice. Twice. Wow.

She slid out from under the covers. Sam wouldn't miss her. Even if he did, she just had to have a drink of water. All the alcohol she'd consumed was taking its toll and she was madly thirsty. She took her dressing-gown off the hook on the door and went downstairs for a drink of water.

After draining the second glass, she refilled it and crept quietly into the downstairs toilet.

Aisling was amazed to find that she actually looked good. She glowed. That was it. Her hair was tousled, her lipstick had been completely kissed off, her eyes were red-rimmed with rivulets of mascara under them and she felt very tired, but the face in the mirror shone back at her.

She'd done it. She'd broken the curse of Michael by sleeping with another man in their bed. Thank you so much, Sam, she whispered to her reflection.

When she slid carefully under the duvet, Sam grunted and moved till he was curled up against her, his body moulded to hers. He moaned again, wrapped one arm around her and nuzzled into her neck.

'All right?' he muttered sleepily.

'Wonderful,' she whispered back, cuddling into him happily. 'Wonderful.'

He woke her by kissing her gently, starting on her mouth and working his way down her neck until she opened her eyes groggily.

'This is your wake-up call, Aisling.' Sam moved further down her body to cup her full breasts in his hands.

'What time is it?' she asked, closing her eyes.

'Twenty to two.'

'Two! In the afternoon?' She shot up in the bed. 'The boys will be coming soon, you've got to go, Sam,' she said urgently.

'Relax.' His voice was amused. 'They're not coming home until six, you told me that last night. So what's the rush?'

'I know, but . . .' Aisling couldn't explain her panic. Last night, it had been different. How could she explain that she wanted Sam out of the house because she felt guilty, as if she'd done something wrong. She wanted him out so she could sort out her muddled feelings, so she could wash up the glasses, change the sheets and rinse him off her body. The boys mustn't see him yet, it was too soon.

'Please understand, Sam,' she began, 'I've never done anything like this before and it feels strange. I can't let the boys meet you yet. It would be too confusing for them, you must see that.'

'Did you enjoy last night?' he asked softly. His fingers played with her hair. He had the most amazing eyes.

'Of course . . .'

He stopped her words with a kiss, a gentle kiss which turned into a long, deep passionate one. Aisling couldn't help responding. The stubble on his chin grazed the soft skin on her neck as he moved down to nuzzle her breasts.

'I love your breasts, Aisling,' he said huskily. She couldn't resist him. He was so sexy and he seemed to know exactly how to turn her on. Before she knew it, they were wrapped up in the duvet, limbs intertwined as they made love.

'I'll go at three. That'll give you loads of time,' Sam murmured.

An hour later, she lay in the bath and watched him finish shaving. He splashed water on his face, dried it and looked at his reflection in the mirror, turning sideways to make sure he hadn't missed a bit with her old razor. Satisfied with what he saw, Sam ran a comb through his hair before pulling on his shirt.

'I'll see myself out,' he said and leaned down to caress one breast.

'God, you feel great. I want to drag you back to bed again. But not that bed, of course.' He straightened up abruptly. 'It's got to go, don't you agree?'

'Why?' asked Aisling, completely at a loss to know what he meant.

'We can hardly make love in the bed you shared with your husband,' he replied in astonished tones.

'Oh. I see,' Aisling said, although she didn't. Making love in Michael's bed hadn't worried him too much the night before. But then, they'd both been so plastered that they could have been making love on O'Connell Bridge with a paying crowd watching.

'We could go shopping next weekend,' he said. 'We've got to get some decent booze as well. I've got a real taste for bourbon after living in the States.'

'Fine,' Aisling said automatically.

Sam leaned down and kissed her gently on the mouth, a lingering gentle kiss.

He blew her another kiss from the bathroom door.

'See you soon,' he said.

She heard him slam the front door and sank happily back into the bubbles. Who cared if he wanted a new bed or bourbon instead of whiskey? He was wonderful, he was crazy about her. Hell, he could redecorate the bedroom if he felt like it. Aisling closed her eyes and thought about Sam making love to her. She'd get up and tidy the house later.

'Well, how was dinner?' demanded Fiona, the moment Aisling picked up the phone. 'Where did you go? Tell me *everything.*'

'Everything?' asked Aisling innocently, trying not to burst with excitement. 'Sam arrived at just after half seven and he was wearing a blue shirt . . .'

'Bugger the blue shirt!' said Fiona in exasperation. 'How did you get on? Did he kiss you, did you kiss him, did you have mad, passionate sex to Ravel's *Bolero?*'

Aisling snorted down the phone. 'The answers to those questions, in order, are, Marvellously, Yes. Yes and Yes – although we didn't have any music. You know I don't have a stereo in the bedroom.'

'Aisling Moran,' shrieked Fiona. 'I don't believe you. You slept with him? You didn't, did you?' she asked.

'Yes, I did. I know I'm a trollop but who cares, it felt absolutely wonderful and I'm glad I did sleep with him. Not that we got that much sleep . . .'

'Has he gone?' asked Fiona.

'Yes.'

'Right. Put the kettle on, I'm coming over. If you can walk into the kitchen without crutches, that is!'

'He's very attractive, of course,' Fiona said five minutes later, as she sat in Aisling's kitchen and lit a cigarette. 'And let's face it, straight, good-looking, single men are practically extinct in this country these days. Since you have me to thank for introducing you to him, I want all the juicy details. I mean *all*.'

'Thank you, darling Fiona, for introducing me to him,' Aisling said with a giggle. 'I certainly owe you. Sam is a fantastic lover. Not that I have anything to compare him with,' she added. 'But it was wonderful. Three times, Fiona, *three times*. I'm exhausted.'

'You don't look exhausted, Fiona remarked wryly. 'You look like they've turned a light on inside you.'

'I know. It's amazing, isn't it?' Aisling sat back in her chair with a practically untouched cup of coffee in one hand.

'We were awake till at least four and I should have a thumping great hangover after all we drank, but do you know what?' She grinned at Fiona. 'I feel fantastic. And different. I can't explain it, but being with Sam, it was as if all this pressure that's been building up inside me since Michael left was suddenly released, I could relax and let go. It was amazing.'

'You're in love,' Fiona said with a laugh.

'No,' corrected Aisling. 'I'm not. I fancy Sam and he fancies me, but that's not love. I don't want to be in love again, not for a long time.' She was suddenly serious. 'Love is just trouble. If you love someone, they have the power to hurt you and I don't want to go through that ever again.'

'That's perfectly understandable,' the other woman said. 'But don't think you can control love, Aisling. You can't.'

'I know that.' Aisling got up and filled up the kettle. The washing machine shuddered to a stop beside her, ending its final spin. She really should hang out the clothes but she couldn't be bothered. Tomorrow would do.

'Getting a job, losing weight and learning how to live on my own – they were all important things, but no matter what I did, I was still tied to Michael,' Aisling explained. 'Now I'm not. I was tied to him even though he wasn't tied to me. He'd escaped but I couldn't. Sam helped me to escape.'

'When are you seeing him again?' Fiona asked.

'Next weekend, for dinner. He wanted to see me tomorrow but he's got to go to Cork for the week. He's ringing later.'

Fiona raised one eyebrow expressively. 'He's keen.'

The last globule of cream squelched out of the piping bag onto the strawberry cheesecake. Aisling dumped the bag in the sink and carefully carried the plate over to the fridge.

Dizzy, the Coughlans' fat black spaniel, watched Aisling's every move, big brown eyes fixed on the woman who'd been cooking all sorts of delicious things in the kitchen all afternoon.

'No, you can't have anything, Dizzy,' Aisling admonished the drooling dog. 'You're on a diet.'

'*I'm* the one who should be on a diet,' wailed Rachel. She hurried into the kitchen wearing a pink candlewick dressing-gown with a wet towel wrapped, turban-style, around her head.

Rachel was short, plump, very pretty and looked at least ten years younger than her husband, who had to be around forty-five. She was also very disorganised, as Aisling had found out when she arrived in the Coughlans' kitchen a few hours earlier and started a lengthy search in hopelessly untidy cupboards for a large plate for the cheesecake.

'The zip on my black crêpe dress won't close. I know I should have bought those tummy-flattener pants,' Rachel said miserably. 'Have I time to race off to Spar and get a pair of control tights, do you think?'

'You have the time,' Aisling said slowly, thinking of the calorie-laden meal she'd been preparing. 'But you'll be awfully uncomfortable by the time you've eaten dinner if the dress is too tight in the first place.'

'You're right.' Rachel stomped over to the fridge and took out a bottle of white wine from the half-dozen on the bottom shelf.

'Oh, the cheesecake looks delicious!' she squealed as soon as she saw it. 'I can't wait to try it. Let's have a glass of wine, Aisling,' she wheedled. 'You've been busy all day and you need a break.'

Aisling had been working hard in Rachel's huge old-fashioned kitchen for over two hours, slicing vegetables, finishing off the cheesecake she'd made at home and preparing the pheasant with apples and Calvados. She'd nearly gone mad making the fiddly timbales of smoked salmon with dill salad Rachel had wanted to impress her snooty American sister-in-law, Antonia.

'When she's gone, I'll tell everyone else that you cooked the meal. Antonia will want to leave early, she always does. Doesn't like spending too much time with her in-laws,' Rachel revealed. 'But I want to pretend that I did everything just to shut that cow up. Do you mind awfully?'

'As long as you sneak my cards into everyone else's pockets when they're going,' Aisling replied, fishing several cream printed cards out of her handbag.

Reservations
Why slave over the cooker when you can relax at your own dinner party? My team and I can cook you an exquisite, mouth-watering menu from fresh ingredients and you won't have to lift a finger. Phone Aisling Moran for details.

This wasn't strictly true. Aisling's team was herself and herself and herself. Still, she *could* get help if she really needed it. Her mother had offered to give her a hand with desserts.

'This looks very impressive.' Rachel admired the rich creamy paper and the elegant copperplate lettering Aisling had picked in the printing shop.

She'd had a hundred made up and was now crossing her fingers that they'd pay for themselves. She took a cautious sip of wine from the glass Rachel handed her. Catastrophic if she ruined her first dinner by getting tiddly with the hostess before the meal.

'Is there anything I can do?' Rachel sat down at the kitchen table and took a bottle of flamingo-pink nail varnish from her dressing-gown pocket.

'No thanks, you relax,' said Aisling quickly. She'd seen Rachel's hopelessly untidy cupboards and the large collection of ready-made microwaveable meals in the freezer. The other woman was obviously not a dab hand in the kitchen.

By half seven everything was ready. The guests were due, the pheasant was cooking gently in the oven, the damned timbales were perfect and even Rachel was ready, resplendent in an expensive-looking gold silk blouse, black trousers and plenty of gold jewellery.

Her daughter, Amy – sixteen and pretty despite the sulky expression on her face – had been pressed into service to help serve the meal. Either Rachel had been around fifteen when she had Amy, or she used lots of miraculous wrinkle-preventing eye cream, Aisling decided.

In a tattered pair of 501s, a skinny black polo neck that was turning grey, and black suede boots with stack heels, Amy looked like a younger, slimmer version of her mother.

'You could have dressed up, Amy.' Rachel marched into the kitchen to find her offspring enjoying a sneaky vodka tonic. 'You certainly shouldn't be drinking. I said one glass of wine, if you remember. And those jeans are dreadful.'

Amy shot Rachel a venomous look.

'Don't look at me like that, Madam,' started Rachel crossly. Aisling knew that a row was brewing. Maybe I should cook the stuff at home and just drive it over, she thought silently. Maybe I should forget the idea of running a catering company at all.

The doorbell rang loudly. Row instantly forgotten, Rachel roared for her husband to answer the door and hurried out to welcome her guests.

It was eight by the time everyone was seated. Jim was on

wine service and winked at Aisling when he rushed past her with two bottles of white and the corkscrew under his arm. Rachel bustled back into the kitchen to help Amy carry in the twelve plates.

'I don't want Antonia to see you,' she whispered to Aisling.

Aisling was grateful that she didn't have to go in and serve the guests. Cooking a meal *and* looking fresh as a daisy when serving it, simply wasn't possible. Her grey T-shirt was damp with sweat and her hair had flopped in the heat of the kitchen, strands stuck to her forehead. She longed for a long warm bath, a nice book and a glass of sweet white wine.

But it would be at least half ten when she got home and she knew that she'd barely have the energy to slump onto the settee and watch some mindless rubbish before going to bed.

When the guests were all eating, she pushed the door between the kitchen and the dining room open just a fraction, and listened.

She heard murmurs of 'Delicious, Rachel' and 'This salmon is fantastic, how did you do it?' They liked it. She only hoped the pheasant went down as well.

'Would you like some pheasant?' she asked Amy when the girl returned to the kitchen after delivering the last plate.

'I'm a vegetarian,' Amy said, then added, 'but everyone in there is gobbling the pheasant up like mad. Even Aunt Antonia.'

'Not a woman easily pleased, I believe.' Aisling filled the sink with hot water.

Amy grimaced. 'She's a cow. I hope she chokes on it. Not because of your cooking,' she added quickly. 'No offence.'

'None taken. If you're hungry, I could make you some nice cheese sauce for the broccoli and cauliflower, or an omelette?' Aisling had noticed that the girl looked tired and pale under her heavy pancake foundation.

'No, but thanks anyway.' Amy was really very pretty when she smiled. 'D'you want a hand with the washing-up?'

Aisling scrubbed and Amy dried.

'Do you cook all the time, for a living, I mean?'

'Actually, this is my first dinner party,' Aisling explained. 'I work as a secretary in a legal firm and I ended up catering for a special lunch when the original caterers made a mess of things. That's where I met your father and he said your mother would love some help with parties and dinners for her new business.'

'That's true. She can't even make tea. So you never did anything like this before?'

'I love cooking and I've done cooking courses but I never actually thought of doing it professionally. Until this year, anyway.'

'Why is that?'

'I was a housewife and I went back to work when my husband and I split up earlier this year,' Aisling said matter-of-factly. She didn't feel her heart ache when she said it, didn't feel the lump in her throat at the thought of Michael. Thank God. She rinsed a copper-bottomed saucepan and placed it on the drainer.

'When people congratulated me on my cooking after the lunch, I decided to do something about it and then your mum rang. With a bit of luck, and if people get my cards when they're leaving, I'll get more jobs like this.'

'Wow, that's amazing. You're a career woman.' Amy dried a wooden spoon carefully.

Aisling smiled at the girl. 'I suppose I am. Strange, I never thought I'd be one.'

'That's what I want to be,' Amy said. 'I don't want to sit around like Mum did for years waiting for something to happen before Dad pushed her into doing something.'

'That's hardly fair, Amy,' Aisling rebuked gently.' If your mother hasn't worked for a few years, it's very, very difficult going back. I should know.

'My first few months back at work were a nightmare. Imagine if you'd been off school for two years and then had to go back to class with girls two years younger and start again . . .'

'I suppose you're right,' Amy said reluctantly.

'I *know* I'm right,' Aisling said firmly. 'You'd feel totally threatened and stupid, because they'd know more than you. You'd be paranoid about not fitting in. It's a horrible feeling, believe me. Take it from me, your mum's been really brave setting up this PR company and I'm sure she could do with your support.'

'Suppose.' Amy dried a saucepan.

'Everything's going wonderfully, Aisling.'

Rachel rushed into the kitchen clutching four empty bottles of wine.

'It is if you've gone through all that booze already,' reproved Amy, as if she hadn't been drinking herself. 'That's nine bottles at least.'

'It's a party. And there are twelve of us,' Rachel retorted. 'They love the pheasant, especially Antonia. She says she's "amazed it's so good". Bitch. Can you put cyanide on her cheesecake, Aisling?'

Aisling grinned. 'I'm not sure how good that would be for my reputation as a dinner-party cook. I'll do salmon timbales but I draw the line at cyanide.'

'They were gorgeous,' Rachel sighed. 'Everyone wanted to know how I did them. And the pheasant too. I think they're all convinced I cleaned out Marks and Spencer's food hall. As soon as Antonia is gone, do come in and I'll introduce you, won't you?'

Aisling didn't really want to but then she thought about her business. 'Of course. I'll need to freshen up first.'

'Use my room,' volunteered Amy.

It was half twelve when Aisling turned the key in her front door lock. The pots and pans would just have to stay in the hall overnight, she decided, dumping everything onto the hall carpet.

Antonia and her husband had stayed at the Coughlans' until eleven, so Aisling and Amy had sat in the kitchen watching Tom Cruise in *Top Gun* on the small TV beside the microwave until they'd left.

When Aisling finally walked into the dining room, everyone clapped.

'The best meal I've had in years,' said one woman, holding up a large glass of port as a toast. 'I do hope you can cook for me sometime.'

'Of course,' Aisling said. 'I'll give you a card.'

The meal had been a huge success and, as she went into the kitchen to look for Flossie, she felt elated but dog-tired. She switched off the lights downstairs and went to bed, not even bothering to take off her eye make-up. Just before turning out her bedside light, she switched the alarm clock off. She was going to have a lie-in in the morning. She deserved it.

'Aisling, that really isn't you. It doesn't suit you.' Sam stood a few feet away from the changing cubicle, eyes narrowed as he looked at the fitted navy dress Aisling had just tried on. She sighed in exasperation. This was the third item she'd tried on and he'd hated the other two as well.

The cream woollen dress with a matching long cardigan was 'too tight', the elegant black shirt was 'too short', and she'd thought he was going to have a seizure when he saw the clingy red lycra top that went with it. They'd been shopping in the Stephen's Green Centre for just an hour and Aisling was already wondering what sort of illness she could fake so she could go home. She'd been so thrilled with Sam's present of a clothes voucher to celebrate their first month of going out together. It was such a thoughtful gift, she'd told Fiona happily.

Aisling cooked a special dinner for the occasion and she was delighted when Sam gave her the voucher which was hidden in a big box of chocolates. It was the sort of gesture Michael would never have made.

'We can go shopping next Saturday,' Sam had said, unwrapping a coffee creme for her.

'I'd love that,' she said truthfully, wondering how to avoid eating too many chocolates without upsetting him. A whole box of Dairy Milk would mean she couldn't eat a proper meal for at least a month. 'I'd love to go shopping with you.'

Famous last words.

'What *would* look good on me, Sam?' she demanded now,

irritated beyond belief. 'A yashmak?'

'Honey, don't get upset.' He looked pained, his eyes troubled, as if she'd really upset him. 'I just want you to buy something suitable, that's all.'

'Suitable for *what*?'

'For going out to dinner with me, for the office. You needn't be so defensive. I'm only trying to help.'

'Listen, Sam.' Aisling looked at him with eyes blazing. 'You and I have very different ideas about what's "suitable". I have the sort of figure I can show off. And I want to show it off!' she hissed. 'Have you got that?'

'Fine. I just want you to look nice.'

The cheek of him, Aisling thought crossly as she retreated into the changing room and pulled the curtains. As if she didn't look nice before.

Men always thought they knew better than you. She hoped this particular phase turned out to be just that – a phase – a brief one. For all his faults, Michael had never been particularly interested in her wardrobe. Then again, maybe that had been part of the problem. Perhaps men were supposed to be fascinated by what their women wore. Perhaps it was a caveman thing, a flattering thing.

Aisling stood in her bra and knickers and looked at the three very nice outfits that Sam had condemned. They all *looked* nice. But after years of wearing sloppy T-shirts and elastic-waisted trousers, she probably wasn't the best fashion expert in the world.

Wearing anything clingy was a thrill for her. But maybe Sam was right and she shouldn't indulge her taste for spray-on lycra garments in case she ended up looking like mutton dressed as lamb.

'Aisling.' The curtain shook. 'Look what I've found.'

She stuck her head out of the cubicle.

'This,' Sam produced a clothes-hanger from behind his back, 'would be lovely on you.'

'This' turned out to be a long, highly patterned pale peach dress that flowed and billowed like a sail, a dress which would undoubtedly make her look like an over-the-hill bridesmaid. Six months ago, Aisling would have loved it, mainly because it was big enough to accommodate a size sixteen. However, she wasn't a size sixteen any more and she wanted to wear something which showed off the fact. Sam didn't know anything about this. He had no idea she'd lost so much weight, she hadn't told him. Aisling had felt it might change his opinion of her, as if he'd go off her if he found out she hadn't always been the slim blonde she was now.

It wasn't fair to expect him to understand her hatred for anything baggy. Keep calm, she told herself. Don't let the sins of Michael Moran be visited on every man after him.

She reached out and took the dress from Sam. His face creased into a smile and she grinned back at him. She impulsively leaned out and kissed him on the cheek. There was something utterly charming about Sam's smile, that mischievous grin which lit up his face. He was quite irresistible standing there in a snow-white cricket jumper and faded denims which clung to his long legs. One of the shop assistants had eyed him up the moment they walked into the shop until Aisling shot her a proprietorial 'hands off' look.

'Bet you a tenner it looks lovely on you,' said Sam confidently, as she slipped back behind the curtain.

His attitude to clothes was probably because he'd lived in the States for so long, Aisling decided as she took the dress off the hanger and stepped into it. Apart from places like California, people in the US dressed in a much more conservative manner than their European cousins, didn't they? Aisling wasn't sure. But she ought to give Sam the benefit of the doubt. Definitely.

'It's beautiful, Aisling.' He held one of her hands high and made her turn so he could admire the dress from every angle. Privately, she thought it made her look like some sort of child-woman instead of a mature woman of thirty-five. But Sam loved it.

'It's so sexy,' he cried with delight. 'You look amazing.'

He grabbed her in a bear hug and whispered in her ear.
'Good enough to eat. Let's take it.'
'And then we can stop shopping?' Aisling asked.
'Absolutely.'
'I'll take it.'

CHAPTER EIGHTEEN

'Sit down.' The builder dragged up a paint-speckled stool for Jo to sit on. He covered it with a newspaper and Jo sat down gratefully. For once, it wasn't tiredness, an aching back or her recently developed varicose veins that made her want to sit down rapidly. It was the state of the cottage.

She'd expected a clean, newly refurbished place but she'd walked into a disaster area, with dust everywhere and the sound of a kango hammer blasting in her ears.

Rhona had often asked her whether she was insane to sell her cosy, modern apartment in Malahide to move into an old, ramshackle cottage in the Dublin mountains.

'You won't be in before Christmas,' Rhona declared when Jo explained that there'd be a two-week gap between moving out of her apartment and moving into the newly painted, renovated and rewired house in tranquil Redwood Lane.

'The contractor's a very reliable man and he says it'll all be finished by the fifth of November,' Jo replied. 'Honestly, Rho, it's not like you to be so pessimistic.'

Rhona looked at her friend shrewdly. 'Jo, if it's finished by the tenth of November, we'll go out to celebrate – you can have dinner and I'll eat my hat. It's a pity you hadn't joined *Style* when Ted and I bought our house. I distinctly remember being told the house would be ready by the end of August. We moved in during a torrential downpour in October. I never got the water stains out of my mother's old cream armchair.'

It looked as if Rhona was going to be proved right. It was already the second week in November, the builders had been working for three weeks and the cottage looked worse than ever.

The tiny hall was filthy with muddy footprints. A week of

rain had stopped work on the roof. The garden had turned into a bog and roof still hadn't been fixed. All the cottage needed was rewiring, central heating installed, a bit of work on the plumbing and a small job on the roof, or so Mark's contractor friend had said.

So why, after three weeks, was the entire place like a building site?

'It's not as bad as it looks,' the builder roared over the din.

'Really, Tom? Well, that's a relief because it looks bad, very bad.' Jo's head throbbed in time to the kango hammer.

'Turn it off,' roared Tom in the direction of the kitchen.

When nothing happened, he left Jo in the tiny hall wondering what the hell she was going to say to the painters who were due to arrive tomorrow.

'Tea?' asked Tom, poking his head around the kitchen door. 'We're just brewing up.'

'OK. Now tell me what's happened?' Jo asked wearily. She got off the stool, walked into the kitchen and stared at the big hole where the sink used to be and at the gash that ran across the recently concreted floor.

'Plumbing problem. We've had to rip up the floor. I did ring you at the office yesterday evening to tell you,' he added, 'but when I couldn't contact you, I just went ahead and sorted it out. It'll add another two days onto the work. We'll be finished by Tuesday, latest.'

'The painters are coming tomorrow,' Jo said in a faint voice.

'I know, I know. I'll ring them up and tell them not to come until Tuesday afternoon.'

'Sugar?' inquired the man who'd been working the kango hammer.

'Two, please,' said Jo, 'and do you have any biscuits?' Or Prozac?

They drank their tea and talked about how the rain had delayed the work, how the plumbing had delayed the work and how there was some problem with the phone-line according to the man from Telecom.

'Oh, did I tell you that he came?' asked Tom.

409

Jo speed-munched her way through three fig rolls and drank a cup of very sweet tea before climbing the stairs. The pale wooden banisters were thick with concrete dust, lumps of plaster had found their way onto the steps. Jo ignored it.

As she walked into the second bedroom, she realised that the painters would have to spend days cleaning the walls and woodwork.

At least the cork tiles in the bathroom would only need a wash. But the pale green carpet in the smaller bedroom was so dusty Jo knew she'd have to replace it. She thought about the mounting bills and decided that judicious hoovering would have to do for the moment. Maybe she could rent one of those industrial carpet cleaners and do it herself. Then again, she thought gloomily, at seven months pregnant she was hardly in any condition to hoover anything except food up from her plate. She felt *huge*. Even her gynaecologist said so. Huge, broke and with a half-finished cottage hanging around her neck like a millstone. She poked at a bit of carpet with her shoe. A cloud of dust rose like white smoke from the Vatican. Blast.

If anyone asked her what she wanted for her birthday in a couple of weeks, she'd ask for a carpet-cleaning voucher.

The kango hammer started up again, the noise practically drowned out the thoughts in her head. God, what a waste it had been coming up here today. But she had to do something on her day off instead of slobbing around Aisling's house. It was lovely of Aisling to have offered her spare room for the two weeks when Jo was homeless – make that six weeks – and lovely to spend time with her friend, the first time they'd actually lived together since their flat-sharing days. But she preferred her own space to living with someone else, even if that someone was as easy-going as Aisling. And now that Sam was there every minute of the day, Jo was beginning to feel like a gooseberry. An enormous gooseberry.

She went into the main bedroom and idled away a few moments imagining how she was going to decorate it. She'd

410

picked a rich yellow paint to go with the cream and butter-milk curtains she fancied. But the curtain material would have to wait. God only knew how much extra the contractor would charge.

She was staring out at the muddy wasteland at the front of the cottage wondering how it could possibly be transformed back into something resembling a garden, when the baby kicked. Jo's face grew soft as she stroked her belly lovingly.

The baby was always kicking these days, but Jo didn't mind, except when it happened all night. On those days when she felt depressed, miserable and lonely at the thought of having the baby all by herself, all it took was a gentle reminder from her little passenger to cheer her up.

'I'm off,' she said to Dick, the kango-hammer man, who'd stopped the machine once he saw her making her way carefully down the stairs.

'Bye, Tom,' she called into the sitting room.

'He's gone,' Dick said.

Charming, thought Jo. Rips up the kitchen floor and buggers off. What a worker.

It had started to rain. Again. She trudged through the mud where she and Mark had once negotiated nettles and long grass, and got into her car.

She'd had to push the driver's seat back so she could fit her bump behind the steering wheel. Her size also meant she'd outgrown practically everything she owned, including her maternity trousers. Aisling was going to bring her shopping tomorrow, 'early, so we'll avoid the Saturday crowds', she'd said. Aisling was great. She'd even sorted through her old 'fat' clothes to find something to fit Jo.

A flowery overshirt Aisling had produced, her own black maternity skirt and a pair of pale grey ski boots were today's deeply unflattering outfit. Wedged into the driver's seat, Jo couldn't see her feet, but she just knew that the ski boots were filthy from the muck outside the cottage.

There was no way she could go into the supermarket in this state. Damn and blast.

She turned the key in the ignition. The engine made a
high-pitched whirring noise, gave a little shudder and then
died. Damn, damn, damn. She turned the key again. Same
outcome. I do not believe this is happening, she shrieked. She
tried again and when the engine made a third half-hearted
attempt to get going, she thumped the steering wheel angrily.
Bloody car! This is the perfect time for you to pack it in!

She levered herself out of the car, marched back into the
cottage and gave Dick the fright of his life when she tapped
him on the shoulder.

'Jesus!' he yelled.

Jo was not in the mood for conversation. 'My car won't
start. Will you have a look at it?'

By the time Dick had pulled off his dusty overalls, tried the
car a few times and spent ten minutes with his head under
the bonnet poking around, Jo was at boiling-point.

'It's your starting motor,' he pronounced finally.

'Which means *what*, exactly?' Jo asked irritably.

'It's not going anywhere today,' he replied.

Jo felt as if she'd been deflated. 'What will I do?' she asked.
'Can you give me a lift to a garage or something?' she
pleaded.

'Tom's got the van and he's not coming back for a couple of
hours. He's running over to check on a job in Bray. But I've
got a mobile. You can ring someone.'

Rhona's mobile phone squawked that she was either out of
coverage or had her unit turned off.

Rhona was out all day, Nikki was in London and everyone
else in the office was at lunch, Annette said when she
answered the phone.

'I can't go anywhere,' Annette said, deeply apologetic, 'the
man's coming to fix Tom's word processor and I've got to be
here. I'll get someone to pick you up as soon as . . . oh, hold
on, Jo, will you.'

Jo sheltered from the rain under the porch of the cottage.
She wouldn't be able to hear a thing Annette was saying from
inside the cottage since Dick had started kango-ing again.

She'd have to get her own mobile phone. More money. Why hadn't she bothered joining the AA? Why, why, why?

'Jo?' said a man's deep voice. She gasped. It was Mark. 'What's happened?'

She'd managed to avoid him for ages, had been frostily polite in the office, disappeared as fast as a heavily pregnant woman could whenever he seemed to be walking towards her desk to talk to her. Now there was no escape.

'My car's broken down. It's the starting motor, apparently. I've got no one to bring me home,' she wailed. 'And I don't know who to ring. It's never actually broken down on me before.'

'Where are you? And how do you know it's the starting motor?'

'I'm at the cottage. Redwood Lane. One of the builders looked at it for me. It's his phone I'm using but he doesn't have the van because Tom's gone to Bray.'

If Mark was confused by this explanation, he didn't let on. 'Leave it to me,' he said firmly. 'I'll arrange for a tow truck to pick the car up and I'll come and get you myself. Give me three-quarters of an hour.'

He must have really pushed the Porsche to the speed limit. Only twenty-five minutes later his car roared down the lane and stopped outside the house.

'Nice car,' said Dick appreciatively, sipping another cup of tea. Too much tea, that was why the cottage was like a disaster area, Jo thought testily. Maybe she should swipe the tea bags and see how much Dick got done without a tea break every half an hour.

'Your fella, is he?' Dick inquired with interest.

Jo sniffed. 'No.'

'Mmm,' Dick muttered, as if he'd noticed the eyeshadow, mascara and lipstick she'd carefully applied in the bathroom mirror. She hoped his nose was too bunged up with cement dust to smell the liberal application of Trésor. If only she'd been able to find her brush. Not that she could have done much repair work when her hair was so damp and frizzy.

Mark swept up the path, a dark brown waxed raincoat flapping around his long legs. He looked far more at home in the wilds of the Dublin mountains than she did. Apart from her ski boots.

He also looked healthily brown after two weeks in the Maldives, the honey colour of his skin made the grey streaks in his short hair stand out even more. He was sickeningly attractive, sexy and most definitely not 'my fella', thought Jo desolately.

'Hello,' she said in a small voice.

'Come and sit in my car while I have a look at the engine.' He put a strong arm around her. They walked slowly down the path. He pushed the passenger seat back, helped her in carefully and said, 'I won't be a moment.'

Jo watched him stride back to her car and lift the bonnet capably. Mark did everything capably, everything from running several businesses to fixing the coffee maker in the office when Annette said it couldn't be fixed.

He'd made her feel safe, comforted and special for a few months. And she'd pushed him away and into the arms of his old girlfriend. Well, he'd hardly gone to the Maldives *alone*.

A few minutes later, Mark opened the car door, threw his raincoat into the back and eased his big frame into the driver's seat.

'It's the starting motor, all right. Someone from my garage is coming to get it. They'll have it for you tomorrow afternoon.'

'Will it be expensive?' she asked tiredly.

Mark shot her a glance.

'No. I doubt it. It's just a small job.'

'Really?'

'Really. I don't suppose you've had any lunch, Jo, have you?' he asked kindly.

Nobody said her name like that but Mark, with that mixture of warmth and something else, something she could never define. Tenderness. Was that it? Couldn't be. Why would he bother being kind to her when she'd been such a bitch to him?

Jo bit her lip and looked out the window at the small patchwork fields speeding by, dark with mud. Cows huddled together in the rain, monotonously chewing silage from big metal troughs. They looked as wet as she was. They looked depressed too. Being a cow couldn't be much fun.

She felt a hand on hers, a warm, strong hand clasping her small, cold one for a moment.

'Let's go to Johnny Fox's. I could do with a decent pint of Guinness and some lunch, how about you?'

Jo couldn't say anything. She just nodded.

'Good. And you can tell me why you're still up to your eyes in builders a month after they started.'

'Don't get me going on builders,' said Jo, brightening up. 'Honestly, I don't know what they're playing at. They know I'm in a hurry to move in but they don't seem to be working any faster to make up for lost time.'

'Have you spoken to Brian recently?' Mark put his hand back on Jo's after negotiating a sharp bend. 'He's the best contractor I know. He usually runs a pretty tight ship.'

'He's away all this week.' Jo was almost afraid to move in case she dislodged his hand from hers. It felt lovely to be touched, so comforting to have his fingers gently curled around hers.

'I'll ring his office later,' Mark said, 'and put the skids under those boyos at your house. Brian must be paying them too much if they've all got mobiles, and I don't want to make them millionaires at your expense.'

'Thanks,' Jo said gratefully. 'I know I should be tougher on them myself, but I'm just not up to it right now. If they said anything back to me, I know I'd cry.' She was sick of acting hard-as-nails with Mark. He didn't have to know that when she felt like crying, it was because she'd messed up her chances with him. Nobody knew that, not even Rhona.

Jo had lost count of the times when she'd lain in bed and wondered what he was doing, who he was doing it with.

She still had the ticket stub from their trip to America in her purse and sometimes she took it out and touched it, remembering the few days they'd had together. When anything seemed possible, even a love affair between a pregnant woman and her boss.

Jo had searched the gossip columns relentlessly, keeping an eye out for mentions of glamorous half-French painters or wealthy businessmen. But there'd been nothing.

Once or twice, she'd thought of telling Rhona what had happened, that she'd lied to Mark about Richard. Then she'd stopped herself. Mark had to be in love with Eva and Rhona knew about it, Jo was sure. Telling Rhona that she was in love with Mark would put the other woman in a difficult position.

Jo could almost hear her words, 'They're getting married, Jo, as soon as she can get a divorce.'

Mark looked over and grinned at her, the tiny lines around his grey eyes crinkled up attractively.

'I have tissues in the glove compartment if you feel like a good sob,' he offered. 'But I hope I can cheer you up.'

You sure could, Jo thought silently.

He stopped the car outside the highest pub in Ireland and hurried around to help Jo out of her seat.

Oh God, she thought, remembering the muddy ski boots.

'I look a mess,' she sighed. 'These horrible boots and everything.'

Mark took her face in both hands and kissed her gently on the lips. 'You look absolutely beautiful, as always, Jo.'

Still holding her upturned face, he stared at her carefully, eyes taking in her huge dark eyes fringed with thick lashes. She stared back at him, wondering if she'd dreamed the last moment. She looked an absolute mess with her frizzy hair and her awful clothes. Had he really kissed her and told her she was beautiful? It was like some glorious dream.

Mark was watching her intensely, fingers warm on her skin and suddenly she knew what he was waiting for. A response. He wasn't sure, he'd taken a chance. What a fabulous, marvellous, perfectly timed chance.

Jo smiled at him, feeling the warmth deep inside her spread onto her face.

She stretched one hand up and touched his cheek gently. She stood on her toes and arched herself towards his lips, not easy in her condition. He slid one arm around her, supporting her back as he bent down to kiss her. This time, it was no gentle, platonic kiss: it was deep and passionate, yet somehow full of love and understanding.

Mark pulled away first. 'I should have done that a long time ago,' he said. 'I've wanted to for long enough.'

Jo couldn't speak. She stood looking up at him, her eyes strangely filled with tears.

'Come on.' He took her by the hand and led her towards the pub's front door. 'It's starting to rain again. We can't have you getting soaked twice in one day.'

He found a pew-style seat for her near the fireplace and banked up cushions behind her to protect her back. After months of looking after herself, this act of tenderness was nearly her undoing.

'Don't cry, Jo,' Mark said softly, sitting beside her and kissing her on the cheek. 'I know you're all emotional. But I'm here to look after you now.'

This finished her off completely. 'It's so wonderful,' she sobbed, the tears finally racing down her cheeks. 'You're being so nice, after I was such a bitch to you. I don't deserve it.'

'Of course you do. It's me who doesn't deserve you.' He handed her his handkerchief. 'Blow.'

'I'm always stealing your handkerchiefs,' she snuffled tearily. 'Sorry.'

'My handkerchiefs are all yours, everything of mine is yours.'

He meant it too, she realised, looking up at his face through the tears.

'What about Eva?' she asked.

'There's been nothing going on between Eva and myself, not for a long time. Certainly not since I fell in love with you.'

'What about the Maldives?' asked Jo anxiously. 'You couldn't go *there* on your own, could you?'

Mark's look of amazement told her he hadn't a clue what she was talking about.

'Your holiday,' she prompted.

'I went to Spain with some friends to play golf. Male friends, I should add. I couldn't stand a beach holiday. Unless you were with me,' he added, planting a gentle kiss on her forehead. 'Think of the fun I could have rubbing sun lotion onto you.'

She drank hot tea and he fed her smoked salmon on home-made brown bread. He only started on his plate when hers was finished.

'You're so good to me, Mark,' she said simply, leaning comfortably against his shoulder as he ate.

'I've wanted to be good to you for a long time but you wouldn't let me,' he answered, taking a bite of bread. 'You're very good at that "I'm an independent woman" thing, very good at scaring people off.'

Jo grimaced. 'I know, I'm sorry.'

'There's no need to be sorry, I can understand exactly why you'd want to scare people off.'

'Can you?' she asked uncertainly. She desperately wanted him to understand everything. 'I was so lonely and on my own when Richard left. I felt like a one-woman disaster area. I couldn't bear to let anyone close.'

'I can see that now,' he said with a low laugh. 'When you split up with him . . . I didn't know if that was the right time to make my move. I was afraid you were still in love with him.'

Jo let her right hand rest on Mark's neck, her fingers stroked the back of his head. She loved feeling the breadth of his shoulders, the sheer physical size of him. He made her feel petite, even now when she was as big as a whale.

'When I asked you to go to New York, it was a gamble. I hoped you'd go. I wanted to find out how you really felt about him despite the break-up.'

'You knew we'd split up?' she asked in astonishment.

He grinned and fed her a sliver of salmon drenched in lemon juice.

'Yes. I haf good informants, *Fräulein*,' he said in a mock-German accent. 'I needed to know if you could ever think of me. And I thought you could – and maybe even did – until you told me about the baby.' He shrugged. 'At that point, I felt like such a heel, as if I was trying to take advantage of you.'

'That's why you started treating me like your long-lost little sister,' she said, finally understanding.

'I didn't feel very brotherly towards you.' Mark stroked her thigh with one hand. 'Not at all.'

Jo felt a warmth in her belly at the thought of Mark harbouring unbrotherly desires for her. She remembered the dream she'd had about him that night in the Manhattan Fitzpatrick, the dream where they were naked and entangled in bed.

'I thought you were disgusted with me, that's why we couldn't talk except on the phone,' she explained, dragging her thoughts away from the picture of them in bed.

'Disgusted? Never. You've got to understand something, Jo,' Mark said, turning to face her, 'the way I felt about you, I couldn't bear to see you alone, alone and pregnant thanks to that bastard, when you should have been loved and your baby should have been loved.'

She loved hearing him talk this way, loved it.

'Christ, I couldn't bear to see you facing everything on your own.' He tucked back a few damp strands of Jo's hair behind one ear.

'So you mean you fancied me when you brought me out to lunch ages ago, before we went to New York?' Jo demanded.

'Yes.'

'And you fancied me when we went to New York?'

'Fancied you? I wanted to drag you into bed and never let you out again. When you wore that brown painted thing, I couldn't take my eyes off you.'

'That's my Mary Gregory dress, not some "thing"! But you liked it?' she added, with an arch smile.

'I loved it.'

'Good. I was beginning to think I'd lost my touch,' she added triumphantly.

'And I love you too, Jo. I just needed the chance to tell you. Today was it.'

'Oh Mark.' Jo leaned against him contentedly. 'I love you too. I thought I'd never be able to say that – to your face, that is.' She sat up straight. 'Do you think we should ask the garage to keep the starting motor for us as a sort of memento?'

'One we can look at on our silver wedding and feel indebted to?' he asked, kissing her again.

'Exactly!'

'We should keep Rhona's telephone as a memento as well,' he added.

'Why?'

'Because yesterday she told me that you weren't really with Richard, that he hadn't come back. Why the hell did you say he had?'

'I didn't want you to think I was pining for you when you were obviously in love with Eva,' Jo said defensively. 'I couldn't bear you to pity me or think I was a foolish pregnant woman.'

'I've never met anyone as imaginative as you in my life,' Mark said. 'Does this mean that if I don't ring you first thing tomorrow morning, you'll suddenly decide that I've gone off to the South of France with someone else?'

Jo didn't answer. She was thinking of the most important question of all, the one thing she had to ask.

'The baby. The baby is the most important thing in my life, Mark. I have to think of her first. Can you love my baby, even though she's Richard's?'

'She *won't* be Richard's baby,' he said simply. 'She'll be *our* baby, *our* child. If I hadn't wanted both mother and child, do you think I'd be here? I'm not like him. I don't just want the beautiful journalist and nothing else, no ties, no commitments. I want the woman, the mother, you.' Mark turned on the seat, held her hands and looked at her.

'I know you've been hurt, Jo, but you've got to trust me. I'll never let anyone hurt you ever again. And as for that bastard . . .'

She placed a finger over his mouth. 'Don't ruin it by even talking about him,' she said. 'He's bad news, always has been, although I didn't realise it for a long time. Let's just forget about him.'

They sat in front of the fire for an hour. Jo warmed her toes after Mark had carefully taken off her ski boots.

'I can't remember when I last saw my feet,' she said cheerfully, as the warmth of the fire sank into her bones.

'Was I always really horrible to you?' she asked, hating to think of how she'd been fatally drawn into disagreeing with every second word Mark had said at the editorial conferences.

'Brutal,' he replied. 'You were so argumentative, always determined to have your say because you had such strong opinions about everything. But I liked that. You were never afraid to have your say. And if you were proved wrong, you always said so, which I like even more.'

'Like the posters with the three words wrongly spelled?' she asked.

'Like the posters,' he agreed. 'You were so angry with yourself that day when you realised they'd nearly gone to the printers incorrectly. And you were twice as angry with me for mentioning it at the meeting. I remember you were wearing that pink cardigan thing, it was really quite see-through.'

Jo grimaced. 'I know, I only realised how transparent it was later.'

'I noticed,' he said with a small smile. 'You came back into the boardroom after the meeting to get your notebook, all barely concealed temper.' He paused and grinned. 'I was trying not to stare at your breasts because I could see the faint outline of your bra through the cardigan . . . It was quite a feat to talk at all.'

'I thought you were a pig and I was waiting for you to make a sarcastic comment!' Jo exclaimed.

'I was trying not to grab you and tell you I was crazy about you there and then,' Mark said.

'Really?' she asked in delight. 'I was going to throw that cardigan out.'

'Don't you dare,' he murmured. 'Next time you wear it, I want to take it off.'

'I might not fit into it ever again,' Jo said ruefully, looking down at herself.

'It doesn't matter. We'll just have to find something else for me to rip off,' Mark said gently.

It was nearly four when Mark looked at his watch.

'I'm afraid that we have to go, darling,' he said, smiling down at her as if he couldn't quite believe that she was his. She knew how he felt.

'I've got to go to this business dinner in town at eight and I've got a meeting in Jurys beforehand.' He got to his feet.

'Oh.' Jo couldn't hide her disappointment. She'd hoped that they could spend the evening together and now he was telling her about his plans, plans that had nothing to do with her.

'You're invited, my pet, so don't get upset. I'll pick you up at half six,' he added, tickling her under the chin.

Jo beamed at him. 'You've certainly got me figured out.'

'I've been doing research for over three years,' he said. 'My God, are you all right? Is it the baby?' he asked suddenly, as Jo let out an anguished squeak.

'No. I've nothing to wear!' she wailed. 'Nothing glamorous that will fit me, anyway.'

'Is that all?' Mark gave her a hug. 'Rhona's bound to have something glam from her three pregnancies and we're not far from her house. We could drop in and pick something up.'

Rhona answered her mobile with her characteristically brusque, 'Yes!'

'Hi, Rho, it's Jo here. Where are you?'

'Stuck behind a bloody truck on the dual carriageway. You sound as if you're on a car phone, Jo.'

'I am. I'm with Mark.'

She was rewarded with a triumphant roar on the other end of the receiver.

'With Mark as in with him in the car, or *with* Mark?' Rhona demanded.

'*With* him,' answered Mark, who could hear his editor's roars.

'Yahoo! Thank you for ringing me to tell me,' Rhona said in a quieter voice.

'Actually, I'm ringing because I need something sexy in the maternity-dress line for this dinner Mark is bringing me to tonight,' Jo said apologetically. 'We're only a few miles away from your place . . .'

'Typical. I personally co-ordinate the match of the decade and you just want to rifle through my wardrobe!' Rhona did her best to sound outraged but failed. 'I'll be home in twenty minutes. Ted will be there so tell him to put the kettle on. Better still, I'll phone him myself.'

When Rhona swept into her sitting room half an hour later, she brought a bottle of rosé wine with her.

'We've got to celebrate,' she said, kissing Jo warmly on the cheek. 'It's only sparkling wine but it's better than tea. I'm so happy for you, Jo,' she whispered. 'You deserve him. He's a wonderful man.'

Mark got up from his seat beside Jo and held Rhona in a bear hug. 'Thanks for everything.' He turned to face Jo. 'If it wasn't for this lady, we'd still be freezing each other out every time we met.'

'My wife is a formidable woman,' Ted agreed, handing them all glasses of frothy pink wine.

A second bottle of rosé had been consumed by the time Rhona and Jo finally made it upstairs to rummage through Rhona's wardrobe with five-year-old Susie and eight-year-old Lynne eagerly accompanying them.

'Do you want to see our room?' inquired Susie, who was holding Jo's hand.

'Of course. Will you show it to me?' asked Jo.

After five minutes admiring Susie's teddies, her dolls and Lynne's latest potato-print picture, she followed Rhona into the spare bedroom.

'I shouldn't drink on an empty stomach,' hiccuped Rhona, heaving open the old pine wardrobe door. 'You had half a glass, and Mark only had one – that means that Ted and I drank practically two bottles on our own.'

'Well, it's not as if you're going anywhere,' Jo pointed out sensibly. 'Oh Rhona, this is lovely,' she said, taking out a long cream silk dress with tiny buttons all the way from hem to neck.

'Lovely if you're six foot and six stone,' said Rhona, sitting down on the bed. 'This is my spare wardrobe, the one the girls like best,' she added. 'And it's where I keep all the stuff I should never have bought because I can't fit into it. Lynne, show Jo the stuff at the back beside the sequinned dress. There's a nice velvet thing I wore when I was having Susie.'

'Can I try it on?' asked Susie. She looked up from the basket of lipsticks she'd taken off the dressing table.

'No darling. It's for big people only.'

'Really big people,' said Jo when she saw it. On the hanger, the long-sleeved empire-line dress in midnight blue looked big enough to fit Rhona and Jo together.

But when Jo put it on, she found that it was amazingly flattering. The high waist drew the eye to her cleavage so that you didn't notice her huge bump, while the long, tapered sleeves gave it a faintly medieval air.

'Perfect,' Rhona said, looking at her deputy editor through narrowed eyes.

'Purfect, purfect,' sang Susie, admiring the broad pink smile and bright red eyebrows she'd drawn on herself with lipstick.

'If Susie does your make-up, you'll look stunning,' added Rhona gravely.

'Thank you, Rho,' Jo said suddenly. 'Thank you for this and for what you've done for Mark and me.'

'Well, I knew that if I didn't do something, the pair of you would never sort things out. Of course, this means I have to sit up at the top of the church for the wedding and I get to wear an enormously mad hat.'

'Anything you want,' replied Jo with a large grin. She sat down on the bed. 'Come on, Susie, put on my lipstick!'

CHAPTER NINETEEN

The answering machine switched on seconds before Aisling reached the phone. She'd only had the machine for a month and she still found herself racing out of the shower or hurrying from the depths of the settee when the phone rang, having forgotten that people could leave messages. She decided to wait to see who was calling before she picked up the phone and carried the groceries over to the fridge and began to unpack what felt like a ton of cat food and an equal weight of the fromage frais that the boys were currently eating by the bucketload.

'This is Carla De Paor,' said the caller, in a high, rather posh accent. 'I'm phoning to see if you can cater for a party before Christmas. Do give me a ring if you can help. My number is . . .'

'Hello, Ms De Paor,' said Aisling, snatching up the phone and turning the machine off. 'This is Aisling Moran. You want to book *Reservations* to cater for a party? When is the party?'

'Friday, December thirteenth. For about fifty people. I know it's terribly short notice, only asking you two weeks before, but my friend Yvonne recommended you so highly. I do hope you can help me,' the caller added.

Aisling looked at the *Cat's Companion* calendar hanging by the phone and did some quick calculations. She had a midweek dinner party for ten that week, her second for Jim and Rachel Coughlan, and a buffet to get organised for the following Saturday, a day after the De Paor party. But the buffet would be very simple and she could always rope someone in to help with the party catering. She'd need to get off work early, of course, but she was owed plenty of time off.

'Yes, I can probably fit you in, Ms De Paor,' she said in the cool, businesslike manner she'd learned to use on the phone.

'A lot depends on how elaborate the party is. What are you planning?'

'Nibbles, a finger buffet really,' the other woman replied. 'The party isn't until nine and it's not dinner, you know. Just something to have with the booze. Oh you're so good to take me on,' she gushed. 'My other people said they couldn't do it at the last minute. If Yvonne hadn't told me about you, I don't know what I'd have done!'

'*Reservations* won't let you down,' Aisling said firmly. 'Once we've taken a client on, we provide a first-class service.' Unless I get sick, she thought privately, in which case the whole thing falls apart at the seams.

'I'd like to meet you to go over exactly what menu you'd like,' Aisling continued. 'Could you meet me on Monday at one-fifteen in the Harcourt Hotel?'

'Yes, yes, no problem. How will I recognise you?'

I'll be the one with the bags under my eyes and the rose between my teeth, Aisling thought mischievously. She said, 'I'm blonde and I'll be wearing a navy suit.'

'Marvellous, thank you so much,' said the other woman. 'Ciao.'

Ciao? Did people still say that? Aisling wondered as she hung up. A mental picture of Carla De Paor came to her – a cosseted wealthy wife with bobbed burgundy hair, a year-round tan from too many hours in the sun and enough gold around her neck to settle Bolivia's national debt.

Once, that type of woman would have overawed Aisling, made her feel gauche and dowdy. But not any more. In the last few months, she'd met more society types than she'd ever dreamed of as *Reservations* made a name for itself as a small but exclusive catering business.

She'd learned that the ones with the posh voices and the expensive clothes were just as likely to have grimy kitchen utensils and mice droppings in the saucepan cupboard. And, when she'd changed her clothes in a bedroom of one luxurious mansion in Foxrock, she'd passed the master bedroom and realised that the elegant lady who dressed in chic clothes and sported French-manicured nails, left the same tangle of tights, discarded outfits and clutter of toiletries on the bed as any woman did. There was no doubt about it, Ireland's most glamorous people were decidedly unglamorous when you got past the façade. Dealing with the De Paors would be no problem.

Aisling had just unpacked the shopping when the phone rang again. This time she picked it up.

'Hiya, Aisling. How are you, honey?' Sam's voice hadn't lost its faint transatlantic twang, a subtle variation on his native accent that made the endearment 'honey' sound deliciously sexy.

'I'm fine, Sam. Just been shopping and I'm going out to pick up the boys in half an hour. We're going to have lunch with my mother.'

'Still on for tonight?' he asked.

'Of course,' she replied. 'It's not every night I get brought to a charity ball, so I'm not going to miss it.'

'Are you finally going to tell me what you're wearing, or is it still a big secret?' he asked.

Aisling stifled her irritation. Ever since Mark had asked them to accompany himself and Jo to the fund-raising ball for Chinese orphans, Sam had been wheedling away to find out what Aisling was going to wear.

'It's a surprise,' she said. 'I want to dazzle you.'

'*Dazzle?*' said Sam suspiciously.

'Yes, dazzle.' Aisling could feel herself getting agitated. What was the matter with him? Every time he mentioned the ball, he wanted to know what she was wearing, even though she'd told him it was a surprise at least four times. Which word was he having difficulty with, she wondered? Dazzle or surprise?

'I just want to know, that's all.' Sam sniffed. Nobody could sniff like Sam. Each one was an Oscar winner, laden with meaning.

'Why?' Aisling couldn't stop herself. She was annoyed by the implication that she couldn't pick something suitable for a posh ball in the Shelbourne without his help. She wasn't some hare-brained bimbo who couldn't tell a black-tie affair from a beery barbeque in somebody's back garden. She was a working woman who'd just arranged *another* booking for her catering business. A business she'd set up thanks to her own cooking skills and entrepreneurial ability. So why the hell was Sam treating her as if she was an imbecile with no clothes sense?

Damn him. He was so square when it came to clothes. Not satisfied with buying her a ludicrously little-girl dress the first time they went out shopping, he'd subsequently surprised her with another maidenly outfit – a ruinously expensive white Ghost dress that made her look like a milkmaid. He probably expected her to wear that to the ball. Well, he could forget it.

'I'd love to see you wearing *my* dress.' He sniffed again. 'You look beautiful in it, so elegant.' There was a pause. 'I'm sorry,' he added in a low voice. 'It's childish to want you to wear my present.'

It was Aisling's turn to sigh. Don't be so hard on him, she told herself. You're just out of sync with normal man/woman relationships. Most men probably want their girlfriends to wear feminine outfits instead of knock-'em-dead sexy dresses. Perfectly normal, wasn't it? She'd ask Jo, just to be on the safe side.

'I love the white dress you bought me,' she said. It was only a half-lie. She *did* like it, but it wasn't the sort of thing you could wear into the office and it was far too impractical to inspire confidence in her catering clients. 'But I've bought a lovely dress for the ball and I want to wear it. You'll like it when you see it, I just know it.'

He'll hate it, she thought as she hung up. It was very sexy – the complete opposite of the white dress he'd bought. A year ago, she wouldn't have dreamed of wearing anything like it. Mind you, a year ago she wouldn't have fitted into a long oyster-coloured halter-neck dress. Especially one that moulded her body like surgical gloves. Still, Jo said it was going to be a very over-the-top affair, so Aisling had felt justified blowing two and a half dinner parties' worth of takings on the dress.

'Hello, Ash,' murmured Jo, walking into the kitchen rubbing her eyes sleepily. Eight months pregnant, Jo was very big and in her towelling dressing-gown worn over a large T-shirt, she looked as if she had a beach-ball tied around her middle.

'Did you sleep?' asked Aisling, pulling out a chair for her.

'Not really. I keep having to pee all night and she's kicking like mad,' Jo sighed.

'I'll make you a nice cup of tea and some toast,' offered Aisling, 'and you can sit inside and watch telly.'

'Thank you. What would I do without you, Ash?' Jo asked.

'You'd get out more,' Aisling replied, filling the kettle. 'I'm afraid the boys will soon think you're their mother. You're here more often than I am.'

'I don't mind baby-sitting at all. I love being with them. Anyway, when you're building up a business you've got to accept lots of work, at least that's what Richard always told me,' she added drily. 'It'll be easier when you've got someone to help full time.'

Aisling put brown bread into the toaster and placed a tray with Flora, marmalade, milk and sugar on it on the table in front of Jo.

'I'll need to hire someone sooner rather than later,' she said. 'I've just got another job, a party for fifty on Friday week. For an awfully jolly-hockey-sticks-sounding woman called Carla De Paor.'

'Well done! That name's familiar, though,' Jo said thoughtfully. 'Aren't they the ones with the huge pile in Greystones and the garage business?'

'Don't know,' said Aisling, making the tea. 'The only problem is that Sam will go ballistic when I tell him because Michael was taking the boys that Friday night and Sam and I were going to drive to Wexford and spend the night in a hotel somewhere.'

'You can do that another time,' Jo pointed out. 'You've got

to make as many contacts as you can now to get yourself established.'

Aisling looked out of the kitchen window at the bird-table where a tiny robin daintily pecked at the nuts she'd put out earlier. It was a freezing November day, the last vestiges of frost still sparkled in the pale wintry sun.

'I know,' she said slowly. 'But Sam doesn't seem to understand that. He knew what I wanted to do when we met, but now he really seems to hate me working at night. I don't know why.'

'I'm afraid that's a typical male reaction,' Jo said. 'Independence is wonderful, an attractive quality in fact. Like wearing sexy clothes, miniskirts or low-cut blouses. Until you become an item. Then, it's "don't go out wearing that dress, cover up your boobs, your legs, whatever, and turn into Little Miss Stay at Home.'

'You said it,' muttered Aisling, thinking of Sam's fascination with her wardrobe. 'Mark isn't like that, is he?'

'No. Not at all. I think it must be because he's so confident and secure in himself.' Jo took her toast out of the toaster and plastered it with Flora. 'He loves the fact that I've made my own way in the world. But not all men are like that,' she added, licking a piece of margarine off her fingers.

'Why do I get stuck with the ones who want to turn me into the bloody housewife from hell?' demanded Aisling.

'Come on, Ash, give him a chance,' begged Jo. 'He's probably trying to protect you. He can see that you're stretching yourself by doing two jobs as well as looking after Paul and Phillip.'

'You're right. It's just that . . .' she paused.

'What?' asked Jo through a mouth full of toast.

'I'm beginning to feel claustrophobic,' Aisling said finally. There. She'd said it, actually said what had been rattling around in her head for the past two weeks.

In the three months since she'd met Sam, she'd had a marvellous time. Most of the time. Nearly all the time, really. He was a handsome, attentive lover and that had doubled her confidence, made her feel happy, relaxed and as secure as a recently separated woman could be.

Sam stayed at her house on the nights when the boys were with Michael and they made passionate love, before falling asleep wrapped in each other's arms. On Sunday mornings, they sat in bed reading the papers – never the *News* – and had breakfast, before making love again, usually with toast crumbs sticking to their bodies.

Aisling was amazed at how quickly she'd got used to his presence in her life and her bed. When Michael left, she'd genuinely thought that she'd never want another man ever again. And here she was in a serious relationship with Sam.

He'd certainly improved her life, made her feel better about herself in every way. But there was something not quite right about their relationship lately. She'd first noticed it one day when he rang her from his office to tell her that his trip to London the following day had been cancelled.

'I thought we could have a romantic dinner for two,' he suggested. 'Just you, me and a bottle of nice Chablis.'

'Sorry, Sam,' Aisling said. 'The boys have to finish a project by Thursday morning, so I said I'd help them with it tomorrow night. It's on "Space", which is great because they love watching *Star Trek*. They're mad about anything to do with astronauts. Anyway,' she added, 'I'm not really able to do late nights in the middle of the week. I'll fall asleep at my desk if I don't get a decent seven hours' sleep. I do hope you understand.'

'It's all right, I understand,' he said sharply. Clearly, he didn't understand at all.

She could imagine how it looked from his point of view. He'd offered her a lovely night out and she'd turned him down, rejected him.

Well, tough, she thought to herself. The boys are more important than a night out, they need me. There's been enough uncertainty in their lives during the past year. They need a stable home life. I'm out often enough because of the catering business, so they need to know that I'm there when

CATHY KELLY

they want me to help them with something.

Sam had become even more annoyed the following week-end when Aisling couldn't spend Saturday afternoon with him. She was cooking twelve huge vegetarian quiches and had to make a smoked trout pâté which a client was picking up that evening.

'You can't work all the time,' he growled. 'You've got to stop working so hard. This bloody business means I never see you.'

Aha, thought Aisling. That's more like it. You're not upset at the idea of me working too hard, you're just cross because it means you can't get what you want. Typical man. She'd been prepared to promise him a romantic evening at home when she'd cook his favourite peppered steak with all the trimmings. But she was damned if she'd do it when he was going to behave childishly.

He'd been so cold towards her the next time they met that Aisling found herself apologising for Saturday. She told him she'd consult him in future so her cooking didn't infringe on their time together.

'I'm sorry, Sam,' she'd said. She sat beside him on the settee and cuddled up close. 'I didn't think. I'm trying to make the business a success and when I get an order, I hate to turn it down. But I'll check with you in future in case you've anything nice planned, all right?'

Even as she said it, Aisling knew she was making a big mistake. Making a rod for her own back, her mother used to say. She didn't explain any of this to Jo, who was eating her toast hungrily.

'All relationships have their ups and downs,' Jo said comfortingly. 'It's a bad patch you're going through, that's all.'

'So says the woman who is blissfully in love and hasn't said a cross word to Mark for the past six weeks,' joked Aisling.

Jo beamed at her. 'Are we sickeningly in love?' she asked.

'You're a living, breathing Danielle Steel storyline.'

'That bad!'

'No, I'm kidding. I'm thrilled for you both. Now, more tea?' asked Aisling.

'I'd love some.'

Aisling topped up the teapot with hot water and listened to Jo read something funny from the newspaper. But her mind was elsewhere.

'Well, what do you think?' Aisling twirled around in her oyster-coloured evening dress in front of Jo who was sitting on the bed in Aisling's bedroom, sipping a glass of milk.

'Absolutely amazing. Fantastic,' praised Jo. 'You'll be the belle of the ball. I wish I looked like that!' she added wistfully, patting her vast belly in Rhona's velvet dress.

'You'll get your figure back in no time,' said Aisling comfortingly. 'You're naturally slim for a start and the weight will just fall off when the baby is born, I know it will.'

Jo grimaced. 'I do hope so. I feel like a supertanker in velvet.'

'You look great, Jo. Your skin is fantastic, your hair is so shiny and the dress is very flattering.' Aisling hugged her friend.

'It would want to be,' pointed out Jo, 'seeing as how it's the only thing I can wear out at night. This is the third outing it's had in the last few weeks and if I meet anyone I know at the ball, they're going to think I only have one dress,' she added gloomily.

'Mark certainly thinks you look great.'

Jo's face softened. 'He does, doesn't he? He's such a wonderful man. So different from Richard. Actually, talking of Richard . . .'

The doorbell rang loudly, cutting across Jo's voice.

'They're early.' She glanced down at her watch.

Aisling hurried to the stairs, holding up the skirt of her long satin dress as she ran.

'I'll let them in. Take your time coming downstairs, Jo.'

Mark and Sam stood at the front door, handsome in their dinner jackets.

'Aisling, you look . . . great,' said Sam in an astonished voice. He stood back. His eyes travelled the length of her body, as he admired the clinging dress which showed off her curves. She'd spent an hour coaxing her blonde hair into soft waves and it rippled as she moved, the silver and golden colours perfectly matched by the shade of her dress.

In fact, the only spot of colour were her eyes, which Jo had carefully made up for her, their denim blue accentuated by smudged brown liner and thick dark brown mascara. Against the pale fawn colours of her hair and dress, her eyes looked hypnotic and intensely blue.

'You look beautiful, Aisling.' Mark leaned over to kiss her warmly. 'Sam's going to have to spend the entire night fighting off competition from love-stricken admirers.'

Sam didn't look pleased at the thought. 'They can look but they better not touch.' He slid one arm around Aisling possessively and kissed her.

'Is Jo upstairs?' asked Mark.

'Mmm.' Aisling couldn't talk properly with Sam glued to her.

Mark took the stairs two at a time and met Jo as she walked out of the bathroom stuffing spare tissues into her handbag.

When he hugged her gently, careful not to squash her bump, Jo experienced that sense of complete happiness she felt whenever she was with Mark. 'How's my favourite mum-to-be?' He dropped a kiss on the top of her head.

'Huge.' Jo snuggled her head into his chest. 'I'm afraid that someone's going to come up to me tonight, break a bottle of champagne on me and say "God bless her and all who sail in her".'

She could feel Mark's deep laugh vibrate in his belly.

'Don't be silly. You look great. You're only a tiny little thing. Will I carry you downstairs to prove it?'

Jo slapped him playfully. 'Only if you want to end up in casualty with a slipped disc, Mark.'

Downstairs, they found Aisling trying to set the video to record something while Sam stood boot-faced in the hall, holding her coat and looking at his watch.

'We'll be late,' he said testily.

'I'm coming,' called Aisling. 'I just want to tape a film later.'

She reached the front door just as Mark opened it and both she and Jo gasped.

'A limo!' Jo said in astonishment. A gleaming black stretch Mercedes was parked in the drive, a black-suited driver holding open one of the back doors.

Mark grinned as he put on his black wool overcoat. 'I thought we should do it in style tonight,' he said, 'because it's a special evening. A very special evening,' he added, glancing at Jo.

He and Jo sat facing the front of the car with Aisling and Sam opposite them.

'We could have had champagne, but since Jo can't drink any, I didn't order it,' Mark said, stretching out his long legs.

'I could have half a glass.' Jo leaned comfortably against him. 'Do you know what this reminds me of?' she said in a much softer tone so only he could hear.

'No.' Mark put his arm around her.

'Remember when we arrived in New York and the hotel limo was there to meet us? I'd never been in one before but I was determined not to appear unsophisticated and say so.' She settled herself even closer to him. 'I kept wanting to open the drinks compartment to see if there was actually anything in it.'

'You never cease to amaze me, Jo,' Mark said. 'I've never met anyone who can act as marvellously sophisticated as you do when you put your mind to it.'

'Acting comes in very handy sometimes,' she whispered. 'Especially when you're chatting up the boss . . .'

When the limo pulled up outside the Shelbourne, Aisling was amazed to see three other equally long limos parked in front of the hotel. Their driver double-parked, ran around to open the door and helped her out as she stared at a tall woman in floor-length fur who was getting out of the limo beside her.

'Get a load of that coat,' Aisling whispered to Jo.

'Definitely ranch mink,' Jo whispered back.

'I bought her a mink and she wouldn't feed it,' Mark pointed out to Aisling, doing his best to sound serious.

The two women burst out laughing. Madame Mink stared at them frostily.

'Silly cow for wearing fur in the first place,' said Aisling.

She walked into the ballroom with a spring in her step. She felt beautiful, sexy and gloriously confident. She could see people glancing at her, men openly admiring her beautiful, elegant outfit. It had to be the dress.

'It's the dress,' she whispered to Jo.

'It's you,' whispered Jo back. 'You look amazing.'

They found their table and the two women were just sitting down beside each other so they could gossip, when Mark arrived with their cloakroom tickets.

'Your lady in mink had a tantrum at the cloakroom. She insisted that they find somewhere extra safe for her coat,' he explained.

'Goodness.' Aisling fanned herself with the small dinner menu. 'I do hope you asked for the same treatment for mine. It's a family heirloom and I know Dunnes are unlikely to ever have anything as gorgeous ever again. I'd be distraught if anything happened to it. I mean, *where* would you get your hands on anything *that* nice for sixty pounds?'

'Was it only sixty quid?' asked Jo, astonished. 'It looks much more expensive.'

'Fiona picked it out for me,' Aisling explained. 'She has the most amazing eye for clothes. Nearly as good as you.'

Sam excused himself to talk to someone he'd spotted at another table. Aisling amused herself by looking around, gazing at the people at other tables. Men looked so handsome in dinner jackets, she thought, as she watched beautifully dressed couples weaving through the tables. Even the ugliest, scruffiest man looked better in a black tuxedo.

The women had obviously pulled out all the stops. Sleek blondes and brunettes in elegant black sheaths, vied for attention with women in flowing ballgowns. A couple of very young and very slim women sashayed across the room in spray-on lycra creations, one bronze and one a startling white that contrasted with the girl's pale golden skin.

You had to be young and slim to get away with that type of dress. Aisling wondered what sort of underwear the girl in the white dress was wearing. All-in-one, vacuum-packed underwear? No, she was thin enough to get away with ordinary undies.

A balloon floated into view, an oversized cream balloon with swirly gold writing on it saying something she couldn't make out. Someone had gone to an awful lot of trouble with the decorations. The entire room was done in gold and cream, gold and cream balloons hung from the ceiling. Glass vases of tiny cream roses, tied up with gold ribbons, stood on the tables, and wreaths of gold and cream silk flowers were garlanded around the room and on the raised dais where seats and music stands were laid out for a band.

There was plenty of gold on the ears, wrists and necks of the female guests, Aisling noticed enviously. She fiddled with her plain gold bracelet and wished she had a gold and diamond necklace like the statuesque blonde in pink satin who was batting heavily mascaraed eyes at her companion.

Then Aisling saw him. He was walking towards their table, talking to another man, not really watching where he was going. He looked handsome, if a little tired, in the expensive tuxedo she'd helped him buy just over three years ago.

'It would be handy to have my own instead of renting one every time I need it,' Michael had said as they trawled Dublin's most expensive men's shops to find what he was looking for.

It certainly suited him, Aisling had to admit, although he'd put on weight and the buttons were ever so slightly strained across his stomach. Her gaze shifted to the two women who walked a couple of steps behind the men chatting animatedly.

Both were dark-haired. One had short, jet-black hair, offset by a brilliant ruby ballgown, the other's brown bob swung as she walked. She wore a strapless white silk dress with a tight bodice which flared out into a full skirt much too wide for someone of her height. Pearl earrings and a pearl choker completed the outfit.

The dress must have looked stunning on the shop dummy. But it was a major fashion mistake on the dumpy, short-legged woman who wore it.

Aisling stared at her husband's girlfriend and wondered why she didn't want to grab her wine glass and smash it over the other woman's head.

So that was Jennifer Carroll. *The* Jennifer Carroll. It was funny, Aisling realised, staring at her in an almost removed state of mind, but Jennifer didn't look anything like the femme fatale she'd imagined. How had Fiona described her? *All red talons, glittery gold outfits and skirts cut up to her thighs.* Something like that.

The woman who was now only a few yards away from her bore no resemblance to the predatory manhunter that Fiona had described.

In the flesh – the not inconsiderable flesh, Aisling noticed in amazement – Jennifer Carroll was short, verging on plump. Her pale skin looked pasty against the gleaming white dress.

Aisling hated the smell of fake tan but, as she glanced down at her golden arms, she was pleased she'd put it on the night before. Jennifer didn't look as if she'd bothered with anything much, apart from having her hair salon-blow-dried.

But maybe Jennifer just hadn't had the time to bother, Aisling reflected, because she was ironing Michael's dress-shirt, finding his cuff links – 'They *must* be there somewhere, Aisling!' – and trying to put her make-up on in front of the mirror while he poked about in the drawers underneath the mirror looking for a particular pair of black socks.

A cork popped loudly beside her. Aisling turned to see a waiter pouring frothy liquid into Jo's glass.

'Let's have a toast.' Jo turned to face Aisling with a half-full glass of champagne held aloft. 'To all of us and . . . omigod! It's . . . it's Michael and . . . her!' Jo's mouth formed a pale pink oval as she stared at Michael and Jennifer. 'I don't believe it!' she gasped. 'Oh Ash,' Jo laid a warm hand on her friend's shoulder, 'are you all right?'

'Yes,' said Aisling, still not sure exactly how she felt. 'Stunned, yes. It's strange but, I'm OK, honestly.'

'He looking at us,' hissed Jo. 'Look the other way!'

Aisling obediently twisted around in her chair and smiled warmly at a surprised Miss Pink Satin who obviously felt obliged to smile back.

'Have we had our toast?' Aisling said brightly to the whole table. 'Let's toast the future!'

Everyone raised their glasses and drank. Aisling drained her glass in a couple of frothy gulps.

Jo's mouth fell open again.

'If I drank that fast, I'd hiccup for a month,' she said. 'Are you sure you're all right, Ash?'

'I'm not sure,' whispered Aisling, a fixed smile still glued to her face. 'In a few minutes, I'll either be over at their table battering Michael and Jennifer with your handbag – yours is bigger than mine – or I'll be perfectly fine. I don't know which. Now, are they sitting down yet? Where are they sitting?'

'What are you two whispering about?' said Mark, leaning towards them.

'It's Michael and his girlfriend,' hissed Jo, 'over there.'

'Where?' demanded Mark.

'The second table on the left, beside the dance floor.'

Aisling turned her head slightly. She had no idea whether she wanted to talk to Michael or not.

'The woman in that dreadful white meringue dress,' Jo told Mark, bridling like a mother hen seeing someone hurt her favourite chick. 'It's a dreadful dress. Doesn't she have a full-length mirror in her bloody house? I can't *believe* anyone would go out looking like that.'

For the first time since she'd spotted Michael, Aisling smiled properly.

'You're a howl, Ryan,' she said affectionately to Jo. 'You're so protective.'

439

'Well, she ran off with your husband,' said Jo indignantly. 'I mean, really!'

'You can only run off with someone who wants to run off in the first place,' Aisling said, in the tone of someone who'd spent an awful lot of time turning the whole situation over and over in her head. 'Look what's happened to me as a result. Michael's leaving changed my life. It was brutal, and not the sort of experience I'd recommend, but it worked. It changed my life and, boy, did it need changing. And now look at me.' She smiled and flicked back a lock of blonde hair.

'You're one hell of a woman, Aisling,' Mark commented. 'There can't be many women who've coped the way you have.'

'Not to mention losing practically two stone and starting a new business,' put in Jo.

'How about a toast to you, Aisling – and to *Reservations*?' said Mark.

'Hello, guys.' Sam slid into his seat beside Aisling. 'What have I missed?'

'Oh, we've just been gossiping.' Aisling shot a warning glance at the other two.

'So I asked him why it was going to take two weeks to put down a wooden floor in the kitchen,' Jo said, 'since it had only taken one week to replaster all the downstairs.'

'What exactly are you having done to the cottage now?' inquired Sam idly.

Aisling stifled her irritation. Sam spent hours in her house and had listened to Jo and herself discussing the renovation of the cottage often enough to know precisely what was going on, down to the last nut and bolt. He obviously hadn't listened to a word they'd said.

'It's nearly finished apart from a few minor details,' explained Jo patiently.

Aisling remembered when she'd indulgently repeated herself every time Michael muttered. 'What?'

He usually said 'What?' halfway through dinner when Aisling was regaling him with details of her day or telling him about the funny thing she'd heard on the radio that morning.

Dinner *chez* Moran. Michael indifferently munching his way through Aisling's delicious stuffed pork with one eye on the newspaper and one eye on his ratatouille – to make sure that his fork didn't miss his mouth and spill food down his shirt front.

Aisling couldn't suppress a shiver. Had she really lived her life like that? Repeating herself endlessly. When Michael hadn't been bothered to listen? Had she really been that quiet little mouse? A mousey mouse, she realised with a grin, running one hand through her blonde mane. A mouse with no confidence, no conversation and no waist. She took a sip of champagne to calm herself down.

Even her hands looked better nowadays, she realised, admiring the fingers that curled around her glass, the short, well-shaped nails painted with a soft opalescent pink. They were never going to look like Vivienne's perfectly manicured hands. But they were improving. She'd been stirring chocolate sauce one night at one of her catering jobs when she noticed that, though her hair, clothes and figure were much improved, her hands let her down completely.

Now she made herself wear rubber gloves when she was cleaning the bath and scouring saucepans, something she hadn't bothered with for years.

Aisling glanced over to Michael's table.

Thank you, Jennifer, she said silently. Thank you. If you hadn't come along, I'd still be living on automatic pilot, still worried about what to cook for dinner, still utterly depressed. You've no idea what a difference you've made to my life. Or my hands.

'Aisling, honey, what are you going to have to eat?' Sam asked. 'I think the lamb sounds nice.' Sam was looking at the menu hungrily, the subject of Jo's cottage obviously closed.

Aisling picked up the small menu. Each course of the five-course meal offered at least two choices. Raw oysters or roast pepper salad, two types of sorbet, consommé or five-mushroom soup, rack of lamb, salmon cutlets or aubergine

441

CATHY KELLY

lasagne, dessert trolley or Irish cheese board. A wonderful menu.

'Oysters make me sick and I hate peppers,' Sam muttered.

He sounded just like Phillip when he was sulking for some reason or other, Aisling realised. And Sam was certainly sulking. He'd been shocked at the sight of her daring dress, but he hadn't been able to make a fuss in front of Jo and Mark. Instead, he was being charming to all and sundry, while being very cool with her. She hated childish adults.

Stop it, Aisling, she told herself sharply. He's funny, kind, very sexy and crazy about you. Don't ruin it. 'Maybe they can rustle up something else, a salad perhaps?' she said in a placatory tone.

'I hope so.' He sniffed.

Aisling reached over for one of the bottles of white wine that had just been placed on the table and filled Sam's glass to the brim. When he drank half, she filled it some more. If that's what it took to keep him amused, then she'd keep filling his glass all night. It was like giving the boys 7-Up when they were sick, or Calpol when they were babies.

Could they rustle up a green salad or some alternative to the two starters? Aisling inquired.

When the waitress promised to bring a mixed salad for the gentleman, Sam didn't even say thank you. Aisling felt her temper rise. If there was one thing she couldn't bear, it was people who couldn't be civil to waitresses, bar staff, whoever. It drove her mad. She looked down to find that she'd shredded her cloakroom ticket.

By ten o'clock, the meal was practically over. A few people were still forking up the remains of some wonderful profiteroles. The classical music, which had been piped through the room all through dinner, was turned off and a woman with a microphone announced that the charity auction would shortly begin.

'We've got a raffle for some marvellous prizes,' she explained. 'The top prize is a luxury holiday for two to Tunisia.' Everyone clapped appreciatively. 'Tickets are five pounds each, or six for twenty-five pounds.'

'Oh, gimme a hundred, then,' Jo said under her breath to Aisling.

The classical music was slapped back on and the organisers started to work their way around the tables, bearing books of tickets and cash boxes.

'What were you going to tell me about Richard earlier?' Aisling whispered to Jo.

'He rang me,' Jo whispered.

'He didn't!' said Aisling, aghast.

'Shush,' hissed Jo. 'I haven't told Mark yet.'

'Why didn't you tell me?' demanded Aisling. 'What did he say?'

Jo leaned back in her chair and said nothing for a moment.

'Sorry. I just felt very faint suddenly,' she said. 'He rang me at work yesterday and he upset me so much, I didn't want to talk about it. The pig. Hand me that menu, would you?'

Aisling gave her the menu and Jo immediately began fanning her face. 'He wanted to see me. He said he was sorry he'd left me and he wanted to try again.'

Aisling was stunned. 'I can't believe it.'

'Neither could I. I told him he could get stuffed,' Jo said with relish. 'And I have to say,' she added, a triumphant smile hovering around her lips, 'he was absolutely gobsmacked when I said it. He honestly thought I'd welcome him with open arms and when I said "Get stuffed", he was speechless.'

'*I'm* almost speechless at the sheer nerve of him,' Aisling said. 'Imagine phoning you for the first time in six months and having the temerity to think you'd have him back!'

'That's Richard for you,' Jo said, still fanning herself. 'He lives in a fantasy world where nothing ever goes really wrong. If it does, he walks away. And to think I wanted him to be a father to my baby.' She shuddered.

'I'm so glad you have Mark,' Aisling said gently.

'Me too. He's involved, he wants to know how I feel and how the baby is doing every moment of the day.' Jo couldn't keep the happiness out of her voice. '*He's* the real father.

Richard may be the biological father, but he'll never be her real dad.'

Aisling didn't want to upset Jo, but she knew she had to ask. 'What if he demands access to the baby?' she asked.

Jo absent-mindedly fiddled with a curl of her dark, glossy hair. 'I'm not sure,' she said. 'He'd have a right to see her, of course, but I'd hate it. I'd hate him having anything to do with her when he didn't want me to have her in the first place.'

'Have you talked all this over with Mark?'

'Yes,' Jo replied. 'We talk about everything – apart from this latest bit of news,' she added hastily. 'I'm trying to find the right time to tell Mark so he won't go ballistic.'

Knowing the sort of straightforward and honourable man Mark was, Aisling could well understand how this fresh example of Richard's appallingly selfish behaviour would send him into a cold, controlled rage.

'We've talked about Richard wanting access and visitation rights,' Jo explained. 'Mark wants to do what's right for the baby. He knows that she's entitled to see her real father. But,' she broke off to emphasise the point, 'he absolutely *loathes* Richard for what he did to me. If Richard has to come to my place to see the baby, I'll need to lock Mark into the hotpress beforehand so he won't murder Richard.'

'Did someone mention that bastard's name?' Mark turned to face them.

Jo blushed. 'I was just telling Aisling that we've been talking about Richard's rights to see the baby.'

The muscles in Mark's face tightened and his grey eyes grew icy cold.

'Ladies and gentlemen,' boomed a voice, 'the auction is ready to begin.'

Saved by the bell, thought Aisling. The loud voice of the auctioneer drummed out of the speakers around the room and made conversation all but impossible. Aisling squeezed Jo's hand affectionately before turning to face the dais.

'What am I bid for this football jersey?' roared the auction-eer. 'A jersey signed by all the members of the Irish team, a perfect Christmas present for the soccer-mad teenager.'

Aisling watched with interest as people bid outrageous sums of money for the oddest things. Two china plates with butterfly designs hand-painted in nail varnish made £1,000 because the artist in question was the lead singer of a rock band. Just as well she'd chosen singing instead of art for her career, Jo said with a giggle.

A beautiful piece of driftwood made into a piece of sculpture went for half that, even though Aisling felt it was ten times more beautiful than the garish butterflies.

'I know the money is being raised for charity, but why do the items have to be so bloody daft?' she asked Jo when the auctioneer was giving his vocal chords a brief break.

'I think it's supposed to be more fun for the seriously wealthy bidders if the stuff is totally useless,' Jo replied. 'Presumably, there's a certain cachet in being able to tell all your rich pals that you spent £2,000 on a biscuit tin which Oscar Wilde's cleaning lady swore belonged to him!'

It was when a man at the next table successfully bid for a tiny watercolour painting, that Michael finally saw Aisling. They'd both turned to look at the purchaser and their eyes locked. Though she was quite a distance away from him, Aisling could have sworn he went pale with shock. Not surprising. The very idea of his estranged wife and new girlfriend meeting at a party would be enough to give any man an ulcer.

Michael probably expected her to race over to his table and throw something at him, or to scratch Jennifer's eyes out. Well, she wasn't going to do that.

Aisling allowed herself a little pat on the back. She'd come a long way from the enraged, grief-stricken wife of six months ago. Let Michael panic. She wasn't about to lose her cool.

Sam had loosened up after numerous glasses of wine and two brandies. He wanted to dance with Aisling.

'Do you think they'll play the tango?' he murmured into her ear. 'I'm quite good at Latin American dancing.'

'We better wait till the auction stops and the music starts,'

Aisling advised, as he started nuzzling her ear.

She could feel one hand moving stealthily up her thigh, gently caressing her through the fabric of her dress.

'So you don't hate the dress after all,' she couldn't resist saying.

'It's very nice. I'd prefer it if I was the only one to see you looking this sexy,' Sam said. 'You're mine and nobody else's. Remember that.'

She wasn't likely to forget it from the way he was holding onto her.

'Sam,' she began, 'you've got to understand, I'm not a *thing*. I'm a person. I don't *belong* to anyone except myself.'

He wasn't listening. The band had just launched into the first bars of Glenn Miller when Sam caught Aisling's hand and pulled her out of her chair.

'C'mon, honey. Let's show them how it's done.'

Normally Aisling couldn't have thought of anything worse than being practically the first couple on the dance floor, but for once she didn't mind. She and Sam made a handsome couple and she wanted to give Michael the opportunity to see what he'd dumped.

When Sam spun her around, she could see Michael's poker face. Jennifer sat a little apart from him, looking strained. Let them watch, thought Aisling, bestowing a warm smile on Sam. She'd put him straight about the question of 'ownership' later.

Sam may have looked good, but he was no dancer. After two fast numbers, she was ready to sit down and rest her bruised toes when the tempo of the music slowed. Sam immediately slid one arm around her waist and started to waltz clumsily, her body crushed against his.

'You look wonderful,' he murmured through boozy breath.

'Thank you,' Aisling replied with the sexiest smile she could muster. Now was not the time to remind him that he'd hated her outfit a couple of hours ago. She closed her eyes and kissed him, a long, passionate kiss more suited to the bedroom than the dance floor. God, but she was enjoying this.

She opened one eye and took a surreptitious look in Michael's direction, delighted to see that he looked as if he'd just had a root canal done at the dentist – and been presented with the bill into the bargain.

Another kiss, I think, she decided. Poor Sam was going to be beside himself with passion if she didn't stop.

'We should go home early,' said Sam huskily when their lips finally parted.

That wasn't part of Aisling's plan.

'We can't just go and leave Jo and Mark after they invited us,' she said hurriedly. 'Anyway, we've all tomorrow morning to lie in bed and . . . read,' she added with a meaningful grin. 'I've had enough dancing, Sam. I want to go to the ladies' room, OK?'

They walked leisurely back to their table. Aisling deliberately chose a route which avoided Michael's table. She'd go over to say hello in her own time – when she'd powdered down her undoubtedly shiny nose and put on more lipstick.

In the ladies', she decided against giving herself another blast of perfume – it would look too obvious. But she brushed her hair and slicked on plenty of the coral lipstick which made her lips look full and glossy.

'Hello, Michael, how are you? Aren't you going to introduce me to your friend?' she practised. No, that sounded wrong.

'Michael, darling, so nice to see you again.'

Too false. How about. 'Hi, Mike, nice to see you. Can't stop. My boyfriend's insatiable and we have to get back to bed immediately. Bye.'

There had to be a right way to do it. Maybe there was a book – *How to Behave When You Meet Your Ex and His Lover for the First Time*. And if there wasn't a book, perhaps she would write it. It would be a bestseller, she was sure of it.

A woman washing her hands at the basins looked at Aisling enviously, a quick peep when she thought Aisling wasn't looking. She was tall and heavily built, and wore the sort of size sixteen dress that Aisling herself would have had to wear a year ago. Poor thing, Aisling thought, sympathetically.

She held the door open for the other woman as they left and smiled at her.

'That's a lovely dress,' the woman said longingly. 'I wish I could wear something like that.'

'Thank you,' said Aisling with a friendly look. 'I'm still not used to being able to wear it myself, you know. Six months ago I wouldn't have been able to get away with this, but I've lost loads of weight.'

'Really?' asked the woman, with the fascinated gaze of the eternal dieter who knows the calorific content of every single type of chocolate biscuit.

'Really,' Aisling repeated. 'And if I can do it, anybody can. See you.' She walked off, thinking about the smile which had spread across the other woman's face – a there-is-hope-for-me-after-all sort of smile. I'd be great as a diet counsellor, Aisling thought happily. She was so busy thinking about how satisfying it would be to help other depressed and miserable women lose weight and regain control of their lives, that she almost didn't realise she had walked straight up to Michael's table.

Here goes, she decided. There's no backing out now.

'Hello, Michael. How are you? You must be Jennifer.' She was amazed at how calm and steady her voice sounded.

'H . . . hello,' stuttered Michael in shock.

Aisling didn't know which of them looked the more stunned. Jennifer stared up at her with wide, frightened eyes, like a rabbit caught in the headlights of an oncoming jugger-naut. Michael looked utterly horrified.

'Relax,' Aisling said. 'I'm not going to bite. We're adults, after all.'

'Of course,' Jennifer said breathlessly. 'Nice to meet you, Aisling. The boys are always talking about you.'

'I'm glad to hear it,' Aisling said. Close up, the other woman looked tired and drawn, plenty of crow's feet around her pale blue eyes. She had to be thirty-five or thirty-six.

'Would you like to sit down?' Jennifer asked politely, gesturing to the empty chair beside her. Michael shot her a withering look and she flushed. Her eyes glistened with what looked suspiciously like tears.

They were having a *row*! Aisling couldn't believe it. She hoped it was about her. She sat down gracefully, determined not to spoil the effect of her perfectly styled hair and beautiful dress.

'How are you both?' she asked graciously, feeling rather like the Queen at a garden party. All she needed were the elbow-length white gloves and the tiara.

'Fine,' said Michael sharply, shooting Jennifer another meaningful look. The other woman's face fell and, for an instant, Aisling felt sorry for her. Michael had always been very talented in the withering-look department.

'Sorry.' Jennifer pushed back her hair clumsily and left, rushing towards the ladies'.

'Was it something I said?' asked Aisling, still with the serene smile on her face.

'No.' Michael sounded as weary as he looked. The band struck up The Carpenters' *Close to You.*

'You always loved that song,' he said absently.

'And you hated it,' Aisling answered.

'Did I? I quite like it now.'

Aisling's eyebrows shot up. 'Are you mellowing, Michael?' she asked.

He snorted. 'No. Yes. I don't know.' He ran one hand through his hair, leaving it standing up in dark peaks. Once, she'd have cried at this point, the point where she realised that she'd never smooth his hair down for him again. Not any more. Her hair-smoothing days were well and truly over.

'Did I interrupt an argument?'

'Sort of. It was a bit of a shock seeing you here, that's all,' he admitted.

'Why?'

'You know why,' he said. 'You've never met Jennifer and she feels so guilty about everything.'

Typical, thought Aisling, *she* feels guilty but you obviously don't.

449

'We have to meet sometime, why not now?' she said.

'I suppose,' he said, reaching for his cigarettes. Silk Cut purple, she noticed. Amazing. She'd tried to get him to stop smoking Marlboro for years. It took six months with another woman to have him down to a lighter brand.

'Things have been difficult recently and Jennifer got a shock when she saw you. You look amazing,' he added. 'You do, you know.'

'I know.' Aisling gave him her cat-devouring-a-meringue smile and prayed that she wouldn't be struck dead for lying so blatantly. When did any woman ever say *I know* to a statement about her looking good?

'Jenny's been sick, she had a bug and she doesn't look very good, so she was a bit freaked out to see you here looking like some bloody superstar.' He took a deep drag of his cigarette.

Score *dix points* to Aisling. He thought she looked good and so did 'Jenny'. Marvellous. Make it *douze points*. At least that explained why Jennifer didn't look like the stunner she'd expected. Perhaps she had better days. She'd want to.

'I shouldn't be telling you any of that, I suppose,' Michael added gloomily.

'I'm afraid that there aren't any rules for this type of situation,' Aisling said, a touch of sarcasm in her voice. 'So we'll have to make them up as we go along. I'm sorry I don't fit in with your version of the dumped wife – a thirteen-stone heifer with a bit of a booze problem,' she sniped. 'It would have been easier for you if I still looked like that, wouldn't it? So you could tell "Jenny" that you couldn't bear to live with me any longer and she'd have believed you. It's not so easy when I look better than she does. Tough, Michael.'

Aisling gazed at him angrily. She hadn't meant to lose her temper but she couldn't help herself.

'It wasn't like that,' he protested weakly. 'You know that!'

'I didn't know *anything*,' she said. 'That's the whole point. You never gave me a chance. But,' she gazed at him contemptuously, 'you did me a favour. After all those years of telling me I'd be no good going back to work, I did.'

'Aisling,' begged Michael, 'let's not go into this now, please.'

'Why?' she demanded. 'Am I causing a scene?' She glanced around. Despite the loud music, people were staring at them. But she didn't care. She'd waited a long time to tell Michael what she really thought and now he was a captive audience.

'Thanks to you, I had to go out and get a job. And thanks to *me* and *my* skills, I started up a catering business. *Reservations*. It's very successful actually,' she hissed. 'But I doubt if you and "Jenny" would be able to afford to hire me. It's an exclusive business, no riff-raff.'

'For God's sake, Aisling, let's be adults about this.' Michael looked shattered.

'Adults? If you want to behave like an adult, why did you bite *her* head off when she was behaving like one? Don't tell me,' she snapped. 'I know. It's because that's the way you are, Michael, isn't it? Difficult. That's the polite way of putting it, anyway,' Aisling added sarcastically. She looked at him with disdain. 'If Jenny's worried that I'm going to steal you back because I'm no longer the frumpy wife, I can put her mind at rest. Our relationship is over, dead as a dodo, *finito*, finished, gone.' Aisling enunciated each word clearly and crisply.

'So she can stop worrying. Get her to come back and I'll tell her,' she offered.

She was pleased to see that Michael looked hurt. There wasn't a thing he could say.

'In fact, I'll get her myself.' Aisling got to her feet abruptly. She walked out of the ballroom. Jennifer wasn't in the ladies'. Aisling found her at the bar, gulping a gin and tonic as if her life depended upon it. Slimline tonic, too, Aisling noticed.

'You didn't have to leave,' Aisling said. 'There's nothing we have to talk about that you can't hear. All we need is to wait another four and a half years and Michael and I can get divorced. So don't worry about me wanting him back. I don't.'

Even as she said it, Aisling knew it was true. She didn't want Michael back – under any circumstances. She'd had twelve years of marriage and that was enough. It had taken many hours of sobbing to figure it all out. But she knew what she wanted now. Aisling had tasted freedom and she liked the taste. Loved it, in fact. There was no going back. Jennifer would find that out for herself. Sooner rather than later, Aisling reflected, if Michael was true to form.

'Would you like a drink?' Jennifer asked tentatively.

'No thanks. I've got to get back to Sam. He's so possessive, he hates it when I leave him,' Aisling couldn't help adding. Was she really here, talking calmly with the woman who'd stolen her husband? No, not stolen, she corrected herself. The woman who'd been there when he decided their marriage was over and that he wanted out. 'You know, new lovers can't wait to get you home to bed!' Aisling smiled wickedly. She idly wondered if the wild start-of-the-affair sex between Jennifer and Michael had dimmed. Definitely, if the strained atmosphere between them was anything to go by. 'See you soon.' She walked away with her head held high.

'Where've you been?' Demanded Sam when she sat down between him and Jo.

'Talking to my husband,' she replied sharply.

'What!' he screeched, pushing back his chair and getting to his feet. 'Where is he?'

'Calm down, Sam,' said Aisling tiredly. She'd had enough trauma for one night without Sam's histrionics.

'What did he say to you? If he upset you, I'll kill him! I'll kill him, anyway,' Sam raged. His face was flushed with alcohol, his eyes were angry and he was actually balling his hands up into fists. 'What did you talk to him for?' He glared at Aisling.

She'd had enough. This was ridiculous. Sam was going to fight Michael over her, probably because he didn't like the idea of Michael seeing her in a sexy dress. Or merely because he wanted to fight with *anyone* who dared to look at her.

Aisling stood up until they were face to face. She didn't even raise her voice.

'Listen, Sam. Who I talk to is none of your bloody business. Michael is still my husband, not even my ex-husband yet, so we have a lot of things to talk about. Like our children, for instance. Do you understand what I'm talking about?' she asked him as if she was talking to a five-year-old.

'Aisling!' he shouted.

'Shut up,' she hissed. 'This is *none of your business*. Do you understand?'

'No. It *is* my business. I'm with you, I'm responsible for you!' he snarled.

'You're not responsible for me, Sam. You never were and you aren't now. Accept that or leave now!'

Shaking with controlled rage, Aisling sat down again.

'I'm so glad you're back,' panted Jo.

'Are you all right?' asked Aisling, Sam forgotten as she took in her friend's pale, damp face.

'No. I don't think so. I feel very strange all of a sudden. Mark went to the loo five minutes ago, and I've been feeling very strange since then.'

'I'm so sorry. I was so busy with Sam, I never noticed . . . Why didn't you come and get me?' Aisling hissed at Sam.

'I didn't know where you were!' he retorted.

'Oh Ash!' Jo's cry was loud and scared. Her eyes were huge as she looked at her friend. 'My waters just broke!'

CHAPTER TWENTY

Mark held Jo's right hand tightly as the limo raced towards the Coombe.

'Don't worry, Jo,' he said encouragingly. 'You're going to be fine, I promise.'

'But you've never had a baby,' sobbed Jo. 'How do you know?'

'*I* have and you're going to be fine,' said Aisling reassuringly, squeezing Jo's left hand.

'The baby's early. I'm not due yet,' wailed Jo. How could she be having the baby so soon? She'd another three weeks to go, the baby was premature. Maybe she wasn't in labour at all. She'd read the pregnancy books and she hadn't had the hours of contractions she'd expected. It had to be a false alarm.

'Aaagh,' she screamed as another contraction hit her.

'Oh God,' groaned Mark. 'Hurry up,' he yelled at the driver.

'He's going as fast as he can,' Aisling said in the calm and controlled voice she used when the twins had nightmares. 'We don't want to end up in the casualty room before we get to the delivery ward, do we?' She glared at Mark.

'You're right, you're right,' he said. 'You've got to stay calm,' he added to Jo.

'I don't want to be calm,' she yelled. 'This hurts.'

And it's going to hurt a hell of a lot more, Aisling reflected. Wait till they got to the bit where Jo screeched that she was never going to let a man get within a fifty-foot radius of her ever again. Aisling remembered that one. Listening to a woman screaming that sex was off the agenda *for ever* was enough to put the fear of God into any man. Never mind one who wasn't even the father in the first place.

Once she'd realised that Jo was going into labour, Aisling sent Sam to her house in a taxi to get Jo's hospital suitcase.

They'd packed it a few days before.

Jo already had a large collection of baby clothes, including beautifully knitted matinée coats and shawls her mother had made, and a selection of pastel-coloured babygros Rhona had given her. Packing for the baby was no problem, she said, reading from the list.

'Nappies, vests, babygros, cardigans, soft towels, a hat, gloves, breast-feeding bras, sanitary towels, nipple cream, the list goes on and on. It's like bringing an entire department store into hospital,' Jo laughed.

'Breathe deeply, Jo,' Mark said in an encouraging voice.

'That's later,' hissed Jo.

'All right, Jo. Don't get upset,' Aisling said. 'You've got to stay calm.'

'Calm? Shrieked the expectant mother. 'How can I stay calm? I'm having the baby in a car!'

'You're not, Jo.' Mark held her gently. The pain of the contraction faded. They sat quietly for a few moments, Jo's eyes closed again, one hand lay gently on her bump, the other tightly clasped in Mark's.

Jo was so glad it was Mark who was with her right now. She couldn't imagine what Richard would have done. Phoned his mother, probably, before retiring to the nearest pub for some Dutch courage. He wouldn't have been much help, wouldn't have been *any* help.

Mark wasn't like that. He loved her and that meant he wanted to be with her all the time. Wonderful, wonderful Mark. She could feel his hand warm and strong around hers.

He seemed to understand that she didn't want to talk. She wanted to stay silent. If she could keep her eyes closed and stay very, very still, she mightn't have another contraction. Then they could all go home.

'Aaagh!'

The pain was intense. And terrifying. There was no doubt about it, Jo thought as she clenched her teeth, she was having the baby. It was going to happen very soon.

'Thank God,' breathed Aisling as the limo pulled up outside the hospital. 'I thought we'd never get here.'

'You and me both,' muttered Jo, between deep breaths.

Within minutes, she was being examined by a midwife who pronounced her as three centimetres dilated.

'Di-lated to meet you,' Jo joked weakly.

'You're wonderful, do you know that?' said Mark quietly. 'Even now you're able to make me laugh.'

'Fear,' said Jo. 'I'm bloody terrified. I'm trying to make both of us laugh . . .' Another huge contraction gripped her.

The midwife, a down-to-earth woman named Paula, took Jo's blood pressure, temperature and pulse before listening to the baby's heartbeat.

'Both you and your baby are doing fine,' Paula said calmly. 'You're definitely in labour, but it could be a long time before you reach the second stage. You've got to relax, Jo.'

'I'm in labour, really?' asked Jo in alarm.

'Yes, but you could have a long wait,' Paula explained. 'I'll be monitoring you all the time to see how you're doing, but you've got to relax.'

Jo felt as if a tight band was being wound around her chest, squeezing her heart and lungs until she could barely breathe. In labour. She was in labour. There was no stopping it, there was no turning back. The baby was coming. She was terrified.

'Mark!'

'Yes, Jo, I'm here.'

She squeezed his hand in terror. 'Oh Mark, it's happening and I'm not ready, I'm not ready at all.' Her voice became a sob.

She clung to him, sobbing with a mixture of fear and pain. Mark looked at Paula in anguish, not knowing what to do.

'You might feel better if you walked around for a while,' Paula advised Jo. 'Would you like to do that?'

Jo nodded through the tears. Anything was better than just lying back on the pillows in pain. She'd love to walk if only she could. It was all so terrifying, so utterly terrifying.

★ ★ ★

When Sam arrived with Jo's things half an hour later, she was feeling more relaxed.

'She's calmed down a lot,' Mark told Aisling when he left the labour ward to get Jo's nightie. 'They gave her an injection of pethidine. She refuses to have an epidural, as you know. I wish she'd have one.'

'Jo's terrified of the idea,' Aisling said. 'I did my best to convince her. Told her *I'd* have had one if I could when I was having the twins, but she won't hear of it.'

Mark rubbed his eyes tiredly. 'She says you should go home, Aisling, and get some sleep.'

'Sleep! I don't think I could,' Aisling exclaimed, pulling her coat tighter around her shoulders. 'I feel so useless out here, I wish I could do something.'

'*You* feel useless,' Mark said, his voice strained. 'At least you've gone through this. I don't know what to do at all, except tell her to breathe deeply. I can barely breathe myself when I see her in so much pain!'

Aisling gave him a hug. 'You're doing great. She simply needs you with her, the hospital will do all the rest. Don't worry.'

'Thanks.'

Aisling watched him go. He looked utterly haggard, but then, they all did. Her eyes had been bloodshot the last time she looked in the ladies' mirror and even Sam, who always looked in the prime of health, was white-faced with tiredness.

'What time is it?' murmured Jo when Mark went back to her. 'I think I dozed off.' She sounded almost drunk. Paula had explained that pethidine could do that to you.

'It's nearly three.' He stroked her face softly. He was glad that she was dozing off, glad that the injection meant she slept between each agonising contraction. He sat beside her, watching her eyelids flutter as she slept. She seemed to be having mini nightmares, tossing restlessly and waking screaming when the pain hit her. Mark held her hand while she slept and wiped her hot face and neck with a cool facecloth when she woke up. Paula was fantastic. She soothed Jo when he couldn't.

'The baby's heartbeat is very strong,' she told Jo. 'It won't be too long now.'

The hands on Mark's watch had crawled around to half four when a red-haired nurse popped her head around the door.

'Mr Ryan, Paula said you should grab a cup of tea and I'll stay with Mrs Ryan,' she said.

'Thanks, but I couldn't leave her,' he replied.

'Go on,' the nurse insisted. 'It could be a long night.'

Mark gulped his scalding tea, not really wanting to wait until it cooled. He was afraid to be away from Jo for more than ten minutes. Who knew when she'd go into the second stage?

'Mark!!' He heard her long before he reached the ward. She was screeching in pain, her face contorted as a powerful contraction hit her. Her eyes were red with exhaustion and sweat had matted strands of dark hair to her forehead.

'Jo, I'm sorry, I'm sorry I was gone,' he cried.

'I've got to push!' she screamed.

'Don't push yet.' Paula's voice was calm and controlled. 'This isn't the time to push. Take two short breaths and then breathe out slowly,' she advised, checking Jo's cervix. Another nurse monitored the baby's heart through the machine they'd connected to Jo's belly.

'You're nine and a half centimetres dilated, Jo. You're nearly ready. How do you feel?'

'Bloody awful,' panted Jo. 'Aaagghh!'

They propped her up with a pile of pillows, getting her into the most comfortable position.

'You're doing great, Jo,' Mark said.

'Ten centimetres,' said Paula.

Jo screamed with pain. 'Now I know why they call it "labour".'

'OK now, push!' commanded Paula. 'A long, steady push.'

Jo pushed, tucking her chin down onto her chest. That was

the right way to do it, she was sure. That was what they'd said at the classes. Oh God, the pain, she couldn't take it. How could the baby come out? How would it fit?

'You're doing brilliantly, Jo,' said Mark encouragingly, one large hand clasped tightly in Jo's small one.

'Take a deep breath as you feel each contraction beginning,' Paula said. 'Ready . . .'

Jo did her best and pushed as hard as she could. She could feel the baby, feel the baby coming out.

'That's great, one more push. It's crowning. Jo, we can see the baby's head.'

Mark squeezed her hand and Jo felt the tears swell in her eyes. The baby, her baby.

'Don't push for a moment, Jo. The baby's head is stretching the birth canal. We don't want you to tear,' Paula said.

'Relax,' Mark said.

'And pant,' added the red-haired nurse.

Jo panted, feeling the pressure lessen.

'Oh Jo, look, the baby's head!' yelled Mark in excitement.

She could barely see, couldn't stretch any farther. She so desperately wanted to see the baby's head.

'Push,' commanded Paula. 'Just a couple more pushes, just two more!'

With one last push, Jo felt the baby ease out. She gasped with relief, and as Paula held the small bloodied body up for her to see, she gasped with joy.

'She's a beautiful little girl,' Paula said triumphantly.

Tears blinded Jo. She watched Paula expertly check the tiny infant. She'd read all about the Apgar score to assess the baby for breathing, heart rate and response to stimulation. Before, the Apgar had been words on a page – now it was the most important thing in the world to her.

'Oh Mark.' Jo held her breath with terror. Please let the baby be all right. The baby let out a loud wail, a healthy sound that brought colour to her mother's cheeks.

'Is she all right?' Jo asked, barely able to speak with fear.

'You've got a beautiful little girl, Jo,' said Paula. 'She's seven pounds one ounce, very healthy. She scored an eight on her Apgar.'

Paula laid the baby, all wrapped up in a soft towel, in Jo's arms. Jo gazed down at the huge blue eyes, the downy dark hair clinging to her head, and the small pink mouth screwed up with crying. She'd never felt anything like it before, Jo thought, the powerful and intense love she felt for her tiny, fragile baby. She held the baby's delicate little hands, marvelling at the tiny fingers.

'She's so beautiful,' said Jo, holding the fragile baby close to her chest. Mark sat on the edge of the bed and stroked the baby's head. His huge hand dwarfed the infant's red face.

As if she had responded to his touch, the baby stopped crying and snuggled instinctively closer to Jo's breast. She made little sucking noises with her mouth and Jo was about to open her hospital gown to feed her when Paula appeared beside her.

'Because she was premature, we've got to make sure that she's healthy,' the midwife said, gently taking the baby from Jo. 'The paediatrician wants a look at her. I'll be back with her as soon as I can.'

Jo felt as if a part of her was missing. She laid her fingers over the mound of her belly, still huge from carrying her little passenger all those months. If something went wrong, if the baby was sick, Jo didn't know how she'd cope. She'd die if anything happened to the baby, she just knew it.

'She'll be fine, Jo.' Mark leaned over to kiss her forehead. It was no good. She loved Mark to pieces, but he couldn't comfort her when it came to her darling baby.

After fifteen of the longest minutes of Jo's life, Claire, the red-haired nurse, returned with the baby and the paediatrician in tow.

'She's fine,' explained the doctor. 'Perfectly healthy. She's quite big for a pre-term baby at seven pounds one ounce. And she's perfect.'

'I know, isn't she?' Jo beamed up at him.

'You hold her, Mark,' she added. When Mark took the

infant into his arms, she mewled like a kitten at first and then snuggled peacefully into his chest.

'She's fantastic,' Mark said in awe, staring at her as though he'd never seen a baby before.

'A daddy's girl already,' said Jo with a smile.

Half an hour later, the baby was sleeping peacefully in her crib when Claire came into the brightly painted hospital room Jo had been wheeled into.

'You need to get some rest,' she told Jo.

'I'm exhausted,' Jo admitted, 'but could I have a cup of tea, please?'

'Yes. Do you want one too?' Claire asked Mark.

'I'd kill for some tea,' he replied gratefully.

'She's so beautiful, isn't she?' Jo gazed into the cot beside her bed where the baby lay sleeping.

'How could she be anything else when she's got the most gorgeous mother in the world?' Mark sat on the edge of the chair beside Jo's bed and leaned over towards her. 'I had this all planned,' he said. 'We were going to leave the Shelbourne early and get the limo to drive us up to the cottage, where I have candles, champagne, flowers and the CD player with your favourite Mariah Carey CD all ready to swing into action. And then,' he paused and looked at Jo intently, his grey eyes warm with love, 'I was going to ask you to marry me. So will you marry me?' he asked softly, so as not to wake the baby. 'I think this is the perfect moment, with our daughter asleep beside us.'

He fumbled around the inside pocket of his dinner jacket which lay on the chair behind him. A moment later he produced a small navy leather box, opened it, and offered it to Jo.

'Oh, it's beautiful,' she breathed, stunned by the square-cut emerald surrounded by tiny diamonds. As she moved the box, the little diamonds twinkled in the light.

She looked up at Mark.

'Oh Mark, thank you so much. I do. I will. Whatever!'

She'd never loved him more than at this moment, with

stubble darkening his jaw, eyes red-rimmed, his face pale with tiredness and strain. He'd been with her for the birth of the baby, *their* baby. *She* was Mark's child, there was no doubt in her mind about that. He leaned forward and kissed her gently on the mouth.

'I'm so glad. I've wanted to ask you for a long time, but it had to be the right moment.'

Jo grinned tiredly as she lay back on her pillows.

'I think we can safely say that we'll never forget this moment,' she said.

The door swung open and Claire arrived in with a small pot of tea and two cups.

'Your friend is still outside. She can come in for a moment if you'd like.'

'Mark, go and get Aisling,' said Jo. 'Tell her we've some news for her.'

462

CHAPTER TWENTY-ONE

'Do I look OK?' Jo twisted and turned in front of the mirror in her bedroom. Did her bum look too big in the cream brocade suit? The slim fitted jacket flattered her curves and the combination of the long straight skirt and high-heeled cream boots made her look like an elegant Edwardian lady. Or at least it had when she tried it on in Amanda Wakeley's shop in London. But now she wasn't so sure.

It wasn't the traditional wedding dress, but as she and Mark weren't having the traditional church wedding, she preferred a low-key outfit to go with the simple civil service. A ceremony attended by their close family and a small reception in the beautiful estate in Enniskerry's Powerscourt was what they'd both wanted.

The ceremony was at three. It was still only half one, there was plenty of time for last-minute panic attacks about whether her outfit looked all right and would she have to insist that Ralph, the photographer, doctor the wedding pictures to make her look slimmer.

Jo examined herself in the mirror. She was still a little pale, even though she'd used at least half a ton of bronzing powder. But at least she'd lost most of the weight she'd put on carrying Isabel.

If only her bum was as slim as it had been before she'd got pregnant, then she'd be totally happy. But you couldn't really tell thanks to those lycra-panelled knickers that sucked everything in.

Her dark hair was piled up on top of her head. A few tendrils clustered around her face. Jo fiddled with these curls restlessly.

'You look great, stop worrying.' Aisling looked up from the bed where she was trying to undo Isabel's babygro to change her nappy.

At three months old, Isabel Ryan was a very energetic young lady and enjoyed nothing more than wriggling madly when she was having her clothes put on or taken off, kicking the undresser in lots of painful places.

'Let me, Ash.' Jo got down on her knees beside the bed and took over from Aisling. 'How's my Isabel?' she cooed, kissing her daughter's snub nose. The baby squealed with delight and kicked harder as Jo tried to ease her tiny feet out of the cream towelling outfit.

'Don't kick Mummy in the tummy, pet. Now you've got to be very, very good while Mummy gets ready to marry Daddy,' murmured Jo, as she expertly undid the babygro and unfastened the nappy. 'Won't you be good, Isabel?' she asked.

Isabel responded with another couple of unco-ordinated kicks and a happy gurgle.

'She's a love.' Aisling sat on the edge of the bed and watched, with more than a hint of longing in her own voice.

'Isn't she just?' Jo said proudly. 'We've been so lucky with her. When I went to the crèche for the first time last week, three of the mothers there couldn't believe it when I told them how good Isabel is. I think they think I'm making it up to make them jealous.'

'Not many babies sleep solidly for eight hours at night.' Aisling opened her handbag and pretended to search for her lipstick. She *had* to get over the maternal feelings which tore at her heart every time she held Jo's little daughter in her arms.

'The twins were awful for sleeping. I'd get Phillip off to sleep when Paul would wake up, or vice versa.'

Aisling outlined her lips with lip pencil and then applied the deep pink colour which went perfectly with the fitted dusky rose wool trouser-suit she was wearing.

It was just as well she'd worn the long-sleeved pale pink body underneath, she thought. It was the coldest day in February, freezing winds whipped around Jo and Mark's cottage in the Dublin mountains.

'Come on, darling, help Mummy put your dress on,' Jo was saying softly.

'I'll help,' Aisling offered, seeing the difficulties Jo was having trying to slip the cream silk overdress, the same colour as her own elegant suit, over Isabel's head. By the time Jo finally managed to put the cream bonnet with the silk ribbons on her daughter's dark hair, Isabel looked like a baby from an eighteenth-century French painting.

'All we need are Marie Antoinette's shepherdess's dresses, bonnets and a couple of sheep and we're all set to be hung in the National Gallery,' Aisling said with a laugh before extracting a camera from her handbag. 'Smile!'

'We've got half an hour before the car comes so I decided to open one of the bottles of champagne Mark left in the kitchen.' Laura Ryan appeared at the bedroom door with a tray, three glasses and a bottle of Cristal.

'Champagne,' cried Jo in delight. 'My favourite. Mum, I didn't know there *was* any champagne in the house.'

'Your husband-to-be is highly organised,' her mother replied with a smile. 'He told me about the case before he left and said he'd hidden a Chocolate Orange in the cupboard under the sink for you to go with it.'

'Oh.' Jo sighed appreciatively. 'He knows I love Chocolate orange.'

'With champagne?' asked Aisling.

'With *anything*.' Jo and her mother laughed at exactly the same time. Aisling was struck again by how alike the two women were. There was no way you'd ever think that the lithe and dark-haired Laura Ryan was a grandmother, never mind the mother of grown-up children.

'Let me take Isabel.' Laura picked up her granddaughter with delight. Isabel gurgled happily and blew bubbles at her adoring granny.

Jo draped a towel across her mother's shoulder so she could cuddle Isabel without ruining her wedding outfit with dribbles.

'Granny has to look good in front of your daddy's relatives,'

Laura explained as she adjusted the towel.

'You look fantastic, Mum,' said Jo sharply. 'There won't be anyone there to hold a candle to you. Anyway, I told you that Mark's family is very nice. His sister, Denise, is lovely, although I have no idea where she got that little bitch Emma from,' Jo added thoughtfully.

'She's the only one I was worried about. I could picture her making snide remarks all day, but not any more. She knows what side her bread is buttered on now,' Jo added vehemently.

'Tell me, what's happened?' demanded Aisling, agog.

Jo abandoned all pretence of putting on her eyeliner.

'Well,' she said with a definite glint in her eye, 'I went into the office last week with my copy and I had Isabel with me, of course. That little cow was there, sitting in my seat as cool as a cucumber and she'd dumped all my stuff on top of my filing cabinet. She didn't expect to see me, I can tell you.' Jo grinned triumphantly. 'She went puce and started moving her stuff off the desk quickly. I went in to talk to Rhona and when I came out she was on the phone bitching about me.'

'I don't believe it!' said Aisling. 'How stupid can she be, talking about you like that when you were there.'

Jo shrugged. 'That girl is a real mystery to me. Sometimes she's so smart and bitchy, and other times she comes across like a complete fool. Anyway,' she took a sip of champagne, 'I waited until she was off the phone, let Rhona take Isabel, then I called Emma into Rhona's office. I told her that I knew exactly what sort of person she was, and I said that even though I didn't believe in throwing my weight around normally, she'd better watch out when I came back to work. "You may be Mark's niece," I told her. "But *I'll* be his wife. You figure it out." That shut her up.'

Aisling and Laura howled with laughter.

'Well done,' Laura said, 'I'm proud of you.'

'That's priceless. I'd have loved to have seen her face,' said Aisling.

'You will. She's going to be at the reception,' Jo pointed out. 'But just wait till you see how nice she is to me. She didn't think I had it in me to be hard, but she knows better now.'

'You could never be hard, Jo,' Aisling said. 'Not in a million years.'

Jo considered this as she screwed the lid off her mascara tube. 'I've wisened up, maybe that's it.'

'Haven't we all?' Aisling thought of the past year and all the changes it had brought to her life. In a short period of time, she'd gone from being a depressed married woman to being a fulfilled working mother who'd managed to set up her own company, *and* hold down another job, *and* look after her beloved twin sons on her own into the bargain. She'd certainly toughened up.

She'd even managed to exorcise Michael's memory thanks to Sam. The affair had been wonderful at first. It had turned into a bit of a nightmare at the very end. Aisling cast her mind back to the day after the charity ball, the day she'd told Sam to get out of her life for good.

She'd just got home after dropping some things into the hospital for Jo and was about to start dinner when the doorbell rang. It was five in the afternoon, the boys were watching TV and she wasn't expecting any visitors.

'It's Sam,' announced Phillip. He stuck his head around the kitchen door.

Just what she didn't need. After last night's confrontation, she could do without another one. She was sick and tired of Sam Delaney. She opened the freezer to see what she could defrost for dinner and waited for Sam to come looking for her. When he didn't appear, she went into the sitting room.

'Where is he?' she asked in a puzzled voice.

'Outside,' Phillip said innocently.

Aisling glared at him. 'Why didn't you open the door?' she demanded. Before Phillip could answer, the doorbell rang again.

'I thought you weren't going to let me in,' Sam said, when she opened the front door.

'That was just Phillip playing games,' she said tiredly,

leading the way into the kitchen.

'Little brat.' Sam's voice was harsh.

Aisling whirled around in fury. 'Don't you dare call my son names! Who the hell do you think you are?' she yelled.

'Jesus, Aisling. Don't fly off the handle,' Sam said, taken aback. 'It's only a comment, I'm sorry. Look, I'm here to apologise for last night, so why don't I do a double apology? Sorry for flying off the handle last night and sorry for saying your son is a b . . . sorry,' he said lamely.

'What's wrong, Mum?' demanded Paul, rushing into the kitchen with Phillip on his heels. The pair of them stared at Sam accusingly. 'What's *he* said now?' Phillip's furious face was so like Michael's, it was uncanny.

'Will we throw him out, Mum?' asked Paul.

Aisling felt her heart burst with pride. Her little heroes, ready to take on a grown-up three times their size just to protect her. She went over and hugged them both. They were growing up so quickly, in a couple of years they'd be as tall as she was.

'No, boys, it's OK.'

Paul relaxed at her words, but Phillip's body was still tensed as if he was ready to fight. He moved out of her embrace and looked up at Sam steadily.

'Our dad isn't here, but don't think you can boss Mum around,' he hissed. 'We don't like you. Why don't you go back to America?'

'Yeah, why not?' said Paul.

Aisling was stunned. She had no idea that the twins disliked Sam so much. She'd thought they got on all right with him. But when she cast her mind back over the few times when the four of them had been together, she realised that when they all went to McDonald's or the cinema, both boys sat on her side, never beside Sam. Funny, she'd never thought about that before.

'It's all right, boys,' she said. 'Everything is fine, everything is going to be fine.' She smiled at Phillip. 'Go on and watch the TV. We'll have dinner in an hour.'

As they left, Sam dragged out a kitchen chair from the table and sat down with a thump.

'You're ruining those boys, ruining them because you're guilty about being separated,' he said in his mid-Atlantic drawl. Aisling realised that she hated the way he spoke, his American twang suddenly sounded so false. 'When I was their age, I'd have been given a good beating for speaking to an adult like that. And that's what Phillip wants. A few slaps would be good for him.'

She turned to look at him, taking in his flushed face and angry eyes. He was a bully, all right. Why hadn't she noticed it before? She'd been seduced by the way he made her feel. She'd wanted to get her own back at Michael by having such a sexy, handsome boyfriend.

She'd let that, and his amazing ability in bed, blind her to his faults. Not any more.

'You're entitled to your opinion about children,' she said evenly. 'But don't think you're going to try your theories out on *my* children, because you aren't. And you're not going to try it out on me, either, Sam. It's over between us. So if you could leave, I can get back to living my life without you telling me where I'm going wrong every five minutes.'

Sam stared at her open-mouthed. 'You can't mean that, Aisling,' he said. 'What about us, about our plans . . .?'

'There is no *us* any more. It's over.'

He grabbed her arm and tried to pull her onto his lap, his words cajoling. 'Please, Ash, don't say that.'

'Let me go!' She wrenched herself free of his grasp.

'Aisling.' Sam stood up and tried to put his arms around her, but she backed away.

'Just go, Sam.'

'Yeah, go.' Phillip and Paul were back, standing at the door like small sentries. For a moment, Aisling felt her chest tighten as Sam's face grew dark. His jaw tensed.

Jesus, he wasn't going to hit them, was he?

'Boys, come here!' she cried. They ran to her and stood in front of her.

'Go!' she said again.

He shrugged. 'I'll go, but you'll be sorry. I know you will. You'll want me back.'

Yeah, when hell freezes over, she thought silently. Nobody said anything as Sam turned and walked out the door. He slammed the front door behind him.

How predictable.

'Well boys, what do you want for dinner?' Aisling asked brightly, determined to hide how shaken she was by the encounter. 'Or should we go to McDonald's for a treat?'

'*We'll* cook,' Phillip announced. He pulled up a chair for her at the table. 'We can defrost just as well as you can.'

Aisling had to laugh. She got herself a glass of icy white wine from the fridge and sat down at the table. 'OK, boys, what are we eating?'

'Are you thinking about Sam?' asked Jo.

Aisling looked at her friend and smiled. 'You know me so well, Jo,' she said.

'Well enough to know that you've done the right thing,' Jo said quietly.

'Oh I know that.'

'I'll take Isabel downstairs while you finish getting ready, girls,' Laura said, taking the baby out of the room.

'Now I know where you get your perceptiveness from,' Aisling said. She sat on the pale yellow duvet and looked up at her friend. 'I'm not upset, Jo. To be honest, I'm very happy. I love my life now, I love the freedom. OK, juggling work, more work and childminders isn't easy, but there's this huge sense of freedom in everything I do. *I* make the decisions, *I* decide what I'm going to do every day, every week,' she explained earnestly.

'It's incredibly liberating. Sam was great for my self-confidence, at the beginning anyway,' she added wryly, 'but being around him made me realise that I don't want another man to worry about. Not for a long time. And when I do want someone else, it has to be on my terms.'

'So you're happy?' asked Jo tentatively. 'I know it's childish, but I want you to be happy on my wedding day.'

Aisling got up and wrapped her arms around Jo.

'I am happy. I'm so happy for you and Mark too. It's wonderful seeing how happy you both are with Isabel.'

'Thanks for everything, Ash,' Jo said. 'Thank you for being here today and thank you for being so good to me when I needed you.'

'What are friends for?' Aisling asked with a shrug. 'Now tell me, this photographer, Ralph, who's taking the wedding pictures. Is he handsome? Is he single?'

'Yes and yes,' said Jo, a tad too enthusiastically. 'He's drop-dead gorgeous. Dark hair, brown eyes, great body. There's only one problem – he's gay.'

'Is he a mature adult?' demanded Aisling.

'Absolutely,' Jo replied.

'Fine. We can work on everything else. Just as long as he's grown-up, that's all I want. Now, shall we go to a wedding?'

'You bet.'

You can buy any of these other
Headline Review titles from your
bookshop or *direct from the publisher*.

FREE P&P AND UK DELIVERY
(Overseas and Ireland £3.50 per book)

Woman to Woman	Cathy Kelly	£7.99
She's the One	Cathy Kelly	£7.99
Never too Late	Cathy Kelly	£7.99
The Only Way Is Up	Carole Matthews	£6.99
Summer School	Domenica de Rosa	£6.99
Missing You Already	Pauline McLynn	£6.99
Desire	Louise Bagshawe	£6.99
Things I Wish I'd Known	Linda Green	£6.99
Take A Chance On Me	Jill Mansell	£7.99

TO ORDER SIMPLY CALL THIS NUMBER

01235 400 414

or visit our website: www.headline.co.uk

Prices and availability subject to change without notice.